THE END OF AN ERA

The memoirs of a Naval Constructor

Published in 2003 by
Periscope Publishing Ltd.
33 Barwis Terrace
Penzance
Cornwall TR18 2AW

www.periscopepublishing.com

A CIP record for this book is available from the British Library

ISBN No 1-904381-18-9

Printed in England by Anthony Rowe Ltd
Eastbourne

The Memoirs of R. J. Daniel

Former Head of the Royal Corps of Naval Constructors,

UK Ministry of Defence

And

Board Member for Warshipbuilding, British Shipbuilders.

R. J. Daniel

CONTENTS

Cover illustration shows HMS Quilliam in a US floating dock at Leyte Gulf in 1945. The author is on the left.

Introduction

The memoirs are an informal record of my work between 1942 and 1991 when I finally retired.

Apart from a few later insertions which are self evident in the text, the memoirs were written in 1991, almost entirely from memory since keeping a diary had always seemed a potential security risk when I was with the Ministry of Defence. The exception is the final chapter on Canada for which I used the reports that I made at the time. The Ministry of Defence and the Foreign Office took only a year to give them security clearance.

They were written because much of our history of naval construction seems to be being lost in the rush to fragment and disband the nations defence equipment research and design capability and place it in the hands of people with quite different abilities and loyalties than those that motivated the Royal Corps of Naval Constructors in the previous century.

The RCNC that I joined designed the navy's ships, oversaw their construction, ran the Royal Dockyards and major Admiralty research establishments and served in the ships of the Fleet. Little of that remains.

The title, The End of an Era, reflects this change.

It is unlikely that ever again, an officer will have the spread of hands-on design experience or responsibility that I had, an aircraft carrier, a missile trials ship, an anti-submarine frigate and several classes of nuclear submarines in addition to research and general design appointments and, later, overall responsibility for such classes as the *Invincible, Manchester*, and MCMV's, among others. It was exciting and rewarding.

With the design of the Resolution Class ballistic missile submarines, we were contributing to the deterrence of the Soviet threat in the most direct way. The threat has since gone but was very real at the time.

The first Head of the RCNC that I served directly had no respect for and a healthy dislike of, politicians of all shades. In more than fifty years since then I have found no cause to think him wrong.

R. J. Daniel, OBE, FREng, CEng, FRINA, FIMarEST, RCNC, idc

Part One

THE WAR YEARS

Chapter One

In 1939 the new T-Class submarine HMS *Thetis* was lost while on trials off Liverpool. This had a profound effect on me; the depth of water was barely 150 feet and for a time the submarine's stern was above water yet by inadequate rescue attempts, the Royal Navy allowed those gallant men to die. Two members of the Royal Corps of Naval Constructors, the Corps I hoped to join, died in *Thetis*; Bailey, the submarine's designer, and Hill, the Naval Overseer at Messer's Cammell Laird's, the builders.

When I graduated from the Royal Naval College in the summer of 1942 I asked to go to the submarine design group. Thus began an association that was to last throughout my career. I was appointed to the Naval Construction Department in Bath to work under the redoubtable Chief Constructor George William Pamplin. What "Pamp" didn't know about submarines was not worth knowing

People ask "Why was the Admiralty in Bath, some 60 miles from the sea?" In the contingency planning for war in 1938/39 it was realised that space would be required in Whitehall for extra operational planning staffs. It was decided to create this space by moving departments out and the departments that could be moved most readily were the technical and logistics people. The answer to the question "Where?" was to send them to the decaying Spa towns which would have lots of hotels to be used as offices. The army went to Harrogate, the air force went to Cheltenham and the navy went to Bath. Clearly the connection between bath, water and boats had not escaped the administrative minds in Whitehall.

The city to which they came was caught in a time warp somewhere about the First World War. The prosperity engendered by the re-armament programme had had little effect on Bath. Tourism as we know it today did not exist and the Georgian houses and hotels were to a large part occupied by people who had retired from the Home, Indian, Colonial or Foreign civil or military services, trying to maintain standards on pensions that were increasingly being over -taken by inflation. The soot blackened crescents and the like might be architectural gems but five floors of stone staircases, dampness, coal fires, and plumbing last 'modernised' in 1910 were hardly conducive to comfort and healthy living. Class differences were still rigidly observed, the ordinary inhabitants were assumed to exist to serve the 'Quality' (and a good number did earn their living in service) but not to obtrude into the 'better' areas of the city. Above all, there was insufficient wealth in the system to support a modern city; it was all running down. There was little modern housing and when the war dragged on and the Admiralty people began to bring their families to Bath, there were few modern schools for them to attend; most dated from the previous century.

Dampness was a problem and a cause of illness. Periodically the River Avon would flood the lower parts of the city and as late as the early-60's colleagues living in low lying parts would have their cellars flooded for most of the winter months.

One of the morning express trains was non-stop from London to Bristol. Passengers for Bath travelled in the rear coach which was uncoupled half a mile or so before Bath station and brought to a halt at the station platform by the guard or brake-man while the express thundered on, unchecked, to Bristol. This 'slip-coach' then had to be moved to a siding between the up and down lines, not by a shunting engine but by a carthorse that lived in a small stable (a one horse affair) at the western end of the up-platform. In the afternoon the same train would arrive en-route to London and stop while the slip-coach was hauled into position by the horse and coupled up to the train. For most of the intervening hours the horse was in its stable with its head over the stable door, placidly watching the steam trains and their passengers arrive and depart. This practice went on for some years after the war.

This, then, was the city to which several thousand civil and naval personnel were transferred at almost a day's notice at the outbreak of war. Most of this civilian and naval staff had houses elsewhere, principally in the London area, to which they expected to return when the departments went back to Whitehall after the war. All believed that the war would be short. They were billeted in houses all around the place. The (usually elderly) residents were moved out of the hotels and Admiralty Departments were assigned to them to make the best possible use of the space available.

This was not done without problems, made more difficult by the state of some of the hotels. The central structure around the staircase in the Empire Hotel was found to be shaky and massive timber supports had to be put in at each floor; they were still there in the 1980's when the MoD finally vacated the place. In the Pulteney Hotel which was said to be ' one of the most splendid in the city attracting a string of titled guests', staff had to be warned to place all filing cabinets against the walls and on no account to gather in the centre of the rooms because the floors sagged so. And so on through the list of hotels The Grand Pump Room, the Fernley, the Spa, the Francis and the others, all of which had been struggling to keep their heads above water in the lean years preceding the war, with little to spare for repairs. Meanwhile, on three sites around Bath the government built hutments, each building being a central corridor with six big rooms on either side. If one imagines hospital wards each side of a central spine, and indeed that's what they were built for, as potential auxiliary hospitals for use should there be large numbers of casualties from bombing or battles. By the time they were completed in 1942 it was thought safe to use them as offices.

In the submarine group we had a senior draughtsman who had joined the Admiralty at the beginning of the century and who remembered the fuss when the first 'typing lady' had joined the old Admiralty Building in Whitehall and had been put in a small room in the basement lest she should distract the male staff., but for the most part the staff were below middle age.

The section which I joined as deputy chief was responsible for all the T, U and V-Class submarines in service and under construction, for all the older classes H, 0, P and minelayers and for all the overseas submarines that had escaped the Nazi invasion and which did not have their own experts. The Dutch and the Free French did have their own excellent naval constructors and some Greek navy constructors had been in my term and would undertake this duty with the British built boats that were passed to their navy. Oh, I forgot, we also had the fast fleet submarines Severn and Clyde.

By tradition, my desk was in the design room. The draughtsmen sat at 10 ft long drawing benches, facing each other in pairs along the room. There was good sense in this arrangement for I was subconsciously aware of all that went on in the office. In quite a short while snippets overheard at the Bath end of telephone conversations would tell me the subject and who he was talking with and where, and kept me abreast of what was going on. One soon learnt a lot about people's ability and judgement and I am sure that they were doing the same about me. Of course one learned something of their personal lives; some of the younger men had been sent to Bath from the Home Dockyards and this was the first time that they had been away from home - a tit-bit that has stayed in my mind was one morning in 1942;

Mr A "This letter is from my old Mum in Plymouth, she says that her hair is falling out. Could it be with worry because of the bombing?

Mr B "I expect that she's washed it with something that doesn't suit it"

Mr A "Oh no, she's still using Persil ".

Wartime Persil would not exactly strip paint off a ship's side but it would have a jolly good try.

The draughtsmen and clerical staff were paid weekly. People from the Navy Accounts Department would sit at a small table in the corridor on payday and the staff would file past and receive a small envelope containing their pay. Back in the design room they would open up their envelope and check the contents. Listening with half an ear, I was mildly surprised at how closely some of the staff checked that they had indeed been paid for every minute of overtime down to the last halfpenny. At the time I was surprised that they were paid overtime at all. Were we not mobilised to fight the common enemy, the men in the forces didn't get overtime so why should Admiralty draughtsmen and clerks? A little thought showed that authority really had no choice, the workmen in industry and the Royal Dockyards had always been paid overtime and it would be a very unwise government that risked unrest and strikes in the factories producing the weapons of war. Our junior draughtsmen had always been 'overtime grades'.

Within two days of joining the section I was ordered to the Clyde area to attend *P312's* sea trials followed by *P339*. This boat should have had the pennant number *P313* but why push your luck? This became the pattern, that I would spend something like a third of my time in submarines, usually in Scottish waters where newly completed submarines did their trials and 'worked-up', but sometimes much further afield, a third in visits to the shipyards and Royal Dockyards to perform inclining experiments to check the submarine's stability and ability to dive and to undertake the initial 'post-refit' diving trials and a third in the office in Bath. One of the early sets of post-refit trials that I undertook was in HMS *Thetis* — recovered, rebuilt and renamed HMS *Thunderbolt*. Secretly I hoped that this hull had already given sufficient obeisance to the fates and henceforth would have a charmed life but this was not to be; an Italian Navy sloop sank her on 14th March 1943 with the loss of all hands.

Submarines were essentially riveted steel cylinders with diesel engines driving two propellers, Torpedo tubes were forward (and occasionally aft), a gun and a battery to supply electric motors to propel them when submerged. The Mark 8 torpedo was carried; a good weapon, so good in fact that it was a Mark 8 that sank the Argentine Navy's *Belgrano* forty years later.

The older submarines were fitted with a predictor in which the torpedo officer would set the dials to where he thought or knew the target to be and its speed and the predictor would give the direction in which the torpedo should be fired. It was in effect a mechanical computer and was known as the Tiswas. More elaborate, but still mechanical machines known to the crews as 'Fruit machines' soon replaced these. In those days torpedoes did not actively home on the targets but they could be angled, a somewhat chancy thing as HMS *Osiris* learnt.

The rules of engagement as I understood them were "the bigger the target, the bigger the number of torpedoes you fire, except a submarine target where you fire the lot". It was none of my business but it did seem to me that the bigger the target the easier it would be to hit it with a single shot, whereas little targets would be more difficult to hit and so lots of torpedoes should be fired. It didn't really matter for most of my friends fired the lot, anyway.

Twenty-five years later we were doing some development work on torpedo launching at depth, when due to some malfunction, the sea pressure pushed a torpedo back into its tube and crumpled its rear end against the tube's rear door. "Cor', we said, and one quite senior officer confessed that in the Mediterranean Sea in the war the same thing had happened to a torpedo that his submarine had attempted to fire. They had opened the rear door of the torpedo tube and found a somewhat bent torpedo; they had hastily pushed it out. At least one other boat had done the same. They hadn't told anyone at the time for they were sure that somebody in Bath would blame them!

One of my more demanding tasks was to supervise, design wise, the construction of all-welded T and V-Class boats. More than a year earlier some senior naval constructors and the shipyard bosses had met and decided that future submarines should be all-welded. This had meant changing the steel and the shape of the frames and all the construction plant and methods. It is difficult to convey how much of the science we had to invent and develop before we could proceed. The shipbuilders made 5-metre diameter rings and butt-welded them together. Constructor George Stunden in Chatham Naval Dockyard built a rig to rotate his rings so that all the welding would be done in the best down hand position. He was ahead of his time. Much, much work was done on developing the steel and the welding rods, remembering that we wanted thousands of tons of the stuff as soon as possible.

An RAF aircraft had captured a German U boat, *U570*, the Graf. It was brand new and as would be expected it was a good design and well built. It was all-welded. We were having some problems with our welding and we took many samples. It was convenient for several reasons to cut a large hole in the top of the engine room and I went to Chatham to plan and witness the re-welding sequence. I recall that it had snowed and was bitterly cold and I had toothache. In due course the submarine went back into service; everyone knew her as Graf so she became HMS *Graph*. For a brief time she operated with our forces- one plan was that she should infiltrate herself into a U boat wolf pack — but it was all too dangerous and she was eventually decommissioned and sank while being towed round Scotland. I saw an article by one of the RNVR officers who had served in her; he said that they had no fear of being sunk by friendly forces because they dived every time they saw any aircraft or ship! This was standard procedure; the navy's concern was that a trigger-happy RAF type in the designated safe area of the Clyde estuary would jump her.

There was certainly some reason for airmen assuming that a submarine sighting would be a U boat. The UK entered the war with 57 submarines and built a further 176; the Germans entered the war with 56 and built a further 1,093 despite the most intense bombing of their shipyards, a truly prodigious performance. To complete the record, the RN lost 74 boats and the Kriegsmarine lost 795 in the course of the war. At 3,083, 38% of British officers and ratings serving in submarines lost their lives, a percentage only exceeded by the RAF's Bomber Command. The German casualty rate was much higher. According to German records, of the 39,000 officers and men who served in U Boats, 28,000 drowned (72%) and 5,000 (13%) were taken prisoner, giving a total casualty rate of 85%. Towards the end of the war there was a much greater than evens chance that they would be sunk on each patrol and yet the U Boats still sailed out, their crews were very brave. What is also interesting about these figures is that if one divides the number of men who served in submarines by the number of submarines, the British service had 35 men per boat and the Germans 34.

For some reason their Lordships of the Admiralty had decided at the outbreak of war that submarines -hitherto named — should no longer have names. Perhaps they imagined that the mention of a P-Boat would have the same mind chilling effect as the mention of a U Boat, little realising that the Germans also gave their boats names. So the Admirals had their P's. On joining *P312*, I found that the officers had christened her HMS *Trespasser* and devised a ship's badge of a man climbing over a five bar gate.

All the other Commanding Officers had done the same, *Tradewind, Tally-Ho, Truculent, Turbulent, Untiring, Usurper* and so on. I mention the last because their do-it-yourself ships badge was a cuckoo in a nest. It was said that matters came to a head when

Their Lordships sighted a report from a young CO reporting an incident to HMS *Winkle* while under his command. In the fullness of time submarines got their names, in the early days those that they had chosen themselves.

Many of the initial trials took place in the Scottish lochs or on the Aran mile but more extensive trials and deep dives to test the hull strength took us much further afield. One of the more simple trials was the forward hydroplane trial, for which the submarine was trimmed down until just the sail (conning tower) was showing and would then porpoise along as the forward hydroplanes, (horizontal rudders) were alternately set to the dive and rise positions by the submarines coxswain. Obviously, all the submarine's hatches were shut. On two occasions I had young commanding officers of U-Class boats, Lieutenants with their first command, who insisted on staying on the bridge despite advice to the contrary. On each occasion we had to stop the trial and rescue a very wet CO who was clinging to the periscope brackets. I would be the last to suggest that the coxswain had deliberately leaned just a little too hard on his levers. One of the two pretended that nothing untoward had happened and stood in the control room with rivers of water streaming from his trousers; the other had the good sense to dry himself while we got on with the trials.

A trial I always enjoyed was the main machinery trial during which the ship would work up to full power on the diesel engines and run for periods of 8 hours while we took instrument readings every 15 minutes. Actually we took readings for about the first hour and then every hour thereafter because they would be absolutely steady and we could rely on the submarine's chief of the watch to alert us should the gauges as much as flicker. Between readings the engineer overseer and I would play liar dice in the little wardroom. In the T-Class the air for the engines came down a special trunk but in the U and V-Classes all the air came down the conning tower making the control room as cold as charity. To climb to the bridge was a struggle against the down-coming gale. Quite fun really, but not so good in a north Atlantic storm when as much seawater as air seemed to enter. On one occasion my chief, Pamplin, came on a V-Class trial. After the first half hour or so he went up on the bridge leaving us to continue our 15 minute readings; we adjourned to the wardroom to play liar dice supreme in the knowledge that the rotund Pamplin was such a tight fit through the pressure hull hatches that he momentarily stopped the air flow, whereupon the engines sucked air from the submarines interior and made everybody's ears go pop. So when our ears went pop, Engineer Captain Herbert Moy and I would go into the engine room and studiously take readings — we had ample time because there would be separate pops as my chief came through the upper and then the lower conning tower hatches.

The propellers in the early U-Class had made an audible noise that could be heard at a considerable distance under water; they were said to 'sing'. The cause was unevenness in the water flow past the hull locally and into the blades, making the blades vibrate. We were aware of the German developments in hydrophones and I used to linger in the back-end listening to the singing propellers and wondering whether the enemy could hear it too. It was calculated that if we made the submarines about 3 metres longer the improvement in the flow would cure the problem. This was done in the second series and worked.

The Constructor Commander on Admiral Submarines staff attended deep diving trials. In 1942/43 this was the (very) tall Bob Newton. We would erect deflection battens to measure the compression of the hull as the vessel was taken down to and beyond its operational diving depth. There were often creaks and bangs as the pressure hull movement strained the external structure. In the earlier boats it was not unusual to have rivets become loose. All of the classes with which I dealt had their circular shape slightly flattened forward to accommodate the six torpedo tubes and aft to suit the twin propeller shafts. This was not good structural design practice but was unavoidable in the circumstances. It meant that high bending stresses and shear stresses were generated, particularly in the pressure hull frames. I actually found this to be useful; irrespective of what the deflection battens were doing in the circular, and hence classically loaded part of the hull, I used to watch the webs of the pressure hull frames in the torpedo compartment that my calculations had indicated might have the highest shear stress and when, or if, the paint started to develop characteristic 45 degree shear lines, I would know that we had gone deep enough. Those were the days! Our problem with the new A-Class design that was being worked on was to persuade the naval staff to accept four torpedo tubes so that we could have the circular hull that would be most resistant to collapse.

There is a well-established service tradition that one should never volunteer for anything. I would add, "Don't show off." One evening in the submarine depot ship's wardroom someone challenged Bob Newton that he couldn't high-kick the ceiling. Hopping like a chorus girl Commander Bob kicked the ceiling and in so doing damaged his knee for the rest of his life.

When in Bath I picked up where I had left off, approving plans, doing calculations and so on. I was required to take my turn for overnight duty on fire watch or as the night-duty or weekend duty officer. As duty officer one had to receive all incoming messages and correspondence and take appropriate action; which usually meant deciding whether to send for the man or men best able to deal with it or to wait until they arrived the following morning. For someone in the rather separate world of submarines it was a good way to check up on the rest of the navy and the ships in which I knew my term-mates were serving. At weekends there would also be a very senior officer on duty and one got to know them, particularly those who could not make their minds up and those who always wanted to talk.

I lunched in the canteen and naturally with people with whom I had been at college. We talked shop and shared problems. Ronnie Lofft was in the cruiser design group and the loss of the small cruisers of the Dido class was a matter of concern. If they were badly hit amidships they turned over and sank, with much loss of life. We had left the naval college knowing that the most important thing was to design the watertight subdivision so as to prevent a damaged ship from heeling over; by all means be prepared to accept a loss of buoyancy but don't lose too much stability and this was the message preached by the damage control school. The Dido class had longitudinal bulkheads each side of the after boiler room which were the problem. We suggested that large holes be cut in the bottom of these bulkheads. Calculation showed that the effect was beneficial. Ronnie Lofft proposed this to his superiors all of whom had been brought up with a battleship mentality and who reacted as if he had suggested that they sell their daughters into white slavery. Two years later, after further serious losses, the sort of solution that had been suggested was adopted.

Travel to Scotland and to the northern shipyards was always overnight; occasionally I could get a 3rd class sleeper, which was one of four berths in a small compartment. More usually I sat up, one of five people squeezed in on one side of the compartment faced with five glowing cigarettes of the people on the opposite seat. Little or no light was allowed lest it should attract the attention of enemy aircraft, but there was usually enough warmth from the closely packed bodies. Since the journey most times started in the dark and finished in the dark one had no idea with whom one had spent the night, mostly they were soldiers, to judge from the kit bags, tin hats and rifles over which one stumbled. Average speeds were seldom more than 40 mph, due in part to the lengthy stops at stations where soldiers and airmen gathered up their kit bags and rifles and lumbered off while seemingly an equal number got on. The trains stopped at all the stations, obscure wayside halts comprising a pub, a church and three cottages now merited a stop because the second battalion the Black Watch or the Royal Blankshires was encamped three miles up the road. Hotels were little better, no heating, no hot water and not very good food. Complaints were always met with "Don't you know there's a war on".

One suspected that much of the food allocated to hotels for visitors - all visitors were on official business — did not reach the visitors. And not only hotels ;I was at lunch in the directors room at Vickers Barrow one day. When coffee was served the Chairman remarked to the head waitress "Is there any sugar, Doris?" to which she unthinkingly replied "Oh no sir, even we don't get sugar in our coffee these days".

Vickers High Walker at Newcastle, a battleship, carrier and cruiser builder, was building V-Class submarines. One night, one of the partially completed hulls slid down the berth and rolled over. Help! It took but one day to pull it upright in its new position where it was eventually completed and launched. On completion these boats went a short way north to the coal port of Blyth for work-up.

We found that the crews, that is, the officers, had a tendency to nit-pick about the state of their boat as it approached completion. With the first boat we assumed that such problems were to be expected when bringing a new submarine builder on stream but when we had the same experience with the second and third boats we took an interest from Bath. We consulted Vickers Barrow, who could find nothing to criticise in High Walkers standards. As an afterthought the Barrow man mentioned that as each submarine was completed at Barrow the company presented the wardroom with a small civilian radio for their use when in harbour. Thereafter High Walker presented each boat with a radio and we had no more complaints. These were young men who daily put their lives on the line in enemy waters yet that radio mattered.

Diesel submarines must surface for several hours in each 24 to recharge their batteries. As the war progressed the intensity of allied air and sea patrols with radar, caused high German submarine losses while recharging. The Germans equipped their boats with a breathing mast, which they called a schnorkel, through which air could be drawn to allow the diesel engines to run with the submarine submerged at periscope depth. When they learned of this device Admiral Submarine's staff asked that British boats should be so fitted; there was an undertone of "why didn't you think of this". The fact was that we had proposed such a system in 1942/43 and had been told by that same staff that such a device was not necessary. We did not invent it, nor did the Germans, the Dutch did. Our inspiration was the Dutch submarine O23, which already had a schnorkel when she came to Britain when Holland was invaded. Quite recently, in 1993 we had some Dutch friends to dinner. We spoke of the difficult choice that those who were occupied faced, reluctant co-operation or open defiance of the Nazis with calamitous consequences for one's family. The husband said that he had been in the shipyard in the war when one day the German navy people had found the 0 23 schnorkel drawings and took them away with some excitement. So in the end, it seems, both the Kriegsmarine and we may have used the same prototype design.

One day I was told that some Russian submarines were arriving and that I would be responsible for the technical work that Prime Minister Churchill had promised Mr Stalin we would do, namely to fit radio direction finding (RDF) and asdic, (now called radar and sonar,) presumably so that the Soviets could copy them. My orders were to arrange and facilitate this. The submarines had started from Vladivostok some months earlier and journeyed via San Francisco, Panama, and Halifax, Nova Scotia. We were not able to discern how many had set out but four reached the UK. Russian speaking

Canadian officers had been attached to the boats for the Atlantic crossing to interpret allied signal traffic and help bring them safely through the approaches to the UK. The Russians had treated them abominably. On arrival in the Clyde the British said that they expected that the soviet sailors could do with a spot of leave after their long journey and that arrangements had been made for them to go to an inland hotel. "No" said the Russian Commodore " in wartime, soviet soldiers do not have leave". Thinking about it afterwards I supposed that if one is serving in Murmansk and lives in Omsk there is not much point in having a crafty 48-hour pass.

The rank structure was confusing; Lieutenants with Lieutenant Commanders as their subordinates commanded some of the submarines. Time in submarines was the criterion for command, not time in the navy. The engineers seemed to be on a different structure, the senior man had four rings. The political officer was a Lieutenant Commander who spoke English and said that he came from a university in the Urals. He was a most attractive and helpful man. My opposite number was Captain 2nd rank Zinoviev from the Soviet embassy in London.

The Soviet submarines were in a poor state after their long journey, with external hull plates hanging loose or missing and a missing hydroplane. The hulls were cylindrical and riveted and the diesel engines were Swiss Brown Boveri. Their auxiliary power system for operating valves, opening bow doors, raising masts and periscopes and the like was low-pressure air distributed in pipes about 6cm diameter. All equipments exhausted directly into the boat causing the pressure to rise. During the brief cruise I took with the commodore, the pressure gradually built up; I wondered how high they would let it go, thinking of the effect on the equipment and the crew. Finally I asked the commodore what they did about the pressure, expecting him to say "start the low pressure air compressor" — which would put the precious air back in the air storage system ready for use again. Instead he reached up and yanked at a lever at the crown of the hull and allowed the air to escape into the sea and hence the atmosphere. This was clearly something you couldn't do at any depth. I never discovered whether this was his party piece for my benefit. Whichever way one looked at it the choice presented to the CO was hazardous in war, either come to periscope depth and release a great big bubble of air or start the air compressor and make a noise.

Everywhere I went in the submarines a non-English speaking Russian sailor with a large revolver accompanied me. In each boat there was a small compartment forward about as big as a toilet with a locked steel door from which the sentry was always keen to divert attention. If as I suspected it contained a rudimentary listening device the operator would have a hard job hearing anything with the steel door rattling merrily behind him.

The Soviet submarines were allocated to Portsmouth and Rosyth dockyards for fitting British radar and sonar. We asked the Russians for drawings to help in the work but none were available so the dockyards had to take detailed measurements and create their own working drawings. Both Royal dockyards did an excellent job. Frequently I would meet with Captain Zinoviev at Rosyth on a Sunday, the day when it seemed we could best get away from other duties. At one such meeting he suddenly said that the Soviets would also like to have a 20mm Oerlikon gun fitted at the after end of the sail, as in British submarines. I said that the gun and ammunition and the bandstand would weigh more than the small single shot cannon already fitted and for stability reasons we would remove the latter. I was very worried about stability and the Soviets would not supply any data. I had to rely on Captain Zinoviev. I put in hand the necessary drawing work and arranged for the supply of equipment and returned to Bath. The following Wednesday morning I received a telephone call from Zinoviev, "Moscow says No", "No to what", I replied, "No to removing our gun, we want both guns".

I repeat this story for one simple reason that dates the event. The German armies had reached the outskirts of Moscow and the Volga and were locked in a life or death struggle with the Soviet armies. Yet with all this going on, Zinoviev had been sending messages about a piddling little gun and someone in their navy ministry had been replying.

When the refits were complete the Soviet submarines sailed to the Clyde to exercise their crews in the use of the new equipment that had been fitted. Inescapably during their period in the UK the rigid soviet constraint on their sailors loosened and many acquired British friends, none more so than the political officer who, rumour had it, had something big going with a Scottish schoolteacher. The outcome of this rubbing of shoulders with the capitalist west was that we had some difficulty in getting them to go back to the war. I forget the whole catalogue of reasons for delay but one boat ran aground and had to be docked. One flooded a battery tank and had to be docked and so it went on.

Just before the Soviet submarines completed their refit we received a request from Moscow to design a complete hydraulic system for their new submarine design. This would replace the bulky low-pressure air systems. Although we were hard pressed we said "Fine, please send us the drawings of your submarine and the broad indication of what the hydraulics will be required to operate". Moscow replied that they would not supply drawings of their submarine but the following spaces were available for hydraulic fittings, whereupon they tabulated a series of small areas in each main part of the boat. We said that we would not proceed on this basis and shortly afterwards were told that Mr Churchill ordered us to. After some debate we asked one of our hydraulic equipment specialist suppliers, McTaggart Scotts of Loanhead to take on the task and this they did. Throughout my long association with warship design and construction I made all sorts of demands on this company and they never let the Royal Navy down.

This was not the last that I was to hear of Captain Zinoviev. The final episode was to be 5 years later.

The British U and V-Classes were rather nice little boats with internal main ballast tanks. These and X comp tank aft were very difficult to get into and required one's body to be bent three different ways at the same time — different bits of course. Coming out was worse; on a few occasions in the shipyards and dockyards people would panic and they would have to be quietened down and guided out when calmer. The mine compensating tanks in the Porpoise Class were similarly difficult of access. My first acquaintance with them had been as an apprentice watching HMS *Grampus* being built at Chatham. Jack Sims was the Assistant Constructor responsible for the build and it was here, one day that he found that he couldn't get out of the compensating tank that he had entered for inspection. The submarines were all riveted and the noise inside the hull during construction was appalling. He had to remain, bent and cramped inside the tiny tank until work ceased for the day when, much calmer now, he was able to ease himself out through the manhole with the help of dockyard staff.

The Porpoise Class minelaying submarines had been designed in the early 1930's to carry and lay the RN's buoyant moored mine. Some 50 spherical mines, their sinkers and mooring chains were stowed on trolleys on rails in the submarine's casing and launched one after another through stern doors. These were contact mines; influence mines had yet to be introduced. To assist in placing the mines in the correct position, the submarines were equipped with taut-wire measuring gear; several miles of fine wire paid out from an external drum at the rear of the casing. The mine laying policy was that they would be laid in narrow waters; thus the submarine would obtain an accurate visual 'fix' some miles from the intended position of the minefield, sink the outboard end of the wire to the seabed and proceed submerged to the mining area, measuring the distance run and hence her position by means of the taut-wire gear.

They proved their worth in 1941 and 1942, not in carrying mines, but in carrying essential supplies into beleaguered Malta –'the milk run'. Every possible cubic inch of space was filled with something essential for the defence of the island, ammunition, food, lubricants, fuel and personnel. Petrol for the few RAF aircraft still flying was the prime requirement but was too dangerous to be carried inside a submarine. The minelayers vast minelaying space inside the casing was suitable for carrying gasoline. I am told that the urgency to get fuel for the Air Force was such that the first run was made with petrol in cans. This was so dangerous that special tanks were installed, running on the mine rails for subsequent trips. My duty was to run my slide rule over the general scheme of things. Since the weight of the of gasoline in its can or tank was about the same as the weight of the water it displaced there was no problem with the submarine's stability when fully submerged but coming up and unloading did require a certain amount of guile when the full load was carried and was massively complicated by axis air raids.

The V and U-Classes relied on the weight of their batteries for stability. If the battery was removed when afloat in the dockyard, main ballast tanks had to be filled, otherwise the boat would roll over. One day late in 1942 a U class boat was doing a post-refit work-up somewhere south of the Eddystone Light. The first lieutenant had some difficulty maintaining the balance between the weight and the buoyancy of the boat -the trim- but thought that this must be due to fresher water and temperature layers close to land. However a check revealed the alarming fact that a battery tank was filling with water and would soon have covered the cells. The submarine surfaced and returned to Devonport Dockyard. The ballast tanks were filled and the flooded battery removed. Water was coming in slowly via the sump, a small pocket to collect any spillage during battery maintenance. The reason was defective welding; that's putting it politely for this was not a weld that had cracked but was a series of pea sized blobs of weld metal that had barely melted at the edges. Repair would require docking and all sorts of tedious things like completely removing the acid proof bitumastic lining of the battery tank and making the repair welds upside down in the very restricted space inside the ballast tank. The original welds would have been made down-hand, in the shipbuilders fabrication shop in relatively ideal conditions.

This piece of shoddy workmanship could have resulted in the loss of the submarine, and in my brief report to my chief, I remarked that the welding was so bad that it must have been rejected by even the most inexperienced overseer 'had it been seen'. At the time we had about 100 overseers at Vickers Barrow whose duty it was to inspect everything including all welding that went to make our submarines. Pamplin sent my report to the principal overseer at Barrow who replied in vitriolic terms that he was not used to having his work criticised by junior officers, especially since it had arrived on Christmas Eve and instead of wishing his team well, he had had to discipline them. Pamplin gave this reply to me; across it he had written 'silly old fool'. I was pleased that it was only the overseers who had a bad Christmas and not the wives and children of the 34 officers and men of the submarine who could have been in danger as the result of this bad work.

One of the duties that I found difficult at the time was deciding the significance of dents in the pressure hulls made by enemy depth charges and bombs. These submarines had riveted hulls. Unless the boat was near the surface, attacks that bent the pressure hull frames usually sank the submarine. Boats that got back with bent frames had those frames replaced, but lesser damage would usually dimple the hull plating between the frames without distorting the frames. The plating in the small submarines was little more than 15 mm thick. My responsibility was to decide how little work should be done to fit these vessels to return to their dangerous duty. The rules I adopted were; if the dent was less than half the thickness of the pressure hull plating, do nothing. If the dent exceeded this, a T bar was put across and welded to the plating and the adjacent pressure hull frames. There were, alas, sometimes dents in places that couldn't be got at without taking the submarine to pieces, such as under a main motor. Where there were several big dents in adjacent frame spaces, a repair was made. Otherwise, individual dents would not limit a vessel's ability to dive to its designed depth but would affect its ability to sustain further action damage in the vicinity. Probability theory salved my conscience and they went back on patrol, little dents and all.

HMS *Tradewind* was the first T-Class submarine built at Chatham Dockyard. She came to the Clyde for trials with the naval constructor responsible for the build and a team of his workmen on board. We set off in the Gareloch for diving trials. The procedure was to set the trim and then to flood the main ballast tanks, two by two, until on flooding the final pair, the submarine would float gently down while going slowly ahead, allowing the First Lieutenant to let more water in or pump more water out until the vessel's weight equalled the buoyancy. *Tradewind's* officers followed this procedure but the boat hung up, partially submerged. The 1st Lieutenant was putting water in everywhere. I said, "Let's start again" and the CO blew main ballast bringing the submarine to the surface. Before you could say Jack Robinson he ordered, "Open all main vents"; there was the bang of opening vents and the roar of water rushing into the tanks and down we went with an increasing bow down angle.

I was at the after end of the Control Room holding on to something and the Chatham Constructor George Stunden was at the forward end against the conning tower ladder. We grinned lamely at each other as if we always did it this way. We both knew that the loch was about 200 feet deep with a sandy bottom (in places) so nothing very terrible was likely to happen but until we got used, some twenty years later, to the large angles that high speed nuclear submarines use to dive and turn, a dive angle approaching 10 degrees was unusual. By now the CO was blowing No 1 main ballast tank. The Chatham workmen had been in the torpedo compartment forward and just as the angle started to lessen, the first of these entered the control room looking somewhat wild-eyed. We then held an inquest. It appeared that the outside ERA had found that No3 main vents had not opened the first time because their hydraulic valves were shut. He had opened them and was in process of reporting this to the 1st Lieutenant when the CO had ordered open all main vents. We pumped tons and tons of water out of the trim and compensating tanks and with a gentle main ballast blow and slow ahead together we regained the surface to start the trials.

The responsibility for the conduct of trials was quite straightforward (?). The trials programme specified the things to be done and it was my responsibility to see that they were done in the way intended and to record the results. The CO was always responsible for the safety of his ship and executed the required manoeuvres and there was usually an experienced submarine qualified commander from the Naval Equipment Department, (DNE), Bath, on board. It was not unknown for something to happen during a trial to make it necessary to depart from the strict letter or order of the programme and this was always agreed between us on the spot with no problem. In my time the commanders from DNE were Dewhurst and Rimington, both of whom had been decorated for their service in command of submarines in the early years of the war. They were rather different. They were of the old school and had spent years in submarines prior to the war before achieving command. They were now supervising Lieutenants as young as 22 years old with their first command, such as Tony Troup and Ian Macintosh.

The sort of pitfall that might attend an unwary emphasis on one's responsibility happened to a colleague, Norman Honey, when conducting the sea trials of the aircraft carrier conversion, HMS *Vindex*. It would seem that Norman rather over-did things and gave the impression on the bridge that he considered himself to be in overall control. "Very well, Mr Honey," said the ship's captain "I am going to my cabin, perhaps you would have someone tell me when we get back to port". Honey hastily explained that he hadn't meant to imply that he was in that sort of overall control…

HMS *Truant* was refitted at the Ailsa Shipbuilding Company of Troon who were still pleased that somebody in the Admiralty had had enough wit to name the Hunt class frigate built there, HMS *Ascot*. At the end of the refit we had to submerge the vessel to check the stability and whether the ballast in the keel (on which the stability depends) needed adjustment. The nearest place for the test was the Holy Loch where we secured the submarine loosely to buoys forward and aft. Actually we had difficulty catching a trim and we went rather deep in the process. When we eventually sailed back to Troon, several shipyard people who had just come for the ride were greyer than they had been when we set out that morning.

The trimming and inclining experiment of the first T boat from Devonport Dockyard earned me a formal indication of displeasure from the Controller of the Navy. This was the first submarine that Devonport had built since the first war. It was a ghastly day in winter. At 7am the vessel was moved to the middle of the dockyard basin where we checked that the depth of water was sufficient and submerged to just bring the hull under water. All of the pressure hull hatches leaked so up we went and renewed the rubbers on all the hatches. Down we went again, more leaks, up and down and finally submerged with just the periscope showing. The vessel was now in trim and we checked the stability. We then came to low buoyancy and checked the stability and finally to full buoyancy and checked the surface stability. All through the day there were minor problems that had to be put right. It was now 8pm and my duty was to finally record the precise condition of all the tanks, stores and compartments so that I could calculate her final weight and have the ballast adjusted accordingly. This was a brand new submarine, the fuel tanks had never seen fuel oil and were simply full of water. In service the fuel is water displaced which means that sea water enters the last oil tank as the engines draw oil from the first tank, with the water siphoning through the system until finally all the tanks are full of water and the submarine is correspondingly heavier because the water is heavier than the fuel it replaces. In the T-Class there were four tanks to each group, so I had tank 1 and tank 4 tested which showed water in each case. So I went back to Bath and did my sums and told the dockyard how to ballast the ship. In due course the vessel was completed and went to sea en-route to trials and found that she was heavy, by about 20 tons if I recall properly. She signalled Admiralty and I was in big trouble. Investigation showed that after the trim and inclining experiment the dockyard had found that in one of the fuel groups the piping had been wrongly connected and tanks 2 and 3 had been empty throughout. They had corrected the piping error but had not told anyone, having no concept of its consequences for the submarines ability to dive. So I earned the Controllers displeasure. The lesson for me was always check everything, then check it again.

My chief Pamplin was a demanding man. The doors of the design room would fly open as he jet propelled himself in with some papers in his hand about which he wanted to speak. He would begin the conversation when some distance away while one struggled to recall what were the last papers sent in. He was a naval constructor in the tradition of the Master Shipwrights, sound on theory and versed in practice, able to design ships and build 'em too. He had given me a very hard ride for the first six months or so after I joined him; I suppose that fresh from the naval college I thought that I knew-it-all and deserved it, but about the Controllers displeasure he was fully supportive. I never heard another word about it.

Pamplin's forthright manner had some interesting results. In the British Foreign Office junior officers do not knock on the door when entering a senior's room. No one would have called Pamp a diplomat but he, too, objected to people knocking on his office door prior to entering and instructed the office lady clerk to put a DON'T KNOCK notice on his door. She duly prepared a notice and stuck it on his door, 'Please do not knock'. She was required to remove this and 'do what I said, 'DON'T KNOCK'. Thus it was. We were all highly amused when the biter was bit. Pamplin lived in a village near Bath and somehow managed to secure a miniscule ration of petrol to occasionally ride a small motorcycle between his home and office. When it rained he got wet and would change his clothes on arrival hopping from one leg to the other with his back to the door. When there was something urgent to discuss one would stand in his room and witness this performance. There came the day when the lady clerk didn't knock, opened the door and knocked Pamp to the floor clad only in his underpants. In 1942, war or no war, such occurrences gave middle-aged lady clerks the vapours.

Pamplin's boss was Assistant Director Lance Williamson, a bachelor, gentleman and a devout Christian. Each morning, on arrival at his desk he would spend ten minutes in silent prayer and meditation. He, more than anyone else, epitomised to me the generation and society that passed with the war.

I never ceased to wonder at the ability for submarines to grow heavy in service. I would complete the trimming experiment allowing for everything that had to be carried on board – with a bit to spare and off would go the submarine to work-up and war patrol. Six months later the boat would complain of being heavy and submit her own readings, which demonstrated that this was indeed the case. She might be 10 tons heavy in a T boat and 5 tons or so in a U. One might argue that due to repeated dives to extreme depth the hull plating had deflected slightly between all the frames thus reducing the buoyancy by a ton or so, but what is the rest? In older ships there is a weight due to repeated painting but not in new submarines. To understand my puzzlement, remember that a solid chunk of steel weighing one ton occupies a volume of several cubic feet. Where and what was the extra weight? We found that a major part was from things the crew carried on board on a come-in-handy basis, extra spare gear, extra ammunition, extra comforts and so on. Where on earth did they put it?

The preliminaries to a trim and inclining experiment usually involved a period of darkness inside the submarine while it was pulled away from the dockside to the deeper water. When he was the naval overseer at Scott Lithgow's, Greenock, Bob Newton was in a boat for the experiment. The lights went out when he was in the torpedo compartment and after a while he realised that he could see dim light near the torpedo embarkation hatch. Probing showed that, instead of rivets to withstand the diving forces, a workman had put in candles. This was not the first time one of HM Ships had been delivered from a Scottish yard with things like candle rivets HMS *Southampton*; the first ship of a splendid new class of cruisers had flooding below the quarterdeck on her delivery voyage south. Tearing up the teak decking showed that far from being welded securely in place, the quarterdeck hatch was just tack-welded and the main welds simulated with putty.

Several of the navies of countries occupied by the Nazi's provided crews for submarines, which were commissioned in their national colours. We did our best to meet any national requests. I recall that in the V Class for the Free French Navy we converted a distilled water tank to a wine tank. I could never quite figure out where the tens of gallons of wine came from in war-rationed Britain; perhaps they had a run ashore in Bordeaux or Algiers each time they went on patrol. My favourite was the V-Class boat for the Greek

Navy. When she was commissioned at Barrow she received the full commissioning outfit of stores and victuals including a few weeks worth of rum in the traditional wickerwork jars. The Greek CO refused to allow the rum on board his ship. The naval overseer felt that it would be a shame to return it to store for, after all, the CO might change his mind, and so after the submarine had completed trials and sailed for the Mediterranean, all had a good time.

There had been several attempts to penetrate allied harbours by determined Italian officers in or on midget submarines and later by the Japanese. When he learned of this Churchill is said to have expressed annoyance that we had not developed such vehicles. Actually, by then, following an initial lack of interest from on high, Naval Construction Department had a small group developing such craft. We had two main lines of development, 'chariots' which were effectively torpedoes upon which two men rode like motorcyclists and X-Craft in which the crew were inside. In each case the weapons were limpet mines to be stuck on the hulls of enemy ships or laid on the sea bed beneath, in each case with delayed action fuses to allow escape, although eventual capture or death was almost inevitable. Of the thirty men who took part in fifteen chariot attacks on the enemy, only six survived. The two-man crew of the chariot was to allow one man to control the craft while the other cut through nets or positioned the explosive charge. Two men were also desirable for psychological reasons; a lone operator is much more likely to abandon a dangerous mission than are two men. The Japanese would have had a far greater ratio of planes entering the final phase of their mission had they had more two-seat kamikaze planes.

To test the first X-Craft it was lowered from the horns of a Boom Defence Vessel. It was hauled up from its test depth with a leaking periscope gland. Our man who was in the craft swore that the water was up to his neck. He certainly had wet feet.

The fact that we were developing midget submarines was a closely guarded secret. They were not built in shipyards and the elderly depot ship from which they trained for their dangerous missions was located near Oban and not in the more densely populated Clyde area. The whole thing was so secret that the favourite game of the little boys on the Oban foreshore was playing 'midget submarines'. One of my jobs was to have the T class fitted with external cradles in which the chariots might be carried to their target area, and eye plates aft for towing X craft. In 1944 I was watching some ships staff welding these cradles in place on the ballast tanks of a T-Class submarine alongside the submarine depot ship in Trincomalee. As I climbed away I heard the petty officer remark, "Fancy a paymaster knowing about welding". When dirty, the paymasters white distinguishing cloth used to look very much like the constructors silver grey.

I have mentioned travel and cold hotels. A colleague and an elderly Lieutenant Commander RNVR travelled to Oban and were put in a small hotel. They were collected the following morning at 6 am and driven some miles to the jetty and thence by boat to the depot ship for breakfast, but first the Captain wished to see them. While they were talking, the Lieut Commander made a vain grab at his raincoat pocket; there was a thud and a glass containing a solid block of ice in which were embedded his false teeth rolled across the floor. That's how cold Scottish hotels were.

I am sure that Campbeltown is an attractive place and was attractive in the war years. I have been there and have slept there several times, yet I have never seen a thing other than the wet dock wall, the wet cobbled dockside road and the door to the hostel the navy used. I always arrived and left in the dark and always by submarine. Perhaps the most enjoyable period was in the autumn of 1943 doing the three weeks of sea trials of the first ship of the V Class, HMS *Venturer*, commanded by Lieut. Jimmy Launders, and the most memorable event was the evening when we anchored in Lochranza on the Isle of

Arran and received the signal that the Italian fleet was safely anchored beneath the guns of Malta, followed by 'splice the mainbrace'. The coxswain produced tots of rum for the wardroom and the wardroom gave the fore-ends a bottle of whisky. Sometime later the coxswain asked for permission to bathe. Permission given, he went to the extreme bow of the submarine and jumped in. I have never seen anything like it before or since, I swear that he came straight back on to the deck, barely touching the anchor chain, absolutely blue with the cold. We assumed that he was responding to some sort of dare and his reward would be paid in tots over the following days – in harbour of course. No one else ventured in, the cosy warmth and fug of a submarine has much to commend it.

An interesting trial was DC 1. I was able to observe this through the after periscope in HMS *Venturer*. We proceeded at periscope depth (obviously!) and a destroyer came up at speed on a parallel course about a hundred metres to starboard. I watched as a seaman on the destroyer's quarterdeck bent down and pulled a lever and a depth charge rolled over the stern. Some seconds later there was a plume of water and the submarine shook as the shock wave and the noise of the exploding charge, reached her. Lights went out and things rattled a bit. The captain called for reports from forward and aft and all was well in this small trial intended for crew training.

To Jimmy Launders went the credit for sinking a German U boat when both it and his own boat were submerged. We take such things for granted today, with active, target-seeking weapons, but in those days, with the trusty Mark 8 torpedo, it was a considerable achievement.

Without question the daily allowance of rum, the Tot was an inspiration when introduced into the navy in the days of wooden sailing ships of the line. Life was unbelievably hard, the food poor and often rotten and the tot must have been the one thing that made life bearable; it dulled the senses. In the wartime navy in 1939 the tot was still much prized, neat for the Chief's and PO's and diluted with water for the more junior rates. There was no question that this substantial shot of spirits affected the crew's efficiency and slowed down their reactions and I was always pleased when the rum issue was in the evening rather than at midday.

Wartime submarines were always short of water. Washing arrangements were primitive and there was a dependence on the depot ship for really serious bathing when in harbour. With longer and longer patrols we had to do something. Now it happened that we were introducing de-humidifiers to reduce the humidity of the boats' atmosphere and improve comfort and hygiene when submerged for long periods. The product from a de-humidifier is (of course) water and the doctors advised us that the water was pure. We had learned from captured German submariners that they had the same problems and that they used de-humidifier water for "wash-wasser". So we told our sailors to wash in it; to prove the point a doctor drank some but we could never get our men to use it; "Wot! Wash in old Chalky Whites sweat, not b****y likely" was the response.

The German U-boat that was captured had a distilling machine in the engine room. It was removed and copied at great expense and in due course distillers were fitted in the T-Class. We had endless difficulty in trying to make them work satisfactorily at sea. The story has it that one of our T boats sank a U boat on the surface and rescued most of her crew, including the engineer officer. He was taken into the diesel room and invited to make the distiller work, whereupon he threw up his hands and said "obsolete".

I have mentioned that many submarine trials were done in the Scottish lochs. I was in a V-Class and we had done something to do with torpedoes at Lochgoilhead and were departing en route to Captain Submarine Squadron 3 in HMS *Forth*. Standing in the control room the pop in my ears told me that someone was coming down the conning tower ladder and a pair of high heeled shoes and silk stockings were quickly followed by the rest of the CO's wife who I was concerned to see was very pregnant. We submerged a little bit to show her how it was done and at the mouth of the loch we landed our lady passenger. Only those familiar with the class can fully appreciate the gymnastics necessary first to reach a V (or U) Class casing, then climb vertically up the side of the sail and straddle over the top to reach the bridge before squeezing through the hatches down another two vertical ladders to the control room. And doing it all in reverse to go ashore and this time getting into a small boat to be out of sight of Captain SM3.

All of this is really a digression because what was undoubtedly my most important task was advancing the production of submarines with all-welded hulls. The 1930's had seen the progressive introduction of welding in place of riveting in surface warships and in non-pressure hull structure in submarines. In 1940/41 it had been decided to weld submarine pressure hulls. Just like that. According to the more junior RCNC officers who had been present the managing directors of the companies accepted the directive with as much reaction as if they had been told to paint the hulls blue instead of grey. Shortly afterwards the submarine design group issued guidance drawings and orders for all-welded T, S, and V-Class submarines and the game was on to produce the right steel, T shaped frame bars, welding electrodes and welding machines and to devise erection and welding procedures and inspection methods for use in such constrained structures.

We had to establish new standards as we built production boats, not for us the aircraft designers luxury of prototypes. We had to devise inspection methods; we had radiography but little experience in interpreting what the X rays showed. The big error that we made at that stage of development was lining up the welds along the hull and the welds around the hull to give four welds meeting like a cross roads. We were conscious that radiography held up work in the vicinity. We decided to radiograph all the cruciform welds. The Admiralty X-ray people said, "We think that there is a crack"; the shipbuilders said, "We are not sure" so we cut them out. I can recall the first time that we did this. It was at Vickers Barrow and Cammell Laird's were present because the problem was general. We cut the hull and found a crack 2 feet long. The Cammells people smiled a little. The next day we went to Cammell Laird's yard at Birkenhead and found cracks 3 feet long. None of us had any reason to smile.

We went through a bad spell until, through the splendid efforts of the shipbuilders, the electrode people, the steel makers and the radiographers; we achieved acceptable standards and produced welded hulls that were stronger and more battle worthy than their riveted predecessors. A problem that we faced was how to demonstrate that we had achieved this standard in the hulls already under construction. We didn't have much time. So we decided to apply internal pressure. This would not load the hull in the same way as external pressure but it would pull at the welds. The obvious solution was to fill the hull with water, after making sure that the slipway could take the weight and this was done in one case but the first of class submarines already had much equipment in them, which could not be flooded, so the decision was made to pressure test with air. This brought a considerable risk; incompressible water would itself present no danger but a submarine hull full of compressed air at over 100psi would contain enough energy to do serious damage if the hull ruptured. At the time we speculated on whether the Cammells boat would cross the Mersey if the end blew off. We went ahead with the tests; John Starks was responsible for the S-Class and I had the T-Class and we showed our confidence by climbing about on the hulls during the tests. (With our fingers crossed). Looking back from today's sophisticated structural analysis methods it all looks pretty ad-hoc, but it worked and the boats could go to war.

The thing that kept me going was my knowledge of how bad riveted joints really were. No one who has seen riveted hulls built can contest this. The textbook situation of accurately drilled holes in plates and butt straps being lined up and nice round rivets driven in is seldom the case. The light seen through the holes in plates brought together is seldom circular and into these, rivets are hammered. One should never forget that to a riveter, if he can see any light at all, 'it's a good hole'. If a Martian who had no preconceived ideas was told that to keep out the sea the Earthlings drilled lots of holes in the hull and bunged bits of ill-treated iron into the holes he would fall about laughing. During our training in the Royal Naval Engineering College we had been given the tools and told to weld two plates together after a five-minute demonstration by our instructor. We had then put our efforts in a tensile machine to measure the strength of our welds, and hey-presto, poor as they were, they were stronger than a riveted joint would have been. Except for one of my term-mates whose specimen joint came apart in his hands. Well, there is always one isn't there.

The welds that we made that first day were better than the weld on the battery tank sump that nearly lost us a submarine.

The introduction of welded hulls significantly increased the resistance of our hulls to damage and loss by enemy action. We demonstrated this by explosion tests against full size sections of hulls, gradually increasing the size of the explosion and measuring the resulting accelerations and damage. The target that I designed in the back of my workbook was built in Portsmouth Dockyard. It had conical, floodable ends, which were flooded to submerge the target for test, and emptied to raise the flooded test section. The origin of these full-scale tests was somewhere about 1926 when someone in the submarine design group had suggested that prior to scrapping, the ex-World War One submarines of the reserve fleet should be used as targets. Their Lordships approved and a submarine was moored on the surface in Spithead as the target vessel. The instrumentation was crude and had to be tried. To do this it was decided to make a small explosion at a considerable distance from the submarine before starting the trial proper. This small charge was detonated and to everyone's horror the submarine slowly sank! When the boat was brought to the surface it was found that far from being its designed thickness, the pressure hull forward was less than 3 mm thick due, not to corrosion but to the constant rubbing of the mooring chain during all those years in the reserve fleet. This was one of the reasons why all of our newer submarines had an extra thickness of hull plating beneath the anchor.

The T-Class had Admiralty or Vickers diesel engines. Overall the Vickers machinery installation was about 6 tons lighter than the Admiralty installation, about 98tons compared with 104tons. The Admiralty engines were designed and developed by naval engineer officers in Chatham Dockyard where the thump of engines under test in the 'Factory' was a constant reminder of this really remarkable work. The U and V Classes had high-speed diesel generators and propulsion was always on the main motor.

Three of the pre-war T-Class were fitted with MAG German diesels. These proved not to be as reliable in service as the British engines but, of course, this could have been in part due to the non-availability of spares as the war progressed. A consequence of this was that the boats spent less time on patrol than their sisters, which improved their chance of survival. There was much good humoured banter of the CO who took one of these submarines on patrol and sank a U-boat within the first week only to have to return to HMS *Forth* with machinery problems the day after while the boat that did a pier-head jump to fill the vacant billet sat through the weeks of the entire patrol without seeing a thing.

There were many losses during my period in Bath. We would prepare the set of documents and drawings to refit such and such submarine only to learn that she had not returned from patrol. Early losses were one a week but gradually things got better. What was especially tragic was when boats were lost during their trials and work-up period off the coast of Scotland. Two of my boats, HMS's *Untamed* and *Vidal* were lost in this way and only the former was ever found. When she sank HMS *Untamed* had been 'ping-running', running up and down at a nice comfortable depth and providing a target to train the sonar operators of the surface ships above. The crew perished. The submarine was located and salvaged and it was found that she had flooded through the speed-log opening. Someone in the crew had decided to do some work on the log and despite the safety interlocks, had partly opened the hull valve resulting in uncontrollable flooding. It is difficult to make things absolutely sailor-proof.

Messers Chernichef manufactured the logs used to measure the submarine's speed and the firm's representative would attend the speed and machinery trials of all new submarines to calibrate the log. He was known throughout the submarine service as Baron Chernichef. I never learned his real name; it was always "Morning Baron" and so on

We were not alone in losing submarines during their trials and work-up period. The German navy lost over twenty boats in the Baltic during the war years but fortunately the depth and other conditions enabled many people to survive.

At the beginning of 1944 I was appointed to the staff of the C in C Eastern Fleet as the Assistant Fleet Naval Constructor Officer and required to familiarise myself with the ships of the fleet until passage was arranged.

Chapter Two

I took passage in the Escort aircraft carrier HMS *Ameer* to Ceylon. The carrier was loaded with twin-engined aircraft for the RAF and carried a large number of personnel for the ships of the fleet. The voyage was uneventful except for a threatened air attack on our convoy off Algiers, for which we made smoke. We did not make smoke the traditional way: *Ameer* had chemical smoke generators which some genius had positioned right beneath the openings through which air was drawn for the boiler room. In consequence all of the engine and boiler room staff were badly affected, the Chief Engineer particularly so. The ship was a 'Woolworth carrier' built in the USA in an incredibly short time, and had only just been delivered. There was one boiler and one propeller. Somewhere between Bombay and Cochin (where the aircraft were off-loaded) we lost all steam pressure and our accompanying N-Class destroyers went round and round us as we drifted while the boiler room staff tried to relight the boiler.

For the first part of the journey we were in a fast troop convoy carrying troops for the Mediterranean theatre. It was sad when almost each third day all ships lowered their flags to half-mast while some unfortunate person was buried at sea. There must have been over 15,000 men in the ships, all of whom had been fit on embarkation and one wondered what accident or sudden illness had taken these young lives 'on active service', so soon after leaving the UK. I had joined *Ameer* in Belfast but somewhat to my surprise, my official duties started before then. When I joined the train for Stranraer (for Larne and Belfast) a Chief Petty Officer with a clipboard and armband marched up to me and said, "You are the senior officer in charge of this draft, Sir". This was news to me, but I had enough wit to ask him how many were in the party and to seek confirmation that each small group of sailors had its own Chief or Petty Officer in charge. The only stragglers were officers and I could rely on them not to abscond.

Everything about *Ameer* was spartan. I occupied a bunk in a largish cabin with eight bunks, four of which were occupied. All the fittings were of steel and the only soft furnishings were the four mattresses and bedding. My three companions were a New Zealand Navy VR pilot with a cavalier attitude to authority, who prowled around the cabin brandishing a large sharp sheath knife that was strapped to his right leg when he was not practicing disembowelling motions. He was a rather unsettling companion. The second was a charming, quiet South African Navy lieutenant who in later years was to become the C in C of that country's navy and the third was a Lieutenant Commander RNVR who had been on Admiral Mountbatten's staff in Combined Operations and was en-route to Kandy to join his old chief. Most evenings we 'took a turn' on the flight deck and discussed many things. He mentioned one day that the navy had taken his yacht. This was not surprising because at the time of the British retreat to Dunkirk in 1940, the marinas and rivers of Britain had been stripped of every thing that would float, to be sailed or towed across the Channel to try to rescue our soldiers. His chance remark came back to me when we entered the harbour at Alexandria; my friend suddenly said, "There's my yacht" and pointed to a ship with funnels, now painted grey, but unmistakably in the style of the Victoria and Albert, called *Stella Polaris*. I began to have a shrewd idea why he fitted so comfortably in Mountbatten's staff – a nice man.

Bombay, like Alex, was a seething mass of humanity. *Ameer's* captain was not a well man and was hospitalised in Bombay while his ship sailed on to Cochin, where we were for several days while our cargo of aircraft was off-loaded at Willingdon Island.

Cochin was small in those days as were the nearby towns. I for one was not sorry when we sailed into Colombo harbour and I could at last take up my new appointment.

The C in C Eastern Fleet's headquarters was in a block of apartments on the seafront near Galle Face Green. Across the road, across a piece of grass to a 4ft drop was the sandy beach and the Indian Ocean and over there somewhere Africa and Arabia. My chief was Constructor Captain F.G. Bogie; he and I were the only constructor officers in the fleet although there were two others in the dockyard activities in Colombo and Trincomalee. One of these was in the Heavy Repair Ship HMS *Ausonia*. Bogie and the Fleet Medical Officer had offices either side of a staircase and shared a WRNS secretary. The Fleet Engineer officer had the rooms beneath. Bogie remained with the fleet staff and I was with the ships of the fleet based on Trincomalee, under the command of the Vice Admiral, second in command. When in Colombo I would occupy a second desk in the captain's room and live in the Galle Face Mess. Bath seemed very remote.

The Galle Face Mess buildings had been built in the previous century and used as a military hospital until falling into disrepair. Like the Royal Naval Engineering College buildings at Keyham, Devonport, having earlier been condemned, the Galle Face buildings had been brought back into use for officers. There were two stone buildings, one for senior officers and one for Lieut Commanders and below. In the grounds were hutments built from palm trees arranged as cabins. The day I arrived from the UK I slept in such a palm-cabin. I was disturbed by rats and the next day and always thereafter I was put upstairs in the main building. The rooms had glass-less windows and bat-wing doors opening on to a wide veranda that stretched the length of the building. The rooms were spartan but airy in the remorseless heat. The stewards tidied the cabins and also did the laundry; one would see white shirts, shorts, socks and other items spread out on big rocks in the sun. The wringing process would precede this, which was to whip the rocks with the garment making a loud splatting noise. I suppose that Messer's Gieves; the naval outfitters did well out of it, eventually, but at first the sound used to wring my withers. There was an anteroom and a wardroom whose Singhalese cooks and stewards were presided over by an excellent RN chief petty officer.

The normal day uniform was white shorts, white short sleeve shirt with rank epaulettes, white stockings, white or black shoes and white cap cover. It was some time before I realised that the rest of the staff had dubbed my chief 'the man with the longest shorts in the fleet'. Now that they mentioned it I, too, could see that his shorts were over his knees. There was much good sense in the seaman's working uniform afloat. Twenty years earlier pith helmets were worn, shirts had a reinforced pad to protect the spine and shoes with stockings were compulsory. Now, partly due to the example of the Australian navy, in ships, shirts were not worn and sandals were allowed. Men were healthily tanned and free from many of the complaints that once made ships in the tropics so uncomfortable.

The Galle Face mess was a Transit Mess into which officers joining the fleet, and particularly people who were on some sort of special or fact finding mission, were put while their itinerary and forward movement arrangements were sorted out. It was a great place for meeting old and new friends joining or visiting the fleet, a fleet that was being augmented as the war in the Atlantic and the Mediterranean scaled down. Apart from professional colleagues, three people come to mind. The first arrived with me in the good ship *Ameer*. He was a pressman who had volunteered as a war photographer, in part for the extra money because he had an invalid wife in London. After one night in Colombo he was whisked off to join a ship that was to take part in the bombardment of Sabang on the western-most tip of Sumatra. The operation was successful and only one of our ships was hit, and that only a damaged mast but that mast fell and killed my press friend. The second was also a non-combatant; I sat next to him by chance at dinner and noticed his "press" epaulettes. I turned to speak to him and as quick as light he whipped an articulated speaking tube in front of my mouth. It transpired that he was an official war artist. I hadn't really thought about the harshness of tropical sunlight until I learned that he was only painting his subject, the battleship HMS *Howe* for about half an hour at dawn and half an hour in the evening. In Sri-Lanka - to us it was still Ceylon - the sun comes up about 6am and goes down about 6pm give or take half an hour throughout the year. When I was in Colombo we used to talk about his work and the sketches he was making. The finished painting is now part of the record of the navy's story.

As a general rule, by 1944, the straight stripe Royal Navy had accepted the entwined stripe RN Reserve and the wavy stripe RNVR officers as (nearly) equals but this did not necessarily extend to the chaps with bright green cloth between their wavy gold braid; these chaps were the 'specials' who had been given officer rank because of some special skill the navy required, but who were not expected or trained for general naval service. In many cases these officers had ability far beyond that available in general, they might be electronic boffins or Japanese linguists or something similar; they were different and they tended to be loners, on the outside looking in at the navy. Such a man was my third friend, Lieut. RNVR (Sp) Callaghan, like myself a man of Kent. He hailed from Maidstone where he had been a tax inspector before becoming a secretary of the Inland Revenue Staff Association. He had been in the Naval Intelligence Division in Whitehall and was now appointed to the Eastern Fleet for similar duties; more than half jokingly he suggested that he had been sent away from Whitehall when they discovered that he was a socialist. We shared much discussion on the likely social and economic structure of post-war Britain and the need for radical change. The bee in my bonnet was the need for a powerful industrial effort on exports because the UK would be bankrupt after the war. In one of our last talks he said that his ambition was to become a member of parliament and that he was on the labour party's candidates list.

Occasionally silent non-European gentlemen in plain clothes would pass through the mess, in some cases destined for clandestine landing in territory held by the Japanese. On one occasion I shared an aircraft from Colombo to Trincomalee with a future prime minister of Burma. Use was made of Walkers Dock in Colombo to dock destroyers. One day I was on the wooden staging around a destroyers damaged propeller when a Singhalese fitter turned and asked me whether Japanese destroyers had the same sort of propellers as the British. I was able to assure him that his job was safe. For some reason Captain Bogie came down in the dock; he literally clung to the dock wall the whole way down the unprotected steps and for the first time I realised why he was so reluctant to fly or climb masts and so on. His distress with vertigo was very severe.

The C in C was Admiral Sir James Somerville of Force H fame. His Chief of Staff was Commodore Edwards whom I was destined to serve in other appointments in later years. His flag Lieutenant was a very capable young man. I warmed to him one day when the Admiral was at sea in his flagship. It was C in C's habit to walk on the quarterdeck in the dog watches, on the starboard side, of course, and he would invite young men of his staff to share a few turns up and down the deck and talk to them about current issues. Obviously he was briefed by his "flags" but it was very good public relations and it did give the Admiral an idea of what was concerning people. Afterwards, back in Colombo he would surprise his staff by his awareness of something that had not yet reached their desks. It was the practice for a destroyer to collect urgent mail for the C in C and race after the fleet to deliver it. This was done by the destroyer coming close alongside the flagship and firing a line across, along which a container would be sent containing the mail. I was present on such an occasion.

As it was coming over the destroyer flashed a message by signal lantern, "What's he saying, Flags" asked the admiral. "He wants his shell case back, Sir," said the flag lieutenant. "Tell him not to be a Jew," said the admiral whereupon flags turned to the Chief Yeoman who was always in attendance and said "Make, don't be a Scotsman". Flag lieutenants are employed to know who is commanding what and he knew that the destroyer's CO was of the Jewish faith. I hasten to add that in those days such expressions were in use without the slightest suggestion of racist overtones although looking back I suppose it could have been hurtful.

Bogie told me that, according to members of the staff close to the admiral, the medical branch of the navy had decided in the spring of 1939 that Rear Admiral Somerville was suffering from tuberculosis and had recommended that he be retired on medical grounds. Somerville and his civilian specialists had vigorously contested this, but the Medical Director General and particularly a certain Surgeon Lieut. Cdr. (lets call him Smith) had insisted that he was unfit for further service. While the case was under review, war was declared and Somerville went back to sea and fame. The Admiralty in accordance with long-term career planning usually makes appointments to admiral's staffs. Admiralty would send a signal proposing to relieve Captain X by Captain Y and C in C would signal his concurrence. In accordance with this procedure the Medical Director General signalled his intention to relieve the Fleet Medical Officer by Surgeon Captain Smith who was currently serving in one of the three hospital ships at Trincomalee. To everyone's horror, for Smith was well liked, the admiral informed the MDG that Smith was not acceptable and he had appointed Surgeon Captain Jones, who was serving in another hospital ship, to the post.

Some weeks after the change had taken place, Admiral Somerville was in Trincomalee and in the course of his visit met Surgeon Captain Smith. Afterwards he turned to his secretary, a paymaster captain, and quietly said, "My God, it's the wrong Smith". There followed a series of elegant moves which showed the wiseacres in the Fleet and in Whitehall that it had all been part of a very complicated plan to benefit both the service and Surgeon Captain Smith.

One of the most interesting tasks was the work to improve the environment in HM Ships. The ships complained that they were hot; they were, after all, near to the equator but they felt that they were hotter than was necessary. This had been bearable in peacetime when warships in the tropics had operated with every opening that could be opened, open. Now, under wartime conditions learned the hard way in the battle of the Atlantic, things were for real and ships were very hot. On station we had found that in many cases the fans that provided the ventilation were not running at full speed, many were running backwards (they don't suck, they blow but not very well), ventilation trunking was often obstructed and control flaps inoperable. The reason that most ships gave for not running the fans at full speed was that they would, or might, burn out and when fans failed they didn't get a replacement! We sent massive demands to the UK for spare motors; starters and fans and soon these were arriving with the Naval Stores organisation. The ships were assured that spares would be supplied promptly and ordered to run all fans at full speed after checking the system over. There were surprisingly few failures.

A habitability mission arrived in mid-1944 to check up and reinforce the measures already taken and more particularly to examine the medical factors associated with ship borne life in the tropics. This was reflected in the composition of the mission, two naval doctors and one naval constructor. I would be available as a fourth member and the mission could, if required, work as two teams.

We visited all of the major ships of the fleet and most of the smaller ones. Submarines were no problem, unlike in the past when the sailors hurried to move on board the depot ship when in harbour, the crews of the modern T and S boats recently arrived on station preferred to remain in their nice cool submarines thanks to the de-humidifiers which both cooled and dried the air. In each ship we asked about problem systems. We looked at all the fans and made system checks, took flow and wet and dry temperature readings and took physiological data on personnel, pulse rates and temperatures, in all living and operational spaces. It was remarkable how many fans were found to be running at reduced speed, notwithstanding the earlier instruction from Fleet HQ to run them at full speed. Some ships thought that they were! Many fans were running backwards and a simple reversal of connections produced a marked increase in airflow. In one aircraft carrier the laundry was unbearably hot and humid. Well, laundries often are but this was really hell. We found that the gas flap on the fan exhaust system was closed and to judge from the paint, had never been opened. In another major warship we found a ventilation trunk that went from the weather deck to a magazine without a single valve or flap. Most common general faults were the result of bad housekeeping with filters and grilles clogged with dirt, paint and grease. A not unusual reason for lack of ventilation in compartments towards the end of a supply system was human intervention, such as cutting unauthorised extra openings in the trunk or introducing some object, such as a pair of old socks, to reduce the amount of air serving other spaces.

The destroyers had the best ship husbandry, presumably because things were more accessible and the smaller crew numbers made responsibility easier to assign and check. Bigger ships had the British tendency to complain without first 'removing the mote from their own eye'. We did not find a single big ship that enforced a routine to regularly clean its ventilation filters and operate its gas flaps; in most cases responsibility was diffuse below department head level. Such an omission would have been quite unacceptable in a USN Ship at that time.

One of the more significant trials was undertaken in a secondary armament magazine of the battleship HMS *Howe*. The magazine was beneath the thick armour protection and in action conditions would only receive fresh air for ten minutes in each half hour, when valves in the armour were opened. The magazine crew's duty in action was to remove the heavy 5.25inch calibre shells from the racks and carry them to the shell hoists, which would deliver them to the gun turret far above. They would be on watch for four hours and then be replaced by the men who were above opening and closing the ventilation valves in the armoured deck. This would continue until the threat of enemy action had passed. Every 15 minutes we took temperature and humidity measurements and the sailor's temperature and pulse rates. After three and a half hours we made them go into action and supply ammunition to the hoists. After 5 minutes our doctors stopped the trial at which point the medical evidence indicated that the sailors were in danger of collapse. And who wants 5.25 shells rolling about the floor? How this condition might have been changed by the stimulus of actual battle we could not determine but the case for substantial magazine cooling was apparent. It will be appreciated that sustained operations on the equator was not a major consideration in the staff requirements for these ships.

The medical officer in HMS *Howe* was an RNVR Surgeon Commander who before the war had received a great deal of publicity as the victim or intended victim of a confidence trick in Plymouth. In *Howe* he devoted much of his energy to the provision of entertainment for the ships company in one of the twin seaplane hangars now allocated for this purpose. The problem was that the opinion that he had of his singing voice and the brilliance of his wit was not shared by the sailors and since, once he had the microphone in his grasp, he seemed to lose all sense of time, the response was somewhat mixed.

Air conditioning had been provided in HM Ships as an add-on feature in certain special compartments to cool the equipment fitted therein, not for the personnel working the equipment. These were radar offices, which had to be located close to their aerials, and were of necessity high in the ship and frequently exposed to the sun on five sides. By a series of gas flaps the air conditioning system could be made to draw air from the ship and exhaust into the ship thus providing a little cooling to the ship or could draw 100% of fresh air, cool it and exhaust directly back to the atmosphere, or combinations of the above. On practically every occasion that I visited these offices I found the system on 100% fresh air, sometimes with the door open and the radar ratings sitting smoking as they performed their duties. Questioned, they would complain that when on re-circulation the cigarette smoke tended to build up. In most cases with the agreement of the ship's officers we locked the system to give about 90% re-circulation; if the radar ratings didn't like the smoke they could stop smoking while on duty.

What became quickly evident was the inboard environment seriously affected the efficiency of HM Ships and that improving that environment might produce a greater effect on ships' performance in action than, say, fitting an extra gun. This and the need to do something about the incredibly bad and overcrowded living conditions that we provided for the sailors were two of the things that I was resolved to do something about when I returned to ship design in Bath. Although it seems self evident today it took several years after the war, in various appointments in which I might shape policy, to establish that the cost in space and money of air conditioning and sleeping the sailors on bunks was a justifiable military expenditure. Once the case was convincingly made, there was little opposition.

The overcrowding was not due to poor planning by the manpower departments but a consequence of the weapons and equipment added to HM Ships due to war experience, notably radar and additional close-range weapons. In the case of the aircraft carriers the problem was made much more difficult by carrying additional aircraft in a deck-park which brought large numbers of additional crew. British carriers designed for the hostile conditions of the North Atlantic were not meant to carry additional aircraft parked on deck but in the kinder conditions in the Far East this was possible and increased the ships squadrons by more than 25%.

The work of improving living conditions on the spot was not always appreciated. The same aircraft carrier that had never opened the laundry exhaust flap complained that the wardroom ventilation supply was deficient. And so it was. Inspection showed that the supply fan was set at half speed and that the ventilation supply trunk was partially obstructed. These faults were corrected and at about 11.30 one morning the fan was restarted at full speed. I went along to the wardroom to judge how improved the air supply was and perhaps to bask in a little reflected glory, to be greeted with pandemonium. The wardroom staff had just completed laying up for lunch on spotless white tablecloths when suddenly stewards and tables had been smothered with several years worth of dust and soot that had hitherto lain undisturbed in the ventilation trunking. Actually they took it rather well. I might perhaps add that this really was a most attractive wardroom, with long wooden tables and sideboards and the reflection of the sea coming through the side-scuttles and dappling the underside of the deck over.

Because of the nomadic nature of their duty the members of the habitability mission had their mail addressed c/o Fleet Medical Officer, Eastern Fleet, from which office one of us would collect it when passing through. It did not take us long to realise that the Fleet Medical Officer's wren secretary always held back the mail for the unmarried RNVR surgeon, making it necessary for this tall, good-looking officer from Guys hospital to go personally to collect his mail.

One should never be surprised at the remarkable span of interests of members of the medical profession. I was discoursing on some aspect of aerodynamics and similarities and differences with hydrodynamics when this doctor showed a more than shallow knowledge of laminar and turbulent flow. It transpired that his research at Guys was in cardio-vascular irregularities and as he said, blood flowing in a vein is sometimes very much like water flowing in a pipe. One day a Professor Basset arrived, it would seem to join the habitability mission in a sort of consultancy capacity although this was never made clear. He was British but teaching in a New England university. His interest was the physiological consequences of high ambient temperatures and humidity. The average age of the ships companies of the fleet was below 25 and anyone over 50 was positively ancient. To be over 50 and a professor from an American university gave Basset film star status, a reputation that spread like wildfire through the fleet when he shaved all the hair from one side of his head and body and let it grow on the other. This was to examine the effect of body hair in the retention of moist air and moisture. He would visit a compartment and put small measuring devices on his skin, the hairy bits as well as the smooth and whirl his psychrometer around while chatting amiably. The sailors loved him.

When ashore at fleet headquarters it was my habit to leave the office at about 17.30 and, monsoons permitting, walk across the grass to the beach and swim until the setting sun just touched the horizon. It was then time to dress, walk to the Galle Face Mess and shower before dinner. The short tropical twilight was always over before I reached my quarters. When they were in Colombo the constructor and the RNVR doctor of the habitability mission followed the same routine. It was thus that a small Singhalese boy named John befriended us. He was particularly taken with the fair-headed doctor of whom he asked endless questions about England and London. The thing that I remember most clearly and still with a sense of the humility we all three felt was when Surgeon Lieutenant Commander Eddie Holling, impressed with the boy's questioning, asked how it was that he spoke such good English, to which the small boy replied "But English is my language, Sir". Holling gave him his uniform belt.

Another aspect of the relationship between nations; there was a lorry with a bench down each side and a canvas top which carried officers between the Galle Face Mess and Fleet HQ. At lunchtime it would wait until 13.00 when one of the passengers would go round to the front and tell the Singhalese driver to depart. One day a very smart Lieutenant in the Royal Indian Navy climbed down and told the driver to go and returned to the back of the lorry. We didn't move so after a while I went round to the front and told the driver that we were ready to go. He said, "Yes master, now I go. I not take orders from a black man".

At the southern end of Galle Face Green was the Galle Face Hotel where we occasionally went for dinner. One sat on cane chairs and it was advisable to wear long trousers because mites in the chairs would bite the back of one's legs. One took one's own alcoholic drinks and it was as well to keep these on the table or firmly between one's feet otherwise the bottles would silently disappear. All in all it was hardly worth the trouble.

I never heard of the theft of anyone's possessions at the Galle Face Mess but Admiralty stores in transit between Colombo and Trinco were fair game. The poverty of the people was so evident and we had so much. Lorries would leave the docks and a case or two would fall off enroute. The drivers would have no idea where they fell off, perhaps when they stopped for tea. Their response to questioning would be to shake (or nod) their heads and share the questioner's confusion. To Europeans the fact that they would say "Yes Master" while shaking their head and "No master" while nodding vigorously did not help. Very occasionally lorries would disappear into the jungle and never be seen again, or at best be recovered less their load and all removable components of the lorry.

Petrol was unobtainable for all but official use but the wealthy, usually ministers in the civil government could be seen occasionally out for an evening drive with their families. The loss of petrol from RN cars and lorries became so bad that locks were put on the filler caps to which only the Naval Stores officers had keys. Within the month ministers were calling on the Governor, Admiral Layton, to protest that it was no longer possible to buy black market petrol and asking that the locks be removed.

The security of the lorries was left to the civil police who were very good. There were restrictions on the movement of rice among the various administrative areas of Ceylon and the police manned roadblocks to inhibit such movement. One day an RN lorry was stopped and a bag of rice was found under the driver's seat. The driver professed himself to be as surprised as were the police, notwithstanding the fact that he had been practically sitting on it. The rice was confiscated and sent to the central depot where, some days later it was found to be of this years crop, but of a variety not grown in Ceylon but very common in Burma.

Despite the war there was still a significant coastal traffic around the coast of India and large dhows would sail right round Ceylon carrying cargoes from the west coast ports to the east coast ports like Madras and Calcutta. The navy monitored this traffic with a small force of motor patrol craft. The big dhows would round the southern tip of Ceylon and gradually stand out to sea as they sailed northwards on course, say, for Calcutta. The poser set by the rice was whether one of the more adventurous had been joining the Burma coastal traffic, risking capture by the Japanese or sinking by British submarines or perhaps the rice had been smuggled from somewhere like Cox's Bazaar to Calcutta and simply purchased by the owner of the dhow for sale on the Ceylon black market.

C in C's staff usually travelled to Trincomalee by Beechcraft but on one occasion I accompanied Captain Bogie by car. The road was a single width of tarmac with a clay verge on each side on to which the smaller vehicle must move when two vehicles met. The jungle was oppressively present and where upkeep was overdue there was already scrub on the clay verge. During the journey we saw a variety of animals including an elephant in the distance; the driver explained that now was the time when the elephants were being rounded up to train the young ones for work. We passed through several settlements, usually near a pond in which most-times someone was washing with a cow or bullock standing in the water nearby. The women bathed by loosening their robe, putting their arms inside and using one hand to keep the robe up and the other to wash themselves, albeit with muddy water. Men and women and children were working in the clearings; their life was hard and I found it depressing.

Staff officers visiting Trinco were accommodated in the staff bungalow when not in an HM Ship. Although the massive naval and military presence in the area was said to have driven the wild animals several miles inland, this seemingly did not apply to the monkeys whose calls were a constant accompaniment to life in the bungalow as were the small lizards who lived on the dining room walls. No one ever tightened their mosquito net, nor slept more rigorously down the centre of their bed, than I did when ashore in India and Ceylon. What a relief to be on board ship; we believed that mosquitoes could not fly more than a few hundred metres from the shore.

As the land battle was joined in Imphal on the border of India, the Fleet's mission was clearly to harass the Japanese lines of communication and coastal installations. Submarines were sinking native craft thought to be carrying supplies along the Burma coast and destroyers were probing inshore. Not without cost, a P-Class destroyer was attacked by an aircraft in very shallow water. The small bomb missed the ship and detonated on the seabed close under the destroyer's stern. There was little damage to the ship in the vicinity of the explosion but the whipping motion buckled the ship amidships in way of the forward boiler room creating a crease more than 10cms high. I was interested to note that the 4-inch guns with which this class was armed were clearly the elderly guns that had been removed from the three-funnel County Class cruisers when they had been modernised just prior to the war

HMS *Tally-Ho* was attacked by a Japanese warship in misty conditions and had her port main ballast tanks damaged. She could submerge but when she surfaced she had a dangerous angle of heel. Her captain, Commander Bennington, a brilliant submariner, managed to escape further damage and sailed back to Trinco, where he came through the boom with an angle of 13 degrees. It might have been Tally-Ho or another damaged boat that had a destroyer sent to tow her home. In securing the tow, the destroyer's stern hit the submarine's bow and there were nearly two to be towed home. There were occasions here and later in the Pacific when I wondered whether we really needed an enemy to damage our ships because we were doing it so well ourselves, thankfully, usually in a minor sort of way.

I have mentioned that ships officers were instructed in damage control - how to limit flooding and preserve stability and put fires out. The basic rule to help maintain stability when partially flooded is to jettison top-weight from as high in the ship as possible. I had not realised the ambiguity in this well rehearsed instruction until I joined the damaged destroyer in the final stage of her journey home and the young engineer officer told me that they had jettisoned top-weight from as high in the ship as possible by removing the contents of the tiller flat (which is about as low in the ship as one can get) and carrying them up to the forecastle (which was as high as they could decently get) before throwing the said contents over the side. They had done exactly the reverse of what was intended.

It was the practice for the crews of ships of the fleet to be given leave and taken to rest camps at Diyatalawa, high in the central hills. Here, for a week or so, they would enjoy relief from the routine, heat, and discomfort of ship-borne life. What we could not help noticing was that people came back with stomach disorders and colds. Admiral Mountbatten, the Supreme Commander, had his headquarters in the ancient capital Kandy, again in the central hills. Rumour in the fleet was that all of the best-looking Wrens were appointed to Kandy. In any case there weren't many of them, Wrens, I mean, not good looking ones.

A story that endured concerned some ratings from a ship visiting Colombo who, it was said came back to their ship in a horse drawn gary, after a good run ashore. Arriving, they cheerfully asked the driver how much they owed him. He, not wishing to ask for too small a sum, dissembled, "Whatever you want to give me, master". The sailor asked his happy messmates. "What shall we give him lads?" and, of course, one wag said "Three hearty cheers" which they did and went on board. All was put right the next day it is said.

I spent most of my time with the fleet. In the early days I naturally gravitated to the submarine squadrons where the T Class boats with which I had dealt from Bath were arriving on station with many old friends. There were three depot ships, Adamant with the forth flotilla, Maidstone with the first flotilla and Wolf (the former Canadian Pacific liner Montcalm) with the second flotilla. In between two of them was an ex-Chinese river steamer called Wuchang, which somehow had escaped from Singapore. I never got round to asking what she was doing in Singapore. The clever trick was to be accommodated in Wuchang where the routine was somewhat less formal than in the bigger ships. It was in

Wuchang that I met Father Murphy; he too had escaped when Singapore fell. He performed his duties with gusto; whenever a submarine was departing on patrol, Father Murphy would be down in the boat handing out blessings and comfort together with cigarettes and chocolate provided by some far distant, and probably protestant, charity in the UK. His good humour and continued good health were much fortified by the produce of Scotland and he had a number of little ploys to ensure that he didn't pay very often.

Wuchang's cooks and stewards were from Goa and were respected for their high level of service. Invitations for Sunday lunch were not lightly declined, for that day was curry day. Two sorts of curry and all the trimmings were offered, medium and hot, both were excellent and enjoyable in the eating; one wondered why the old hands spoke in hushed tones about the hot curry; that is one wondered until about an hour or so after the meal and then one was consumed with inward fires. If the Japanese could have attacked one Sunday afternoon, victory might have been theirs.

In the mess in Colombo I had chatted with a newly qualified submarine sub-lieutenant who was on his way to join the squadrons in Trinco. He was an upper-yardman, which meant that he had started his naval service as a boy seaman in HMS *Ganges* at Harwich and had survived a training that was both physically and mentally daunting – the sort of chap to have playing in one's team. His ambition was to be appointed to Commander Bennington's submarine, HMS *Tally-Ho*. Bennington was himself an upper-yardman and was already a legend. I met the sub-lieutenant next in the submarine depot ship where he was spare crew, available to fill any chance vacancy that might come up due to sickness and so on. Then one day he was appointed to Bennington's boat, not as spare crew but a full time billet. Off he went on his first full war patrol. While on the surface one night they were attacked by a Japanese craft, and the sub-lieutenant who was on the bridge at the time was mortally wounded. Life can be very cruel.

On one occasion I was at sea in a T-Class submarine with the second in command of the squadron, Commander Anthony (Crap) Miers VC. The velvet sky was filled with stars as we sailed eastwards, rolling gently in the ever-present swell, recharging the battery. Crap and I were leaning on the starboard side of the bridge talking quietly when he remarked that he couldn't understand why anyone should want to be a naval constructor; he had joined the navy to be an admiral and he had never met a constructor admiral. I said that, in later life, we hid our stars under a bowler hat, but I could see that he considered this a poor reward. I am pleased to say that he made Rear Admiral.

Rear Admiral Destroyers was Rear Admiral "Hooky" Walker, so called because he had lost his right hand and had a hook instead. He managed beautifully but had some difficulty getting onto and off the decks of his destroyers. The classes of destroyer that we had in 1944 were about 1600 tons with the weather deck about 2 metres above the waterline. They did not have sloping accommodation ladders like the larger ships when in harbour, but Mediterranean ladders which were like rope ladders with small treads. Admiral Walker couldn't manage these very well so he would come alongside in his barge and thrust up his hook and shout to the teenage sailor frozen to attention on the destroyers deck "Get hold of it, man, and pull me on board".

Before visiting her as a member of the hability mission I spent a month in HMS *Howe* as a watchkeeping damage control officer. There was in my time a well-established service tradition (call it natural justice) that those responsible for the design of the navy's warships should experience their worst features as well as their delights. Most warships suffer some vibration aft at high speed and noise at most speeds in the vicinity of the propellers and it was no surprise to me to find that the cabin assigned to me was in the after cabin flat immediately over the propellers and beneath the armoured deck. Access was through a manhole, which was kept shut at sea. I was to learn that this cabin flat was not normally occupied at sea and there was only one other occupant. The propellers were no problem, once into the watchkeeping routine I could have slept through anything. I found that I had little awareness of the passage of time other than the routine set by duty. I did however help prepare the defect list for her next refit.

The family name of the Earls' Howe is Curzon and Lieutenant Commander Viscount Curzon RNVR was serving in the family battleship. He was a charming shipmate with whom every chat somehow came round to sport, it might be a request by Able Seaman Bloggs for a compassionate draft to the UK because his wife had run off with an American airman. The conversation would be something like "Ah, yes, sad isn't it, he is an absolutely splendid fellow and would soon be a leading hand. What a silly girl his wife must be, he has good leadership qualities and did well in inter-part soccer, could well play for the navy one day." "Yes Curzon, but how soon can he be spared?" "Oh, when we get back to harbour. I say, have you seen my new cricket bat, it just arrived from the UK in a batch of uniforms." His Division loved him and to him they were all swans. His father had earned fame as a racing car driver and Curzon told me that he personally had some difficulty in getting car insurance and then only with clauses stipulating that his father should never be allowed to drive the car.

One evening, when in harbour, I noticed that large numbers of Royal Marines from other ships were assembling in HMS Howe; the fleet RM force was about to embark on an exercise. The Fleet RM colonel, a short square peppery man and our major, who rumour had it had an active intelligence background, were much in evidence as were sundry more junior officers who, with one exception, seemed somewhat less enthusiastic than their superiors. A friendly RMVR subaltern who, I gathered, would much prefer to be mustering the ship's confidential books than fooling around in the local jungle, told me that the force was to embark in three landing craft and leave the naval anchorage-- go outside the boom-- into the big bay where it would land on the distant beach at first light to find and capture an objective some miles inland. I assured him that there were not too many sharks in the bay, more barracuda in fact. The colonel and his staff, which I understood included Howe's navigation officer, would exercise control from a harbour defence motor launch.

With some five hundred Royal Marines, complete with weapons, helmets and jungle boots, moving about two decks above there wasn't much chance of sleep. I had done a study in Colombo of how many small assault landing craft we might carry on the cruisers and bigger ships of the fleet in readiness for landing this same RM force on one of the islands off the coast of Burma or in Burma itself. Tonight's event was too good to miss, The landing craft would be LCM's, each capable of carrying a third of the force and disembarking them over the bow ramps.

Although the ships in harbour maintained a state of alertness against enemy frogmen and the like, limited deck lighting was permitted and so it was that when, sometime after midnight the landing craft came alongside, the marines fell-in in their platoons and clumped down the accommodation ladders to take their places in the craft rolling gently in the black water in pools of light cast by HMS Howe. Size 12 boots, rifle butts, helmets and sergeants' exhortations to pass right down in the craft and keep silence in the ranks ensured that soon a good part of Howe's ships company was there to good-humouredly wish them a sailor's farewell.

Loaded with their somewhat subdued cargo, the landing craft made off and hovered audibly but not visibly outside the illuminated area. The colonel and his team embarked in the HDML via the stern boom and a rope ladder - all good commando stuff.

With all safely embarked the small force disappeared into the blackness towards the boom.

Late the following afternoon Howe's RM detachment returned with uniforms salt caked and dirty, climbed wearily on board and dispersed, dour and silent to their messes. During the following days the picture of the exercise emerged somewhat as follows although I cannot vouch for every detail. Furthermore it can be guaranteed that the account that was reported to the C in C and hence to the Commandant General Royal Marines bore little resemblance to the following account gleaned from the more junior officers. The force passed through the boom and made the long passage to the far shore. It was here, it is said, that the control launch discovered a hitherto unknown sand bank upon which to impale itself, which happening took its collective eye off the exercise for quite some long time. Careful planning on the part of the keen officer had suggested that starting to lower the bow ramp so many seconds after the point at which the craft crossed the imaginary line between a headland and a particularly prominent palm tree would result in the bow ramp being down just as the landing craft hit the beach. Unfortunately, in the half light of dawn, one palm tree looks like any other palm tree and the ramp went down just a little early putting the troops up to their armpits in water before they disembarked.

From this promising start the day had got worse as the various units crept around in the jungle looking for the objective, mindful always in most cases that the natural perils from the fauna and flora posed a greater threat to their future well-being than did an imaginary enemy. Unthinkable things seem to have happened that day. Suffice it to say; the day after the exercise, HMS Howe's Royal Marines were their usual smart, well-polished and cheerful selves.

The Eastern Fleet did not consist only of British warships. Australian, New Zealand and Indian navy ships were attached for periods together with ships from the Netherlands, Italy and France. The Italian sloop "Eritrea" had been the personal yacht assigned to the Italian Foreign Minister one Count Ciano, husband of Mussolini's daughter. His amorous exploits had featured in that organ of the British press most read in the fleet, "The News of the World", and the sailors all believed that if you pressed the button beside the bed in what had been the principal stateroom, the bulkhead would open and the bed in the adjacent cabin would smoothly slide in.

Eritrea was used to escort our submarines through the coastal shipping lanes east of Trinco. She was diesel driven and had a very slight oil leak such that one could just see her track. Her captain steadfastly refused to let us put her in dock to cure the leak and we didn't press him very hard because docks were at a premium. This led to a view among the submariners that the only way the Eritrea got back to Trinco was by back-tracking along her own oil slick.

The Netherlands cruiser *Tromp* was very spick and span as was her captain who fascinated me because he was so square in the rectilinear sense. Physically, dressed in immaculate white shirt, shorts and socks he resembled a white detergent packet with arms at the top and legs at the bottom corners and a head on top. He clearly felt his position as his country's representative and I judged that Tromp was not exactly a happy ship.

The French battleship, *Richelieu* arrived at about the time that HMS *Valiant* was damaged by the collapse of the big dock. *Richelieu* was a truly splendid ship.

It was a requirement that midshipmen should pass a written examination in naval subjects for promotion to sub-lieutenant. One of the subjects for written examination was Ship Construction, intended to give them an awareness of stability and buoyancy, in short what makes the darned thing float upright and how best to keep it so. The paper carried

100 marks and a mark of 40 was a pass. It was my duty to set the paper. The young officers were carried in large warships and taught by Instructor Officers who would mark the completed papers and subsequently forward them to Fleet HQ for review. I set the paper and some time later they came to me for review. One of the questions that I had set required just a few lines of calculation and was designed to show a vital piece of seamanship, namely that when an object is lifted by a ships crane or derrick, even just a few centimetres, the weight behaves as if it is all at the top of the crane or boom. Many ships have listed badly when somebody wasn't aware of this.

All of the midshipmen had got it wrong and their teacher had marked all correct. In commenting on the staff paper I said that while I would not wish to change the midshipmen's marks, perhaps their instructor's attention should be drawn to the fact that the weight always behaves as if it's at the point of suspension and that ships' officers have got into big trouble in the past by lack of this knowledge. I proposed a draft letter that the Fleet Instructor Officer might wish to send.

I thought no more about it until one day the Fleet Instructor Captain's secretary asked me to come and see the captain. As a Lieut Cdr. he had been one of my instructors at the RNEC in 1939 and I assumed that he wished perhaps to discuss some detail of my suggested letter. His office was not in the Fleet HQ but in a bungalow nearby. I was quite unprepared for the angry dressing down that he launched into.   He would not accept that his Instructor Officers needed instruction in stability and he demanded that I should withdraw what I had written on the Staff docket. I said that I couldn't do that, Sir, because this was an important aspect of seamanship and there was an increased emphasis on carrying and offloading heavy loads like assault craft from HM Ships and Auxiliaries. Would he prefer the Fleet Naval Constructor to write to all the big-ship commanding officers? I was dismissed with the remark that he intended to take the matter further. The next day he raised the matter at the end of the C in C's daily meeting and had been ordered to send out the letter and make sure that his officers understood this most important matter of seamanship. To quote Denis Healey "When you find that you are in a hole, stop digging"

Admiral Sir Arthur John Power had relieved Admiral Somerville. Both of his sons were to become my friends.

The occasions when my chief, Captain Bogie was absent from the office were rare indeed. On one such occasion he went to Bombay with the Fleet Engineer to visit an aircraft carrier in dock. I was sitting in the office one afternoon when in came the Fleet Medical Officer with a considerable pile of HQ staff dockets under his arm. He seemed not to be his usual self and his exact words were "You constructors are clever chaps, deal with these papers for me. I am going back to the Galle Face" and he turned and went down the stairs and away to his quarters. The papers were in the main submissions concerning medical cases by doctors in the ships and hospital ships and in most cases their recommendations or requests were logical and safe. The staff work by the doctors was excellent and I was able to draft minutes or letters, which the FMO's secretary typed ready for his signature. For the two or three that only the FMO could decide I suggested options. I learned from his secretary that he signed the lot the following morning. He never referred to the incident when I was FMO for a day. Well, for a half day.

The technical officer with the biggest parish was the Fleet Engineer, responsible for the machinery of the fleet and for its engineering personnel. The latter performed miracles in keeping ships, old and new, fully operational under the most severe conditions. Afloat, the task fell increasingly on the junior officers and the senior artificers for whom the periods in harbour were not an opportunity for a run ashore or a swim, but a chance to catch up on overdue maintenance and repair work. When visiting ships it was not unusual for a term-mate to emerge from beneath some defective piece of machinery; often they were the only people on board who had stripped down or seen stripped down such equipment before, usually in the workshops at Keyham. Over an evening drink the FEO would discourse on the status of the engineering officer and the failure of the powers-that-be to implement the promises made at the end of the first world war to give the engineer officer full equivalence with the executive officer. The executive curl (the gold circle above the gold rings on sleeves) had been granted to non-executive officers in 1919 or thereabouts but not full equivalence to Board and Command opportunities. This rankled with this most loyal of officers.

The naval construction, engineering and electrical departments of the Admiralty Bath seemed very far away and increasingly irrelevant to the task of keeping the fleet operational. We were much thrown on our own professional judgements. All sections of the Staff had experience of reporting something that had actually happened - perhaps several times - only to be told by some gentleman sitting at a desk in the UK that it could not possibly have happened. My conversion to the ranks of the cynics was the Victorious rudder.

I admit that both the Captain and I were most surprised to read the urgent signal from HMS *Victorious* reporting that, without human assistance, the ships rudder had moved over causing the ship to execute a circle some kilometres in diameter to the surprise and consternation of Captain Michael "Ginger" Denny and his officers and the pilots of the aircraft that were trying to land back on. What was puzzling was, if this had happened as signalled (that was the Bath training coming out) why should it happen now, apparently for the first time, in a ship that had been in service for several years during which she had steamed thousands of miles. The assistant Fleet Engineer and I went to the ship and asked the obvious questions and checked the steering gear. We found that for some considerable time, to check a tendency to wander, the steering gear system pressure had been raised by about 15% by screwing down the relief valves. This time the rudder had really taken charge.

C in C reported the incident to the Admiralty. We suggested that this was belated evidence that the rudder located directly behind the centre propeller was over-balanced and that action should be put in hand to produce new rudders for the class with less area forward of the rudder stock. Admiralty Bath's aircraft carrier design group replied that if the ship had actually behaved the way C in C said (and they clearly doubted this) it must be due to some other cause; the rudders were not overbalanced. Meanwhile we screwed down the steering system valves and the ships continued to operate. Some long time later new rudders were fitted.

The land forces in the theatre were commanded by General Bill Slim, whom some consider to have been the best British field commander of the Second World War. Slim had performed the remarkable feat of holding his largely Indian army together under intense Japanese pressure as it retreated a thousand miles across Burma to the border of India and turned to stand fast at Imphal. Now it was poised to break out.

The personal relationship between Admiral Power and General Slim was excellent, but one could not help wondering sometimes about planning from the South East Asia Command HQ at Kandy. I was instructed to fly to Trinco to join HMS *Indefatigable* for a forthcoming operation. The Beachcraft aircraft took off but could not fly over or round a tropical storm that extended right across Ceylon; we returned to Columbo. I knew that the fleet was due to sail the next day and was told to fly to Trinco that morning where an aircraft would fly me out to join the carrier. Thus it was that on arrival at China Bay airfield, I was put in the back of an Avenger torpedo bomber piloted by Lieut. Cdr Stuart RNVR and off we went. This flight was of enormous interest. I sat behind Stuart beneath a large canopy through which the tropic sun gave a pleasant heat; there were no clouds. The task force had been at sea for several hours, the sea was calm with a low swell from the east, and the ships wave systems, divergent and transverse from both bow and stern were beautifully defined like a hydrodynamics textbook. Ships heeled ever so gently as they turned and the sky was filled with aircraft - ours I am glad to say. With our longer endurance we were last in the landing pattern; over Stuart's shoulder I could just see the carrier ahead and suddenly the waves were very close, I was jerked out of my seat as the aircraft was stopped by the ship's arresting gear and we were safely at rest on the carriers deck. As I walked from the aircraft with my bag I felt that I must look like a travelling salesman, Mr Gieves representative strikes again.

This was not to be the end of it; having experienced a landing it was the air-engineering officer's view that I had to learn what it was like to take off. Lieut. Cdr. 'Atty' Turner had been my term officer at the RNEC and he went on to become a member of the Board of Admiralty, the first Engineer Admiral so to do, I believe. This duly took place that afternoon. I sat rigidly in the back of a trusty Avenger and, whoosh, we were airborne and in due course landed back on again. The whole exercise reinforced my admiration for the bravery and skill of the naval aviators who do this sort of thing daily and not only in the flat calm conditions that I was fortunate to encounter.

The next day the task force reversed course and returned to Trinco. We had been destined to do an armed reconnaissance of the islands on the coast of Burma and it was understood that the Supreme Commander had recalled us because the 14th Army was mounting an operation to capture islands along that coast. Some days later the force sailed again, this time in a more southerly direction and we attacked Japanese installations on the Andaman Islands. The 3rd Commando Brigade did in fact invade Akyab and Myebon in January 1945.

The most distant operation in my time with the fleet was a sweep across the Indian Ocean to the south of Sumatra and Java to the coast of Australia where we refuelled in Exmouth Gulf before returning the way we had come. En route our aircraft attacked targets in Sumatra including Palembang. There was already a British naval presence in Freemantle, a depot ship and some submarines. The subs were making patrols of many weeks duration to pass through the Sunda Strait between Sumatra and Java or the Lombok Strait to harass Japanese shipping in the South China Sea.

One day in early August 1944 a number of US B-29 bombers landed at China Bay. These were the first we had seen and they looked enormous. Some days later they flew off to bomb enemy targets before returning to another allied airfield. The operation fuelled speculation in the fleet, which had an element of truth in it; that our probing of the Burmese coast was intended to capture an island from which bombers could fly in support of General Stillwell (who was operating in China) and General Slim. Later I learned that the B-29's had bombed the oilfields in Palembang on which Japan was dependent for some 78% of her aviation fuel and 22% of her naval fuel and that the mission round trip of 3,600 miles was the longest aerial mission yet undertaken.

We were all conscious that the tide of war had changed, the Soviet army and "General Winter" had broken the Nazi armies in eastern Europe, the allied armies were firmly established ashore in France and the US navy and marine corps were moving, island by island, closer to Japan. I was particularly excited by the latter for I had no doubt that while operations such as ours on the periphery were important, they would not determine the eventual outcome of the war; Japan would only be beaten by an assault on the Japanese homeland itself

One night while I was with the submarines in early August, I had just climbed into my bunk in Wuchang when the adjacent depot ship's public address system piped "away all sea boats crews, away captains 35ft motor launch, away " and so on until all boats had been called to readiness. It's the sort of pipe you expect to hear just before the man says, "abandon ship". I got up and went out to see a most amazing sight; all ships of the fleet had their searchlights lit and trained on the floating dock which with the battleship HMS *Valiant* inside it, was heeled over at about 10 degrees and under water at the after end. I got across to the depot ship and the Commander gave me his boat. We sped towards the dock and were intercepted by the Vice Admiral in his barge, he said, "Oh it's you Daniel, go aboard and do what you can". I stepped from the Commander's skimmer directly on to the *Valiant's* quarterdeck (which was normally about 3 metres above the sea level) where her crew were assembled, and made my way with some difficulty to the ships damage control headquarters.

The dockyard support for the fleet at Trinco was centred on an island called Sober Island where a skilled force of men called up for national service from British shipyards was quartered and worked. These were the SRD's. They were backed up by the Heavy repair ship HMS *Ausonia*, also manned by SRD's, and by the giant floating dock AFD 8. The dock was a copy of the dock that had given yeoman service in Malta Dockyard for some years. This one had been built just south of Bombay, in three sections. The sections had been towed to Trinco and joined together and fitted out. The dock was in process of being commissioned by docking ships of different types. *Valiant*, the heaviest, was the last test. The procedure was to sink the dock sufficiently to enable the ship to be floated into the dock by flooding the pontoon tanks, and then carefully raise it until the centre-line keel blocks were just touching the ship's keel and then pump out the dock's tanks to lift the pontoon deck and the ship completely out of the water. The ideal state is when there is enough buoyancy in the pontoon tanks immediately under the ship to lift her. When this is not so, tanks towards the ends of the dock and not under the ship are pumped out, this puts a bending moment on the dock which tries to bend - to make it sag in the middle - and this sag is called "breakage". The dock designer sets the maximum permitted breakage and the Dock master in charge watches the breakage throughout.

When I reached *Valiant's* Damage Control HQ I found the naval constructor from *Ausonia*, Lieut Cdr Roy Anscombe and the ship's chief engineer, Commander Cooper who told me that after a whole day trying, they had got the pontoon deck clear and dry during which the dock had shown excessive breakage. The operation had been stopped for the night, dock valves shut, dock boilers secured and the dock crew reduced to sentries. Some time later there had been a tremendous bang aft and the ship and dock, locked together, had heeled over and sunk by the stern. *Valiant* was taking in water forward and had also been damaged aft. *Valiant's* engineers were in the dock trying to flash-up the boilers to run the dock's pumps and her shipwrights were in the battleships fore ends trying to shore up damaged bulkheads and decks. *Ausonia's* SRD's were in the dock walls trying to shut one set of valves to preserve the water-tightness and, above all, the stability of the dock walls. It was evident that we had to sink the dock to try to bring the battleship and dock upright by opening the other set of valves that would flood the pontoon tanks. Many men were working in water, sometimes up to their waist.

I was much concerned about the stability of the battleship-dock combination. The ship would have been in a light condition for docking - not her most stable state; she had an unknown amount of loose water and hence free surface in her forward spaces and water had been lapping her quarter deck when I had stepped aboard. As far as I could judge the ship was being kept in position in the dock by the breast shores between the dock and ship. There was the possibility that the shores would push into and rupture the dock walls with catastrophic results. The dock had to be submerged without immediately removing the vital contribution that it was making to the combination's stability

No praise is too great for *Valiant* and *Ausonia's* personnel who worked at great personal risk to save the day; in the dark, in water and not knowing when some additional failure or the progressive flooding might result in the whole lot capsizing. They managed to close and open the majority of the right sets of valves and as the night progressed we began to feel the heel reduce. One of the reasons that it had been so difficult throughout the day to pump out the docks pontoon tanks to lift *Valiant* was an inability to maintain suction on the dock's ballast pipe, which must have been leaking. This now worked to our advantage allowing the dock's tanks to fill and cause the dock and *Valiant* to sink bodily and the heel angle and trim to gradually reduce. At about 2.am tugs were able to pull the badly damaged battleship clear of the dock, which subsequently sank.

Damage to the battleship was serious. The initial dock failure had pushed the twin rudders upwards by about an inch and damaged the two inner propellers and their supporting shaft brackets. The after part of the dock had then flooded and fallen back and this had trimmed the dock to put enormous forces on the battleships forefoot and keel, resulting in structural damage and flooding extending a hundred feet aft from the bow.

A Court of Enquiry was convened, of which my chief was a member. The court took evidence concerning the design of the dock, its lifting capacity and method of operation and the trials and inspections undertaken prior to docking *Valiant* as well as events leading up to and after the failure of the dock. The court was aware that a dock of the same design built in the UK was in service in Malta Dockyard and had docked the navy's battleships without problem. I provided the court with an estimate of the dock loading at the time it broke, showing that there had been a considerable bending moment on the dock because the tanks under the ship had not been enough to lift her. Judged by the breakage measurements taken when the docking operation had stopped for the night, the pontoon tanks at each end of the dock were substantially empty and, one suspected, some of those under the ship, were not.

From the evidence the dock bottom appeared to have fractured at the joint connecting the after section to the middle section. The after section had hinged up, buckling the dock wall structure and the pontoon deck had hit the bottom of *Valiant's* rudders and inner propellers. This had ruptured the pontoon deck destroying the buoyancy of the after pontoon section which progressively bent backwards and downwards tilting the dock and battleship bow upwards and imposing huge forces which deformed and flooded the battleships fore ends. Clearly the damage and flooding of the dock had not been symmetrical, hence the heel.

On advice, the court ordered that the fleet's diving resources be used to make a survey of the sunken dock to establish the extent of the damage and recover some of the bolts used for connecting the dock sections. Day after day teams of divers and their attendant pumpers assembled in boats over the wreck, four boats to each side and slowly I was able to confirm the picture set out above. The divers recovered several intact and several broken 3 inch bolts and nuts. They did not seem to be of high quality and mechanical and metallurgical tests showed them to be poor quality black mild steel and not the high strength steel the designer had specified. These bolts had been put in and tightened under water by the Indian dock builder. There were no records of inspection and quite extraordinarily it seemed that no UK government activity had been associated with the construction or inspection of the dock.

The Ship Repair Detachments (SRD's) were housed in primitive hutments on Sober Island. They had been recruited from all the shipbuilding and ship-repair centres in Britain, some were volunteers but in the main they were discharging their national service liability in the best way possible with the minimum of bull. They had a job to do in rough and uncongenial conditions and the sooner it was done and they were back in Glasgow or Tyneside or Merseyside the better. Tales of their fights were legion but oh, how they worked when they had to. Ask them to help and they would move mountains; order them about and they would tell you to get stuffed, until they got to know you. There were stories about the night the dock collapsed. Several of them were on the dock wall above where the pontoon deck buckled; there was a loud bang, bits of dock flew past, the lights went out so they jumped into the water; one of them was fished out still clutching his hammer.

Meanwhile a salvage vessel, the *Sea Salvor*, came alongside HMS *Valiant* to assist with repairs. The reputation of these civilian salvage workers - to steal anything portable and a good many things that weren't - had preceded them and sentries were posted on the gangplank, 24 hours a day, with strict orders to examine every item that was removed from or taken aboard *Valiant*. We accepted that this was deterrence rather than total cure. It didn't seem to bother the salvage workers one little bit. The first necessity was to make the ship watertight and remove all the floodwater. Much trial and error pumping took place at the outset; not for the first time in the war (or the last time) I assisted in the grand old game of pumping the ocean round in circles until the divers, working outside, located the leaks and plugged them sufficiently for us to get into the compartment and make more permanent repairs. The flooding forward extended aft to the forward 15-inch magazine and the Cold and Cool Rooms. The work of removing the decaying meat and dairy produce was particularly nauseating and was done by the Royal Marines with their usual stoicism and good humour. One came to expect that the really rotten jobs always fell to the stokers or the marines.

The forces forward had pushed the bottom up several inches such that 6-inch pillars in the magazine were bent. Aft, it was possible to jack the rudder crosshead down to render the rudders capable of slow rotation. The inner propeller shafts were bent and the brackets that support them and the propellers were damaged. To make them safe for passage to wherever the ship would go for repair, it was decided to fit bolted reinforcing plates, which meant drilling about 24 in number 1.5 inch diameter holes in each of the massive shaft bracket arms. This took a great deal of time and effort. The requirement for air for the divers was so large that manual pumps could not meet it; we had petrol driven pumps for the power drills and so we broke the regulations by supplying the divers from the air-compressor. The safeguard was that they were using facemasks, not suits. I have to confess that sitting on the propeller shaft in beautifully clear and warm water watching other people work, is not unpleasant.

In its report, the Court of Enquiry was critical of the dockyard officers for not being present at this final docking and hence for leaving the responsibility with the unfortunate Lieutenant Dockmaster. The senior dockyard officers in Ceylon and Trinco were both reduced in rank as a result.

Attendance at the Court meant dressing properly in white shorts, shirt, stockings and shoes. It was my practice to visit the diving teams en route to obtain their latest reports. One day, while doing this, there was a loud bang in the distance and a small drift of smoke appeared from somewhere behind Sober Island. Shortly afterwards the admiral's barge came for me and I was told that there had been an explosion in one of our civilian manned oil tankers and that I was to do everything possible to secure the situation. The barge put me aboard the damaged tanker and departed. The tanker was clearly in no danger of sinking; on the trip over I had reasoned that the tanker would rise rather than sink and that the danger would be fire. Action was in hand to pump the remaining oil into other tanks and there was much less pollution than I expected. One man, a greaser had been killed. The ships officers showed me their loading diagrams and stability diagrams and clearly were in complete control of the situation. The trivial thing that stamped that day in my mind was that the explosion had blown oil everywhere including on the overhead aerial wires and everywhere that I went they dripped on me and ruined my nice white uniform.

A submarine had torpedoed the oil tanker, moored safely in Trinco harbour. No, not a Japanese or German submarine, but one of ours.

Submarines on patrol had all their torpedo tubes loaded. Unless they fired their weapons at the enemy, the torpedo launching system was not tested throughout the length of the patrol. It was therefore the practice of vessels returning from patrol to withdraw the torpedo and fire a water shot from each tube. HMS *Severn* had returned from patrol and was alongside the depot ship. She had six torpedo tubes forward and two tubes mounted externally angled aft just behind the sail. In accordance with the established procedure her torpedo crew withdrew each torpedo in turn, flooded the tube and fired the water shot. When they came to the two after tubes they withdrew the port torpedo and fired the starboard one. Not unreasonably, a torpedo shot out of the tube and screamed across the harbour, passed narrowly astern of a Royal Fleet Auxiliary loaded with sea mines and struck the unfortunate oil tanker.

HMS *Severn* was the one operating survivor of a class of three Fleet submarines built before the war with a surface speed sufficient for them to accompany the battle fleet. The second survivor HMS *Clyde* was also in Trinco, non-operational and being cannibalised to keep Severn running. I had been responsible for them in the submarine group in Naval Construction Department, Bath, when their advancing age had made it sensible to reduce their operational diving depth. High surface speed had been the watchword in the design and their shape had been optimised for this at the expense of rugged structural strength. In the submarines that I was to design in later years, longitudinal strength was never a problem but in HMS *Severn* one could see the after engine room bulkhead move as she went ahead at high speed in rough seas.

Having no floating dock or graving dock closer than Bombay in which the damaged tanker could be placed for permanent repair, it was decided to make temporary repairs to strengthen the ship for an ocean voyage to a distant repair yard. This work was entrusted to HMS *Ausonia* and her SRD's. Because the ship was registered at Lloyds, the oversight of this work would be the responsibility of the Lloyds surveyor in Colombo. Periodically we would ask Roy Anscombe how he was getting on and he mentioned that he was having difficulty in satisfying the surveyor. More and more steel was added until Anscombe refused to do any more work, stating that he had already used more steel and man-hours of labour than he, as an experienced dockyard officer, would have used in making a permanent repair.

The matter came up at C in C's morning meeting. Admiral Power immediately asked how long the tanker's captain and officers had been away from the UK, remarking that non-service personnel who had been away for more than three years were exempt from UK income tax. Enquiry showed that delaying the tankers departure for repair in a UK yard would certainly be of great financial benefit to some of them. C in C ordered that the ship should sail forthwith for the UK via the Suez Canal. C in C's area of command extended to the Red Sea; the next we heard was that the ship had been diverted to Buenos Aires for repair.

Following temporary repairs HMS *Valiant* sailed for the UK. After much thought it was decided that she had sufficient power and manoeuvre ability on two propeller shafts to be routed through the Suez Canal. The man who expressed the strongest reservations concerning this was *Valiant's* captain who thought that, on balance, going the long way round the Cape might be advisable. Admiral Power thought that this view might perhaps be influenced ever so slightly by the fact that the captain's wife was thought to be in Capetown. *Valiant* sailed up the Red Sea and the Suez Canal authorities were not happy with the statements provided regarding her manoeuvrability. She sailed back to Massawa where, believe it or not, another naval constructor, Len Kirkpatrick, cheerfully supervised the underwater work of cutting off the two inner propeller shafts and shaft brackets that we had worked so hard to make safe and preserve, and allowed the whole to fall to the sea bed. *Valiant* then tried again at the canal but grounded and was refused passage by the canal authorities. The first that we at the coalface knew of all this was when *Valiant* reappeared on the Eastern Fleet's plot, routed round the Cape of Good Hope.

Sometime during this period I was asked to look into a small problem in HMS *Whelp*, one of the W-Class destroyers newly arrived in the fleet and found that a few fans were still running backwards or at half speed. That evening I met the rest of her officers including a young lieutenant called Mountbatten who clearly shared a lot of his uncle's charm and ready wit and greeted me jokingly as a naval destructor.

Towards the end of 1944 there was much activity with the movement of landing craft from Europe into the Eastern Theatre ready for the assault on Burma, Malaysia, Singapore and Indonesia. Materially the early signs were not good, those that reached Aden were stated to be in need of substantial repair before they could cross, or circumnavigate, the Indian Ocean to Ceylon and across the Bay of Bengal. From C in C down everyone in the fleet realised that we had it easy compared to the soldiers of the 14th Army and much thought was given to ways in which we could give tactical support by such means as bombardment of important targets, interdiction of supplies along the enemy coast and sea borne landings. Submarines played the major role in the last two. Most of the coastal traffic was in dhows and our submarines would board them, take off the crew and then sink the dhow. The submarine crews were not proud of these sinkings because in most cases the skipper of the dhow was the owner and the crew his family and the dhow represented their home and life savings; this was not their war and what they had on board was goods for their own people further up the coast. The submarines duly chalked them up on their Jolly Roger but I didn't know one CO who liked the task. The occupants of the dhows were brought back to Ceylon. One submarine actually brought back a pig that had been on a dhow but it jumped overboard as she entered harbour and was drowned. Where does one keep a pig for several days in an S-Class submarine?

A task for submarines was landing and recovering Special Boat Service personnel in enemy held territory. Submarines departing for patrol would motor past the depot ship with the forward and after casing parties closed up and the CO on the bridge. Captain Submarines would return the submarine's salute from the depot ship's quarterdeck. The same procedure would be followed on the submarine's return from patrol. It was not unusual on such occasions to see two or three khaki clad figures at the salute beside the submarine's CO. Having a natural aversion to swamps, jungles, snakes and other crawly things my admiration for the SBS chaps was profound; they had to contend with all of these things as well as the Japanese and their fellow travellers.

Perhaps the most helpful thing that I did personally for the 14th Army was to design a river patrol craft for use in Burma. The army was confident of its ability to break out of Imphal and advance south into Burma once the monsoon was over. Intelligence provided by Orde Wingate's Chindits supported the view that the enemy was over extended and that General Slim's advance might be rapid once the breakout was achieved. Slim was concerned that the advance forces might outrun their logistic support or rather, that the next monsoon might so impede their logistic and manpower support that they would lose their momentum and then be vulnerable to counter attack. Thoughts turned to the rivers that run north to south, could they be used, could the navy help? The army said that there was much seasoned teak available, trees that had been ringed for felling in 1941/42 before the British left, were still standing. The Indian Army Corps of Engineers could fell these trees, convert them to planks and build a craft, given a design. I sat down one afternoon and designed a scow-ended craft propelled with three petrol engines taken from assault landing craft and equipped generally with fittings taken from these craft. I added a 20mm gun. The whole to be built of 2 inch thick teak and consisting only of flat surfaces. At the speeds this craft would achieve, streamlining would be a sick joke.

Instructions were issued to cannibalise three assault craft to yield six engines and sets of fittings and Lieut "Dicky" Bird (more recently Vice Admiral Sir Richard Bird) was posted to Calcutta to liase with the army and air force logistic people whose duty it was to fly essential supplies 'over the hump' into the war zone. Allocating priorities under the prevailing conditions was not easy; items given a 'red hot' priority that failed to make it had to be argued up to 'white hot' to get on an aircraft. Whether these were the terms used by the experts I do not know but they became a familiar part of the cheerful Dicky's vocabulary. Having arrived in the forward area all of this bulky kit had to be carried hundreds of miles by truck behind the advancing army. One can imagine a major somewhere deep in the jungle who has been screaming for ammunition or rations or more engineers or something and some trucks appear loaded with, of all things, boat engines. Construction took place eventually somewhere close to the Chindwin River.

The Indian engineers did a grand job. They cut down the trees, cut them into planks of the required shape and joined them together to form the hull. They built supports for the engines and the gun, put in the fuel tanks and bored the long sloping holes for the propeller shafts using a red hot bar of iron. In went the engines and the gun and sundry other items and Lieut. Bird had what was, I believe, his first independent command. Only one craft was completed because the army advance was rapid and secured objectives that could be supplied in a more orthodox way.

At the end of 1944 I was told that I was promoted Constructor Lieut. Commander and appointed to the newly formed British Pacific Fleet who's C in C was Admiral Sir Bruce Fraser. I would be the only constructor officer on the staff but there would be others in a mobile support force called the Fleet Train and in dockyards in Australia. I hoped that I might take passage in a county class cruiser. These big roomy three funnel ships were the only ships that could do the run to Freemantle without refuelling whereas the more recent and smaller cruisers had not quite enough margin. Earlier in the year the ship on this run, shadowing merchant ships which never saw her until they neared the Australian coast, had brought back a consignment of Australian beer and soon was making the return trip laden with vast amounts of the amber nectar for distribution to the ships of the fleet. It was too much of a good thing; it reached the Admiral's ears and he ordered that it should cease.

Having received my orders I went to close my account with the Hong Kong and Shanghai Bank. This they flatly refused to do requiring that I leave a nominal sum to keep it open. I suppose that its still there. The only expatriates that one met were members of the governor's staff and people at the bank. The latter were not very friendly, the Japanese threat having receded they seemed to resent the large service presence, perhaps because the sailors treated the native population with some compassion but really, I suspect, because they subconsciously recognised that the good old colonial days had gone for ever. They couldn't object much to the officers many of whom had accounts with them, but one could not help getting the message that the sooner we all went away, the better pleased they would be.

Actually, the whole fleet felt the same.

Chapter Three

In the absence of a suitable warship sailing to Australia I took passage in a Norwegian motor ship bound for Melbourne. The ship's speed was less than 8 knots and there were three other passengers. The ship had been at sea when the Nazis invaded Norway and the captain had not seen his family since early 1940. His most cherished possession was an aerial photograph, taken by an RAF Hudson aircraft flying very low up 'his' fjord, which showed his house with his wife and small son outside, waving vigorously. It said it all. I spent hours each evening leaning on the bridge rail talking or rather, listening, to this most learned man. He confessed that his ship's slow speed did not displease him because it gave him longer between port calls. Dealing with port health authorities, immigration, customs, commercial agents and, in war, naval control authorities, filled his time in port and getting once more to sea and its familiar routine was always a relief.

We proceeded majestically across the ocean, well to the south of Sumatra and the Cocos Islands. I was reminded that in Ceylon I had met two employees of Cable and Wireless who were receiving medical treatment; nothing unusual in that except they were from the Cocos Islands station maintaining essential communication links with Australia and beyond, right under the Japanese noses.

One of the passengers was a young merchant navy engineer who was returning to Australia to take the exam for fourth engineer - the initial step. He had been employed in this rank for some time on a temporary basis but now was being required by the Australian authorities to regularise his position. He had the syllabus for the exam with him and so I offered to help him prepare and tried to explain a few fundamental laws, starting with perhaps the most basic of all - Force equals Mass x Acceleration. In my efforts to have him understand or accept this I gradually got down to asking him to believe that one cubic centimetre of water weighs one gram; would he please accept my word for this so that we could get on. He steadfastly refused to accept this and after two days we both found other things to do. He spent a lot of time with the ship's engineers in the machinery spaces and talking in the saloon and it was evident that as a practical engineer, keeping slow speed diesel machinery running, he had their respect. Perhaps he never, ever, passed the written examination and couldn't go back to sea in a reasonable rank; if this was so the merchant marine lost a good, sound, practical, junior engineer.

The ship had a 4-inch gun on the stern and two 20 mm guns on the superstructure that were manned by a small Norwegian navy detachment. One day the ship threw a smoke float overboard and the crew had target practice. They were very good although the range was not extreme. On another day we met an S Class submarine rolling gently as she made her way back to Ceylon.

From Melbourne I travelled by train to Sydney. To be absolutely accurate I travelled by two trains since the gauge of the railway track in the state of Victoria was different from that in New South Wales and, for good measure, both were different from that in Queensland. The Premiers of the states were all agreed that this situation should be changed. By the other states adopting their gauge.

On arrival in Sydney the naval travel people sent me to the transit mess at Sydney Racecourse. I found that I was allocated a billet in a bell tent! The next day I reported to C in C's HQ and learned that the dockyard team had already arrived and set up a base using the piers and warehouses of Woolloomooloo Docks. They were living in a guesthouse at Rose Bay, the bay in which the pre-war Empire flying boats of the UK-

Australia service used to land. I moved in with them. Constructor Commander S.J. Palmer who, years later, was to precede me as Head of the Royal Corps led this team. His assistant was the ever-cheerful Lieut. Arthur Matthews. Because of the distance between Australia and the forward operating area, the BPF would be supported by a 'fleet train' consisting of replenishment ships, aircraft carriers to provide replacement aircraft and pilots, ammunition ships, victualling ships, oil tankers with fuel oil, diesel oil and aviation gasoline, and repair ships. There was even a brewery ship. What genius thought of this with Australia awash with XXXX to the south, I do not know. The senior naval constructor in the theatre was in the fleet train in the person of my old submarine chief, Constructor Captain Pamplin. There was in fact another captain, Victor Hall, on the staff of Vice Admiral Q in Melbourne, responsible for long term logistic planning.

After the privations of wartime Britain and Ceylon, Australia was the Promised Land. If there were war shortages, these were not apparent to visitors such as myself. I was first struck by the variety, colour and freshness of the fruit and flowers on sale everywhere, all of which seemed to be in season somewhere in this vast country. Cities still had tramcars and motoring in Sydney involved doing things at intersections somewhat differently from the way they were done in Britain, even though both nations drive on the same side of the road. The men did not seem to be the tall, bronzed strapping Aussies that we were used to meeting in uniform, most noticeably were rather ill-mannered; not to me I hasten to add but to each other and particularly to their womenfolk. A couple would be out shopping; the man would be half a pace in front of the lady who would be carrying two heavy shopping bags. They would wait for a tram, the man would climb aboard and the lady would clamber up as best she could and perch beside him. No one thought that this was rude. No wonder that so many Australian girls went to America as the brides of US servicemen.

In 1945 the licensing laws in New South Wales required the public houses to close at 6 pm. Around large industrial sites such as the dockyards the pubs would have schooners of beer lined up on the bar by 5 pm ready for the homeward rush, resulting in so much early evening drunkenness that even the churches were campaigning for a much later closing time to allow men to go home to their families first and thus spread the time and the locality of drinking. At that time it was said, the major opposition to later closing came from the publicans themselves mainly on the grounds that they wanted their evenings free.

The British ships under Admiral Fraser (ashore in Sydney) were assigned to the operational command of US Admiral Nimitz and formed a task group within the US fleet, alternately the 3rd and 5th fleets under US Admirals Halsey and Spruance. The general pattern of operations was that the ships and aircraft of whichever fleet it was called (it was the same ships) would attack enemy targets for four days then withdraw and replenish from the Underway Replenishment Group (URG) for two days and then resume the attack and so on for some four to six weeks. There would then be a withdrawal to base areas for essential repairs and battle damage repairs during which there would be rest and recuperation for the aircrews and others. The big ships always came to Sydney.

While the 3rd fleet was operating, the 5th fleet staff would be busy preparing the plan for the next operational period and while in Sydney the ships of the fleet would receive their sack or sacks of documents detailing their role in the coming operations.

After ten days or so the same British ships would sail northwards again, this time as part of the 5th fleet. Since my duties were largely concerned with the material state of the warships and remedying defects and damage, I was destined to spend most of the ten days in, or around, Woolloomaloo.

My appointment to the Pacific fleet was to the staff of Rear Admiral Destroyers. On first reporting to C in C, I was told that this was not so, it had been decided to assign me to the Vice Admiral, second in command of the fleet, principally for service with Rear Admiral Aircraft Carriers, Philip Vian. Unspoken, but understood, was the fact that as the principal means of striking at the enemy, the carriers must expect to be the major targets of the Japanese and most liable to damage. Having heard all that, I was told that first, however, there was a job to do for Rear Admiral Destroyers!

While in Sydney I was required to be one of a marching column of officer mourners at the funeral of the assistant fleet engineer officer. At the graveside I could not help watching the funeral firing party with a professional interest. At college I had always rather enjoyed field training, rifle drill and the like. One of the drills with the Lee Enfield rifle was 'fix bayonets'. To ensure that all the squad did it together was explained by our Gunners Mate instructor as follows; "On the command Fix Bayonets the right hand man of the front rank takes three paces forwards except at funerals where he stands fast. 'Cos why, 'cos he'd fall down the bleeding hole".

During the periods when the fleet was in Australian ports their supply officers would re-stock their cold and cool rooms with fresh produce.   For the first week or ten days of the voyage northwards towards the war zone we enjoyed fresh salad and fruit dishes before reverting back to more usual ships fare. While the officers wardroom might regret this, the sailors didn't; the general consensus on the lower deck was 'Good, that's the last of that rabbits food, now we can have some real grub, like chips and plum duff".

The journey north always saw a great outpouring of letters to loved ones in the UK. There were much better things to do in Sydney than write letters and perhaps consciences were being exercised concerning runs ashore. The usual censorship rules applied, no mention of where the ship had been, was now or where she was going.   There were always attempts to circumvent the rules, such as references to kangaroos, koala bears, Aunt Matilda taking lessons to learn waltzing, seeing things upside down, winning the Ashes, having a nightmare and seeing little yellow creatures, with or without slitty eyes and so on. I had one chap who felt great because he could now tie reef knots and this would no longer be a barrier to promotion. His problem was that he doubted whether the little woman was clever enough to understand his message so he underlined the words great, barrier and reef.   The letters for censoring were unsealed and most had a final message on the envelope flap. 'Swalk' was a favourite, 'sealed with a loving kiss', but the kiss came from a sponge in the ships mail office. Much ingenuity was shown in compiling these acronyms; I had to seek advice on the meaning of 'Norwich', suffice it to say that the last four words were 'when I come home' and that a degree of licence was acceptable in the spelling.

Personally at that stage of the war I could see no great reason why their families should not know that they had been in Australia; the pause in the allied attacks told the Japanese that our ships had gone somewhere, so what. I hasten to add that if they had taken advantage of the lull to send their ships out, the waiting US submarines would have sunk them.   Incidentally, years later in the Korean war a US sergeant was heard to remark to his men that if they saw a figure silhouetted on the skyline, "Don't shoot, its bound to be one of ours". Conversely, in 1944/45 our pilots and submariners had learned that if they saw a plume of smoke from a distant ship's funnel, it was bound to be Japanese. It always was.

I marvelled that so few of the crewmembers missed their ships sailing by being absent without leave, most of those who did, did so because they were drunk and surrendered the next day. These mis-musters rejoined their ships via the next ship to sail north or were flown up by the RAAF.

I took passage north. As I have already said, one of the duties that were politely pressed on passenger officers was censoring the outgoing letters. This ship had just arrived from the UK. Some personal details were embarrassing; ERA Smith was writing in loving terms to two Mrs. Smiths and their small children and in even more passionate terms to a pregnant girl in Dunoon and so it went on, piling up eventual heartbreak. But usually they were the sort of letters that children write, longing to be home but accepting their duty to fight for King and Country.

I joined the Destroyer depot ship HMS *Adamant* at Manus in the Admiralty Islands. This was quite the most crowded and uncomfortable ship, with the worst food, that I served in, however briefly, in the war. I was assigned the captains sea cabin on the bridge. We sailed to Leyte Gulf in the Philippines, which still showed all the marks of the landings by the US forces.

The build up of forces was proceeding apace with the arrival of fleet units and freight. I had learned en-route that one of our destroyers had been badly damaged in recent operations, in fog she had run into the back of the RN aircraft carrier she was escorting and was in a US Navy dock. I was to ensure that the temporary repair would get her back to Sydney. On arrival I was transferred to the US repair ship USS *Markab*, the headquarters ship of Commander Service Squadron 10. It so happened that my arrival coincided with the departure of the US Commodore on promotion to Rear Admiral and literally no sooner had I set foot on board than I was bidden to his cabin as a guest at his farewell dinner with his staff. I recall the fulsome praise that was heaped on the Commodore and his diplomatic rejoinder that he owed it all to his coloured steward, Sam, who at that moment, was serving me and who said in my ear "Aw, shit Admiral, I was just doing my job".

Halfway through the dinner the ships executive officer was called out as a matter of urgency. It transpired that some enlisted men had used cutting equipment to make a hole through a main bulkhead to gain access into the secure store containing torpedo alcohol and had drunk the stuff in the mistaken belief that it was the same alcohol that occurs in fermented drinks. Already one man was dead and others were in process of going mad and blind despite the frantic efforts of the squadron medical staff.

The British destroyer was HMS *Quilliam* and she was docked in YRD 18, a floating dock with a shaped bow to facilitate towing, small workshops, lots of welding and cutting gear and an on-board repair crew. She had been towed from the US and was commanded by Lieut. Commander January US Navy Reserve. *Quilliam* was Captain (D's) Ship and he, Captain Richard Onslow, was still on board, He was a tall man and his party piece, which was quite disconcerting to the unprepared visitor, was to stand up straight and put his head in the overhead ceiling fan which would go bang, bang, bang, as the horizontally rotating blades smote him. He was slightly bald.

The US crew would do the repair work and it was decided that I should be accommodated in the dock. The dock's repair officer Lieut (Jg) Finger US Navy Reserve was distinctly distant for some days but soon came to terms. Captain January was absolutely splendid, as one would expect from a man whose peacetime job was sailing around the Pacific islands in a schooner collecting copra. We had a unique situation. Ever since the hard drinking Secretary of the US Navy, Josephus Daniels, had enacted the law prohibiting the carriage and consumption of alcoholic beverages in US Navy ships, the ships had been 'dry' (except for a bottle of medicinal brandy in Captain January's sick locker, kept in his cabin). High and dry (in the literal sense) within this US Navy ship, and hence technically carried on board her, was an RN ship whose crew enjoyed a tot of rum each day and whose officers had a fully stocked bar. On the other hand the US Navy had better ice cream and movies.

An evening pattern emerged of drinks in the destroyer, dinner in one's own ship followed by movies and ice cream on the dock, I say on advisedly because it was in the open air. This arrangement suited everyone but not long afterwards a US Navy Ensign serving in the dock said that he had written to his father who was a judge in Chicago, questioning the legality of what was going on in this US Ship. He showed us the reply, which was simply "I suggest that you keep quiet, my boy, and accept your good fortune".

Incidentally, the very sofa that Josephus Daniels used to snooze on in his office in the afternoons was still to be seen in the corridor outside the Secretary of the Navy's room when I used to visit Washington DC.

The dock's repair crew worked three shifts and I learned to look with some wonderment each morning at the results of the night's labours. It seemed that they didn't like taking measurements or putting up pieces of wood or steel to mock-up the shape required; they did it all by eye and so one would find that, say, the deck-edge angle was a long bit to which was welded a shorter bit to which was welded an even shorter bit to which was etc until they got it right. Lieut. Finger didn't find this in any way extraordinary, and so after a couple of smiling attempts to suggest how it might be done with less effort, I accepted the US judge's advice "and accept your good fortune" that the US Navy was putting on the stubby bow that would take *Quilliam* back to Sydney where a permanent repair would be made.

US Navy ships continued to arrive in Leyte Gulf. At one time before I left there were over 1,000 ships and landing craft there. Several were battle casualties and one aircraft carrier became a casualty before my eyes. A US Essex Class carrier came in with the forward end of her flight deck hanging down, like two triangular ears, one each side of her bow. She had been in a typhoon and this was the result. Another ship of the class came in. While she was at anchor US Army - Air P 38 fighters were making practice diving attacks on her. One aircraft failed to pull out and hit the forward end of the carrier's flight deck and then there were two with triangular ears hanging down. I have learned since that the controls locking-up was a known problem with the P 38.

An interesting case was the US Destroyer lying nearby with a very badly damaged bridge caused by a Japanese kamikaze. The ship's captain was President Roosevelt's' son who had saved his own life by jumping into the sea just prior to the moment of impact. The others on the bridge had been killed as the plane struck home. My American friends thought this to be a remarkable example of quick thinking. It was, but I asked when was he to be court martialled for deserting his post in the face of the enemy; think how embarrassing it would have been if the kamikaze had just missed.

One day Captain January and I went ashore in Leyte. This was the biggest US Army landing thus far in the fight across the northern Pacific and the build-up of men and equipment was most impressive. Our area seemed to be quiet but bitter fighting was taking place in the main island of Luzon. At the army transport depot we exchanged a bottle of Johnny Walker for a jeep and we drove a long roughly circular route around Leyte Island. The people were very poor and friendly and I am sure were genuinely pleased to have the softhearted Americans back. It was by no means unusual in the Pacific theatre for there to be pockets of Japanese who were still resisting; it transpired that there were several thousand on Leyte and skirmishes continued until March. Perhaps I would not have enjoyed the ride as much had I known that a Japanese might be lurking behind every second bush.

Just as HMS *Quilliam* was completing, I received a signal requiring me to take the first available flight to Manus to examine a cruiser that had serious hull cracking. I replied that I must accompany *Quilliam* for the first part of her voyage south as far as Manus and would be there in a few days time. There is much discussion on the relative importance of pitching, rolling and heave as the cause of seasickness. In meeting the Pacific swell, the shortened, snub-nosed *Quilliam* had a markedly different motion from an undamaged ship and there were many absences from meals the first day out. The next day we took part in the search for the plane to Manus that I would have taken and which had gone missing en-route.

On arrival in Manus I was transferred to the New Zealand manned cruiser, HMNZS *Black Prince* where I learned that fuel oil had been leaking through a crack in the hull on the starboard side and the ship felt that they should sail to Aukland for docking and repairs. I looked at the ships drawings and asked that the tank be emptied. I went into the tank and as I suspected there was a crack about 30cm long athwartships between two frames where the external bilge keel ended. This ending was a construction fault that had led to a fatigue crack. The basic fault could not be corrected out of dock but I could stop the cracks from getting any bigger and once stopped they would present no threat to the ship's strength. I had the ship's shipwrights drill 10 mm holes at each end of the crack. The holes would reduce the very high stress at the end of the crack to a very modest one and the crack would run no more. I reported the facts to the captain and that his ship's radius of action would be reduced by the loss of the fuel tank that must now be filled only with water and advised him that the same remedy should be applied to the other three tanks (at the ends of the bilge keels) if leaks occurred. We drafted a signal to inform the C in C that *Black Prince* could now safely resume operations. I had the feeling when I left the ship that I was likely to be voted the weeks most unpopular person by a ships company who had been sure that their crack would mean at least a quick docking back in their home port in New Zealand.

When I left the ship I was landed on the island of Los Negros and driven along a well-made road built by the US engineers to the airfield. The road passed through thick vegetation and I wondered how many pairs of Japanese eyes were watching. US personnel manned the airfield and the quarters were tents near the beach. Everything was in the Kilroy spirit and positively shrieked "Kilroy was here". My flight south would be the next day. After the evening meal, which was largely "K" rations, there was a movie on a small screen held up on an easel on the beach. The audience, all ten of us, sat on benches. It was pitch black, the light from the movie wiping out any sensitivity to the stars; as I sat there something walked over my sandaled feet. I leapt up and brought the show to a halt, to be told that it was 'just the crabs". I began to understand why the US servicemen always wore their jungle boots.

The Royal Australian Air force provided transport between Australia and the forward areas. The aircraft were DC 3's and one sat sideways on like paratroopers in the movies. On flights north vital cargo and personnel were carried and on flights south there were often medical cases attended by navy nurses of the QARNNS. The aircraft departed Mascot airport, Sydney and landed for the night at Townsville, Queensland. Next morning it was an early start along the Great Barrier Reef and over New Guinea to Manus for an overnight stop before flying on to the Philippines. Not all flights did this last leg. Flying over New Guinea the aircraft could not climb over the Owen Stanley Mountains so we flew along the valleys. Only after the war did I realise that down there were people who had never seen (or tasted) white people.

Occasionally the aircraft would land at Fort Moresby. The one time I went there it was oppressively hot and humid: leaving the cool interior of the aircraft was like entering a Turkish bath. The primitive airport buildings were made of plaited palm fronds and set among palm trees for shade. The whole effect was of vivid greens and red earth. The problem with getting into an aircraft at Port Moresby was that one's shirt was wet with perspiration and one shivered for the rest of the journey as the plane climbed once more to cooler altitudes.

Mention of New Guinea reminds me of Sydney Racecourse. After it ceased to be a transit mess it became the Royal Navy's detention barracks for the Pacific fleet. There was the problem of selecting an officer in charge. They lined up a lot of newly arrived people and asked if any had police experience. Finally a sub-lieutenant RNVR admitted that he worked as a clerk in Scotland Yard. He was an excellent choice-until the rains came. Sydney, that sunny Mecca of the southern seas has a bigger annual rainfall than London but it doesn't spread it out over the whole year the way that London does. The story is that when the rain came the racecourse became flooded so our hero lined up his worst offenders, gave them picks and shovels and told them to dig ditches. They did, under the barbed wire and away. This rather focussed attention on the place and authority realised that there were sailors who would prefer the ignominy of being labelled an offender to serving in a hot, seasick-making ship and being bombed by the Japanese, to boot. The solution was to move the detention barracks to Lae on the North coast of New Guinea where the high barbed wire fence was meant, not to keep the prisoners in, but to keep the headhunters out.

The overnight stop at Townsville was spent at HMAS Magnetic situated on a spit of land forming one side of a bay, which, in common with practically every bay in Australia, was said by the local population, to have the biggest concentration of sharks in Australia. The entrance to the bay is dominated by the green hill of Magnetic Island. HMAS Magnetic had a golden sand swimming beach protected by a steel mesh fence from seabed to surface. The first time that I stayed there I went swimming and I saw something quite big the other side of the fence. I came out, noting that I was the only person in the water, in direct contravention of Daniel's tropical swimming rule No 1, "always be sure that there is someone further out (and hence closer to the sharks) than you are".

Magnetic Island got its name because many shipwrecks on the Barrier Reef were claimed to be due to ships compasses being affected in this vicinity. One evening as the aircraft was approaching Townsville, the RAAF navigator, a pilot officer, pointed to the island and spoke of the reason for its name. I said that obviously the island must be made of iron ore, to which he replied that it wasn't. I said that it must be. After all, was I not a Naval Constructor and hence a person of infinite wisdom? That evening in the bar of HMAS Magnetic, the navigator was pointed out to me as the state geologist for Queensland. I made my peace and remain to this day quite ignorant of the particular aberration in the earth's magnetic field that affects compasses near Townsville.

Someone had the good idea of printing UK newspapers on thin paper for transport to the Far East. I recall that the packages that reached an aircraft carrier each contained 500 papers, consisting of 10 Sunday Times and 490 News of the World. It was from the Sunday Times pinned up on the wardroom notice board, that I learned that my friend of the Galle Face Mess, James Callaghan, had been elected to parliament as one of the members for Cardiff

This was in an aircraft carrier sailing north for operations to the south and east of Japan. The British task group was the northernmost of five and consisted of some four fleet carriers and supporting battleship, cruisers and destroyers. The usual pattern of operations was four days of attacks on enemy targets followed by two days replenishment. Each time we withdrew for replenishment the aircrew were encouraged to relax on the carriers sheltered quarterdeck where the ship's Royal Marine band would play. After a while I realised that on the first day the band played light music-Noel

Coward sort of music- but on the second day, when the boys would be flying the next dawn, the programme was more marches and patriotic music.

At the beginning of the war the British aircraft carriers were far superior to the US Navy's. The American ships had aviation fuel stowed in normal hull tanks like bunker fuel and did not have armour around their hangars. If they were hit by a torpedo the petrol exploded and burnt, if they were hit by a bomb or shell the contents of their hangar exploded and burnt and since their hangars extended right across the full beam of the ship (to enable the greatest number of aircraft to be carried) crew members were trapped below. British carriers had their aviation fuel in special tanks and had 3-inch thick armour on their flight decks and 2 inches on the sides, calculated to be sufficient to withstand a 500 lb bomb dropped from 10,000 feet. Their hangars did not extend the full width of the ship and access was always outside the hangar. The one kamikaze that hit a British carriers deck made a hole about 2ftx2ft, which was filled up, and aircraft were flying again within an hour. However, fragments from the bomb or armour did penetrate the decks beneath and damaged a steam line.

The lesson we had all learned was that we needed the maximum number of anti-aircraft guns and the allied ships positively bristled with 40mm guns in twin and quadruple mountings.

What the British carriers did not have at the beginning of the war was good aircraft. The Sea Spitfire was the best, when some could be spared for the navy. It was not until the arrival of US aircraft such as the Corsair and the Avenger that the performance of the machines started to match the ability of their pilots and the full potential of the carriers could be realised.

US battleships were superior to the RN's King George V class in sea keeping. It was a matter of extreme embarrassment to me to see how serenely the US ships sailed through the Pacific swell while our ship was shipping water over the bow making the crews principal recreation area unusable. The US ships had a full form above water; good freeboard and sheer at the bow while ours had none of these things. This was due to three causes; first the rigid adherence of British ministers to the letter of the Washington and London Naval Treaties that Battleships be limited to 35,000 tons loaded displacement; secondly, the failure of my predecessors, in these circumstances, to build a bigger hull than strictly necessary in order that things might be fitted later, and thirdly, the insistence on the part of the RN naval staff gunnery division, that the forward 14 inch guns should be capable of firing directly ahead at zero elevation. It is difficult to imagine any tactical situation in which this might have been used.

Of these, the second was in my view the biggest failing. Thus it was that the British ships were more than 5 feet deeper in the water than designed due to all the extra 40mm anti-aircraft guns, radar, protection and other things that war experience and common sense had dictated be fitted and this made them far wetter at sea than they should have been. The gunnery division was made to see the light by the end of the war and the new battleship design; HMS *Vanguard* was given forecastle sheer sometime after construction had commenced.

We all have our 'thank God I missed that plane' stories. The major part of the fleet had departed Sydney on their way north. I had remained behind to see some work completed on one of the aircraft carriers and intended to sail north in her. After a day or so I received orders to fly north immediately and join Admiral Vian's flagship.

The flight was arranged for the next day, Friday 13th, a fact pointed out to me by the transport people, who asked, "Would I like to delay to the Saturday?" I said something silly like "I was more scared of the C in C than I was of superstition". Shortly thereafter I received a personal call from the naval provost marshal instructing me to see him on a serious matter. I said that I was sorry, I was busy finishing my work ready to depart for the forward area the next day on C in C's orders. The provost was angry and I agreed that I would come if possible; I was now intrigued. Later that day I went. When I announced myself in his outer office there was a hush and a certain amount of grinning behind hands and I was ushered in to the captain. Almost immediately his phone went and he spoke into it saying "Don't bother me, I have a serious case concerning an officers behaviour in the Hotel Sydney". As he put the phone down I remarked that I had never been in the Hotel Sydney in my life and didn't even know where it was. He looked at me and said "You're RN, the Daniel we want is RNVR, sorry". He had the grace to escort me to the outer office and say in a loud voice "This is the wrong Lieutenant Commander Daniel". I have no idea what the other Daniel did but as late as 1948 the Admiralty was still getting bills in his name and forwarding them hopefully to me. Judged by their nature, he seemed to have had a more entertaining time ashore than I did. The last that I saw was for excess baggage on a commercial flight from Australia to Ceylon in 1947.

I duly took the Friday flight and flew on to Manus from Townsville the following day. When we reached Manus we learned that the Saturday flight had crashed on taking off from Sydney and a number of C in C's staff captains and other officers had been killed.

When the fleet withdrew south, the Fleet Train would be dispersed to best advantage among the islands, principally the Admiralty Islands where they were themselves re-supplied from bulk carriers and tankers. On such an occasion I called to pay my respects to Constructor Captain Pamplin in the Heavy Repair Ship. I was startled at the change in him. In the submarine design group, in the shipyards and in the Royal Dockyards grown men had trembled at his approach, yet here he was in the Pacific, relaxed and docile as a kitten. Mercifully, we had not suffered massive battle damage and he had, in consequence, not much to do and instead of worrying his head off, Pamp had clearly come to terms with the situation. Next week he might have a badly damaged aircraft carrier or cruiser to salvage but today we sat on the deck and talked about our submarine days. I mention this because we both served in the Admiralty after the war and our paths crossed many times, but as far as I could judge, the old fire-eating Pamp never reappeared.

Like the British, the US forces had initially been ill prepared to meet the attacks by the elite Japanese formations and had suffered great losses in limiting the enemy advance on land, sea and in the air. By 1943 the tide had turned and in a number of epic engagements US naval aviators severely damaged the Japanese fleet and its air forces. In so doing the US naval aviators established an air superiority that was never to be seriously threatened. The Japanese sought by all means to halt the US advance but they did not use what they had to best advantage. They trained and committed new air fleets to attack the allied task groups and these air fleets were literally shot out of the sky. In the Battle of the Philippine Sea the Japanese fleet lost 438 out of the 473 aircraft carried; on one day they lost 243 aircraft and their crews for the loss of 30 US aircraft from which about 20 pilots were rescued by submarine or flying boat.

The Japanese did not use their submarines as effectively as they should have done. Perhaps because the generals were in supreme command they seemed to use them to support their army instead of as a naval attacking element. The island of Truk is one of my favourite examples. It was planned as a powerful forward base for the Japanese Navy but was attacked by US carrier borne planes in February 1944 when 33 ships were sunk and 250 aircraft destroyed. Thereafter the US forces ignored it. Bypassed and left behind the US advance yet the Japanese continued to keep it supplied with ammunition and troops by submarine. They even submarined-in 'good time girls'. Whether they were persuaded of Truk's continued importance by the practice of the BPF I do not know, but it was not unusual for new ships sailing north, to be routed past Truk and to loose-off a few shells to try their guns out ready for the real thing some hundreds of miles to the north.

It had long been evident that while the allies might recapture territories overrun by the Japanese they would only be finally defeated by an attack on the Japanese mainland itself, by devastating bombing and blockade followed by an invasion. We were quite sure that in the latter eventuality they would fight us on the beaches and on all the other places that Winston Churchill had promised that the British would resist a Nazi invasion - only more so. We knew that invasion would cost thousands of lives; sustained bombing would reduce this. Thus, just as there had been the hope in the SE Asia Command that we would secure an island where an airfield suitable for B 29 bombers could be built, so C in C Pacific's sights were set on capturing islands from which sustained raids might be made on Japan. Such desirable islands were the Marianas Group. In all of this carrier borne aircraft would be an offensive arm as well as mounting combat air patrols to defend friendly ships and forces. The carrier was paramount.

I have stressed the overwhelming superiority of the carrier borne air groups over the Japanese, which gave a large measure of immunity to the surface forces. The picture changed dramatically when the Japanese began kamikaze attacks on the fleets. Allied aircraft still made a high proportion of kills but some of the enemy got through at low level for desperate dives at ships. The proportion of kamikaze pilots who actually made that last dive was small and the proportion that actually inflicted serious damage was even smaller, certainly much less than 10% of those who set out.

Many of the casualties in allied ships were caused by our own gunfire. The kamikazes that eluded the allied fighter aircraft did so by flying low and came in low over the horizon. All ships in the vicinity would open fire with rapid-fire 40mm guns filling the air with a curtain of steel. The gunners would follow the aircraft down and often would be firing across the deck of a ship in company. The 40mm shells had proximity fuses which would explode their charge when the shell passed within about 10 ft of a solid object and so shells passing over a ship's deck would explode. I don't think that this friendly fire problem had been solved by the end of the war.

The kamikaze that hit HMS *Formidable* and made the 2ft x2ft hole in the deck was travelling slower than a free fall bomb would have done and did less damage. The remains of the plane and its pilot were simply pushed over the side. Another of our carriers had her radar aerial knocked off

In the Eastern and Pacific fleets we were operating with the maximum number of aircraft using a deck park in addition to the hangar or hangars. Each carrier could put up about 90 aircraft and the British Pacific Fleet's air group was about 350 planes and somewhere to the south were about 1500 US Navy planes; a truly formidable force. The airborne commander of the British air group was a Royal Marine pilot, a subaltern - acting half colonel. I used to watch these splendid young men depart to fight our war while we sailed serenely across the ocean awaiting their return. Often the rugby song that we would sing at the naval engineering college to distinguish those who did the work (we junior officers) from those who didn't (senior officers in general) would cross my mind –

"Captains, Commanders, Commander (E)'s too,
With hands in their pockets and sod all to do."

In addition and thanks to some really remarkable work by the US Navy's CB's and the Army Engineers, there were now airfields on Guam, Saipan and Tinian with runways 6,500 feet long, from which B-29 bombers were operating, each capable of reaching Tokyo with more than ten times the weight of bombs carried by a navy plane.

Saipan had been captured in September 1944 and the first raid mounted on North East Tokyo on the 9th of March 1945. 325 planes took part in the raid, which found the capital unprepared. 100,000 people were killed and over 500,000 injured. 250,000 buildings were destroyed at the cost of 14 aircraft missing. Raids on this scale went on day after day, bringing ordinary life in Japan virtually to a standstill and decimating the industrial production upon which the military depended.

The flight profiles of these huge army air force planes was quite remarkable. They would come off the end of the runway at a weight of 65 tons, including 7,000 gallons of fuel, climbing at a few feet per mile. Hundreds of miles closer to Japan they would pass over us still only a few thousand feet up. I was in HMS *Stalker* one night when they passed over in such numbers that her radar displays were completely saturated for more than an hour... and they did it again many hours later on the way back. We didn't know at the time that a few of these B-29's were from the 509 group practicing for dropping the atomic bomb by arriving over their target at 31,000 ft with a ten ton bomb load.

Occasionally I had to respond to the pipe "Constructor to the Admirals Bridge" where I would receive some observation on improvements that we might make when the ship returned to Sydney or perhaps to note for new designs. Vian was not the easiest of masters but he had a remarkable grasp of detail even while conducting major events. On many occasions I would hear him comment on something occurring in the formation, which we would hear being reported to the ship's captain more than a minute later. He missed very little. As I have noted earlier an Admiral's flag lieutenant has an important role in smoothing things between his master and other people. Vian's flag was Lieut, the Marquess of Milford Haven RN, who made singularly little effort to be sociable to anyone.

Many, indeed most, of the ships that I visited in the fleet had passed through the Eastern Fleet while I was there and had received advice on making the best of their ventilation systems. By and large the Pacific was less humid than the Indian Ocean area and there was usually a pleasant breeze which gave some relief when off-watch. Rainstorms were always welcome and the crew took full advantage of them when not closed-up at action stations. Where possible I visited new ships joining the fleet and found one or two fans going backwards and / or running at half speed and all the other things we had found in the Eastern Fleet Habitability Mission. There was an officer on the staff at Woolloomooloo specially appointed for ventilation matters and he usually sorted out these problems as the ships passed through.

One day I was summoned by the Admiral and told to arrange for the air defence lookout positions to be removed because they interfered with his views up and aft. These lookout positions were arranged on each side of the top of the carrier's island structure and prior to radar were the prime position for detecting the approach of enemy aircraft. Four sailors on each side would solemnly scan the horizon with mounted binoculars to warn of approaching aircraft. They were a carry-over from pre-radar days and I readily assured the Admiral that I would have them removed. Vian very reluctantly accepted that we could hardly burn them off and drop them on the flight deck during operations. I prepared the documents to have it done when we got back to Sydney. Admiralty, Bath, now seemed even further remote.

I was fully with the Admiral in this. I had ridden in countless submarines in which four lookouts were in position on the bridge when we were on the surface, each with his binoculars and a quarter of the horizon to watch. Our lives depended on their vigilance. An aircraft would appear on the distant horizon, by the way it hung in the sky it was a Sunderland, (say) and so no panic. The officer of the watch and I would exchange glances and he would say. "Lookout, why didn't you report that aircraft bearing Green three-five." Upon which the lookout would say "Aircraft bearing Green three-five, Sir, I think it's a Sunderland." This ritual was repeated on numerous occasions; it was axiomatic that the officer always saw it first and that after ten minutes or so, the lookouts were effectively asleep with their eyes open behind their binoculars. Perhaps it was simply a matter of their eyes focussing a few feet in front of them, as is the case with airline pilots at high altitude over clouds.

Transfer of personnel and light objects at sea was by breeches buoy. A light line would be fired from one ship to another when steaming at say 18 knots and 100 ft apart. This would be attached to a stronger line which would be secured to a high point in both ships and along this line would move a sling with the person being transferred pulled by a team of sailors on the receiving ship. If the ships got too close or the sailors slipped someone got wet or worse. I was a frequent transferee and was sprayed a few times but never immersed. During the last fourteen days of the war against Japan, I was in ten different ships. Some were destroyers on which I was on board for only a few hours as a means of transfer to another, usually larger, ship.

On the evening of August 8th I transferred to HMNZS *Gambia*. *Gambia* was commanded by Captain Ralph Edwards who had been Chief of Staff to Admiral Sommerville when I joined the Eastern Fleet in Colombo. He told me that he had asked for me to join his ship because the "morrows operation would be a valuable experience". In company with a sister ship HMS *Newfoundland* and four destroyers we separated from the British Task Group. Although the thing sounded ominous I was pleased to be there, not least because my sister's husband was one of *Gambia's* officers.

When dawn broke we were in company with three US battleships, four US cruisers and about twelve US destroyers, steaming line abreast with a line of destroyers ahead and a line of destroyers astern of the bigger ships. We were at the left hand end of the line. Normally I would be in the damage control HQ somewhere down in the bowels of the ship at action stations but Captain Edwards invited me to observe the action from his bridge. We were many miles north of Tokyo, steaming straight towards the coast and as the tops of hills appeared above the morning mist we went to "action stations" and hoisted our battle ensigns on the main and foremasts.

Steaming at about 24 knots with the ensigns cracking in the wind above and behind the bridge it really was inspiring and all the while the hills of Japan got higher and higher. Our target was the industrial town of Kamaishi where, we understood, 10% of Japans steel was produced. At noon, when it seemed that the line of destroyers ahead must run aground on the headlands protecting the bay, the whole force turned 90 degrees to starboard into line ahead and we were instructed by the US Admiral in command, to commence firing independently at our assigned targets. The US battleships fired at the steelworks with deep-throated salvos heard above the crack (by comparison) of our triple 6-inch turrets. Gambia's initial target was the oil storage depot consisting of a score or more of large storage tanks and soon these were ablaze. We shifted target to the railway marshalling yards.

After steaming north for a few miles all ships reversed course by turning inwards and ever closer to the coast. The destroyers had silenced the coastal guns which were said to be on the headlands-I never saw them fire at us- and we continued the bombardment of industrial targets. We continued thus, up and down, north and south, always turning inwards and ever closer to the coast, for well over an hour, with Gambia's gunnery officer controlling his guns from the bridge with the valuable assistance of a spotter plane launched from one of the US cruisers. Finally there came the order to cease-fire and we all turned together into line abreast and sailed due east away from the coast of Japan. In due course we slowed to enable the US cruisers to recover their amphibian spotter planes and later in the day we learned that a second atomic bomb had been detonated, this time on Nagasaki.

What I found remarkable was how one's perceptions were sharpened during the event. A year later when working for the US Manhattan Project I was to become blasé about events lasting millionths of seconds -a purely intellectual exercise- but in the bombardment at Kamaishi physical events seemed to take on a new timescale .I would hear the gunnery officer direct that "A" turret should fire on such and such oil tank farm. The guns pointing broadside beneath the bridge would fire; seconds later the side of a large oil tank would bend inwards, then seemingly minutes later there would be a plume of black smoke and seemingly minutes later again a slowly developing glow of fire. Yet in reality it had been almost instantaneous. The same with the railway yards; with my unaided eyes I could see individual wheels spiralling through the air as wagons were hit, rose and fell apart.

By the morning we had rejoined the British Task Group where I was transferred to the carrier flagship.

Later, we were ordered by the Fleet Commander, Admiral Nimitz to cease all offensive action against the Japanese and if approached by Japanese aircraft, "to shoot them down in friendly fashion". The Japanese were making overtures for surrender.

Ships that had just arrived in the Fleet, such as the battleship HMS Duke of York, sailed for the forward area and those who had borne the brunt of the battle, withdrew southwards. On 14th August the Japanese accepted the allied terms of unconditional surrender recently re-iterated in the Potsdam Proclamation. The war was over.

The government in London declared V J Day and Their Lordships of the Admiralty signalled 'Splice the Mainbrace'. Our commander suggested that the Wardroom tots (of rum) be used to make a punch of which we all partook. Informed opinion was that half of our tots didn't reach the punch bowl but the chief steward and his men seemed happy.

It was quite evident that the crew were not enamoured at the promptness with which V J Day had been declared. In the spring there had been much ceremonial at V E Day to celebrate victory in Europe with parades and much fêting of the soldiers, sailors and airmen.

V J Day by contrast paid no heed to those who had sweated through the Indian and Burmese jungles or served in ships in the Far East. In the European theatre they gave medals for each war zone; in the Far East there were the Burma Star and the Pacific Star but the sailors could only have one medal for both theatres, if they served in both fleets they got a bar. To the sailors in the fleet this confirmed their view that ministers hadn't really been concerned much about them and the war in the Far East.

I must confess to a similar feeling about my superiors in Admiralty, Bath; they were pleasantly remote and didn't bother us much.   I am reminded of a comment by Harold Wilson "What commentators fail to realise is that negotiating teams abroad so often 'go native' and think that London has gone mad or perverse, while London quickly forms the same view of them"

We felt that we could get on with things like minor changes to improve ships efficiency or habitability or in repairing action damage without bothering them and I would most certainly have cut off the air defence lookout's positions from the flagship's island if peace hadn't got in the way. But in our hearts we knew that this could only go on for so long before we would be asking Bath for help.

I feel that even to the present day and despite the several films portraying the battles in the Pacific war, the British people do not have a true appreciation of the prodigious effort the US Government and armed forces made to bring about the defeat of Japan and the casualties that this entailed, casualties that rose more steeply as the battle moved ever closer to Japan.

The naval engagements were titanic. The biggest in the number of ships engaged was in the Philippines where Japanese fleets of battleships, carriers and cruisers in the Sulu Sea, the Sibuyan Sea and San Bernardino Straits were engaged simultaneously by US fleets guarding the landings on Leyte and Japanese naval power to all intents and purposes destroyed in a series of running engagements. US carrier borne aircraft largely inflicted the damage but one Japanese battleship was sunk by gunfire from a US battleship. The Japanese casualties included the battleship *Musashi*, sunk by carrier aircraft south of Luzon. And so it went on, the US Navy and its air-arm were supreme after early, devastating, losses.

Musashi was the second ship of the Yamato Class, the biggest battleships ever built at 69,000 tons with 9x 18-inch guns. *Yamato* was sunk by aircraft bombs and torpedoes north of Okinawa in April 1945. Neither ship had ever fired her guns at an enemy ship. The third ship of the class, *Shinano*, was converted to an aircraft carrier during construction and commissioned on 18th November 1944 for trials in Japanese home waters. The US Submarine Archerfish sank her ten days later. The fourth ship of the class, *Kil*, was never completed

The same for the ground forces. A fight back from early reverses, island by island across the Pacific until the Japanese homeland was within their sights. This was not done without casualties. To capture Okinawa it took 500,000 US troops three months to overcome a garrison of 110,000 Japanese who fought and died almost to the last man. More than 49,000 Americans died in this operation, 34 US ships were sunk and over 350 seriously damaged. The number of casualties that would be sustained in the planned Operation Olympia, to land over 600,000 men in southern Kyushu on 1st November 1945 and a further 1,200,000 near Tokyo in Operation Coronet some five months later, might be imagined. The Japanese High Command had already anticipated the Kyushu invasion and were preparing defences in depth right up to the Inland Sea, using the 2 million reserve troops already in Japan and a further 2 million being brought back from China. The use of the two atomic bombs saved the Allies, (principally the US,) and even more so, the Japanese, from truly horrendous casualties. Those who consider that nothing could ever justify the use of such a weapon often reject this; pointing out that Adolf Hitler had used the same argument to explain the destruction of Rotterdam in 1940.

A disturbing thing about peace was the requirement of the US government that all Lease Lend equipment be either surrendered or scrapped, leading to what was to me a heartbreaking sight of brand new aircraft being pushed over the side of our aircraft carriers into the Pacific Ocean as we withdrew South.

This account would not be complete without drawing attention to the remarkable performance of the machinery and equipment of the ships of the fleet. In the European theatre it was unusual for ships to operate for more than three weeks without coming into a harbour or anchorage where they could be at so many hours or days notice for sea and hence able to shut down a boiler or some other major component for maintenance. In the Pacific Fleet the ships would be under way for eight weeks or more at speeds exceeding 16 knots and yet require little or no repair at the end of it.

One of the most interesting accidental casualties was HMS *Queenborough*, which had a boiler room fire. The fire was so intense that the complete boiler casings and all of the boiler tubes melted, leaving just the distorted drums with the ends of the tubes protruding. When the oil fire started the Boiler Room had been shut off and steam drenching initiated. The heat was so intense that this served no purpose.

I was not destined to rejoice in Sydney. Awaiting me were orders from the Admiralty to proceed to Japan and report on the damage due to the atomic bombs. I sailed north in HMS *Manxman*, a high-speed minelayer commanded by Captain Geoffrey

Thistleton-Smith GC. He had won his George Cross sitting alone on the sands off the Essex coast dismantling the first Nazi magnetic mine. Even with this behind him he surprised me by telling me that he regretted the war being over; he had trained all his life to fight wars and wanted it to continue. I recalled the toast used in gunrooms a century earlier [when promotion was slow] " Here's to a bloody war or a sickly season".

Being a pre-war ship, and a bit of an oddity, Manxman had a captain's cabin aft with a brass bed in it. The captain complained that the springs were such that he rolled out of bed; they must have been like it since 1936 and no one had done anything about it. Could I help? With a little thought, a pair of pliers and a few bits of wire I cured his bed and made a friend. We fuelled in the US base in Guam; after years of Japanese occupation it seemed to me to be like Sheerness Dockyard with mangrove swamps.

When we arrived in Yokohama I reported to the C in C's staff in HMS *Duke of York* who took me ashore and to the British embassy that had re-opened that week. I quickly discovered that possession of the embassy was already a bone of contention between the representative of the Foreign Office and the navy - The British abroad!

Documents now released show that the US had to be persuaded to accept a British naval presence in the Pacific in 1945. They had been more grateful, after their early losses, to have the aircraft carrier, HMS *Victorious*, operating in the theatre a couple of years earlier but I can see their point in 1945, they had come so far, their commanders and men were battle hardened and had the measure of the enemy and an ally might be more of a nuisance than a help.

Chapter Four

While in HMS *Duke of York*, the Fleet Intelligence officer and I had prepared a set of orders in triplicate, on green paper, in the form familiar to US personnel, directing Lieutenant Commander R. J. Daniel to proceed to Hiroshima and Nagasaki to survey the damage to the cities and port facilities and report.

The journey to Tokyo was by jeep with an escort of Royal Marines. I had not until that time realised what a complete job the carrier borne aircraft and the B-29's had been doing in bringing the war home to the Japanese capital. We passed through whole areas of total destruction from fire and bombs and learned that Tokyo was 57% destroyed, mainly by fire. Travel was difficult because bomb craters were unfilled in the roads or, where repaired, say, to support tramlines, the material had been taken from the footpaths or other portions of the road itself. In what seemed to be quite important side roads, telephone wires hung a few feet above the ground or were down altogether. We learned later that, whole forests had been destroyed, to allow fuel for aircraft to be distilled from the wood, such was the shortage.

The British embassy had been in the care of Switzerland as the protecting power and was almost immediately ready for use. The Japanese cleaners and maintainers still lived in a compound in the grounds and presumably had continued to be paid by the British, via a Swiss bank account! Having regard to the destruction all around, it is remarkable that the embassy itself had escaped undamaged although bombs had landed in the compound.

Some days before my arrival in the embassy, a man from the Foreign Office had arrived. He was the political adviser to C in C British Pacific Fleet of whose existence in the theatre I, and probably most other members of the staff, had been ignorant until that time. The Fleet Intelligence Officer, Commander Shepheard said that the embassy was a naval mess and the F.O. man insisted that it wasn't; it was his embassy, or rather would be when diplomatic relations of some sort were established and meanwhile he was in-loco-parentis. What he objected to was the succession of Royal Marine messengers/escorts/guards etc who marched into the drawing room with their caps on, stamped their feet, saluted and gave their messages to Shepheard. By this time, of course, the marines had got wind of the F. O. man's objections and were stamping for all they were worth.

The embassy had been completed a few years before the war and I was interested to see that the Office of Works in the UK had supplied every fitting. Thus each light switch, coat hook and bath bore the coat of arms of King George VI. The person who put this on the inside of the WC's had a sense of humour well ahead of his time or, perhaps, none at all.

The Supreme Commander, General Douglas McArthur was busy moving the vanguard of his staff into the Dai Itchi and other hotels and was in no state to process a lone Briton so I went for a walk. I spent some time looking at the Carp in the moat surrounding the Emperor's palace and noted the policemen in Nijubashi opposite the bridge leading to the palace, whose duty it was to ensure that all passers-by stopped and bowed in the direction of the palace. Whether the Japanese thought it funny (peculiar) to have a lone ex-enemy wandering among them, I don't know. I didn't give it much thought at the time.

The next day Shepheard and I went to the Dai Itchi hotel, to Supreme HQ. I was interested to note that, not unreasonably, all of the features of the hotel were scaled to suit the Japanese physique; narrow corridors, ceilings lower and smaller sanitary fittings. Being me, I wondered how McArthur would sit on that. We found our way to the US Army Air Transportation Section and were directed to one of about forty colonels each seated behind a desk and telephone in a large room. We were not invited to sit down and I am not certain whether there was space or chairs for such pleasantries. Our Colonel was about 28 years old and about 250 lbs in weight. Every button of his khaki shirt was under severe strain; he had lots of medal ribbons. On his desk he had a cardboard box, divided like a crate, containing twelve small open pots of jam, and packets of biscuits. Throughout our discussion he proceeded to dip biscuits in the various jams and munch them. He was laid back and eventually helpful; the following morning there was an aircraft taking equipment to Nagasaki and I could have a ride in it.

When I was delivered to the airport the following morning by the ever-dutiful marines I found that there was a change of plan. The aircraft in which I would ride was stopping in Nagoya and I would transfer to another aircraft coming from somewhere else which would have a jeep for Nagasaki. The airfield was crowded with aircraft but miraculously we found the right one. I was the only passenger and sat in the back while they wound up the engines and we were off. I should add that all US personnel had revolvers; I had a tin of Spam which someone in the embassy thought might see me through the first day or so, and a blanket, ditto. I suppose that in extremis I was expected to use the Spam to stun anyone one who hadn't got the message that the war was over and conceal the body in my blue blanket.

In due course we landed at an airfield at Nagoya. Many US aircraft were passing overhead -it seemed they were sightseeing as they went about their duties-but I felt pretty lonely on the ground notwithstanding the small company of US soldiers who had come to collect the equipment we had brought. My aircraft left. Mercifully the second aircraft arrived within the hour and after a bit of local sightseeing we took off for Nagasaki. The most comfortable seat in the cargo space was in the driving seat of the jeep. After a while I was conscious of a strong smell of petrol and found that a spare can of petrol in the rear of the jeep had fallen over and emptied itself into the rear well. I went forward and told the flight crew who took the matter seriously and switched off lots of circuits and partially opened a cargo door to increase ventilation. By now we were approaching Hiroshima and circled three times around the damaged city before resuming course for Nagasaki.

We circled Nagasaki and flew inland seeking the airfield. We found an airfield and landed. There was not a building or person anywhere to be seen. The aircrew said that they had expected soldiers from the 'bomb people' to collect the jeep; but they were some two hours later than planned and further, they were not sure that this was the right airfield. They thought it was, but where was everybody? After a while they said that they had to get back to their base and off-loaded the jeep, which I signed for. I asked them the direction for Nagasaki and they took off. I was now alone with a jeep in a country with which a month ago we had been at war and upon whom we had unleashed a terrible weapon that had killed tens of thousands of people about twenty miles to the south. For the second time in one day I was alone on a Japanese airfield. How the hell did I allow myself to get in this position?

I left the airfield and joined a rough road, which I judged from the sun -it was afternoon - to being south. I continued to drive southwards and westwards until I came to a small village where I stopped at the largest building to try to ask the way. Fortuitously a black uniformed policeman appeared. Having the British gift for foreign languages I shouted "Nagasaki" at him a few times and he pointed the way I was going. I climbed into the jeep and he bowed as I drove off. After a while the road got better and after I had been travelling for some time, I slowly realised that I was motoring down the main north-south road into what had once been the city of Nagasaki, in this part there was not a single building standing.

I was quite unprepared for what I saw as I approached the harbour, a US cruiser and two US hospital ships but immediately recalled some messages that I had seen and commented upon in the embassy concerning the number of allied prisoners of war held on the Island of Kyushu and how they would be brought out through Nagasaki. It transpired that the US marines had established a perimeter around the Customs House area where the hospital ships were alongside. I drove up to the customs house and was halted by a marine sentry. I explained who I was and waved my orders at him. He explained that I could only enter the customs area if I had a pass signed by his Captain. The system clearly did not allow for odd-bods arriving out of the wild blue yonder. I explained again that I had just flown from Tokyo; he indicated that I should tell that story to the marines so I repeated it. And again He said that had I been one of the prisoner of war contact teams he would have let me in, so I hastily said that I also had to look for British prisoners of war and he let me in. I felt a bit smug as I parked the jeep, only to find a very large marine sergeant standing beside me to whom I had to repeat the whole story. Just at that moment an Australian navy Lieutenant POW contact team member came up and vouched for me and I was let into the actual customs house and issued with a camp bed and a pair of those rather nice jungle boots. I explained my mission to my Australian friend and some time later he reappeared and told me that a British aircraft carrier had entered harbour and some of her officers were at that moment downstairs at a reception with US Rear Admiral Byrd and the nurses from the hospital ships. I learned that the aircraft carrier was the support carrier HMS *Stalker* in which I had been briefly in the last series of operations of the war. I went down and poked my nose in the door and was immediately spotted by *Stalker's* commander who came over and said, "What the hell are you doing here?" I explained my mission and he introduced me to Admiral Byrd and Colonel Stafford L Warren who was in charge of the Manhattan Project assessment team. Admiral Byrd invited me to call on him the following morning when he would arrange for me to join the team from the Manhattan project. Well satisfied, I collected my kit, reluctantly gave back my unworn boots and was taken home to HMS *Stalker* for the night.

The next morning one of *Stalker's* boats delivered me to the Cruiser USS *Wichita* and I stated my business to the officer of the deck. I was taken to the Admiral's outer-outer-outer office where after a while I was informed by a slightly embarrassed Lt (jg) that the Admiral had no recollection of last night's conversation and they would be pleased to deliver me back to the British aircraft carrier. I decided that it was up to me and asked to be put ashore. On the Customs House pier I found a room with a paper notice "Interpreters" in which were about eight black clad Japanese. I went in and asked to be taken to Colonel Warren. A man detached himself and drove me about a mile to a large school building in a part of the city that had suffered less damage, due in part to being shadowed by a hill. Here I was introduced once more to the Colonel, Doctor Warren, and he in turn introduced me to his small team of medical specialists, physicists and engineers supported by an intelligence major and some enlisted men. I was accepted by the team as someone doing the same thing as they were.

The team was accommodated in a small hotel in the nearby village of Mogi. Mogi was on one of the many branches of Nagasaki Ko, the broad estuary leading to the port and city of Nagasaki. The hotel was on the waterfront. The autumn mornings were like Japanese paintings with distant hills rising from the mist and nearby bamboo trees swaying gently in the breeze. Colonel Warren invited me to occupy the spare bed in his room; we lived mainly on "K" rations.

We left Mogi each morning and returned in the early evening seven days a week, otherwise we seldom left the hotel and its small waterside garden. I was, however conscious that whenever I looked out or ventured out I seemed to see the same black suited Japanese man. I learned that the Emperor had decreed that no hostile action should be taken against allied personnel and that my rather shady man was the man in charge of the secret police unit charged with our protection. If they were secretly in attendance in the daytime when I walked about in the devastation of what had once been downtown Nagasaki, I didn't know; I never noticed them. The only Japanese that I encountered in the bomb-damaged city were dead bodies (usually badly burned in the fire that followed the bang) and teams of Japanese men with shovels and rough planks who were collecting the bodies. Unlike the US personnel I was quite unarmed and totally alone and it was a bit eerie to have them pass close by carrying a body on a plank or rough box and solemnly bow to me. I could not help reflecting that had the positions been reversed someone would have hit someone with a shovel. God bless the Emperor. Japanese society was based on conformity, perhaps best exemplified by the Japanese proverb 'The nail that sticks up gets hammered'.

It must be appreciated that with the exception of the intelligence officer, Major "Bud" Uanna and one of the enlisted men, none of the Manhattan Project people had heard a shot fired in anger in the war and hence their attitude to the Japanese was quite different from mine. They viewed the Japanese as poor little people who had suffered as the result of their leaders megalomania and greed and who really were not responsible for the dreadful things that had been done to allied prisoners. They were right of course, it was just that at that time I didn't see it that way. All I saw were the sacrifices that brave people had made fighting their way back from the east and from the west to defeat the Japanese invaders and the evidence of gross ill treatment of all who had become their prisoners.

The selection of targets upon which the first atomic bombs would be dropped had nominally been undertaken by a Target Committee in the Manhattan Project, but had largely been done by General Groves. Groves was only too aware that with the surrender of Germany there were some among the few who knew the purpose of the work going on at Los Alamos who would advise the President not to use the bomb (if it worked). Groves was totally persuaded that the use of the bomb would shorten the war and save thousands of American lives. The first choice of target was Tokyo, really on emotional grounds, but this did not meet the criteria that the Target Committee had laid down, namely that it should be relatively undamaged up to that point, should be configured to display a spectrum of damage, (hopefully to military production capability) and should be unlikely to have rain - and hence clouds- to impede bomb aiming.

The next selection of possible target cities was Kyoto, Kokura, Niigata and Hiroshima. Groves favoured Kyoto, but when it was eventually put to him, Secretary of War, Stimson rejected this choice because of the city's religious significance. By the end of July 1945 the choice was Hiroshima, Kokura and Nagasaki in that order and on the fateful day of August 6th each of these could have received the first bomb if there was cloud over the others. Reconnaissance aircraft dispatched ahead of the bomb carrying aircraft reported 3 tenths cloud over all three and so the first bomb fell on the first choice, Hiroshima.

Nagasaki was not the primary target for the second bomb. The aircraft found ten-tenths cloud over Kokura and ten-tenths cloud over everywhere else. The bomb was primed and all systems were 'go' and those on board the aircraft began to reflect upon the prospect of having to take the thing back to Iwo Jima or to their base in Tinian. The story is that they radioed their base and asked them what they should do. The reply was

"Repeat slowly after me, Our Father which art in Heaven...." Major Bud Uanna swore that this was true. Anyway the aircraft flew south over a complete carpet of cloud to its second, alternative, target, whereupon at exactly the right moment a hole appeared in the cloud right over the city. The exceptional thing was that if one had wanted to produce the maximum amount of damage to the town, the shipyards and other industries, one would have detonated the bomb exactly where it went off. By such a chance was the fate of 60,000 people settled.

The bomb had detonated about 1,000 ft in the air. It had caused damage to people and materiel in three ways; by direct radiation of gamma and neutrons, by heat radiation and by blast. People can live for a while after being irradiated but they become progressively more ill and eventually die. The process is irreversible. Similarly for heat radiation but many of the heat deaths were in the fires caused by the blast upsetting things that caught fire. The blast also killed indirectly by hurling people against things or things against people.

At the moment of detonation the bomb emitted an intense shower of neutrons and gamma radiation (and some beta) and the fission process created a mass of middle density elements - the fission products — which rose with the cloud while emitting intense gamma radiation and eventually moved away downwind. Neutron emission was confined almost entirely to the moment of detonation but much of the gamma radiation received by people was from the cloud as it towered over the city.

The mushroom shaped cloud contains not only fission products but also radioactive dust swept up in the explosion. This radioactivity decays at different rates according to the elements and the radioactive particles settle out from the cloud to earth according to their size and the climatic conditions. An important part of the US teams research work was to determine the extent of residual radioactivity at ground level and whether there was any selectivity in the substances on which they were measured.

The direction in which the cloud had moved away could be detected and followed by the use of Geiger counters and the team took readings for several kilometres in the surrounding countryside to determine the rate of deposition of identified fission products from which the efficiency of the nuclear reaction might be determined. I went out with the teams a few times. On one occasion a jeep broke down somewhere out in the country and two very tired team members walked back to base. I went out with two others to recover the broken down vehicle; when we got there a large boulder, which remained on the drivers seat, had smashed the windscreen. Not everybody obeyed the Emperor completely.

The shipyards along the western side of the harbour were a shambles of corrugated iron and toppled cranes. There had been a model-towing tank for predicting the resistance of ships; it was destroyed. Documents, plans and textbooks were blowing about in the wind. I was interested to note that in the hydrodynamics and ship construction textbooks English and German technical words were used buried in the Japanese text.

Reinforced concrete buildings had done better; at least one could see that a building had been there. Typically at more than 1,500 feet from ground zero (the spot immediately under where the bomb had been detonated) a building with 6 inch thick walls had its front bent in, internal floors buckled, back wall fallen out and roof gone, due to the long duration shock/blast wave followed by the suction phase. The people inside had died where they stood. The building would not be repairable. It was an exchange of comments when looking at my photograph of this particular building that caused the British Chief of Naval Staff to dismiss me summarily from his room when I eventually got back to Britain with my report.

One day I went with Colonel Warren to visit a large naval hospital outside Nagasaki to which thousands of casualties had been taken. The wards and corridors were filled with sad people showing all the signs of what I was beginning to realise were the symptoms of radiation sickness, loss of hair, purple blotches on the skin, loss of nails and sickness. Most would die; they had seen their neighbours and fellow patients die and there was massive resignation. We took tea with the Japanese Surgeon Vice Admiral in charge. Six tall men in grey civilian suits that claimed to be Koreans and who made loud sucking noises when drinking their tea to show their appreciation accompanied him. We silent drinkers must have seemed very rude to them. The Admiral must have thought me important because he gave me his collar badges of rank; for an awful moment I thought that he expected me to take him prisoner; Navy to navy sort of thing.

Parts of Nagasaki had survived due to the shadowing effect of hills and physical distance from ground zero. Life went on as best it could for the Japanese as they struggled to come to terms with reality. The building from which Colonel Warren's team operated in Nagasaki was one of the substantial buildings that had survived - albeit without any windows - and was also being used by the Japanese as an administrative HQ. Our paths crossed the Japanese in only one place; we used the same toilets. There were urinals down the centre and cubicles along the walls. Males and females used this facility and it was not uncommon for a female to stand talking to a man as he used the urinal. This was accepted and there was nothing improper in it. Both sexes wore baggy black trousers and looked much alike to me.

From the time that I was disowned by Admiral Byrd, I saw no-one except the Manhattan Project team but activity continued around the Customs House area as the remaining prisoners of war were collected from the remoter parts of Kyushu and brought to the port for processing and medical care before shipment home. There had been large numbers to start with and now the numbers were quite small. The project team people relied on the navy for communications and rations and obviously were in touch.

The project teams senior enlisted man was a sergeant of Japanese parentage, born in the United States - a Nisei. He was a wheeler-dealer who had been advanced to sergeant and demoted to private on several occasions. At Mogi he had moved into the landlord's house next to the small hotel. The landlord's family appeared to include a daughter.

One day Colonel Warren told me that we had been invited to have dinner with the Governor of Nagasaki Province. It emerged that in accordance with Japanese custom; this would be at a Geisha house. Notwithstanding the strict 'non-fraternizing' orders from the Supreme Command, many of the team members wished to accept. Colonel Warren was not keen and felt that we (he) might get into hot water for fraternizing but on the other hand the Governor had eased our path in the work we had to do. I said that I didn't wish to attend but on the day we were persuaded that it would be ill mannered for the Colonel not to attend. The Colonel and I set off about half an hour after the rest of the team; it was dusk as we turned into the geisha street and saw a milling mass of Japanese and in the middle, the white helmets of the US Marine Corps military police. We turned back and abandoned our teammates for the present. The next morning Colonel Warren was summoned to the Customs House and thoroughly dressed down by the marine colonel who was ex-Iwo Jima and all points south, for allowing his troops to fraternize with the enemy. Little did he know that Warren had nearly been among the fraternisers The story doubtless improved with the telling, but our nisei sergeant had explained that he was only there as the interpreter and in this role, the geisha lady had asked him to have the marine policemen remove their boots in accordance with Japanese custom when they entered her establishment. This they did with some reluctance. Our chaps, of course, were caught with their boots off.

The teams work was drawing to a close when, about a week before we actually left, I sensed a change in some of the US officers attitude to me; they sent me to Coventry. Colonel Warren said that he had received orders that I was to be returned to Tokyo forthwith. I could only assume that, starting with Admiral Byrd's curious reversal some weeks earlier; those in Nagasaki had been querying my presence and had finally got an answer. Major Bud Uanna, the intelligence (and security) officer remained his friendly self, he knew that I had not openly sought classified information and that on the contrary I had contributed materially to the contents of those parts of their report dealing with estimates of blast pressures and other engineering matters. One thing that he said to me was that the Russians were going to be a nuisance post-war and we should use the giant new B-36 bomber to drop an atomic bomb on them now to show them who's who.

At this time I noticed that bulldozers had started to level the damaged area and on the day we pulled out I saw two Soviet officers in uniform walking in the vicinity of ground zero.

Typhoon force winds precluded my leaving early and it was clear that they were not going to let me freelance my way around Hiroshima. In the event I left Nagasaki with the Manhattan Project team in their C-46 aircraft. There was a minor hitch at the airfield when the Nisei sergeant, who had arrived in Nagasaki with just his kitbag, arrived with two large trunks containing objects that he had 'been given' in Nagasaki. Warren refused to take them on the plane and handed them to the military police for return to the hotelkeeper at Mogi. We eventually departed for Tokyo, via two circuits around Hiroshima. As we approached Tokyo, Mount Fuji 's snow covered peak was above the clouds on our port side.

When we arrived in Tokyo, I was taken to the Supreme Commanders HQ, to the office of a Major General Newman, US Army, who reprimanded me for going to Nagasaki and Hiroshima and thus prejudicing Anglo-US relations. He went on to say that the US had produced the bomb and delivered it and that the US would tell the British anything they (the US) thought the British should be told and much more in this vein. I ventured to point out that there were British scientists and engineers in the Manhattan Project but this was brushed aside, they were subject to General Grove's orders and I wasn't. This extra-ordinary performance went on for an hour with the General actually shouting. I was totally at a loss as to what I was expected to say other than "I'm sorry you feel like that, Sir but we did clear my orders with these headquarters." This provoked another out-burst, this time against his own air force people and so on. He would probably have had apoplexy if I had told him about the B-36 bomber. I told him that I had seen Russians in Nagasaki on the day we pulled out and he made no comment. Eventually I asked if he could kindly give me transport to the British Embassy. This prompted a comment about "the cheek of the British", but I got a jeep and driver and was duly delivered to the embassy.

I am now aware that this 'anti-British' attitude was not simply the reaction of an individual officer but reflected General Groves' intention to frustrate the US President's policy of collaboration with the British on matters to do with nuclear research. To be fair to Groves, he had created a vast industrial organisation at a cost of over two billion dollars of the US taxpayer's money and he was intent on keeping this and the awesome weapons that it could produce, solely in hands he could trust. It is sad that Groves sought to play down the contribution that the émigré Europeans made to the Manhattan project because in a way it seems to detract from the US achievement, which, in engineering, was so gigantic. The first scientists arrived at Los Alamos in March 1943 to begin their work on the bomb. By that time the vast plants to isolate the isotopes of Uranium were already well advanced in build at Oak Ridge and Hanford, a truly formidable achievement.

At the embassy Commander Shepheard told me that they had tentatively posted me as missing. Within the embassy the Royal Navy - Foreign Office power struggle was at fever pitch, with Shepheard stoutly maintaining the naval mess argument and Mr Mc something arguing that he was in charge of this piece of Foreign Office territory. I recall that he sought my support for his territorial rights argument. I was simply worn out and tired and extremely bedraggled - I had been away more than a month. The Royal Marines were still a bone of contention, throughout the evening they would enter the ante room (sitting room) and the wardroom (dining room), stamp their boots, salute and hand Shepheard a signal just received or a copy of one just sent. Mr Mc something objected to the whole performance, as would have most Admirals of my acquaintance, but particularly that "they had their hats on in what, after all, is my home". A fellow visitor was the novelist C. S. Forester who said that he had been in Honolulu and had somehow hitched a ride to Tokyo. I hoped that Major General Newman didn't know this further example of British cheek. C. S. Forester said that he had serious reservations about the ethics of using atomic bombs against Japan. How easy it is to adopt strong moral poses when one is absolutely sure that one will not be among those called upon to battle their way ashore and fight across a Japan defended to the last by four million soldiers and a hostile population.

One of the messages handed to Shepheard was from the Supreme Commander's HQ requiring Lieutenant Commander Daniel to surrender the photographs and notes that he had taken in Nagasaki and Hiroshima to SCHQ at 08.00 the next morning. At 05.30 the next morning three Royal Marines took me to the harbour where I joined a British destroyer, which took me to Yokosuka where I transferred to HMNZS *Gambia*, which sailed almost immediately for Sydney. I was known to *Gambia's* captain and wardroom, most recently I had been in *Gambia* when she had taken part in the bombardment of Kamaishi on the day the bomb was dropped on Nagasaki; it was like coming home. They said that I arrived on board looking like a tramp and I can well believe it. My shoes were beyond repair. Throughout the voyage I wrote my report. It was typed by C in C's staff in Sydney and my photographs were developed, one copy of all this remained with C in C for safety lest the top copy and I should not reach London.

The last part of my report suggested that a combination of atomic warheads on ballistic missiles like the German V2 would make a formidable weapon, which it might be almost impossible to counter. One method might be to fire one's own missiles with nuclear warheads to detonate near to them in space. I didn't call it 'Star Wars'. Two years later when serving in Admiralty Whitehall I was to learn what the Admiralty's Chief Scientist thought of this idea.

In October 1945 I was flown back to Britain in a converted Lancaster bomber. I was surprised at how much the wings flexed under loading in flight. We were delayed at the RAF airfield near Haifa for an engine change and while there; there were some explosions in the distance, which I was told was quarry blasting. When we landed at Bournemouth airport we were questioned about the raid on the air station's arsenal during which Israeli terrorists had stolen large quantities of arms and ammunition in an action that was to start the Israeli's fight for their homeland; the bangs had been the air station arsenal being robbed of its contents.

In the UK I started a round of visits to important people in government and Whitehall. Responsibility for atomic matters had remained with Sir John Anderson (of air-raid shelter fame) who had had this role in the previous Churchill government. He made encouraging noises. The military clearly wished the whole thing had never happened and still wished that it would go away. The navy just did not wish to face up to the fact that one weapon could sink one of their battleships (and the accompanying destroyers). The First Sea Lord, Sir Andrew Cunningham really did not wish to hear what he was being told. He looked at the photographs and pointed to the wrecked reinforced concrete building that I described and said; "There you are, its still standing." I, who had stood in that shell of a building, in a flattened city, surrounded by dead bodies, said in some exasperation that he seemed not to wish to recognise that such weapons would change the whole concept of naval warfare and the make up of future fleets. He became angry and ordered me out of his room. He was a great man with a brilliant war record and I suppose that such a quantum advance in favour of the attacker was difficult to face up to. Some years later when he was President of the Royal Institution of Naval Architects he was good enough to say "You were right, my boy."

Eventually I was appointed to Admiralty, Bath to work on the design of the battleship *Vanguard*. That's not exactly true because the ship was nearly built; the task that I was given was to calculate the effect on the ship of hypothetical damage from torpedoes and other weapons, which would cause flooding. The sums showed that the message that we younger officers had tried to put over in 1942/43, that asymmetric flooding must be avoided at all costs, had still not been fully absorbed by our seniors. I was however pleased to see that *Vanguard* had been given a reasonable sheer - slope on the forecastle deck - even if this was patently a late change.

In December the US Secretary of State wrote formally to His Majesty's Secretary of State for Foreign Affairs, Mr Ernest Bevin, requesting that Constructor Lieut. Commander R. J. Daniel RCNC be seconded to the US Government's Manhattan Project for service at the forthcoming tests of atomic weapons.

In January 1946 I flew the Atlantic in a converted Liberator bomber. Entry was through a hole in the bottom of the fuselage. At that time one could hardly pick up a newspaper without seeing a picture of General McArthur, waving or saluting while emerging from or getting into the door of an aircraft. I bet that he avoided Liberators like the plague.

Our landfall in North America was Goose Bay, Labrador. We taxied to within a few yards of the airport buildings and a Canadian Air Force bus came to carry us. This seemed an unnecessary luxury since we had been cooped up for about twelve hours and I said that I would walk to stretch my legs, only to realise as I reached the aircraft's exit that the external temperature was about 30 degrees below zero. So I took the bus. That night was spent in Montreal and all of the next day was occupied in getting to Washington DC.

In Washington DC I reported to Sir James Chadwick at the UK Scientific Office and met Dr. William Penney whose assistant I was to be. Chadwick is famous for his work on the structure of the atom and in particular for discovering the atomic particle we call the neutron. Penney was a mathematician and an expert on the effect of bombs and other weapons. Tragically, his first wife had been killed in the London blitz. For the past several years he had been one of the small British contingent working in the Manhattan Project at Los Alamos.

The operation on which we were to be employed was to be called Operation Crossroads and would detonate three atomic weapons at Bikini Atoll in the Pacific Ocean, one in the air, one on the surface and one deep underwater. The targets would be surplus US and captured enemy warships and auxiliaries on which would be placed items of naval, army and air force equipment and animals to obtain data on the effects of blast, heat and nuclear radiation.

Because of its essentially maritime nature, the task force commander was Vice Admiral Blandy USN. His technical director was Dr Ralph Sawyer, to whose staff Penney and I were appointed. Other senior service officers of 2 star rank were responsible for assembling the vast array of target ships, for logistics, for army, for air force and aviation and so on. Penney was well known for his work at Los Alamos on the bomb and its effects and his reputation had preceded him. He was included in many planning meetings and because I carried his bag, I went along too.

At the top level there seemed to be broadly three schools of thought concerning the arrangement of the target ships in the Bikini lagoon. The air force wanted all the ships to be close together, presumably so that they could sink the lot and prove navies to have no future in war. The navy wanted to spread the ships widely across the lagoon and presumably show that fleets could survive without catastrophic losses. The scientists said lets not waste this unique opportunity to gather data at all distances and so the target ships should be spread out from ground zero like the spokes of a wheel. Fortunately the latter view prevailed.

What about the point of aim? The air force kept on about how accurate their bomb-sights were - "we can drop the thing through a barrel" was the oft-repeated claim. One began to wonder would they miss by two feet or three?

The facts were that the bomb would be released from a height of about 30,000 feet (nearly 6 miles up) and taking account of the variables like drift, wind speed and temperature, probability theory would suggest that on a clear day with good visibility, a good bomb aimer would have a 20% to 50% probability of placing the bomb within a circle of 1,000 feet radius. The 509 Group specially formed and intensively trained for these high-level missions, had regularly placed their 10 ton practice bombs within a 300 foot circle. Analysis showed that on August 6th, 1945 the Hiroshima bomb had detonated some 600 feet from its point of aim, the Aioi Bridge.

Wise voices prevailed, it was decided that the point of aim would be the battleship *Nevada* ringed at 900 feet radius with six ships of various types. If the air force couldn't miss by more than two or three feet, six hundred yards should be a safe enough margin, I thought. The remaining target ships would be moored along slightly curved radial lines of ships of the same type to give a graduated damage profile. To help the bomber, bright lights would be aimed up in the sky towards the point at which it was calculated the aircraft would release the bomb and there were other radio aids.

These top level discussions were given a high security classification but after a while I came to realise that the extreme secrecy was usually a device to guard a piece of information until a general officer was ready to be the one to tell the press, rather than to preserve the national interest.

It was many years before I realised that the same thing occurred in Britain. Usually it was a Minister of the Crown who sometimes hinted of things to come. That was their prerogative while we lesser mortals followed the Official Secrets Act to the letter. In any case there were so many high level defections to the Soviets - Burgess, Maclean, Philby, Blake and others - that we had a sick joke that we were more concerned with preserving our nuclear secrets from the UK press, and in particular from a Beaverbrook man called Chapman Pincher, than from the Russians, "Who probably knew it anyway".

I was, however, surprised to read in Chapman Pincher s book, 'Inside Story', published in the USA in 1976, that "Over several years, Sir Frederick Brundrett, the Defence Ministry's chief scientist, was briefing me on secret matters quite openly, believing that it was helpful in promoting defence policy". In his book, Pincher gives several more examples of leaks by very senior officials made simply for the purpose of showing-off.

The same man, Brundrett took it upon himself to brief the Labour Member of Parliament, George Brown, on the nuclear facts of life, when in opposition in 1959. Brown lived up to his reputation as a wild gun and promptly stood up in the House of Commons and demanded that Prime Minister Macmillan should undertake an enquiry to establish which official of the MoD was responsible for claiming to have authority to disclose figures on H and A bomb stocks.

Another interesting security 'leak' occurred when the Japanese surrendered, General Kenny, a US Pacific Air Force Commander had allowed several journalists to see an atomic bomb and had told them that its weight was 4 tons and that the production rate was 6 per month with 8 already in store. He was wrong on both counts but was this deliberate? It happened that one of the reporters was an Australian of markedly left wing sympathies, such that he subsequently reported the Korean and Vietnam wars from the Communist side and lost his Australian passport in consequence. We know now that the Soviets probably already knew all this from Fuchs and his fellows within the Manhattan Project.

In Washington I had a room in a modest hotel in Franklin Square and ate in the local White Tower snack bar; most of my money went in sending food parcels back to Britain. I spent my free time enjoying the art galleries and museums and generally exploring this beautiful city. I found the public buildings very impressive. I rode the elevator up the Washington Monument and learned from the disembodied voice that accompanies the trip that the top sways 18 inches in a gale. I was impressed by the Jefferson Memorial and learnt much about his singular contribution to the formation and the regulation of the nation that has stood the test of time so well and I reflected upon how much the architects of the US Constitution drew from the Magna Carta. I brooded with Abe Lincoln in his monument and read and re-read his Gettysburg address carved in the wall that curves behind him.

On a quite different plane I was surprised at the number of statues in public places in Washington. Somehow I had associated statues with decadent European royalty, noblemen and generals and expected better of the New World without appreciating that vanity and bootlicking are universal in intent and effect. This might not have been; when the founding fathers were formulating the American constitution in Philadelphia, Thomas Jefferson argued strongly that the clause that prohibits occupiers of official positions from adopting or accepting titles should also prohibit the erection of statues. Had he been present throughout, instead of injecting his views by mail from Paris, he might well have had his way. The Smithsonian was smaller in 1946 but I liked it better than what I saw in 1986.

In 1946 there was a Washington Post building immediately opposite a large Fire Station on 14th Street and my evening walks usually included a little detour past the latter in the hope that there would be an alarm, when the traffic lights would flash red, the station doors would open and out would come one or more of the mighty appliances. Best of all this might be the long one with the ladder and a man sitting on top that, I understood, steered the back wheels. Perhaps one day he would fail to be in place in time and the back of the fire engine would go through the front of the newspaper building opposite. Of course I saw nothing; it was usually when I had just got undressed that I would hear the noise and sirens of the fire engines departing to some distant emergency. One night they started up, gave a few mournful hoots and stopped. "Aha", I thought "they have hit the Washington Post" and put my trousers on again to have a look, only to find that it was my hotel that was on fire. Actually someone had fallen asleep while smoking and it was a mattress that was alight; the firemen dealt with this by lowering it to the ground through the window.

The new cathedral was being built in a style that reminded me of Canterbury. I was told that many of the stonemasons and craftsmen had recently come from Europe and that there was a growing awareness that the sort of craftsmen needed for the detail work were in short supply and would become even more difficult to recruit as the huge task of restoring Europe's war damage gathered pace. As a result the sequence of work was being modified to make the best use of them.

Usually with Penney, I visited various government facilities to discuss the instrumentation they were preparing to deploy at Bikini. Some of it would depend on accurate timing vis-à-vis bomb detonation and much of it seemed to me to be liable to problems when exposed, as it must be, for some days to the temperature, humidity and salt laden atmosphere of a pacific atoll. Visits that were memorable were made to Woods Hole on Cape Cod, Martha's Vineyard, the Aberdeen Proving Ground Naval Ordnance Lab and the David Taylor Model Basin, memorable really for the old and new friends that one met.

The small townships around Cape Cod have names of English towns from which doubtless the early settlers came, such as Falmouth (several variants!) Barnstable, Harwich, Sandwich, Yarmouth and Chatham and, further north, Plymouth and Plymouth Rock. I stayed at the Cocktail Inn a few miles from Woods Hole. There was deep snow and it was very cold especially when I witnessed some explosive tests at Martha's Vineyard with Arnold Aarons. We were transported too and from in a small steam propelled launch in which the only source of warmth was the funnel, upon which in desperation I placed my gloved hands and ruined a perfectly good pair of leather gloves.

The small towns were unspoilt and charming. The daily train to Boston left at 6pm. I was taken to the depot and waited with the other prospective passengers in a restaurant-cum drug store up a slight slope from the track. In due course the train arrived and after discharging its passengers started to toll its bell, at which we few trooped down the hill and climbed aboard and off we went through the dark wooded countryside to Boston and thence overnight to Washington D.C. I was destined to visit Boston next, some years later when my flight was diverted from New York. It seemed that Logan airport was the only airfield still open on the U.S eastern seaboard; we descended through the clouds and suddenly there were ships masts outside the cabin windows and bump, we were safely on the ground. When my flight arrived they were rapidly running out of parking space for aircraft. We were taken to the railroad station and put on trains by harassed airline staff. I stood all the way to New York. In the hundred or more crossings that I made this was the only time that I was diverted. It was my ambition to be diverted to somewhere interesting, like Montego Bay or Nassau, but no such luck.

Aberdeen Proving Ground was what one would expect of a wilderness site for testing high explosives. It was here that I first met the DTMB team and saw the aluminium foil gauges being tested and marvelled that someone had sufficient money to approve the extensive use of such an expensive scheme. Even then the team did not seem to be united. The gauges, of which more than 50 were to be erected on the target ships, comprised a steel cube about 40cm side mounted on a massive tubular steel frame about 3 metres high. Five of the sides of the cube were double plates pierced by holes of increasing size. Aluminium foil was placed between these plates and the trials that I witnessed were to establish some relationship between the size of hole and the pressure to rupture the foil, recognising that the millisecond pressure pulses given by the hundred or so pounds of explosive used in these calibration trials would in no way simulate the pressure pulse of more than a second that would arise from the atomic bomb. I asked what they were doing about corrosion and was assured that this was no problem. In the event, of course, the foil corroded rapidly in the Bikini air and had to be replaced with treated foil. In ———. time would show that the results were only capable of rational interpretation after we had produced the pressure-distance curve derived from our cans.

It was at this time that I met Greg Hartman and Curtis Lamson and the Naval Ordnance Laboratory people and their gauges.

The happening that I most regretted during this time was when Penney and I visited the battlefield at Gettysburg. Most Europeans grow up within 50 kilometres of a place where a battle of some sort took place in the past 2,000 years. In many cases these were the scene of thousands of casualties but in the UK most of the engagements down the years were skirmishes in which a few hundreds were slain and today merit little more than crossed swords on the road map and, occasionally, a roadside plaque. I knew something of the scale of the American Civil War. That it had divided families, had been savage and had caused more casualties than in any previous war but I was not aware or prepared for the national shrine that Gettysburg represented.

On entering the park a uniformed guide climbed into the seat beside the driver and off we went along roads lined with neat piles of cannon balls, all freshly painted and in the distance one could see high lookout towers from which to obtain panoramic views over the battlefield. Our guide directed us to the wood where it all began; the opposing armies had been moving along adjacent valleys and were not aware of the others presence until a patrol of mounted scouts entered the wood and detected the other army. Instead of withdrawing quietly to report, somebody fired a shot and soon units from each side were engaged. Our guide recited this as if reading from a text and went on that "hearing the gunfire, the colonel of the scouts rode up, dismounted and entered the wood where his head was knocked off by a cannon ball and he died without saying a word". Like an idiot I said "Ah, a man of few words" and Penney said "Not a very communicative man" and we grinned, upon which our guide indicated that we were expected to behave with great reverence and climbed sulkily back into the car. We drove on to the first watchtower at which the guide said "You Britishers know it all, you can go up there by yourselves". This was not quite the intellectual disaster that it sounds because Penney was extremely well informed on US history and on the war between the states but sitting in the car with a guide who just sulked was not pleasant and we decided thereafter to drive on round the circuit and quit. In any case, one cannon ball does look rather like any other.

The tour guide would not have appreciated my term of sub-lieutenants at Keyham. We were drilled by splendid gunners mates from Devonport Naval barracks who taught us to march, drill, and bear arms and to fire them as well. The instructors were not unintelligent but had learnt the drills parrot fashion and if interrupted or asked a question, would go back to the beginning and start again. After he had been through this a couple of times some mischievous young man would say "Sorry chief, but what does No 3 do?" upon which the gunners mate would immediately start "At the command Load, No 1 opens the breech." and so on through the whole routine.

Photography demanded much thought. Some things had to be recorded at a very high speed and these cameras would be started two seconds before detonation, which would be about forty seconds after the bomb had left the aircraft. The bomb would be sending signals as it fell from which the moment of detonation could be calculated and all the remote instruments switched on by radio signals received by black boxes (actually these were brown) tuned to act on the 30 seconds, 15 seconds or 2 seconds alert.

It was my job to arrange Penney's instruments to measure the air blast pressure from the air burst bomb. In contrast with the very expensive instruments that the US laboratories were using the total cost of the British things was about 1,000 dollars, and for this we were able to make measurements at more than two hundred locations. The "instruments" were some 500 x 5 gallon gasoline cans, 50x 55-gallon oil drums and several sets of 2-inch diameter mild steel tubes of various lengths arranged in groups of five.

There were problems with the Congress concerning the amount of legislative work and on 27th March the President ordered that the operation be delayed to enable congressional observers to attend. The US armed forces were being run down at an increasing rate and budgetary limitations were beginning to be felt. Further, most of the reserve officers and civilian experts had only agreed to participate in the tests provided that they would be back home to rejoin their universities and companies when the next academic year commenced in September. Admiral Blandy could not extend the test period and to all intents the decision was taken then to eliminate the deep ocean test. The decision had already been taken to make the surface test an under water test inside the lagoon, which meant that the depth could not be greater than about 200ft.

The first stage of the journey was by troop train from Washington DC to Long Beach. I got out of the ChuChu at Chatanooga at 2am just to say I had been there. At some places we were required to detrain for a meal while the engines were changed. Thus it was that we were followed round Memphis by a drunk who claimed that we stole his whisky (or perhaps whiskey). It was also in Memphis that the waitress serving us suddenly said "I come from Romford in Essex, dear". Further west along the track there were Indians selling native work at every halt. At El Paso we stopped long enough to put a foot into Juarez and thus add Mexico to the countries visited. And finally Los Angeles and the USS *Kenneth Whiting* at Long Beach. We were here for several days and I explored Los Angeles. There was some sort of controversy about a film called the Outlaw at the time. My only sight of celebrities was in the Brown Derby one lunch time when Betty Grable came in with Dick Haymes who I noted had higher than usual shoes to increase his height and walked a little oddly. Betty Grable drank carrot juice.

The USS *Kenneth Whiting* was a seaplane tender which was to be the home and workshops of the technical directorate for the duration of the trials. Dr Sawyer had two naval aides, Commander McReynolds and Lieut. Commander Debenham. The former was from Texas and the latter was a qualified submarine officer. We spent a week in Pearl Harbour during which Jack Debenham and I spent a night at the submarine officers club, better known as the Royal Hawaiian Hotel, and took a ride in a pacific fleet submarine from which I photographed said hotel by pressing my small camera to the periscope eyepiece and pressing the knob. It worked.

One night Pearl Harbour seemed to be surrounded by forest fires. I learned that this was the first part of harvesting the sugar crop to burn off the hard, vicious leaves ready for machine cutting the blackened stalks. Another novelty was to see and smell miles of green pineapples ready for harvest. Years later Liz and I visited Hawaii. On our return she was enthusing about the lovely fresh pineapples to an elderly friend, it transpired that the pensioner had never tasted fresh pineapple and so Liz gave her a big ripe one. When they next met the old lady said that she hadn't enjoyed that raw pineapple because "all those prickles had hurt her mouth".

Before the Kenneth Whiting left Hawaii, the local government arranged a steak beach party for the visitors on a beach to the east of Diamond Head. Debenham and I decided to get to the party by driving west and around the island. Along the north coast many wooden houses were still on their backs as the result of the tidal wave that struck on April 1st, the result of an earthquake some thousands of miles to the north. We arrived at the beach party just as a line of cars arrived and decanted about twelve girls wearing grass skirts and beautiful smiles. They lined up and did their Hula Hula dance for not more than ten minutes, climbed back in the cars and disappeared. The second disappointment was the steak sandwich. I am sure that it was an absolutely splendid steak sandwich but I was just not prepared for a piece of bread upon which was placed a steak about half an inch thick and topped off with a second piece of bread. Almost before I could get it to my mouth, the grease from the meat had dissolved the bread and what do you do now when stuck on a sandy beach? One evening Dr Sawyer, Penney and I and a few others had dinner in a shore-side restaurant. Afterwards we wandered down on to Waikiki beach where Diamond Head was silhouetted in the moonlight behind a palm tree (a view much used in travel literature in following years). Almost immediately a US Navy patrol arrived and asked us to leave because the beach was "off-limits" at night. Doubtless a sensible precaution.

I went with Dr Sawyer to call on a friend of his who was a visiting professor at the University to study the water resources of the Hawaiian Islands. The demand exceeded the rainfall and there was concern that the lens of water deep beneath was being depleted. At that time he said that there were indications that it was not being depleted as much as had been thought and was being replenished from some distant subterranean source.

When we arrived at Bikini on 29th May, most of the target ships were in their final positions and we set to, assembling our equipment and positioning it on the ships. Our gasoline cans and drums were put in positions where they would not be blown away by the front of the blast wave and I selected the exposed positions for the arrays of steel pipes and asked the US navy personnel to weld them in place, which they did. One day I was sent for by the Director of Ship Material, Rear Admiral Solberg, a USN naval constructor. I supposed that he had learned that there was a British naval constructor in the Task Force and was doing the decent thing in saying "Hello". In no way, I was roundly told-off for welding my steel pipes on the top of the ex-German cruiser *Prinz Eugens'* turrets. I said that I was sorry, I had been asked to nominate desirable sites and being aware that it had been announced that the cruiser was to be scrapped after the tests, I had included the top of the turret in my list. If there was a reason why this site should not be used it was up to his organisation to say so; the welding had been done by his own USN people. Doubtless, like me, they had seen the statement that the ship was to be scrapped at the end of the tests. I repeated that I was sorry that I had caused him concern, but what was the problem?

This was the third 2 star officer whose manner in dealing with me, his junior, was to bully and shout. Bullying as a management style is true of the lesser ranks in most services, perhaps unavoidably when dealing with new recruits, but to find it so at flag rank was surprising. I was to observe this trait in almost every US Admiral and General I met over the rest of my career - almost as if they take a course on harassment at the US National Defence College. With one exception, Vice Admiral Levering Smith, who was probably the most able of them all.

In the preparatory period in Washington we had each been photographed with an identity number across our chest (like a convict) and issued with our official Crossroads plastic identity card. I was dimly conscious at the time that the photographic crew were suddenly keen to finish with me and get me out of the way and learned the reason some months later at Bikini when my pass was suddenly withdrawn. The man who had followed me in the photographer's booth had been Admiral Blandy. In the confusion they had forgotten to change the numbers across his chest and so for several months the British spy and the task force commander had had the same identity number.

In the weeks before the explosions one became aware of the undercurrents between the various laboratories and between personalities within those laboratories, including the civilian- uniform divide. This was particularly acute within the DTMB elements where no one could get on with the naval leader. Identity is a problem; when Penny and I visited a ship almost invariably the uniformed officers would address me because I was in uniform and therefore could be fitted into their scale of values, rather than the slightly portly civilian ambling along behind. I would step to one side and say loudly something like "Doctor Penney, Sir where would you like to go first?" and of course they got the message that he was the man who mattered.

The organization and provision of supplies and boats and so forth was first class and all the teams had their instrumentation in place and tested where possible by Test "A" day minus 2. The last thing to be done in the target ships was to put cargo nets down the side and hoist a red flag and in those ships with animals, to feed and water those unfortunate creatures.

The task force ships sailed out of Bikini lagoon on 30th June 1946, the night before Test Able. Penney was to be one of the initial re-entry team and he spent the night in a naval rescue tug. At dawn *Kenneth Whiting* was in position about 10 miles from Bikini.

The bomb dropping aircraft "Dave's Dream" had departed Kwajalein at about 5.30 am and made a practice run over the target. The aircraft was broadcasting a heterodyne note, which would cease when the bomb left the bomb bay; as we assembled on deck with our very dark glasses at the ready we could hear this note. An essential pre-condition for the test was that the wind should be blowing in the same direction at all altitudes to avoid the possibility of the radioactive cloud rising and then blowing back over the task force ships and killing us all. The air force had held a competition among the B 29 aircrews, dropping dummy atomic bombs and the team above us that morning had the best bombing record. They only made one of the four practice runs permitted and we heard the cry "bomb away" and the heterodyne note stopped. We all knew some 40 seconds before we saw the flash that the thing was on its way and we put our glasses on.

The flash was brighter than the sun but was slightly lost on us because our dark glasses were so dense. They were quickly discarded as the fireball and cloud towered up into the heavens rising five miles in as many seconds. Drone aircraft were busy collecting samples and measurements. They and their controllers in 'mother' aircraft did awfully well. One flew through the cloud and mother lost control; it was picked up on ships radar miles away and control re-established more than 30 minutes later and the drone was landed as planned-even if a little late. There were also drone boats, which re-entered the lagoon and took radiation measurements.

While all this was going on, I received a message that I was to take Penney's place in the re-entry exercise; he was a bad sailor and had had a wretched night of seasickness. Having regard to what had to be done to recover our gauges it was foolish for him ever to have been asked to be a member of the re-entry team. A launch took me to the rescue tug and returned Penney to the Kenneth Whiting. Following the initial monitoring for radioactivity, the navy rescue tug re-entered the lagoon. Some ships had already sunk, others were in trouble, several were on fire and most of those in the centre had received crippling damage to their upper works.

I suppose that I was so well integrated into the scientific director's staff that no one thought it odd that the first person to board the target ships would be a Briton. My duty was to leap from the tug and climb up the side of the target vessel using the cargo net left there for this purpose, run along the deck and climb up to where the gasoline cans were, cut them free and take them back down the cargo net to the tugboat, hopefully without receiving too much radiation from some local source. There I filled them with water and weighed them and consulted the graphs that I had already prepared which related weight to volume and volume before and volume after, to blast pressure. Bingo, I knew the pressure to which the can had been subjected. I could do these sums before we reached the next ship and I had to repeat the Tarzan of the Apes bit to recover some more cans. En route I also studied the steel pipes that we had welded in exposed positions on the target ships to see which length had just started to bend and again from charts I could relate the aerodynamic drag force to which the pipe had been subject to cause yield at the base, to a blast pressure. Meanwhile many millions of dollars worth of much more complex US instrumentation that had been drenched with salt spray and dust, lay in the tropic sun awaiting recovery and analysis of the results.

It was soon evident from the pressure figures as well as from the pattern of ship damage that the bomb had not exploded where it was meant to.

My most unnerving moment was when I climbed over the side of an APA to retrieve some cans and heard footsteps. Oh my God, I thought had someone been left behind despite the most stringent precautions and checks? Was some poor demented wretch around behind that deckhouse? I took an iron bar provided for tightening watertight doors from its clips and advanced, when around the corner came a large white goat. The people in the USS *Burleson* who had looked after the animals had treated them well and this goat just wanted to be friendly -he hadn't seen any of his friends for quite some time and he wanted to make up for it. I didn't know whether his coat was covered with radioactive dust or whatever but my route to the cans involved stroking him and then coming down a different ladder and running for the cargo net. It appeared that the air blast had rocked his big cage and opened the door. In a US report on the animals it said: "Some of the goats taken along were selected for their psychoneurotic tendencies. Psychologists thought that the severe explosion phenomenon might change these tendencies" I will never know whether 'my' goat was an ornery cuss that had been changed by the severe explosion or just a nice unchanged friend of man.

It was sad to find so many animals dead that day and the next as more ships became accessible; in most cases it seemed to me that their end was in part due to their water supply being blown away by the bomb blast. But in clinical terms their job was done the moment their little bodies had received the radiation and death was nearly inevitable thereafter.

One of the gauges that I couldn't get to the first day was my private venture Pabst beer can placed in the after casing of the submarine USS *Skate*. This can turned out to be the closest survivor to where the bomb went off and recorded a pressure of 95 pounds per square inch.

Shurcliff's official record " Bombs at Bikini "states; "Oddly enough one of the most valuable of all the pressure results was that obtained from a specially-mounted beer can whose graceless collapse filled an otherwise serious gap in the pressure story."

I like the "specially mounted" bit, for even Penney didn't know about my beer cans (there were six in all) until after the test and Shurcliff's US record does not even have the grace to admit that I was there.

The ships of the Task Group re-entered Bikini lagoon late on "A" day and I returned to the *Kenneth Whiting* with the pressure readings and the cans, which were left in the landing craft assigned to us. Penney reported the results to Dr Sawyer. That night President Truman announced that the test had been satisfactory and the power of the bomb had been equivalent to that dropped on Nagasaki. I don't know what contribution fission product analysis might have made at this time concerning the efficiency of the bomb but I am pretty sure that the answer given to the President that day and broadcast to the world relied pretty heavily on a few 5-gallon gasoline cans put out by the British.

It will be recalled that the debate concerning the target array had resulted in a circle of ships at a radius of 900 feet. On the unspoken assumption that with modern bomb aiming techniques, no enemy flak and the chance to make repeated practice runs over the target, no-one could fail to get the thing in a circle 1,800 feet across. - Well, they did! The official US report says; "For reasons that can not be discovered, this bomb missed its point of aim by 1,500 to 2,000 ft."

This is untrue. Our measurements showed conclusively that the miss was at least 2,100 ft. from the centre of the target array. So much for 'where will it go off?'

There was much physical data that we wished to record with high-speed photography, such as the growth of the fireball and the build-up and propagation of the shock wave and the behaviour of the targets. These cameras had to be started by radio signals from Dr. Holloway's group in the USS *Cumberland Sound,* which in turn were generated by a sequence starting with the bomb in free fall, radioing back its acceleration from which its time to detonation could be simply calculated. There were other instruments, including pressure gauges that relied on a radio-timing signal. Due to what the official record says was; "Caused partly by imperfect reception of a preliminary radio signal and partly by human error", the master timing signals all went out nearly 20 seconds too late and so the 15 sec. and 2 sec. signals, so vital to capturing the exact moment of detonation and fire ball growth and blast wave generation, were received in time to record clouds and clouds of dust and debris. It was stated that; "Plans were such that nothing short of this coincidence of ill-luck could have thrown off the master signal " It was in fact a monumental, inexcusable, human cock-up. So much for 'when will it go off?'

Luckily, one young officer, Ensign O'Brien in a destroyer several miles away operated his special camera manually and recorded what we particularly wanted to see, the growth of the fireball in millionths of seconds.

Many towers were built on Bikini and Amen Atolls to support cameras and other instruments. One that interested us was the responsibility of an army outfit that wished to shield their film from possible exposure by the radiation cloud. Not without some difficulty, they clad the room at the top of one tower with thick plates of lead. Many of our colleagues advised against this but to no avail. In the event the lead chamber proved to be an excellent solar oven.

A consequence of the bomb missing its point of aim so badly was that those instruments that had an element of directivity in their operation, and which were metaphorically looking towards the centre of the target array with their mouths open, were struck a hard blow on the back of the neck and quit. It occurred to me while in the tugboat that had the air force had their way and packed the ships in side-by-side they might well have missed the lot. (I'm only fooling General)

On 2nd July onwards target ships were declared safe for boarding and the people responsible for the animals, for instrumentation and for recording the extent of damage were able to get on with their work. We had a small landing craft and crew with which to visit the ships and collect cans and examine the extent of damage sustained by ships and equipment. We were required to wear radiation dosimeters, which were collected each night, and new ones issued the next morning. At the end of the first day I gave in my badge and sometime later was told that I had exceeded the permitted radiation allowance and would not be allowed to visit the target ships again, ever.

This was somewhat serious because I had a second task to perform for Britain, which was to gather as much information on ship damage as I could whilst performing my other duties. This was understood and accepted by the US Navy. I should at this point remark that there were two other sets of UK witnesses at the tests, two Members of Parliament and six Naval officers who were given escorted visits to some target ships. Constructor Commander Norman Hancock RCNC was one of these and so all would not have been lost had my radiation ban been insisted on by the doctors but clearly I, with complete freedom to go anywhere, would be in the much better position.

These 'official observers' had also travelled from Washington DC to the West Coast by train. To be helpful the US Army had posted the names of the occupants on each railway coach and the sole Russian captain was running up and down the platform complaining that there were six British, led by Captain Stephen Roskill RN and only one Russian. Some days later the scene was repeated when the lone Soviet press representative protested that there were several British reporters on the train conveying the representatives of the Congress and the press. After Shot Abel, this man was being taken round the anchorage with the press team to view the damaged ships. He protested to the young ensign who was in charge of the boat, the young man asked him what paper he represented; 'The Red Fleet,' said the GRU man; "Oh", said the ensign "where is that published, Milwaukee?"

The radiation present was almost entirely gamma. Radiation badges on the target ships showed that a massive 100,000 Roentgens reached them and this would have given fatal doses even through 12 inches of steel. There is no hiding place and no cure. The initial heat and radiation burst lasted about one thousandth of a second. There was heat radiation from the fireball for a further few seconds and gamma radiation for somewhat longer as the mushroom cloud rose. The thermal and gamma radiation would injure personnel and the shock wave would damage ships.

Clinically, exposure to several hundred roentgens would be fatal and 50 to 100 rem per day (say) would cause serious harm. The limit set for personnel at Bikini was not more than 0.1 rem per day, a safe small dose. I pleaded with the radiological people to allow me to continue and they agreed this once. There would be no second chance. This presented a problem for I was here, there and every where, noting damage in my little notebook. The solution was simple; thereafter I only wore my shirt with the dosimeter attached when travelling in the boat between target ships, and left my dosimeter in the boat while I was on the target ships. During the course of the day as I travelled between ships, my body would re-radiate sufficiently to produce a low reading on the dosimeter and no one questioned my readings again.

For the record the US inspection teams that were engaged on the same task had printed instructions detailing how each part of a ship and each piece of equipment should be inspected and standard forms on which the inspection results were to be recorded. Two thousand copies of the instructions and five thousand inspection notebooks were issued. The result was impressive; by July 6th Admiral Solburg's organisation had completed an 85-page summary on damage to ships and animals, and by August 1st had prepared a 2,000 page interim report. Five months later it had completed 150 volumes on the damage caused in the 5 seconds after the Test "A" bomb went off.

Various treatments were tried for reducing the residual radioactivity of the target warships. It was correctly discerned that this radioactivity was mainly arising from the salts and other materials that had been deposited on the hulls and subject to the ionising radiation. Could this be washed off and if so would fitting a pre-wetting system to ships be one of the useful recommendations from the test? Would adding things like detergents to the spray make it more effective? One problem was that in the tropic sun these solutions dried on the ship's upper- works and fell off as dust as we climbed about and a certain amount must have been breathed in. After two weeks or so all visits to the target ships were stopped; it was rumoured that traces of plutonium had been found and this is a virulent poison. In any case I had seen all that I required.

For the second test, Test "B" for Baker, the bomb was suspended in a steel caisson beneath Landing Ship, Medium 60. The depth of the lagoon was not more than 200 ft and the bomb was more than half way down. The detonation would be initiated by a series of radio signals and time clocks to ensure absolute safety and to avoid the timing fiasco of Test "A". Of the 120 press representatives who had been present for the air burst test, over 80 had remained for Test "B". They questioned the safety arrangements and Admiral

Blandy allowed them to witness the rehearsal of the firing sequence, with a flash bulb substituted for the bomb. After describing the elaborate sequence of signals that must be received in the correct order and at precisely the correct moment, the process was started and the flash bulb went off exactly 15 minutes before it should have done!

On the day the bomb went off at the time intended and at the place intended. The column of water rose 5,000 ft and was 2,000 ft in diameter. I mention this because there was some difference among the experts as to how high the column would rise. The air force wished to have a drone aircraft immediately over the spot when the detonation occurred and asked the simple question, "How high should we fly?" One famous professor said that the column would rise 60,000 feet; examination showed that he had ignored air friction (among other things). Penney said "About 5,000 ft and 2,000 ft across" and so it was. The aircraft took some remarkable pictures.

The count down to detonation was by Ernest Titterton; a British scientist who worked at Los Alamos but in the official US film of the Bikini tests this was cut out and replaced by a voice with an American accent. This was probably just a public relations man doing his stuff, but as far as General Groves and his senior officers were concerned there was the intention to exclude the British from the atomic project. Grove worked actively against the policy planned by his government and agreed at the Quebec conference in 1943, of collaborating with the British on atomic matters and saw to it that official US publications concerning the development of the atomic bomb minimised the contribution of the European and Canadian participants. Groves never changed. In 1954 he boasted, " I had not been responsible for our close collaboration with the British. I tried to make it as difficult as possible".

The task force had stood out to sea the previous night with the flagship and those who had made the last minute adjustments aboard the bomb carrying LSM 60, leaving early the following morning. The awesome sight of the column engulfing ships and the resulting base-surge as it fell back laden with fission products the equivalent of more than a hundred tons of radium is now familiar. The ship killer was underwater shock and the man killer was the residual radioactivity. The LSM 60 rose on the crown of the fireball and was blown to pieces; I saw a fragment measuring about 3"x3" that had landed on one of the target ships.

It was several days before we were allowed to board the target ships and ten days before it was feasible to board them all. Admiral Blandy's flagship USS Mount McKinley led the re-entry. When it was our turn to enter, our executive officer, a naval aviator, decided to do things properly as an evolution in seamanship and instructed that when we reached our berth there would be a single bugle note at which the anchor would be dropped, the boat booms swung out and accommodation ladders lowered. I was standing with him on top of the seaplane hangar when he suddenly caught his breath a microsecond before a single bugle note rang out as we came abreast and saluted the flagship. Down went the anchor, out went the booms and down went the accommodation ladders. Panic on the bridge; stop main engines, full astern and so on. In what seemed to me to be a remarkably short time, order was restored and we crept ahead to our berth.

My other profound memory was the agony of seeing the USS Saratoga sink. This mighty aircraft carrier was the last ship to sink. When awaiting the tests I had been surprised at her rolling motion in Bikini Lagoon. She had been fitted with bulges to improve her stability many years before and these provided a welcome platform midway between the waterline and the flight deck. The rolling motion was such that the ladder platform was moving up and down about 6 ft. day in, day out and boarding necessitated a courageous leap and good timing. A senior officer got it wrong and fractured his hip. She had been about 500 ft from LSM 60 and sank by the stern seven and a half hours after the shot. There was the thought that she might be beached but the water around her was too radioactive to allow a safe approach. Just as well, really, because her hulk would have been an embarrassment in the longer term.

After Test "A" there had not been much inter-team consultation about results, in most cases because, through no fault of their own, the US teams had few reliable results to discuss. After Test "B" there was much to discuss. What did this mean? What was the significance of that? And so on. Team after team would come to consult Penney about their results and the mathematics thereof. They would come to me as an intermediary and we would go to Penney's cabin, pull back the curtain (US warship cabins have no doors) and Penney from his bunk would grunt something like "What do you want?" I would say something like "Curtis has got some equations here that he would like your help with." Penney would take the paper as he swung himself off the bunk, look at what might be a number of simultaneous differential equations and solve the thing almost before he had sat down.

As the days passed one became aware that the majority of the civilian scientists were keen to return home to take up their old or in some cases new, university posts and most of the VIP's including Penney, were taken to Kwajalein and flown back to the United States. There was some rearrangement in accommodation in the *Kenneth Whiting* and I found myself sharing a cabin with Professor Brian O'Brien, whose son had taken the pictures of the initial microseconds of detonation of the first bomb. After some days he confessed that, as an Irish patriot and for reasons to do with the battle of the Boyne, he hated the British. However he admitted that he had only met about three Englishmen and they had all been nice people.

When we sailed from Bikini, the ship and all in her were monitored for radioactivity. I have already mentioned my disappointment at leaving my US Army issue boots behind within two hours of receiving them on the day I arrived in Nagasaki. For the Bikini tests I had been issued with another pair; they were no longer pristine but they were mine. Imagine my concern to learn that my boots, the boots that I had worn every day for the weeks that I had been climbing all over the target ships at Bikini, were the most radioactive item on the ship and must be thrown overboard without a moments delay. Luckily the supply officer was a man of rare compunction and gave me another pair; which I still have 50 years later and put on when I have to walk on icy roads. My old pair was thrown into the Pacific Ocean from the fantail of the USS *Kenneth Whiting* and, as you would expect a naval constructors boots to behave, they floated the right way up. I wondered as the years passed, whether there was a native somewhere on a Pacific island who was walking around in a pair of gently decaying radioactive boots or perhaps a shark that glows dimly in the dark.

To reconcile the requirement for alcoholic drinks with the "dry" regime of US warships and to provide some recreational and sports facilities, a club was built on Bikini Island where one could drink and swim. From our anchorage it was an hours boat trip to get there and the same thing coming back. Penney and I went once and decided that standing in a boat for two hours was not worth it. After Test "A" the club was closed and swimming not allowed. I was interested in my shipmate's behaviour when we reached Hawaii on the way home. They rushed ashore and drank pints of milk. The Royal Hawaiian Hotel had been returned to the Matson Line and the rooms that Jack Debenham and I had for $7 a night were now $90 a night.

On arrival in San Francisco most people were met by their families and would take a leisurely drive across the nation to their homes or universities. A topic of conversation was the giant 200-inch telescope, which was nearing completion, and a friend went to see the 200-inch mirror being ground. This was most impressive and the people doing it said that it was a pity that he couldn't spend more time because they had nearly finished. He was due to leave the next day but thinking that he could stay a little longer he asked, "How long will you be?" " Not much more than three months" was the reply.

In 1945 San Francisco had been the venue for the international gathering at which the United Nations was born. The Soviet delegation took over several floors of a hotel and also had a ship in the harbour full of Soviet food (and I suppose, duty free vodka). They brought their own security guards and to make them less conspicuous they gave them all trilby hats. Unfortunately the quartermaster who issued the hats, which were all the same colour didn't know that one is supposed to press the top inwards in a crease. Thus it was that for two days all of the Russian strong men walked around looking like film extras from a gold rush movie. What was more curious to the FBI was that several men not registered as part of the Soviet delegation also appeared briefly in these hats.

In Chicago I had time to visit what was once the tallest building and to experience waves several feet high on Lake Michigan before taking the train for Washington DC. In those days one went to the washroom at the end of the coach to wash and shave and I found it a place to avoid at popular times as men shaved with cut-throat razors and waved them wildly about as the train took the sharp curves of the valleys.

While we had been at Bikini the Congress had passed the McMahan Act, which prohibited the transfer of information on nuclear matters to non-Americans without the approval of Congress in each case. Legally, we were out on a limb but it was agreed that we could keep our notes and the Technical Director and his staff would still wish to consult and have the benefit of our, that is, Penney's, advice. Doctor Sawyer's office was in the Navy Department, which was still in the temporary buildings built in 1919. The US Navy in the Pentagon and Crystal Plaza were still in the future.

We developed a procedure of visiting the director's office each morning sometime after 11.00am. They would seek Penney s advice (and sometimes mine) on various draft reports and go to lunch. We would take the reports to the UK Scientific Office where I would remark on the tables and diagrams and text while Penney would prepare his comments. We returned the documents immediately they returned from lunch. In most cases the documents did not justify the security classification often given them. Conversation with Commander McReynolds from Texas was always slow. Richard Condon in his book "Death of a Politician" describes a West Texan lawyer as speaking at minus 2 miles an hour; just about right for Mc Reynolds. I was struck by the politeness of US naval captains who were quick to salute me as I left the Navy Department. After a day or so I realised that my uniform gold braid, two and a half stripes with two strips of silver grey cloth between them (for naval constructor) looked exactly like the broad decorated gold band of a US navy Commodores uniform, especially to people with the sun in their eyes. Although it was a warm autumn I took to wearing my uniform raincoat to avoid embarrassment.

During this time Penney was offered a chair in the University of Chicago. He told me that the offer would give the University the right to publish his work and that he would have to deliver a minimum of three lectures each year. For this he would receive a house on the campus and a very substantial salary, far greater than he expected to get in the UK. One wonders whether this approach had something in common with that made to Heisenberg in the summer of 1939 when he visited the USA and effort was made to persuade him to remain and thus to slow down or stop the possible development of atomic bombs by the Nazi's. The means of persuasion were the offer of a professorship at Colombia University made by Dr Pegram, the chairman of the Physics department and, separately, an offer by Fermi of a chair at Ann Arbor. Heisenberg said after the war that in the summer of 1939 twelve people might still have been able to prevent the construction of atom bombs by mutual agreement. As it was the German scientists made their own decision not to push the idea of developing atomic bombs

It seems not to be widely known that the possibility of developing explosive power from Uranium 235 was known to a number of leading European scientists from the mid-thirties onwards. The principal universities engaged in theoretical or experimental work in the field were Gottingen, Copenhagen, Paris and Cambridge and as the danger of the Nazi's became more evident many of the most brilliant men gravitated to these centres and thence to Denmark, England and eventually, the United States. At the April 1939 Spring meeting of the American Physical Society, Nils Bohr had stated in public that a bomb containing a minute quantity of Uranium 235 bombarded with slow neutrons would be bound to set off an explosion powerful enough to blow up, at the lowest estimate, the entire laboratory and most of the surrounding town. This was reported in the New York Times. In July 1939, Otto Hahn's assistant (at Gottingen) briefed the press about the possibility of a chain reaction in Uranium. This was reported in the Deutsche Allgemeine Zeitung. At about the same time the head of the German Government research organisation called together a team to discuss the subject of getting power from atoms. The Soviets were also active – indeed Soviet ministers seem to have appreciated the possibility of obtaining enormous power from uranium somewhat earlier than in the West. The subject was discussed openly; in 1939 Brodsky published an article on the separation of isotopes of uranium and Kurchatov an article on the fission process in uranium. The 1940 New Year's edition of Izvestia carried an article entitled 'Uranium 235' – 'a new source of energy surpassing a million times everything that has hitherto been known' and in October 1941 many Soviet newspapers reported a lecture by Kapitza (who had been Rutherford's assistant at Cambridge and had been prevented by the soviet authorities from returning to Cambridge following a visit home) in which he said that theoretical calculations prove that an atom bomb can easily destroy a large city with several million inhabitants.

The secretaries in the UK Scientific office were Canadians and I assumed that the male staff in the photocopying room were also from the north. The man who did most of the work for me was keen to get into plastics when he finished here. He told me he would set up a little moulding company. Conversationally I asked him "Where, in Toronto?" He looked at me in some amazement and said "Gee no, in good old New York where I was born." That day we put everything we had in diplomatic bags and took them to the British embassy for onward transmission. The flow of reports was drying up in any case and Penney decided that we should leave. Even this was complicated by a strike at New York docks and we travelled by train to Montreal and thence to Halifax NS through the glorious colours of the Canadian fall.

We embarked in the RMS *Queen Mary* which was making her last run in her troopship outfit before being made back to a luxury liner. I was surprised at how much she rolled in the Atlantic swell. General Eisenhower and Mary Martin were on board and I shared a cabin with about five reporters, one was the late James Cameron. I would retire at a decent hour and be wakened about 1.00 am and a glass of whisky thrust into my hand. The press would then hold court and I learned much that they dared not print about those in high places in Washington and London.

Part Two

THE USEFUL YEARS

Chapter Five

On return from the United States I was appointed to the post of Professional Secretary to the Director of Naval Construction, in the Old Admiralty Building in Whitehall. The principal talking point in naval and military circles was the effect of atomic weapons not only on future strategy and equipment but also on the nature of life itself and clearly the fact that I had been in Japan and Bikini was one of the reasons that I was selected.

I joined on the 1st January 1947 and found my chief, the DNC, strangely pre-occupied. He took and made many private phone calls and as I was to learn, unusually for him, he went and saw people. The next morning all became clear when an addendum to the Official Gazette was issued promulgating his appointment as a Knight Commander of the Order of the Bath; thus .I was serving Sir Charles Lillicrap, Director of Naval Construction and Head of the Royal Corps of Naval Constructors, whose name, with one other, had been omitted in error from the previous day's New Years honours list.

To be pedantic, I was serving Mr Charles Lillicrap, K.C.B. Before the war, protocol ruled that one could not (and did not) use the title until one had actually knelt before the king and been dubbed. One had to keep one's eye on the Court Circular in the Times to see when people had actually been to the palace, perhaps months later. But in 1947 the old order was changing and everyone started to address him as Sir Charles, a much more sensible practice.

The DNC also carried the title of Principal Technical Adviser to the Board of Admiralty. It was a post that I was to fill some 27 years later when titled Director General Ships. This did not align with the titles of comparable posts in the land and air divisions of the new style Ministry of Defence and D. G. Ships subsequently became Deputy Controller Warships.

Domestically this posting was not a great problem; I lived with my sister in rural Kent and commuted by bus and train, a journey of 90 minutes each way. The senior officers were in their seats by 10.00 am and so I was there by 09.59 am and I usually got the 6.42 pm from Charing Cross station for the return journey. On Saturday's we worked until lunch time and it was acceptable to wear a sports coat and flannel trousers on the assumption that one would do something sporting in the afternoon.

Occasionally when I emerged from Charing Cross Station and crossed Trafalgar Square on Cup Final day, there would be a little group of three or so bedraggled people huddled out of the rain and wearing black and white or red striped top hats and coats. When they had left Newcastle or Manchester the night before with several hundred others all sporting their teams colours they had felt ten feet tall; now separated, tired, cold and lost in the big city they just looked and felt daft. This was in the days before whole towns were terrorised by football supporters on Saturday afternoons and before wearing ones team's colours was sartorially acceptable and a source of great profit to the clubs.

While serving as DNC's Secretary I held the parallel post of lecturer in the Resistance and Propulsion of Ships — Hydrodynamics to the more academically minded — in the Royal Naval College, Greenwich, which required my attendance at that seat of learning for all or part of a day each week. I had been unimpressed by the course when a student and I found that the professor was still giving out the same course notes that I had been given, six years earlier. I could recall my frustration when a student. What I had wanted to know was how to predict the resistance of ships and to design propellers to turn the ships engine power into thrust to overcome that resistance and all that I was being given for nearly two whole terms was an endless dissertation on the mathematics of waves and boundary layers, subjects that were being covered at the same time and in a more erudite way, by the RNC mathematics department. The train journey gave me time to completely rewrite the R & P course. So I rewrote these sections and made them appendices and plunged straight into the prediction of ship resistance and so on. The other thing that struck me in lecturing to these splendid young officers was that I could see myself sitting there as a Constructor Lieutenant as I must have appeared to my seniors just a few years before, polite but a bit arrogant.

I received an allowance for my Greenwich work. I was still not overpaid and so I enrolled as a lecturer in the Medway Technical College and took a class of about ten keen young men in the Principles of Physical Metallurgy each Friday evening. I took my class in Gillingham, Kent, twixt train and bus. It seemed to me amusing that these young men gave me full marks for letting them go home ten minutes early rather than sticking out for the full 2 hours when the fact was that I was desperate to get the last country bus myself. I enjoyed writing the course work and lecturing in both jobs, not least for the quality of the young men that attended.

I was much indebted to the typists who cheerfully accepted all this additional work. In the days before copying machines and word processors, if more than five or six copies were required the typing was done on a waxy skin and the copies run-off on a Gestetner machine. The statuesque Eve typed away and always made ten or more typing errors. When I checked it and pointed them out she would say, "Damn" and crumple the skin up; she would then type a new one and make ten quite different errors. It was possible to make corrections on the skins with the use of some red stuff and when we eventually got her to stop crumpling them up, Eve's products looked as if they had chicken pox.

DNC's Secretary was a splendid job. Admirals Power, Fisher and Vian on whose staffs I had served were members of the Board of Admiralty and in a relatively short while changes in personnel brought in Admirals Lord Fraser, Edelston and Edwards. Rear Admiral Ralph Edwards was an Assistant Chief of Naval Staff. Perhaps more importantly their naval secretaries, now of captains or acting captains rank, knew me and would yarn to me about their problems and so enable me to keep abreast of their thinking. There was a tremendous camaraderie in these years and most conversations would move around to some shared experience or what old so and so had done in the war. Sometimes the outcome was not what was expected. I was present at a black tie affair and was with one or two people speaking with Admiral Edwards when along came a baronet who was in the business but not known to the admiral. After the usual pleasantries he said "Where were you in, in the war?" to which the baronet replied "In the RAF" Predictably, (we always said it) the Admiral said "Fighters or bombers?" to which the reply was "Actually, I was a dog handler".

Within the Admiralty, the First Lord was Mr George Hall. The Parliamentary and Financial Secretary was Mr Dugdale, and the trio was completed by the Civil Lord, "Stoker" Edwards, so named because he had served in the fleet in that rate. My friend of the Galle Face Mess Colombo, James Callaghan MP was now the Parliamentary Secretary in the Ministry of Transport in Attlee's labour government and would shortly be moved across to the Admiralty in the same rank.

Sometimes I would come out of the main entrance of the old Admiralty Building, on a cold rainy night to face an hour and a half journey in a cold train and bus, just as the First Lord was being ushered into his official Daimler limousine for the short journey up Whitehall to the House and as he passed, cigar in hand with a rug over his knees, I would wonder whether this was the sort of socialism that the soldiers had in mind when they voted.

When he visited an Admiralty outpost, Admiral Vian preferred to travel by car, in uniform with his little admirals flag mounted on the car wing. He was by nature an impatient man who did not suffer fools (i.e. the rest of mankind) gladly and most journeys were punctuated by orders that the driver should 'go faster' and 'pass the car in front'. His assigned driver was quickly dismissed, and then the next and so on. There came the day when he made the driver sit in the passenger seat and drove himself. This was the straw that broke the camels back and the civilian drivers all refused to drive him. Thenceforth he had a naval rating driver.

Britain was only slowly recovering from the war. Food and fuel were still rationed and indeed some of the shortages were worse than they had been in the war as industry and commerce were re-orientated to produce consumer goods. Exports had priority. The winter of 1947 was severe; there were heavy snowfalls and no thaw. The Southern electric trains were badly disrupted due to ice packing hard on the shoe that collected electric power from the "live" rail and the drivers were supplied with pieces of wood with which to hit these shoes to dislodge the ice. All of the track and station lights would be out and so would those on the train. Trains would gradually grind to a halt, where-upon the driver would climb down and attack the ice, and climb back in and off would go the train for another few miles. Because the lights were out people were liable to think that the train had reached their station and open the carriage doors; several stepped or fell out. Being clever and catching a steam train bound for the Kent coast with stops at Chatham and Faversham was one way of keeping a little warm but they couldn't make great speed due to the stalled electric commuter trains on the line ahead. An acquaintance working in Naval Stores Department who didn't know the steam trains route thought that they had reached Faversham and stepped out into space, rolled down the embankment and badly tore his suit and overcoat. This was a serious blow since clothing was severely rationed; as he said "He would rather have broken his arm".

Yet there was a general acceptance that people were doing their best and little vicious sniping at authority. Complaining and claims for compensation had not by then become a national pastime.

One soon recognised the same faces on the trains to and from London and exchanged a (very) few words. The steam trains coming up from the Kent coast conveyed their quota of bankers and stockbrokers and the like and I soon learned to judge the state of the market from their demeanour; if the market was buoyant they were relaxed and swapped stories; if the market was dull their eyes were glued to the pages of the Financial Times.

A memorable event came when, one evening, after some weeks of stout denials (what else could he say?) the Chancellor, Sir Stafford Cripps, devalued the pound. The following morning the train positively throbbed with the collective will of its passengers urging it towards London and the City. It made excellent time and they were all lined up in the train's corridor with umbrellas and briefcases at the ready, ready to sprint for the taxi rank, when the train stopped on the bridge over the River Thames right outside Cannon Street Station and with the locomotive practically abreast the end of the platform. Bowler hats leant out of windows and umbrellas were flourished; after about seven minutes one impatient soul opened a carriage door and climbed down to the track. Others followed. Consternation, for the track had a third, live rail for the electric trains. Whistles blew and the Guard, who couldn't get through the crowded corridors whose occupants would by now have throttled him and all the other railway employees, himself climbed down and raced to the front of the train to prevent more people leaving and to close the doors. After a while some semblance of order was restored and with much further whistling and hooting, the train entered the station and we disembarked. The few, foolish, heroes who had jumped train were being interrogated by some rather dour faced railway police who were doubtless reciting phrases such as trespassing on railway property, disembarking from a moving (?) train, opening a carriage door while the train was in motion, and so on. Nothing appeared in the press so I suppose they got away with a caution, but missed a vital morning's trading.

A programme of considerable importance during these years was the Ship Target Trials Programme. Some hundreds of warships were scheduled for scrapping at the end of the war, in part to provide steel to help rebuild Britain and her industries. There was a limit to the rate at which the scrap yards could receive and deal with ships and Their Lordships agreed my Department's suggestion that the ships should be used in a series of trials to provide statistical data on the effectiveness of weapons and the ships' ability to resist them. We were much concerned with influence mines and the scrap yards did not mind, within reason, whether the ships arrived somewhat bent and with holes in them.

Gradually the scope of the trials was broadened. A series that interested me enormously was that in which three submarine hulls, A, S and V-Classes, were lowered on wires from salvage vessels until the hulls collapsed. They were then hauled up, beached and examined. In each case the hulls collapsed almost exactly at the depths and hence the pressures at which our somewhat unsophisticated calculations had predicted. Of particular interest was the S boat which my memory tells me collapsed at something under 560ft. Some years earlier one of our S-Class boats commanded by Lieutenant Duff had been under sustained attack by German surface forces off the Norwegian coast and had finished up on the bottom in about 525 feet of water. Duff and his crew sat out the German attack and eventually brought their submarine home. We had run our slide rules over our calculations at the time and said something like "Coo", and the post-war test had confirmed what a close run thing it had been.

The Old Admiralty Building did not have central heating and each room had a coal fire that was laid and lit by someone before work started each morning. A coalscuttle contained the day's fuel. I am not aware that it ever ran out. My desk was in the alcove beside the fire and one day I picked away with my penknife at a round bump on the wall that was covered with many, many layers of paint, to reveal a bell push; so I pushed it. Half an hour later a little man in a striped waistcoat appeared and said, "You rang for some more coal, Sir". The Lifts dated from the ark and there were basements below basements and tunnels leading to other Whitehall buildings. Beside the Admiralty on the Mall was a new windowless building with massive walls designed to be bomb proof. Sometime after I had joined, DNC was told confidentially that in the event of war he and I were allocated a space in this Citadel.

My chief was a wiry little man who wore a bowler hat. He collected first editions and was a devotee of Samuel Johnson. Small in stature with a much-lined face he was 60 years old and looked much older and in the years that I was with him he became mentally much less agile. He was mean in silly little things, more than might be explained by carefulness. A small example was diaries. Each December companies would send him pocket diaries for the coming year. He would remove the fifty or so for the dying year from the bottom right hand drawer of his desk where they had rested for the past twelve months and put them in his waste bin to make room for the new intake. He only ever used one and we had a small staff of about forty in London who would have been glad to have the diaries he didn't use.

He seemed not to like politicians. If the First Lord or Financial Secretary sent for him or if they wanted him on the phone I quickly learned to pop in and ask him first.

Invariably he would say "Tell them I'm at a meeting" or, depending on the time, "Tell them I'm at lunch". In the latter case he would shoot over to his cupboard for his bowler hat and coat and out of the door like a rabbit while I went back to my phone to reply. There would be a pause and I would be asked to step up and see the minister. Mr Dugdale, and later Jim Callaghan, used to ask me to see them more than once a month to explain things. I recall that the proposal to modernise the aircraft carrier, HMS *Victorious* was a hot-potato at the time and the proposal to build a new Royal Yacht to replace the aged *Victoria and Albert* shook the organisation to the core, such was the opposition of Labour Members of Parliament.

Lillicrap's attitude towards (Labour?) politicians was not unique. He attended many formal dinners and would bring the menus in to the office the next morning. I would find little comments in his crabby handwriting, such as "Silly old fool" against the name of a minister of the crown. There might also be written exchanges with his neighbours like small boys at prep school. One that I recall was when the Minister of Transport was the principal guest and was being long-winded and dull. In Lillicrap's hand "Did you write this?" In another hand " No, I have never written speeches for bloody politicians and I don't intend to start now". This second hand was the newly appointed permanent secretary of the Ministry of Transport.

The other thing Lillicrap attempted to do was to make cryptic notes to help him recall particularly witty after dinner speeches. We have all made a mental note to remember funny stories for possible use by oneself at another place with, hopefully, another audience; stories that were so funny that one could not possibly forget them. The next morning the feeling of well-being is still there but the story has gone. Lillicrap's recollections based on his cryptic notes sans alcohol were seldom sufficient to rise more than a polite smile and certainly not to have grown men rolling in the aisles. It happens to all of us but he was particularly unworldly.

In Jack Aspinwall's anthology of after dinner stories, Lord Porritt is credited with the tale of the senior civil servant who observed to his assistant "Quite extraordinary, Smithers, but I can now understand why the country doesn't prosper; I have been watching the workmen out there and they haven't done anything for the past hour". One morning Sir Charles seemed to have zero output and papers piled up in his tray. Unusually, he seemed not to be firmly fixed behind his desk. Finally, just before lunchtime, I caught him looking out of the window that overlooked The Mall, which was being resurfaced at the time. "I say, Daniel" he cried, hopping from one leg to the other and burying his right fist into the palm of his left hand as was his habit when he was excited, "I say Daniel, come and look at this steam roller".

One of the things that all good aides have to master is the art of reading upside down. "What's all this about" he would say or "What does the Second Sea Lord mean by this" pointing to a document before him. From across his desk I would be required to get the gist of the paper and comment. In time it became second nature and I still have a tendency to push instead of pull, glass doors that are marked PUSH on the other side.

There was to be a royal tour to South Africa and there was much discussion about the vessel to serve as the interim royal yacht. The Admiralty floated the idea of a Dido Class cruiser. The king said "No thank you, Dicky Mountbatten says that they roll like pigs and that wouldn't suit the royal ladies. What I want is Britain's latest (and biggest) battleship, HMS *Vanguard*." And thus it was.

Vanguard incorporated some habitability improvements. One was centralised messing in which the crew no longer ate in their separate messes but in central dining halls adjacent to the galley. The ship was fitted out for the royal party and sailed. The new messing arrangements were popular; too popular in fact for it was found that the ships company of about 1500 was consuming 1800 meals at each sitting as young men 'went round the buoy' and joined the back of the queue for a second helping. Perhaps more serious, we received urgent demands for additional cutlery, and more. It was found that unless closely supervised, some of the ratings were not removing the cutlery when scraping the plates into the garbage disposal unit prior to loading them in the dishwashers. HMS Vanguard had four state of the art control rooms for the anti-aircraft armament. At Cape Town one of these caught fire.

Previously I mentioned the problems that we had to overcome to build all-welded submarines and how lightly the decision to embark on this course had been taken by the bosses of the ship builders and industry. A similar meeting of the all-highest was called by the DNC to mark a step change in destroyer construction. After much careful planning and preparatory work my chief and his Deputy Director Production called the meeting to discuss building Daring-Class Destroyers. Senior executives of all the shipbuilding companies and marine engineering firms were present. Marine engineering standards for the navy had virtually been frozen since the start of the re-armament programme in 1936 and now was the time to catch up. Civil power station engineering had advanced and the navy wished to match those standards with solid turbine rotor shafts and higher steam pressure. It was also intended to introduce alternating current in at least four of the eight ships of the class to enable comparisons to be made with direct current generation and supply that was then the norm in HM Ships. The armament would be new too.

The meeting ground its way forward taking account of the long lead times to produce turbine rotors and other strategic materials, shipyard berths, dock and labour loading, effort for design development and so on, yard by yard and firm by firm. Gradually the outline programme prepared by our production people was endorsed.

The meeting reconvened after lunch and turned to the armament items at which the Director of Naval Ordnance's representative, a junior captain, indicated that the production of the gun mountings would not support the shipbuilding dates shown in the programme. It was now clear to me why the DNO had not come himself. Actually what his man said was something like "I don't know why you wasted all this morning talking about programmes for building the ships because you won't have any guns to put on them". At least he smiled while he said it.

Lillicrap apologised to the people from industry and closed the meeting there and then. He was apoplectic with rage. The next day there was a very frosty meeting at which the DNO in person was called to London to explain why he had changed his position without warning and after his Department had agreed to the master production programme. Lillicrap insisted that his own people should examine the armament manufacturing position in detail and after a few private meetings with the companies a better gun-mounting picture emerged.

In the immediate post-war years the emphasis was on turning industry around to produce the materials and goods to rebuild the damage of war and start to produce civilian goods to satisfy years of neglect. Clearly, someone thought, the Royal Dockyards were well equipped for this and they played their modest part. Not without some fun, however. Chatham was asked to produce dustbins; they were superlative galvanised-iron dustbins but so heavy that no one could lift them.

Each year the Royal Corps would hold its annual dinner in the Painted Hall of the Royal Naval College at Greenwich. This was always a splendid affair with many distinguished guests. Socialist ministers were good value and always remained behind to chat when the formal proceedings were over. One year the First Lord was our guest, he was now Lord Hall; after the dinner he said to me "Why don't you young chaps join the

Labour Party. Look at me, I went into the pits when I was 14 and worked on the surface. When I was old enough at 18 I went underground; it was a hard life and I couldn't stand it. When I was 23 I joined the police. I then joined the labour party and now I'm a peer". There was an even more splendid dinner given by the government at which overseas guests were present. My chief was there among the VIP's and I was seated somewhere below the salt. What I recall most vividly was a former First Lord, A. V. Alexander playing the piano quite beautifully after dinner.

After the end of the war, the staff that had been evacuated from Whitehall, many of whom still had houses in London, expected that the Department would return there. By 1947 there was considerable agitation through staff channels and this being a political matter, the First Lord addressed a packed gathering of civil servants in the Bath Pavilion. The senior directing staff also had to be present; they wouldn't have missed it for a fortune. Notwithstanding the 'Back to London' banners at the back of the hall, the staff was told that the naval departments would not return to London and would remain in Bath. Some years later, as part of a cost cutting exercise it was mooted that the department would return to London. Such was the furore that a senior officer came to Bath to explain, to be greeted by the same people who had carried the 'Back to London' banners now carrying 'Stay in Bath' banners.

This enthusiasm had all to do with the difficult housing situation and little to do with historic Bath which an American visitor described at this time as "a graveyard with traffic lights" (and there weren't too many of those, either).

The Third Sea Lord and Controller of the Navy was my namesake, Admiral Sir Charles Daniel, a man who seemed to find it difficult to smile. It seems that this was not only in the office; his wife Lady Olive used to chat with me at official do's and she confessed that he was greedy as well as miserable, he insisted on eating her one a month egg ration, giving as the reason that his two predecessors in the Controller's post had died while in harness and he wasn't going to let that happen to him! This confidence might have been at a Greenwich Garden Party where my chief and his wife were announced over the public address system as "Sir Charles and Lady Lilly Crap". I heard it and thought "Oh no" but Lady L. just couldn't leave it alone and spent best part of the afternoon going up to her acquaintances and saying "Did you hear what that silly man said?" to which if they diplomatically said "No", she would spell it out.

A story that Lillicrap liked to tell concerned the construction of a submarine at Yarrows. On the wall of the director's dining room at Scotstoun there is a painting, which shows all the warships built by this famous company at or about the time of the First World War. There is one World War One submarine although I was told that one could still discern the outline of a second submarine that was painted by mistake and then painted over; I could never see it, but no matter. Lillicrap's story of how Yarrows came to build the one submarine is worth telling.

It appeared that the Controller of the Navy was dissatisfied with the time the established submarine builders like Vickers and Chatham Dockyard were taking to build submarines. He was sure that it could be done in less than 12 months for, after all, did not Portsmouth Dockyard build the battleship *Dreadnought* in a year? He called a meeting of the managing directors of all the shipyards, including yards that had not built submarines, to discuss how this might be done. Privately he asked Sir Harold Yarrow (the first Sir Harold) for help and the latter not wishing to offend his principal customer, agreed that when asked by the Controller at the meeting whether it should be possible to build a submarine in 10 months, he would say "Yes".

The meeting came, the Controller harangued the shipbuilders about the time taken to build submarines and urged them to do better. They stood their ground and

94

Controller turned to Sir Harold and said, "You could build me one in 10 months, couldn't you?" Startled at the form of the question, Yarrow said something that sounded like "Yes" and the Controller said, "Very well, I will place the order with Yarrows". That's how the destroyer builder came to build one submarine and needless to say it took longer than 10 months.

One learns in this business that the most confident and optimistic bidders for any project are those who have not done it before. I recall a conversation many years later when I had jokingly asked Len Redshaw why it was that everyone else seemed to be able to tender a lower price than Vickers for the contract to build a follow-on Type 42 destroyer. "Because they haven't bloody well built one" was his serious reply. This is why some wise person years ago agreed that we didn't necessarily have to accept the lowest tender.

These were the years of post-war reconstruction when the organisation and salaries of staff was under review. The senior admirals were much of the view that the Royal Corps should cease its separate quasi civilian-naval existence and be absorbed totally into the navy, while the Secretariat advised that the Corp's preponderance of senior ranks could not be preserved if the present arrangement, which is enshrined in the Geneva Convention, was changed. With my entrée' into the admirals offices I was able to provide my chief with frequent opportunities to discuss the alternatives with those whose creature we were, but he declined every such chance. To hear the principal technical adviser to the Board say that he could not discuss anything with the Vice Chief of Naval Staff without first telling the Controller, was hardly encouraging.

This reluctance was not only in matters to do with future organisation. One day Admiral Edwards had me in for a chat and said, "What's up with your master? When I was a commander on the naval staff before the war, the DNC was always coming up with ideas for new equipment and ships. Nowadays, with your master, we get nothing and when in desperation we make suggestions, we are told that they are rubbish".

In part it was due to my chief's insistence on attending high-level meetings alone; he positively refused my offers to carry his papers. I was astounded at his willingness to go unbriefed to meetings. Even when he had a brief he would hardly look at it beforehand. Following a meeting to discuss a new submarine, John Starks who was Flag Officer Submarines staff Constructor Commander and had accompanied his admiral to the meeting, came to me and said "Why do you let your chief go to meetings alone, he sits there and doesn't say anything and when he is asked questions about design or cost or building he either doesn't know the answers or says something silly, whereupon FOSM turns to me, his staff constructor, and asks me to supply the answers. If I don't know the answer it's me that has egg on my face, not my admiral. Your man has no one to turn to and so the egg is on his face and that's bad "

This really was a cause for concern in a man occupying the DNC's chair, a man who according to Lord Chatfield in a House at Lords debate "could lose the Empire in a single engagement".

One of Lillicrap's stories concerned the appointment of Eustace Tennyson d'Eyncourt as the Director of Naval Construction in, I think, 1912. d'Eyncourt had been trained as a naval constructor at RNC Greenwich but had gone into industry. In 1912 the DNC was about to retire and a man called Smith was to succeed him. The First Lord of the Admiralty, Winston Churchill, secretly opposed this and wrote to d'Eyncourt who was in Brazil trying to sell Armstrong's cruisers at the time, urging him to return to the UK and he, Churchill, would make him DNC. Although he does not appear in the 'List of past DNC's,' Lillicrap insisted that the unfortunate Smith had occupied the post for one day before he was brushed aside and Winston Churchill's man appointed. When one takes into account the time for passengers and mail to travel between the UK and Brazil and for negotiations between the parties, it is evident that this was a long-standing intention on Churchill's part and that d'Eyncourt was privy to the plan. The retiring DNC swore that he had no inkling of what was afoot.

I relate the story not only because of Churchill's intrigue but because in telling it, Lillicrap added that d'Eyncourt was very popular with the younger RCNC officers because he always took the young men to meetings - even to Admiralty Board meetings - and when asked a question would invite his juniors to speak and then enlarge upon what they had said. Lillicrap 'supposed that this was because d'Eyncourt had no previous naval background'. He was quite oblivious to the good sense of d'Eyncourt's methods and his own shortcoming in this respect.

In the pre-war days the DNC always retired at the age 60 and there was intense interest in how long 'the old man' would continue, not least among the two or three officers who might take his place. Both of the front-runners, Shepherd and Pengelly had served in battleships in the Grand Fleet at Jutland. I would find myself being engaged in circular conversations which would touch on my chief's engagements in the very long term and so on. Since I had no idea when he intended to go, I was on safe ground here. Similar attempts would be made to elicit what I knew about the post-war reconstruction of the Royal Corps and here I had to be more wary because these papers did pass through my hands. One day I learned that the senior man in Bath had returned from London and summoned a meeting of Assistant Directors to tell them what he had learned (from me) which was pure conjecture for his benefit and I resolved henceforth to know nothing, even if it did make me look stupid on occasion. Recently I came across the Admiralty pattern pin-cushion that I had at the time and still pinned to the front was a piece of paper on which I had written KYBFMSD in big red letters — Keep Your Big Fat Mouth Shut, Daniel.

Actually it seems that Lillicrap had no intention of going voluntarily. Some time after I had ceased to be his secretary a friend in high places sent me a copy of a letter from the Permanent Secretary to Lillicrap, informing him that the Board did not wish to retain his services after the following September. Like the vicar who scored a hole in one, I could not share this knowledge and it was not until the very last moment that his successor, Victor Shepherd was told.

Lillicrap had obtained early recognition from his work as d'Eyncourt's assistant on Churchill's "Landships Committee". Seeking something to break the awful stalemate of trench warfare in 1916, Churchill had asked for a 'battleship on land' and had turned to his protégé d'Eyncourt for help. From this, with the cooperation of the War Office, the early tanks were developed. Lillicrap was appointed a MBE.

He was a cruiser man. Discussing cruiser design he was a different person entirely. He glowed with enthusiasm. He had designed the County Class cruisers in 1922 and the variants that followed. They were excellent ships, big and roomy with space and weight to spare for later weapons and extra armour, good 8-inch guns, high speed, good sea keeping and good endurance. Having served briefly in one in the Eastern Fleet they had the Daniel Seal of Approval. We talked much about this design and the subterfuges that he had had to adopt to get his own way or as he put it to prevent 'them' messing it up. When the time came for me to move to Bath at the end of 1949 he took me to his cupboard behind the screen and took out a bundle of official documents, all dated between 1922 and 1926 and explained that these were proposals concerning his cruisers that people had made and with which he hadn't agreed so he had conveniently 'lost' the paper; he felt that sufficient time had now passed and there was no reason for him to keep them. He asked me what he should do with them. Since the ships whose purity he had been guarding for some 25 years had already been sunk or scrapped or the few survivors extensively modernised, I took them outside and tore them up. Some time later there was a minor scandal in the MoD when a colonel vacated his room and the floor under the carpet was found covered with official papers that had gone missing.

The strength and the hydrodynamic properties of warships are obviously a major concern of the DNC and he had major research establishments in each field. Each dealt with theoretical and model and full-scale trial work. Strength and resistance to damage research was done at the Naval Construction Research Establishment at Rosyth (called UNDEX in the war) and hydrodynamics at the Admiralty Research Establishment at Haslar. AEW was the daddy of them all. In the late nineteenth century a gifted member of the RCNC, William Froude, persuaded the Board of Admiralty to provide funds to build a water tank some hundreds of feet long in which he would pull ship models along and from which he claimed he would be able to calculate the power required to propel full scale ships at various speeds. He devised the mathematical laws, which govern the prediction of skin friction and wave making resistance between model and ship. The first model test tank was built at Torquay in the West of England - a plaque still commemorates the site. The techniques having been proven it was only a matter of time before much bigger test tanks were required and where better to build them than at Portsmouth; well, just across the harbour. In Lillicrap's time, Dudley Offord was the Superintendent of NCRE and Richard Gawn the Superintendent at AEW. Each had made a signal contribution to the Royal Navy's successful war at sea. Dudley was the disciplinarian who swept opposition aside while Doctor Richard smiled his way around problems as if they didn't exist.

Lillicrap's training and early career was based on the expectation that war at sea would be decided in battle between mighty battle fleets; fast cruisers would be the eyes of the fleet and would draw the battleships into engagement. There were no aircraft or radar. To Lillicrap, the cruiser designer, every bit of a knot extra speed and sea mile of endurance was gold dust and ships shapes and propellers were honed to perfection. He liked dabbling in hydrodynamics and we saw a lot of Dicky Gawn.

The US Navy's pioneer in ship resistance was Rear Admiral David W. Taylor, a member of their old style Construction Corps. The USN's model basins were built at Carderock, outside Washington DC and named after the admiral. Taylor wrote a classic treatise on "The Speed and Power of Ships" and in about 1947-48 another US naval constructor; Captain Harold Saunders was engaged in revising Taylor's book. His entrée' into the British navy's vast amount of data was through his friend, Lillicrap and I spent a good deal of time seeing that answers eventually went back across the Atlantic.

Another little friendship that I enjoyed was with Captain Donaldson. He claimed that the only reason that he had advanced beyond the rank of Lieutenant Commander was because a naval constructor had saved his bacon. It was in the Mediterranean; his ship had been bombed and damaged and they had poured quick setting cement into the damaged compartments and limped into Malta for repairs. In those days of incessant bombing one did not hang about and the dockyard asked the ship to use explosives to break up the concrete. "No problem" said Lt Cdr Donaldson, "leave it to me." Fortunately the constructor came by and learning that a charge of several pounds was in place suggested that they should first do a small trial with a couple of ounces of explosive on a nearby chunk of concrete the size of a truck that had once been part of the dockyard real estate. The charge was duly laid and detonated and the chunk of concrete was reduced to rubble. Donaldson hastily removed about nine-tenths of his demolition charge and went on to become a Rear Admiral.

An important series of official dockets or papers was the "P" series that was used for production and purchasing topics. The most important of these, dealing with the orders for new warships or modernisations came back to DNC's London office for custody. I spent some interesting hours studying design submissions going back to the beginning of the century. One of the most noteworthy was a pre-war paper by Lillicrap's predecessor, Sir Stanley Goodall who had drawn their Lordships attention in the mid-1930's to the inadequate armour protection, particularly deck armour protection, of HMS *Hood* making her vulnerable to modern gun and bombing attack; he recommended that this mighty battle cruiser be withdrawn from service for extensive modernisation, failing which the ship "was not fit to be in the line of battle", that is, to be put in the situation where she might be fired at by enemy battleships. Their Lordships regretted that, for reasons of prestige, this, the largest British warship, could not be spared for the 2 or 3 years necessary for modernisation. Within 5 years HMS *Hood* was sunk by gunfire by the German battleship Bismarck, which was itself then sunk by other British ships. One cannot help believing that the 1500 men who were lost in *Hood* would have had a better chance of surviving that battle had their Lordships been able to heed their DNC's warning and allow the ship to be given thicker deck armour.

One of the early things that I had to learn was that the Board of Admiralty never made mistakes. Not in a public way like saying "We made a mistake; cancel X". What it would do in these circumstances would be to blandly promulgate the correct decision and everyone who knew the score would heave a sigh of relief and obey the last order. The Controller's Secretary explained this to me with some feeling when I drew attention to something about nuclear responsibility that would not stand the test of time. One recalls the advice given to rising politicians; "never resign, never apologise, never explain" and the notorious former governor of Louisiana, Huey Long's advice, "Always be sincere, even when you don't mean it".

Following the end of the war the UK had asked the Russians to return the equipment that had been supplied to them to prosecute the war. The navy had loaned some of the four stack lease-lend destroyers that had been supplied to the RN by the Americans early in the War — they were old even then — and the battleship HMS *Royal Sovereign*. The Russians replied that the ships were unfit to make the passage from the Northern Fleet to the UK. The British said we would like to see for ourselves. At that time the Iron Curtain had not quite closed and after the usual prevarication it was agreed that a British naval expert would travel to Murmansk via Moscow. Constructor Commander "Reggie" Hughes duly arrived in Moscow and waited for permission to travel north. The embassy put him in a room on one of the ring roads and the steady stream of trucks on the road kept him awake. He noticed that more than half of them going in both directions carried no load. He reasoned that even if the system did not seek return loads, half the trucks should have a cargo and after a while he recognised the same empty trucks going around and around the ring. Perhaps it was the KGB class of 1947 qualifying in truck driving-cum-surveillance.

After a week he boarded a train for Murmansk with a Soviet naval escort who pulled down the blinds occasionally, presumably when they passed a military installation. In the naval base the officers expressed surprise that he had come and were even more surprised when he opened his case and put on spotless white overalls and said "lets go and look at the ships". He examined the ships structures, boilers and equipment and pronounced the ships seaworthy for the trip to the UK and in due course, home they came.

The battleship had been renamed *Archangelski* and after some haggling - and probably a threat to send Constructor Hughes back - the ship set sail at the end of January

1949. Her passage was monitored by allied aircraft as she came down the Norwegian Sea and arrangements were in hand to receive her at Rosyth Naval Base when suddenly she reversed course and sailed north only to swing south and then go round in a big circle. After a day or so she resumed her course southwards and reached the UK. As part of the post-war reparations the Soviet navy was to receive the Italian Battleship *Giulio Cesare* and the return of the *Archangelski* was timed to coincide with the sailing of the newly refitted ex-Italian ship. What had happened was that the senior Russian naval officer in charge of the refit and transfer had been found dead in his cabin just when the ship was leaving. His name was Captain Zinoviev (First Grade now), the man with whom I had dealt in London in 1942/43 when some Russian submarines came to the UK to be fitted with radar and sonar. The Italian authorities established that he had taken his own life and so the Soviets resumed normal business. I believe that he just could not face going back. The ex-Italian battleship became the Soviet navy's *Novorossiysk* and sank in Sevastopol in October 1955 as the result of a mine explosion.

When our people examined the returned HMS *Royal Sovereign*, they found that most of her deck equipment was unworkable and that the gun turrets seemed never to have been rotated; they were stuck fore and aft. The ship was scrapped.

Quite early on, Penney arranged a symposium attended by the nation's top military and civil officers to tell them something of the effects of atomic weapons. It was held in the Royal Academy of Arts building in John Adam Street and was classified Secret. It will be appreciated that atomic weapons and their effects were the No.1 matter of concern in international and domestic politics and every scientist was treated with respect, for, after all, he might be one of those atomic people. There were sessions on naval, army, air force and civil defence and my chief was invited to present the scene-setting paper to open the naval session. I wrote the paper. I also prepared a general paper covering the ground that I expected the other services to present, in short, a summary paper that he might find useful. Lillicrap brusquely rejected this; saying that it was none of our business. Penney's aide who played a prominent part in the symposium and who I met for the first time that day, was Klaus Fuchs.

Lillicrap did his stuff introducing the maritime session and late in the afternoon we came to the final session — Summing up. To Lillicrap's consternation, Penney called on him to make the opening speech. The little man looked momentarily stunned while I fished the paper that he had rejected out of my case, thrust it into his hand and steered him up to the lectern. He read it out and it sounded just great; just what was required. Lillicrap could sense that the audience was with him; he gained confidence and towards the end, at the penultimate paragraph, he departed from my script and added a line of his own. That one sentence showed that he didn't understand much of what he was talking about. Penney said afterwards "it was a bit of a howler, but never mind, most of the distinguished audience would know no better". Penney didn't know what a close run thing it had been even to get my chief on his feet for that final item.

Some months later Klaus Fuchs was arrested as a Soviet spy and it seems that he had been passing them information all the time that he had been at Los Alamos working in the Manhattan Project. Fuchs' father was a protestant pastor in East Germany and doubtless much pressure was put on him. I thought at the time that he was probably the most useful source the other side had on the West's atomic work; but since then it has been stated that one at least of Americas most prominent and trusted nuclear physicists had been keeping the Soviets informed for several years before that. There are some queer people about.

In the immediate post-war years nations had begun to make claims for ownership of bits of Antarctica. Good sense prevailed however and it was agreed that there should be discussions leading to international exploration of the continent. In the interim it was agreed that no nation would send ships south of a certain latitude — somewhere about South Georgia. There were no satellites to spy from the sky and aircraft couldn't reach the place so how would decent law abiding governments like the British know that the other nations weren't about to present the world with a fait accompli? Remember that in 1947 the powers that be in Britain were more convinced than they are today, that God is an Englishman, so they secretly sent a small warship. The wretched thing got stuck in the ice some hundreds of miles south of the no-go latitude. For several days radio messages flashed to and fro. The ship was in danger of being crushed and finally it was decided that if there was no improvement by the Sunday, Her Majesty's Ambassador in Buenos Aires would inform the Argentine government that due to a failure of her navigation equipment, HMS *Sparrow* had deviated to the south and had been trapped in the ice and Britain had no alternative but to cross the forbidden latitude to rescue her crew. A matter of hours before the time set for the ambassador's admission, the wind changed, the ice parted and our sloop freed herself and sailed north. Obviously God was an Englishman.

DNC's small clerical registry in London was presided over by the redoubtable and rotund Mr Jones. Mr Jones was an ex- service man and an active member of most ex-service organisations. He was the Quartermaster of the Admiralty Home Guard. Clerical registry work was definitely not his forte, not because of lack of ability but rather lack of interest, but if one wanted the near- impossible or the unorthodox, like an air ticket to Timbuktu or the supply of some obsolete spare part to an ageing warship in Singapore the next day, Mr "Fixit" Jones was definitely your man. His contacts in most government departments and establishments were legion, people like himself who in the war had kept their ships, battalions and squadrons supplied with unobtainable spares and creature comforts by one means or another. Such NCO's were prized in the war and living conditions in Britain in 1947 were little different from the war years.

In a London back street in October 1948 I found a shop that had a small stock of fireworks. I bought some and showed them in the office ready for Guy Fawkes Night, November the 5th. "Oh," said Mr Jones "I'll let you have a couple of flares" and on the day he produced a couple of olive green objects that I proudly bore homeward to rural Kent. The fireworks that I had bought each measured about 10cm long and 1cm diameter; Mr Jones' flares were about 20cm long and 6cm diameter and would be the centrepiece of the evening. As the bonfire glowed I struck their tops as instructed and they ignited. They flared but there was no danger that they would be mistaken for, say, a lighthouse, more likely, a candle. But they made smoke, boy did they make smoke, thousands of cubic feet of the stuff all over the main A2 trunk road to Dover bringing traffic to a halt and eventually the local Bobby on his bike. The smoke also covered the main railway line but the big steam trains were not bothered.

Some time later Mr Jones left the service. Years later he appeared in my design room in Admiralty, Bath looking very prosperous and accompanied by two of his grown-up sons. He was now in the road surfacing business and was seeking future work. Not for Mr Jones the contract to repair the roads on the Foxhill Site, what he wanted was advice on how he might get contracts to re-surface air force and naval airfields and runways, or perhaps Heathrow.

There was only a small DNC staff in London with the bulk located in Bath and in the shipyards and research establishments. Important matters would usually be sent from our office to Bath who would propose the action to be taken over my chief's signature Some other official papers might be recognised by Bath as requiring the chief's attention and reach us that way. It did not take me long to realise that the standard of staff work coming from Bath was poor. Most times the professional content was sound but the presentation and policy slant left a lot to be desired Frequently I would bounce the things straight back with a note saying that "DNC would be grateful if you would examine..." or "DNC wonders why you did not consider..." This was not conceit; I had the drift of how the Naval Staff and Board were thinking.

So I took to rewriting the worst of them and gave them to my chief together with the original; he always signed my version. This was not without its perils; I came back from lunch one day to find a very irate Assistant Director Pengelly with our records opened at something that he had proposed and demanding to know why I had dared to modify it. The girl clerk had broken the rules that only the chief and I should have access to those files and was standing unhappily nearby. She had been Pengelly's clerk in the battleship section when he was designing the King George V class and clearly her old loyalties still mattered. I said that my chief had not been happy with the Bath version and I had rewritten it to take account of xyz etc. Perhaps he would like to discuss it with Sir Charles, "You have your copy of the minute and so he need not know that you have had access to his confidential files". That stopped him.

I had to do the same with Chief Constructor Merrington who was appointed to Whitehall to take Bakers place when the latter went to Canada in 1948. Merrington came into my room on Day One, shot his cuffs as was his wont and said "Very well Daniel, give me all of DNC's correspondence. From now on I will deal with it." I said "In no way, Sir, my orders are that only I am to handle DNC's papers and until he changes them I am afraid that's what I must do. Perhaps you would wish to take it up with Sir Charles?." I had reason to know that the last person that Lillicrap would wish to have handling his papers was Merrington who had been forced on him from Bath and who's posting he had accepted with considerable misgivings. To his credit, John Merrington never raised the subject again.

In the years immediately after the war, service and civil service officers who had received accelerated promotion were reverted to their substantive rank. There were of course hundreds of marginal cases and also, cases that were caught up in post-war reorganisation. The Royal Corps cases that gave Lillicrap most concern were the term-mates Sims, Baker and Hall. In the dark days of the war, Sims had been on Admiral Submarines staff at Fort Blockhouse and Baker dealt with merchant ship conversions for war purposes. With the creation of the Combined Operations organisation, Baker moved into Admiral Mountbatten's sphere and was soon promoted to Chief Constructor to reflect the importance of designing and building the thousands of ships and craft required to transport and land men and armour on hostile shores. Although nominally junior to Sims, Baker had been promoted to the higher rank some years before Sims. Hall, who had been the Constructor Captain on VA (Q's) staff in Melbourne in 1945, was no problem, he was reduced to constructor, but Lillicrap absolutely refused to accept that Baker's wartime promotion should give him precedence over Sims. Lillicrap told me that he didn't care if Baker was reverted to constructor but he would flatly refuse to revert Sims.

John Murray of LLoyds Register was a friend of Lillicrap and a more than occasional visitor to the office. John had been associated with our development of welding techniques for submarine hulls during the war and then with the construction of the combined operations landing ships and craft and I sensed that he felt that all things considered, Baker, the brash, loud, Kentish boy had benefited a great deal from other peoples inventiveness. In particular that Baker's deputy, Constructor 'Moses' MacMurray and latterly some clever Americans had not received due mention for the outstanding programme for which Baker took most of the credit. How much of this Murray told to Lillicrap I do not know. Anyway, Lillicrap certainly had no doubts about Sims. It was about this time that the need to replace Harrison in Canada came up and Baker was spared the axe.

The rule in the Admiralty was that the First Lord always wrote or had typed on official papers in red ink. The First Sea Lord used green ink and the Vice Chief of Naval Staff used purple. Merrington also used purple ink and I used to wonder how he got away with it. Obviously nothing that he did in manuscript ever got near to a Board member. Why I remember his ink was because I often had to act as a scrutineer for the Royal Institution of Naval Architects and we could always recognise Merrington's secret ballot when, like everyone else, he voted for himself.

In 1949 I presented a paper at the RINA entitled "The Royal Navy and Nuclear Power". The paper was largely concerned with the effects of nuclear weapons on warships and the measures that might be taken to improve their chance of survival but it did briefly discuss the possibility of harnessing the fission process to produce power for ship propulsion particularly for submarines. This was the day when Admiral Cunningham said "'you were right, my boy".

I had long discovered that if I allowed something to go to him in manuscript, my chief would amend it in his small angular hand. If however I sent in the same thing typewritten, he signed it.

On more than one occasion when we didn't know what his preference would be, such as attending a lecture somewhere, I would have the girl type two notes, one accepting and one declining the invitation. Sometimes both would come out signed!. He always used black ink and a broad nib and his writing was rather like Adolf Hitler's, all short up and down strokes.

Most of us are conscious of a wish to develop a flowing signature instead of the school- boy 'write your name at the top of the paper' style that serves us for the first 20 years or so of life. A few appreciate the advantage, career wise, of a signature that is both flowing and legible. For many, however, the flowing style becomes an unintelligible squiggle. A story that says it all appeared many years ago in The Pelican, the journal of the RN Staff Course. Commander Mountbatten was serving as the Communications Officer on C in C Mediterranean Fleet's staff in Malta. It was the practice to write ones comments on the internal staff dockets. A more senior staff officer became frustrated at the difficulty they all had in reading these manuscript remarks and proposed that in future all comments on staff dockets should be typed. He wrote and signed a staff paper setting this out. The paper reached Mountbatten who wrote −Concur with Czqalyt Zyptokx'.

Victor Shepheard had an impressively legible signature. He was ambidextrous and I recall watching him standing before a wall mounted blackboard at Greenwich and writing the same thing simultaneously with a piece of chalk in each hand; the right hand writing from left to right and the left hand writing from right to left, to produce mirror images.

Two mentions of A. Hitler. We were receiving translations of the Fuhrer Conferences and most times he seemed to make sense. One did not need to agree with him but if one is going to act outside the standards hitherto accepted between nations for the conduct of warfare, one might as well be a realist and go the whole hog. At the opening of hostilities against Poland he personally instructed his generals "What matters in waging a war is not righteousness but victory. Close your hearts to pity, proceed brutally". He was talking about the media pretexts for waging the war; credibility he dismissed as unimportant on the grounds that "the victor is never asked afterwards whether or not he told the truth". An item that I liked was when Speer asked for more steel to put bulkheads in the landing craft carrying men and materials to North Africa because the British submarines kept sinking them. Hitler replied that they would sink anyway and it would make more sense to provide more life belts than more bulkheads.

The other mention concerned the small plastic identity cards with our photographs and signature with which we gained access to the Admiralty each day. The Engineer in Chief of the Fleet was a Vice Admiral called Venus Ford although it is difficult to imagine anyone less like Venus than he was. He had a Professional Secretary -a commander-called McGilvray. McGilvray had an extra identity card made with a photo of Hitler and signed A. Hitler. Each morning he would flash this pass to the elderly messengers who manned the Whitehall entrance and walk on to his office. It was a source of some amusement at parties until on one wet morning he waved his pass and paused to fold his umbrella and heard one elderly messenger say to the other "There goes that bloody fool McGilvray with his Adolf Hitler pass ".

Britain tested its first atomic weapon at Montebello in 1952. The planning was well advanced by 1949 when Lillicrap made it clear that he thought that I had seen enough and I shouldn't go. I saw some of the en-route signal traffic after I had moved to Bath because the force sailed in one of 'my' older aircraft carriers. The Admiralty received a constant stream of signals from the senior officers of each service and the scientists, which were asking in a roundabout way, who was in charge? The Commodore was insistent that this was a naval operation so would everyone do as he said. I recall clearly that the Brigadier said that he intended to position his men to face the hazards they would face in a future battlefield scenario; I think that he was told not to be so daft. I did not realise then how serious this might be in years to come. Obviously Penney straightened things out when they arrived on-site. I could only but compare this British make-do as we go, with the tight, well-documented organisation of the US Operation Crossroads. But at least we had learned the lesson not to drop the test bomb from an aircraft and it did go-off at the correct time.

In the Department in Bath we had two small sections that dealt respectively with armour and with the non-explosive part of armour-piercing shells. They had fingers in the steel industry and their products came together somewhat violently on the test range at Shoeburyness. I was lunching in the Strand Lyons Corner House with the armour man, who was old enough to be able to exchange polite banter with the waitresses. They were known as Nippies. We were being waited on by a particularly beautiful girl, who seemed a little flustered, such that my friend said "What's the matter today, you are all fingers and thumbs" and she replied "Yes I know, you see yesterday I was chosen as Miss Nippy". Some days later I saw her picture in the paper and her name — Joan Rice. She went on to star in several films.

A big event in 1948 was the Safety of Life at Sea Conference held in London. There was a difference of view between the Admiralty, which had a division concerned with the protection of trade at sea and the Ministry of Transport, which administered the regulations governing plimsoll lines and such things. The navy said that in two wars it had been called on to escort and protect merchant ships that would turn over and sink if an enemy as much as breathed on them or words to that effect and the rules should be changed to ensure that they had a measure of strength and stability to continue to float when moderately damaged.

The Transport Department said that this was really nothing to do with the navy and commercial aspects must be paramount. Its Chief Ship Surveyor was a rather unattractive man called G. Daniel. The matter went to Cabinet level and it was ruled that the Ministry of Transport should lead for the UK.

In those days we were close to the US Navy and US Coastguard and their views were the same as the Royal Navy's. We got together with our cousins and at the conference they presented the common view. At the time I thought it unusual that the navy which, with the merchant navy, had paid such a high price in getting supplies through to Britain in the war, should have its views rejected by the civil Transport Ministry and be forced to conspire with the Americans who took a much more realistic approach to the subject of safety at sea.

As is usual, the results of such a maritime conference were the subject of a learned paper presented to the Royal Institution of Naval Architects at its next Annual Meeting. The paper was presented by Chief Ship Surveyor G. Daniel and in the question period the naval side made much of the opportunity that had been missed of ensuring safer merchant ships, particularly the need to restrict flooding on wide open decks and the consequent loss of stability. I took part in the questioning in what was called, later, by Sir Stanley Goodall, the "Battle of the Daniel's".

Only in the mid 1990's is action being taken by these civil authorities to remedy the design shortcomings to which we were drawing attention in 1948 and this only after massive loss of life in seagoing ferries.

Perhaps the most important discussions on future naval construction were to do with future frigates. It was decided that we required three types, anti-aircraft, air direction and anti-submarine. By and large the first two would accompany the fleet or convoys to direct the airborne air defence and fire their guns at those that got past the fighters, while the ASW frigates would fight their separate war against submarines. Providing all three roles on one hull resulted in a ship that was too large and too costly. The Engineer in Chief was adamant that the ships should be driven by diesel engines because the people called up for naval service in a future emergency would likely be more familiar with internal combustion engines (and hence be easier to train) than with boilers and steam turbines. The aim was to provide a common hull and machinery package, which could be built rapidly and cheaply and fitted out for one of the three roles according to how an enemy threat developed. A sort of MEKO. The problem was that tactically the ASW frigate required higher speed than would suffice in the AA and AD versions and whereas the necessary power could be provided by medium speed diesel engines for the latter, the ASW frigate would require a significantly higher power, and for hydrodynamic reasons, a longer hull, than the other two types. The decision was made to have a common diesel hull for the AA and AD frigates and a longer steam hull for the ASW.

War experience had demonstrated the importance of numbers of ships at sea and the Controller argued that in addition to the First Rate ASW ships there should be less expensive Second Rate ASW ships; thus was born the Type 14 frigate with one propeller and a smaller armament. They were to have many shortcomings compared with their bigger cousins but they were to prove invaluable in future years in meeting commitments that otherwise would have gone by default. The next cry was for a general purpose frigate capable of doing a little of everything in the more remote areas of the world, with a gun, a helicopter, single shaft propulsion and limited cost; this was the Type 81.

This debate went on long after I had left the London office and, of course, was part of the plan to spread the fleets resources among a large number of smaller ships to counter, or as a consequence of, the possibility of attack by atomic weapons.

I was amused and interested by the opening chapters of Peter Wright's book "Spycatcher" because a few of the people he mentions were known to me and in my young view at the time were well past their best days, put politely, were clearly exhausted by the war. The lasting impression that I have of Sir Frederick Brundrett, the senior scientist serving the navy is of eggs, since he was at the same time the Chairman or some such thing of the Egg Marketing Board and one couldn't go into his room without becoming aware of this other interest. In a nation rationed to one egg per person per month his work with the chickens was probably better value than his other work. There were some other odd characters, one day Chief Constructor Pamplin arrived in my room directly from a meeting at which a senior scientist had expressed such outspoken communist views that Pamplin wanted him reported to the security services.

A secret official paper arrived on my desk en-route to my chief. It was the report on the atomic bomb damage in Japan that I had written at sea in the Pacific nearly two years earlier. The most interesting thing to me was the treatment of my final chapter in which I had suggested (in October 1945) that ballistic missiles armed with atomic warheads would be most deadly weapons and that perhaps the only way to counter them might be to intercept them by detonating a similar weapon close to them in outer space. A similar conclusion was reached by President Reagan's advisers in 1988 and called Star Wars. The reaction of the highest defence scientist in my case in 1946 was to draw a red line obliquely across the page and write; "This officer is not qualified to comment on these matters"

Lord Denning's book, "The Family Story" tells of his brother's experience. In the 1930's Paymaster Lieutenant Norman Denning was serving in Singapore. He noticed the large number of Japanese fishing boats and fishery research vessels equipped with all modern navigational aids that were prospecting the waters all around Singapore Island. He was suspicious; he knew that the whole defence of Singapore was based on the assumption that in the event of war with Japan, the attack would be a frontal assault from seaward. From his investigations, Denning thought that the attack might come from the landward side, from a Japanese force landed on the Malay peninsular. He prepared a report for submission to the Director of Naval Intelligence. He did not know what had happened to it until he made enquiries some six years later. He found that it had been dismissed with the comment; "This young officer is over-exercising his imagination. The Japanese have no sea borne assault force; it is ridiculous to imagine an army advancing hundreds of miles through jungle territory". One wonders how many more "young officer's imaginings" have and perhaps still are, being dismissed.

I must hasten to add that someone recognised Denning's potential and had him serve in the Naval Intelligence Centre in the Citadel in the 1939-45 war, interpreting all the diffuse data that came to hand. He retired as Vice Admiral Sir Norman Denning, having filled the most senior service posts in both the Paymaster Branch and in Intelligence.

In this post-war period the need to devote the nations resources to reconstruction and manufacture of consumer goods, reduced defence budgets, and declining manpower as personnel were released from national service and military obsolescence forced the Board to sell, give away or scrap many ships and to place many more in a reserve fleet. Those ships on which work continued did so at a slow pace. Work on many was suspended pending final decision.

The decision was taken to complete the cruisers *Tiger* and *Blake* building on the Clyde. The Managing Director at John Browns described the decision as a 'dirty trick' because it would divert effort away from more lucrative commercial work. My chief had a very high regard for this man, Jimmy McNeill and repeatedly recommended that he be knighted. At the same time my chief was being lobbied endlessly by McNeill's opposite number in the shipyard, a man called Skeffington who left no stone unturned in his efforts for preferment. In the end both were knighted, McNeill on the Admiralty's list, and Skeffington through the Scottish old-boy network that never fails. To this day the same system works, no matter how much the recipient's actions may have cost the country.

A warning about honours. There was a man at English Steel who Lillicrap considered deserved recognition and recommended him for the CBE. Time passed and after his name had failed to appear for the fifth or sixth time, Lillicrap asked why. He was told that the same man had been recommended for an MBE in 1919 for his work in the war on steel production and had declined the honour. This put him on some sort of black list. Actually he had declined it because he felt that his men were just as worthy as he was and they couldn't all be given medals.

It was no surprise to me that when the political hurdles were finally overcome by calling the vessel a medium hospital ship masquerading as a royal yacht and the ship ordered, the contract went to John Browns of Clydebank. Labour Ministers at the time were strongly opposed to the idea that the scrapped *Victoria and Albert* should be followed by a new Royal Yacht. It was considered to be an unjustifiable expense and was only finally approved after the most vigorous argument by the First Sea Lord, fronting for the Palace. Like several ships from that yard no sooner was it delivered than it came to a southern royal dockyard to be put right, in this case the ventilation system to the royal apartments was totally rebuilt.

Although my chief, as head of the RCNC, was the most senior naval constructor officer, there were other senior members who headed departments of the Admiralty. In particular the Director of Dockyards whose writ ran not only over the five home yards but also the naval dockyards at Bermuda, Gibraltar, Malta, Singapore and Hong Kong plus staff in Simonstown in South Africa. Officers returning from the normal three year appointments to such places or about to take up such exciting posts would call on my chief and I would get all the news as well. How I envied them. All RCNC personnel would serve in dockyards but when more senior, would tend to specialise either on design or dockyard work. I found the wartime and immediate post-war dockyard managers a source of great practical and costing expertise and profound industrial knowledge and it should be a matter of shame that the measures taken in later years "to improve efficiency and raise management skills" which were in effect to provide jobs on the buggins-turn principle for less qualified naval and civil officers in the dockyards, should have destroyed one of the few areas where the services were way ahead of industry.

One of the senior RCNC officers who occasionally called on my chief was my boyhood hero W.J.A. Davies. Bill Davies was undoubtedly the best known and most popular member of the RCNC in the inter-war years. Not for anything to do with naval construction but because his partnership with his friend Kershaw on the rugby field had enabled the Royal Navy fifteen to sweep the inter-service board and better still, the pair of them had done the same for England for several years - a truly lovely man. Incidentally, and apropos Crap Miers comment to me one night in a submarine somewhere in the Indian Ocean in 1944 that he had never met a constructor admiral, Rear Admiral W. J. A Davies did serve in that capacity early on in the 1939 war.

Amid the plethora of medals was a modest thing called the Imperial Service Medal that was awarded to long serving subordinate officers on retirement. The people who had been moved to Bath but had retained their homes in the London area would elect to receive their medals from my chief in London and on the appointed day would attend, accompanied by their close relatives. I would provide my chief with a brief summary of the man's career and the small staff in London would be required to form the audience. Although the medal itself was fairly trivial, to the recipient the event was always emotional, representing in most cases the end of some forty years of service and most of them cried when making their little acceptance speech. There was one senior draughtsman of the London staff who always found this a matter for sarcastic mirth afterwards. In 1949, he retired and was awarded the ISM. He brought his wife and daughter to the ceremony and sobbed uncontrollably throughout.

Dating from earlier years like the ISM was a greater than life size bust of Sir Phillip Watts, a distinguished former Director of Naval Construction. The bust was mounted on a plinth and located in the wide passage outside the room of the Admiralty's top civil servant, the Permanent Secretary. Sometime in the war, someone had placed a cigarette between its lips and it was still there, many years later. I am not sure what this tells us about the British but if anyone had wanted to make a bust of me I would have given them a cigar. I don't know the provenance of the Watts bust but it reminds me of the Goodall portrait. Sometime in the 1930's someone decided that the Royal Corps should present its Head, Sir Stanley Goodall, with his portrait by a well-known artist. Sittings were arranged and the senior Corps officers informed the members how much each was expected to contribute, according to rank, towards the cost. It seems that someone took a dim view of this and (doubtless after making his contribution) wrote to his MP. A question was asked in the House of Commons about officers being required to make gifts to senior officers. After some rapid Whitehall footwork, the Admiralty stated that the painting would belong to the Corps, not to Goodall, although he, as head of the Corps, would be responsible for its custody. He took it home. And thus it was that when he died the painting was returned to the RCNC who were pleased to donate it to the Royal Institution of Naval Architects.

At that time the Permanent Secretary was Sir John Lang. He had started as a boy clerk and had risen to the topmost rank, as had more than 20 of the 47 or 48 Permanent Secretaries heading government departments at that time. One day he personally brought a sheaf of papers to my chief. They contained a draft submission to the Director of Public Prosecutions alleging fraud by a member of the RCNC. It concerned claims made by the officer for 'Excess Rent Allowance'. This was an allowance by which people who were appointed to a new station could claim a contribution from the state towards the extra cost of accommodation at the new place. To receive the allowance one had to provide some documents, including one from the landlord at the new station. The navy accounts people had paid the money to the officer but for over a year had been unable to get the documents until they threatened to stop paying, when a document was supplied with an almost illegible signature. Further pressure revealed that the landlord had the same name as the claimant and finally they established that this senior officer's wife had bought the house in Great Pulteney Street, Bath, and had taken her husband in as a lodger. John Lang was determined to prosecute, however my chief thought that this would be bad for the Service. I was set the task of finding a loophole, which turned out to be that nowhere did the regulations actually prohibit what had been done. No one had thought that a gentleman would do such a thing. As is so often the case, they were intended to prohibit it but they could be got round. So the papers didn't go to the public prosecutor and Mr S was never promoted beyond the rank he held when he and his wife invented the great excess rent fiddle. They were great socialites in Bath, Friends of Bath Abbey, Patrons of the Theatre and the Festival and so on. I would see Mrs S dancing languidly at various balls and wonder what the reaction would have been had I told those present that I had helped save her from prosecution by the Crown for fraud.

An event that brought Mr S a degree of disfavour with his colleagues followed a Corps dinner at Greenwich. It was the practice to provide a coach to take officers to Paddington Station after the dinner to catch the midnight train to Bath and beyond. The coach was timed to depart the college at 11pm but everyone knew that at that time of night with little other traffic on the road in the mid 1950's, the journey would take much less than an hour and so people would aim to board the coach sometime about 11.10pm. On this particular year Mr S boarded the coach just before 11pm and when the college clock struck the hour, notwithstanding the fact that he was the only passenger on board, instructed the driver to leave, giving himself a 54 seat taxi and stranding about forty [some quite senior] officers in south east London.

An even more senior officer was on the staff of the Control Commission in Germany. The senior naval officer on the commission had written several times to my chief suggesting that a change was desirable and finally he called one day and said in effect that Mr C was fraternising too much with the ex-enemy, well actually with the female half of the ex-enemy. Sir Charles told me that they could lump it; Mr C could stay there until he retired in a few months time; he certainly wasn't having him back. This was no surprise to me because this elderly officer with his thick spectacles and thinning grey hair had pirouetted in my room some months earlier, on a visit to London, and urged me to seek a transfer to the control commission in Germany where, he assured me, by frequenting the dance floors, I would be able to purchase untold delights for the cost of a packet of cigarettes. Alas, another lost opportunity. It was some time before I realised that Mr C was the uncle of Chatten, a colleague who had been at Greenwich with me.

There was always much that was amusing. One quite senior officer used to invent all sorts of reasons why I should go to lunch and hence leave my room. Such remarks as 'the fish is very good in the canteen today but it is likely to run out quite soon" and so on. Actually the canteen smelt so much of generations of fish and chips that one's clothes smelt afterwards and I seldom went there. Anyway, Mr B would seek the private use of my phone to ring his girlfriend in the Admiralty, Bath and would then spell out messages in a code, which a child of eight could have deciphered. It was really quite a relief when he married the girl.

Sir Charles used to chat with me about earlier DNC's and their lives. Before the motorcar they were expected to have their own coachman and horse drawn carriage and of course they lived much closer to the office. I learned how Sir William Berry had a mistress in Mayfair; if his staff tried to contact him, he would have "been at the club". "Sir we tried your club" 'Ah, I wasn't at the Athaneum, where else did you try?" When a list of clubs had been exhausted he would say "did you try (say) the Cavalry Club" If the answer was "no" then that's where he would claim to have been. We agreed that notwithstanding the praise heaped upon him after the first war, Sir Arthur Johns' submarines were not all that to write home about.

Mark you - the Royal Navy didn't help. The K-Class was designed to accompany the Fleet with a surface speed of some 23 knots. The power was provided by steam generated in boilers whose stored heat was sufficient to drive the turbines for up to half an hour after diving. The environment in the boiler rooms must have been hellish. Each time the submarine surfaced the funnels had to be raised and hull valves opened to allow combustion air to enter and smoke to escape and the reverse procedure each time the submarine dived.

According to David Frost's ' Book of the World's Worst Decisions' published by Andre Deutsch, 'A specially striking triumph of British naval planning came in 1917, at the height of the Great War, when the British Admiralty decided to construct a flotilla of K boats – giant 325 foot long steam powered submarines.

K2 caught fire on its first dive.

K3 sank to the bottom with the Prince of Wales on board and had to be salvaged.

K3 was then rammed by K 6 on manoeuvres and sank.

K4 ran aground.

K5 sank with the loss of all hands.

K7 rammed *K17* and had to be scrapped.

K14 sprung a leak while still in dock.

Later, at sea, *K14* rammed *K22* and sank.

K17, during the same sea trials, rammed first an escorting cruiser and then *K7*. *K17* then went out of control and sank.

K22 was rammed by another escorting cruiser.

In 1918 the K boat project was abandoned. 250 British sailors had been killed'.

What bothers me about this story is that it doesn't mention *K13* which sank in the Gareloch and whose crew is remembered with a memorial in the local cemetery.

Towards the end of my time with him, Lillicrap admitted that he relied greatly upon my memory in the conduct of day-to-day business but could remember the events at the early part of his career in great detail.   In particular he could remember how, on returning from the period of sea training that followed graduation from the naval college, he had been appointed to HM Dockyard, Devonport and could recall with startling clarity the bearded gentlemen who were to be his senior colleagues for the next three years. He added wistfully 'we who thought the old men odd, are now the odd old men".

It was probably even more stressful, he thought, for the young wives who would be required to make and receive calls (always with the correct number of visiting cards) from senior officers wives, most of whom would bring prayer books and bibles for study there and then and suggest attendance at their particular church or chapel with hints that the retribution for non-compliance might be in this world rather than in the next.

He liked to reminisce. We spoke a lot about the ships in which I had served and he knew that I gave the King George V Class battleships a small minus and the fleet carriers and his County Class cruisers, a big plus. He told me one day that he did not think that one of our senior officers had been treated very fairly. The man, W.A.D. Forbes had been the head of the new design aircraft carrier section and largely responsible for the design of the Illustrious and Indefatigable Classes. It had been due to his persistence that many of the most valuable characteristics had been adopted, such as the extent of armour on the flight deck and sides, big lifts and so on, things that made the ships bigger and more costly than the D.N.C, Sir Stanley Goodall wanted or would, initially, accept. Forbes had persisted. Lillicrap explained that Goodall was a battleship man and was 'Fleet action minded'. The idea that the carrier would prove to be the decisive naval weapon as it had in the Pacific, never crossed the Board's mind. Lillicrap felt that, perhaps, Forbes might have been given more credit for his work.

The offices that d'Eyncourt and subsequent DNC's had occupied in the Old Admiralty Building overlooking the Horse Guards were badly damaged by a German bomb in the war and we were now on the north side. Each spring I would receive a phone call from the secretary of the Admiralty Cricket Club asking for the return of the challenge trophy — the Admiralty Cricket Cup — that the DNC Department had won in 1939. Each spring I would explain that the office where the cup was on display had been demolished in the war and the cup had probably been demolished also. For all that I knew it might well be on some long retired or dead persons mantelpiece. I did make a search the first year and asked the Corps in Bath to do the same. No cricket cup but the Boyland Cup for billiards re-appeared and has been played for ever since.

As a general rule, letters addressed in manuscript and bearing a postage stamp, were taken unopened to Lillicrap.   There were not many such but every three months or so one of those airmail envelopes with red, white and blue edging would arrive from New York. They were never left on his desk after opening. Then one day when she had emptied his out tray, Kate, his shorthand typist (they weren't called secretaries in those days) found one of these letters trapped between two other papers. So I looked at it; it was from a lady who confessed that all the other men had wanted her for her body but Charles wanted her for her mind and more in the same vein and she would be in London on so and so. I managed to put the letter back in his room.

Quite soon thereafter he went on three weeks leave for which one of the girl clerks bought two railway tickets to the Lake District and reserved two seats for the following Wednesday. On the first day of his leave, which was on the Monday, all hell broke loose and everyone wanted DNC. I told everyone that he was on leave and they demanded his holiday telephone number. Being ever helpful I told the First Lord's secretary and others that he was not travelling north until the Wednesday. At about 2.00 pm I had a phone call from Lady Lillicrap asking me what was going on and why was she getting phone calls for Charles "Isn't he in the office?" I thought quickly and said that he wasn't back from lunch and she volunteered that he was probably browsing in a bookshop in the Charing Cross Road. I packed up my papers and took a train to his local railway station, Lea Green, hoping to intercept him on his way home reasoning that, in the circumstances, he would do this at his usual time. Not so. At 8.00 pm I gave up and went home. Two weeks and a bit later he returned from leave and late in the morning he demanded to know what had gone on, on the first Monday of his leave. I told him who had wanted to speak with him urgently and that they had demanded to know his holiday telephone number. I had had no alternative but to say that he was not scheduled to travel north until the Wednesday and that since his wife seemed to be under the impression that he was in the office, I had sat on Lea Green station for about four hours to warn him of this. His only comment was "I went home by car" and the matter was never mentioned again. I am sure the whole thing remained cerebral.

One day we received an instruction that we were to give serious consideration to a sewage disposal system proposed by some friends of Mr Churchill who had an Italian sounding name. The system involved some separation and chemical treatment that would leave solid matter in the bottom of the ships tanks, which the sailors would then have to dig out. They sent a sample of the solid material. We rejected the system. We were then told by the First Lords office that Mr Churchill did not like us rejecting his friends sewage system and that we should reconsider the matter, whereupon I wrote a brief note asking how the Minister would reply to a question in parliament asking how it was that the labour government now had the Royal Navy shovelling s***. We never heard another word about it.

In the Royal Naval College Greenwich the external examiner in Hydrodynamics was usually an RCNC officer serving at AEW, the Admiralty's hydrodynamics research establishment at Haslar. The procedure was that the examiner would submit his proposed paper together with solutions for the numerical questions. This went well for my first two years but a new examiner was appointed for the third year. His proposed paper arrived after the deadline for printing and it took extreme pressure to obtain his worked solutions whereupon I found that out of six calculations, he had five wrong. He was in no way abashed and continued thus for the next 30 years.

In my time there was a strong tradition for navies with close links with the Royal Navy to enrol their young naval constructor officers on the 3-year course at Greenwich. There had been two Greek officers in my term and in 1947 I found that there were Chinese and Portuguese officers in the terms to whom I lectured. One of the Portuguese lieutenants 'lived ashore' that is he lived in a flat in Blackheath instead of in a room in the Naval College. One series of my lectures was immediately after lunch and on one or two occasions the Lieutenant was not in his place; then the door behind me would open and he would appear, facing the rows of students already in their seats and sidle past to his place. I vaguely noticed an outbreak of face rubbing. On the third time that this occurred I realised that he had walked back across Greenwich Park and through the Naval College with large smears of lipstick on his face. Having regard to the distance that he had to walk each lunch hour, he couldn't have had much time for eating.

I went to a few receptions in the Portuguese Embassy. At the last it was suggested that there would be a job for me if I would transfer to the Portuguese navy. It was explained that the pay would not be as good as the British but that I would be encouraged to work at the same time for the big private shipyard in Lisbon and more than double my pay.

Lectures in service establishments after lunch are not a good thing. Many years later it fell to me to lecture on Ship Construction to the Senior Officers Technical Course. You will think this to be a splendid idea -to lecture to these newly promoted Rear Admirals on the latest technologies, but really it was more a device by the appointers, to park these people somewhere until suitable vacancies appeared into which they might be put. My lecture was immediately after lunch; my audience was four; they had had a good and somewhat liquid lunch and one by one they proceeded to fall asleep. This was disconcerting, to say the least, for what does one do? The alternatives seemed to be to stop lecturing and quietly wait until the time had expired, to shout wakey-wakey or to carry on as if nothing had happened in the best traditions of the service. After all, they might simply be resting their eyes, Bristol fashion, the better to concentrate on the spoken word. (If so, why snore?) But then what does one do in the time generously allowed for questions? Towards knocking-off time I spoke loudly and they were once more on active service. The senior officer told me how much they had enjoyed my talk.

In the 19th Century. Gilchrist Alexander remarked that flippant young barristers dropped heavy volumes on the floor or banged the flaps of their seats when they suspected that the learned Judge had dropped off.

As a lecturer at Greenwich I was aware that the young officers were not impressed with certain college departments. The mathematics department was always good but elsewhere standards gradually fell away as eminent professors retired and were replaced by less eminent men. In 1940 the professors of applied mechanics and mathematics had been Haigh and Milne- Thompson. Haigh was the nephew of the Great Western Railways locomotive designer and had followed the classic route to engineering greatness by learning the practical aspects of his trade as an apprentice at the railway works at Swindon, before going to university. He, it was, who 'discovered' corrosion fatigue – the fact that engineering components subjected to an alternating stress regime in a corrosive environment fail at a less number of stress reversals and/or a lower stress than those in a non-corrosive situation. It is fitting that his classic work should have been triggered by an investigation of premature failures of railway carriage axles on the Great Western Railway; he found that the failures were due to the discharge from the carriage toilets falling on the axles. It was typical that this gentle professor was the one senior staff member who made it his business to come into the Royal Naval College to meet the newly joined Constructor Sub–lieutenants, on the evening that we arrived. We had been on a submarine course at Chatham while the Battle at Britain had been fought in the skies above us and now the night bombing raids on London were in full spate. The professor had come through the rain of shrapnel and bombs. He was to die shortly afterwards as the result of enemy action. Professor 'Spike' Thorne succeeded him. Many years earlier, Thorne had been associated with the construction of the airship R 101.

In much earlier times the RCNC had been responsible for the design of the navy's airships (as it had been for the design of the GPO's radio masts and the Army's tanks) but in due course specialised agencies took over these tasks. R101 was designed by industry for the RAF. According to Thorne, the design and build was a disaster because when the engines were delivered late in the construction sequence, it was found that they were not rigid enough. They had run splendidly on the rigid test bed but when mounted in their lightweight nacelles they seized up. They had to be made stronger and hence heavier. By this time the airships structure was complete and most of the gasbags had been installed. The only solution was to provide more buoyancy lift by modifying the hull; this took time and meanwhile the installed gas bags chafed against the structure and became set in creases and so on. The consequence was that when finally commissioned the craft was a mass of leaks. There was a commitment to fly to India that the Minister was determined to honour and R101 departed. She reached her planned cruising altitude but then progressively lost height and crashed in northern France, killing all on board. Professor Thorne used this to emphasise three lessons; always be sure that you test things in properly representative conditions; always endeavour to order in batches (if R102's hull had been following, its material could have been used to modify R 101) and third, but not least, *never* let your engineering judgement and safety be overridden by a politician.

The mathematics department was in the safe hands of Professor Milne-Thompson and his deputy (and successor) Prof Broadbent, the editor of The Mathematical Gazette. M-T had written the standard work on Hydrodynamics using vector analysis and so we learned our mathematics in this way. It provided many elegant methods and we passed our examinations. The trouble was that the rest of the world used Cartesian methods and Lamb's classic textbook and so those of us who must work in this field had subsequently to convert to Lamb or remain isolated in our own vector world. M-T had been crippled by polio in his youth; he was a delightful man but somewhat shy and a lecturer who fixed his gaze somewhere high at the back of the room and pressed on regardless. It was T.A.A. Broadbent who brought mathematics alive for me and made the whole thing enjoyable.

Having embarked on the Greenwich story, mention has to be made of Professor Ruddock and the Chemistry and Metallurgy department and his deputy Doc. LLoyd, both Sheffield graduates from an age when Sheffield meant Steel. This was fun. Then there was Physics under Professor Simms — to us this was largely electrics and the infant electronics.

Languages meant French under M. Harrault. He was an unhappy man trapped in England while his beloved France was no longer free. He had been at Verdun with General Petain in the First World War and was still devoted to him. He had no time for the upstart de Galle and, it seemed to us, even less for the English. For a variety of reasons I challenged the mandatory French tuition, 'Why not German, in which I was reasonably proficient? 'OK' said Authority, 'M Harrault was a prisoner of war after Verdun, so he shall teach you German'. Perhaps he was much more clever than I thought because after a few periods of Germanspeak by a Frenchman who had learned his German from prison guards in Alsace, I gladly rejoined the French class - end of digression.

As officers graduated and were appointed to various Corps posts there developed a groundswell that something had to be done and my chief was persuaded to take the matter up with Instructor Rear Admiral Hall, the Director of Naval Education. The Corps for its part put in a first rate professor of naval architecture but even then the sands were running out. Many years later the academic training of naval constructors was moved to University College London where they are required to obtain a masters degree in an engineering course tailored to the Corps requirements and for which an RCNC professor is appointed to the college.

Towards the end of 1949 I was told that I was to be promoted and appointed to Bath to take charge of the Light Fleet aircraft carrier design section. Although neither he nor I knew it at the time my seniority was to be reviewed later and advanced by two years, giving me the rank of Constructor at the age of 27 years. Notwithstanding the promotion, I left the job of DNC's professional secretary with genuine regret, not least for the fact that I had quickly realised that I wielded much of my chief's authority without sharing the responsibility. Many years later I was to take strong exception to senior scientists in the Ministry of Defence doing just this. but then, they impeded progress whereas I jollied the department along.

When Jim Callaghan left his ministerial post in the Admiralty we exchanged letters. I had expressed the hope that he might return quite soon as First Lord and was a little surprised when he replied that he hoped not, 'because the Admiralty was no longer in the main stream of political advancement'.   More than 40 years later, in his autobiography 'Grand Inquisitor', Robin Day commented about the ex-Home Secretary, ex-Foreign Secretary, ex-Chancellor of the Exchequer and ex-Prime Minister Callaghan 'James Callaghan was not an intellectual. He did not have a first class brain, as did Macmillan or Wilson or Healey or Jenkins or Gaitskell. But he had a first class instinct of what public opinion wanted or did not want, on law and order, on education, on taxation and even (though belatedly) on trade union bloody mindedness'.

Recalling the near to anarchy state to which the nation fell in the late 1970's due to the Callaghan's governments inability or unwillingness to curb the trade unions – its paymasters - some would feel that Robin Day was more than generous. I suppose that one could equally comment that it is the responsibility of leaders to lead, or to quote Bonar Law from much earlier times "I must follow them, I am their Leader".

Chapter Six

Now for some real work… There were five sections in the Aircraft Carrier Design Group, dealing respectively with the Ark Royal Class design, the Hermes Class design, the modernisation of the Victorious Class, the construction of HMAS *Melbourne* for Australia, and Arresting gear. I was responsible for the design and construction of the four ships of the Hermes Class and in accordance with established practice, my section also looked after the Colossus Class, 1942 Light Fleet aircraft carriers already in service and thus had an immediate awareness of what was going on in the carrier world at sea.

The Hermes Class was known as the 1944 Light Fleet carrier. My predecessor had selected the hull shape and materials and the first three empty hulls had been launched before work was stopped at the end of the War. Steelwork on the fourth ship had scarcely begun. In typically British fashion, this last ship was the name ship of the class, HMS *Hermes*. The class would have two propellers and be somewhat smaller than the Ark Royal Class but would operate the same aircraft.

The hull shape was a good compromise between the requirement for high speed and the requirement for economy and the hull structure was designed for ruggedness and long life. My task was to update and complete the design and in particular the aviation and electronic arrangements, to match the rapid advances taking place in these sciences, and to get the ships built.

The aviation problems were quite complex. The sort of aircraft to be carried would have to be catapulted off the deck to reach flying speed. Similarly they would have to be arrested, that is, caught and pulled back on landing, otherwise they would run into aircraft waiting to be catapulted off or, failing that, run straight over the ships bow and into the sea. The new catapult, the last RN hydraulic catapult, the Mark 5, was being developed and also the new Mark 8 arresting gear. The maximum acceleration allowed on catapulting was just under 3.5g and the maximum retardation by the arresting gear just over 3g. If our gear exceeded these amounts we could pull the nose or the tail off the aircraft.

Clearly, the deck length required for landing must not overrun the length for catapulting and we also had to arrange a safety barrier between to prevent any aircraft whose hook didn't catch an arresting wire or whose hook broke, from running into aircraft parked forward or on the catapults awaiting take-off. This barrier would normally be down and could be quickly raised in an emergency. Its supports had to be massive to take the load of an aircraft being brought to a stop in the barrier. I had seen an aircraft land off-centre and hit the barrier support which broke and swung up to kill the ships Instructor officer who just happened to be taking a photo of the landing from the small island wing 'goofers platform' and never knew what hit him.

The problem with all these equipments was the different types of aircraft to be carried, catapulted, arrested or caught in the barrier. They are worth rehearsing; there were those with one propeller, two wheels and a tail wheel, like a Seafire. Similarly with two propellers, like a Brigand. Next came aircraft with tricycle undercarriages and two contra-rotating propellers like the Gannet or with two jet engines like the Sea Vampire. Other aircraft types featured other combinations.

This really was serious stuff; the forces and powers to launch or arrest or catch a 15 tonne aircraft at over 100 knots are in the thousands of horsepower and failure usually resulted in someone's death. It is difficult to convey the intensity of the coordinated team effort involved in flight deck operations. In my experience as I had seen it in the war, this was the epitome of naval drill and it was done so well. My job in the Hermes Class was to arrange things so that the next generations of naval aircraft and their weapons, could be operated as smoothly and safely.

There were about twenty men in my staff of whom four or five looked after the Colossus Class including those sold to, or on loan to, Commonwealth or foreign navies. For the new design our task was to produce guidance drawings, which would go to the shipbuilders for them to produce working drawings, which would come to us for approval and then be used in the yards to build the ships. The three shipbuilders who had orders for the ships shared the task of producing the detailed plans. The plan approval procedure was by no means a formality; most of them went back with many amendments in red. There was no doubt that the people in the yards did not check their subordinate's work thoroughly before sending it in. I soon became only too aware that the buck stopped at my desk.

I was fortunate that my colleagues on the engineering and electrical sides were old friends. The electrical engineer Charles Helps and I had been at school together from the age of 11 years, we won naval cadetships at the same time and were together at Greenwich .The marine engineer Bob Himms and I had been at sea together in the war. Liaison with the Naval Equipment Department was principally with Commander Richardson, a naval pilot who was in his last appointment prior to retirement. He had qualified many years before the war and had flown ancient biplanes from such ships as the *Furious*, *Argus* and *Glorious* before flying from the carriers that were commissioned during the war. When he had first flown the aircraft were made of wood and canvass and were not very heavy. The arresting gear consisted of young seamen who ran alongside the plane as it landed and grasped the wing tips to bring the aircraft down on to the deck (to overcome the ground effect), to bring it to a standstill, to move it out of the landing area and, perhaps most importantly of all, to prevent the aircraft being blown back along the deck or over the side as the aircraft carrier steamed head-on into the wind at full speed.

Organisationally I had two assistant constructors and two senior draughtsmen who were towers of strength. The senior draughtsman on the Colossus side was within a year or two of retirement. He still affected Whitehall standards of dress with striped trousers, a waistcoat and black jacket, a trifle worn now and with miscellaneous stains. He was a student of Shakespeare and had a quotation from the Bard for most occasions. He enjoyed a liquid lunch and was usually a trifle late in returning. Our design room was as far as it was possible to be from the entrance that everyone used and he would weave his way along the long central corridor after leaving his topcoat in the first gents toilet that he came to. He had a theory that if a senior officer saw him in an un-fortunate position and he made some gesture of submission like popping into the nearest toilet, then honour was satisfied. He was like a character from Dickens and I rather enjoyed him.

A senior officer just returned from service with the British Services Staff in Washington DC was given a temporary office overlooking the entrance. After a few weeks he presented the top man in Bath, Victor Shepherd, with a list of persistent latecomers. He was thanked and moved to a new office where he wouldn't be distracted by looking out of the window. Needless to say, my Dickensian senior draughtsmen was among those noted. We gave Shepherd full marks but years later, when Shepherd was the Director of Naval Construction and located in Whitehall, he picked this officer to be his Principal Deputy in Bath. There was a view that he was chosen because he could always be relied upon to say "Yes Sir" to Shepherd and "no" to everyone else.

The Colossus Class hull had been designed in Naval Construction Department in 1942 and passed to Vickers for development of the detailed structural arrangements for rapid building. Some genius there had decided that a flat deck would be easier to build than the traditional ships deck that is cambered with the middle a few inches higher than the edges. The net effect was that when built in the ship the flat flight deck and the flat hangar deck sagged down in the middle. I was in the Dutch ship Karel Doorman in Rotterdam in 1951 in a rainstorm and the centre of the flight deck was a lake several hundred feet long and several inches deep. Moral; you can't build a flat deck, it will always sag, so give it curvature as our forefathers did, they weren't stupid. This fault had been corrected in the later ships of the class in which the flight deck was given camber.

Fire is an ever-present danger wherever there is aviation fuel. The US Navy had paid a terrible price at the beginning of the war due to its unsatisfactory method of carrying aviation gasoline and we knew that we could never relax. We took elaborate precautions with the aircraft fuel storage and supply systems. We wanted a reliable petrol vapour detector and spent some tens of thousands of pounds developing a device that worked on infrared. We took it to sea in a Colossus class aircraft carrier and spilled some microscopic quantities of aviation fuel just above the pump space. The pointer of our detector stubbornly refused to budge from the zero mark but sailors miles away complained about the ' bloody smell of petrol.' If only we could have mechanised a human nose that did not become saturated and tolerant to a persistent odour.

One of the biggest problems in designing a warship is providing acceptable accommodation for the crew. Almost invariably this is made worse by the manning departments adding extra men as their requirements become better defined while other departments discover that their two cabinets of electronics are now six and, by the way, they now require cooling by water.

In the original ideas for the Hermes design my predecessor had proposed to fill the compartments at waterline level on both sides of the ship with 50-gallon oil drums coated with bitumastic as a means of preserving buoyancy and stability in the event of flooding. In my view these would have lasted at the most five years and thereafter been a nightmare. I calculated that by subdividing these large compartments and allowing access only from a hatch in the deck above, I could utilise all of this space for storerooms, bathrooms and auxiliary machinery and much improve the design while still preserving the damaged stability of the ship in the way the drums had been intended to do.

I had returned from the war much concerned at the conditions under which the crews existed and determined that we had to do something about it. I had nagged Lillicrap on the subject and, frankly, had been surprised that there had been such little comment in official and press circles about the large number of ex-navy personnel who were suffering from chest complaints, in particular, tuberculosis. Conditions in HM Ships in the North Atlantic positively encouraged the spread of such illnesses with large numbers of men in cramped quarters, dampness with inadequate drying facilities and above all, sleeping like a chrysalis in a hammock with spine bent, chest compressed and breath condensing on one's bedding. Doubtless the incidence was reduced in the final years of the war as ships went to the less hostile climate in the Far East, but it was plain to me that getting rid of hammocks would bring a substantial improvement in the health of the fleet. Furthermore, what had sufficed for people recruited in the years of pre-war depression and under the pressure of war would not do for the sort of recruit we would require to operate and maintain the high technology equipment of the future. In an enlightened society the services would have to compete with industry and the lure of home comforts for their recruits.

Each warship has a 'Ships Book' in which are placed important documents pertaining to the ship, such as her Stability Statement and trial results. Perhaps because of complaints long ago, an Admiralty Form to do with crew numbers and hammock billets is filled-in for each ship and placed in the book. It is often less than honest ~ I recall that for the Colossus Class Light Fleet carrier, *HMS Theseus* the number of slinging billets (places where a rating could hang his hammock to sleep) was recorded as over 1,200 but more than 300 of these were in the open cable deck forward and the quarter deck aft and not useable at sea. The old hands will point out that at sea one third of the crew is on watch but unfortunately half of the rest cannot be slung when the ship is operating aircraft. This is by way of an example.

The officer accommodation position in an aircraft carrier is always difficult because of the large numbers and kit to be stowed. In the Hermes design the number of officers was over 70. Then one day their Lordships (rightly) abandoned the 'rating pilots' category and the number of officers requiring accommodation rose to 130.

The rating pilots schemes (sergeant pilots in the RAF) were an anachronism. When aircraft were introduced into the forces they were seen as reconnaissance vehicles. Earlier when cars had been introduced the driver was seen as analogous to the coachman and the officer (and gentleman) sat in the back. So when aircraft came in, the officer sat in the back and the pilot drove the thing. The navy had an observer branch and it was not unusual early in the war to see a CPO pilot with a Commander sitting in the back, but I don't recall seeing it much after 1941.

I now had two problems. Examination showed that with the established areas per man/rank structure for officers I would have Lieutenant Commanders sharing six or eight to a cabin, a quite unacceptable situation in my view although not unknown in USN carriers. The other problem was how to provide a personal bunk for each rating and then persuade the entire naval manpower drafting and logistics organisations that men drafted to Hermes Class carriers did not need hammocks, but would require a mattress.

I was fortunate to have imaginative staff and we soon evolved a scheme for portable bunks, which could be cleared away to provide a recreation area as well. We were aware that in service most of the bunks would remain up all the time and we configured the messes accordingly. Harry Neal, a young Leading Draughtsman did much of this work; He was typical of the good people we had in those days, he had been an officer in the Admiralty Home Guard and a family man as well as performing his duties in office throughout the war. I prepared the required submissions for the DNC's signature en-route through the victualling and naval personnel departments and to the Board of Admiralty for approval and was mindful that I was about to alter centuries of naval tradition.

Nothing happened and after about three weeks I called on Sir Charles in Whitehall to ask after my proposal. He had it in his drawer and he took it out and said, "You do guarantee that this will work, Daniel?" and after a few exchanges he signed the paper and I took care to carry it away with me. Contrary to what one might have expected the naval departments and the victuallers (who would have to provide mattresses and so on) were fully supportive of the change and we had, together, taken the first step towards making the hammock obsolete in the Royal Navy. No longer would Jolly Jack with his kitbag and hammock, grace the nations station platforms and jam the railway trains' corridors.

It did not occur to me until much later that I had also changed the Royal Navy's first line of defence against small leaks due to enemy action. Standard doctrine in the event of splinter damage was to put a hammock or hammocks over the hole and shore them into place. The hammocks would adapt to the jagged edges of the hole in the hull plating and much reduce the ingress of water. I supposed that they would now use the mattresses.

Looking back, there was no press release or publicity about this change to centuries of naval tradition, no spin-doctors, no TV pundits, in fact no-nothing. I make this comment because I see that the MoD has just commissioned a study of sailors accommodation by some commercial agency and this was splashed all over the front of the local press.

The solution to the officers cabin problem came to me while lying in the bunk of the ancient ferry steamer crossing to Larne, for Belfast, where two of the Class were being built. It was quite simple really; if the bunk were raised up, it would be possible to put a chest of drawers and a desk with drawers under it. Put an 18inch wardrobe at the end of the bunk and a washbasin beside its head and the whole cabin need not exceed 40 sq ft in area. Having that to oneself would be much better than a one third share of a 200 sq ft cabin.

There are other considerations that affect accommodation. In a ship the forward end experiences more motion and sea noise than aft of amidships; this is not too important in a 20,000 tonne carrier but here the spaces beneath the flight deck forward are very noisy during flying operations due to the catapults. Since most of the flight deck crews are busy during flying times it was not unreasonable to allocate these spaces to them.

The other bee-in-the-bonnet that I had brought back from the war was that the efficiency of personnel was paramount and in ships closed up for action the environment must be controlled to keep them alert and fit. As a consequence of the threat from atomic weapons no-one disputed that the normal design condition had to be with all openings closed but we were only now beginning to realise how much heat our 'new' electronic equipments (which still had thermionic valves or tubes) generated and how we would be driven to cool them with chilled water and air. In short, our ships had to be fully air-conditioned.

A small battle that I fought and lost was that the tins of provisions supplied to HM Ships should be square rather than round to make the most economical use of storeroom space. In those days I was simple enough to think that the Armed Forces orders were big enough to merit such a change in manufacturing methods and that the civilian market would also welcome such economy. I cited the corned beef tin as proof that it could be done. I learned that far from being the brand leader of the square tin brigade, the entire corned-beef-tin-manufacturing industry had for some years been trying to get people to buy their corned beef in round tins, rather than those truncated pyramids with a key.

The Dutch navy was close to the RN in those days with Dutch aircrew flying Sea Fury airplanes and cross training with their British counterparts. Since they had a Colossus Class ship I was responsible for ensuring that all modifications applicable to the class were sent to them through their naval attaché in London. This had its funny moments such as the time he sent me back all of my records on deck landing control positions that my section clerk had sent to him in error. There was worse to come. She had a habit of asking questions when I was talking on the phone or talking to someone and I would fend her off by replying something nonsensical. One day she apparently had asked me where to send something and I had said "Hong Kong". Many weeks later whatever it was reappeared with a plaintive letter from Commodore Superintendent Hong Kong wondering why he had been sent information concerning Hermes Class.

The Dutch naval constructor with whom I dealt was very apologetic that he had worked in the shipyards during the German occupation. He went on and on about it. I said that faced with deportation and starvation for my family I would have done the same. He insisted that I meet his wife. His house was full of books in simple rough wood shelves. Sitting in the corner was a grim faced old man in black who said not a word. I learned later from the naval attaché that this was his father-in-law who had been a leading Dutch Nazi and who had been imprisoned after the war. It made me wonder about the 'being forced to work for the Germans story'; perhaps they didn't have to twist his arm too much.

The other thing about visiting The Hague was that the British Naval Attaché's office was in a house some distance from the Embassy. I was given the address and when I was quite near I asked a seemingly elderly lady for such and such street. She fled from me saying "Niet, Niet". Trust me to pick on a Russian Embassy wife. There was a Dutchman across the road who was vastly amused and who told me that the place I wanted was just round the corner.

Returning through Harwich on a cold wet miserable morning with about twice my duty free allowance of tobacco in my raincoat pocket, I walked boldly into the customs shed and found myself confronted by four customs officers., including one with two and a half stripes. They were not interested in me, they had opened the cases of a tall man with a gangsters hat on and cigarette lighters and other innocent contraband had poured out all over the counter. I stole a look at the sharp-featured smuggler; if one had lined up all the passengers who had crossed that night and played 'pick-the-smuggler', one would have picked him.

The other simple thing I learnt that morning was, if you have successfully smuggled the crown jewels past the customs, don't unpack them while the train is still at Harwich station because that chap who looks like a porter wheeling a trolley along the platform idly glancing into the train windows, is actually a customs officer. In these days when the emphasis in smuggling is with drugs that ruin people's lives and make other peoples fortunes, it seems ludicrous for someone to have been smuggling cigarette lighters. Of course an extra 100 grams of pipe tobacco was different.

The first three ships of the Hermes class would feature the new radars types 982 and 983 and the Operations room was in the Island at flight deck level. My chaps struggled with plans of the room and just could not get in everything that the radar experts wanted. The lay- out was a joint responsibility with the radar whiz kids at ASWE Portsdown. so we sent it to them.; imagine our surprise when it came back with everything neatly laid out. It took us a little while to realise that the draughtsman at Portsdown had accomplished the impossible by solemnly drawing the compartment outline to the correct scale and then drawing everything inside it at nine tenths of its proper size!.

The next event in the Op's Room saga was when the Director of Navigation and Direction asked for a change of some sort. We did it but I could not resist being clever (they were all my friends) and remarking on the official docket that DNC was surprised that at this late stage the DND should wish to make changes. About a year later as the result of flying trials at Farnborough we had to make changes to the supporting arms of the aircraft safety barrier and could only do this by taking some extra inches from the Operations room. I sent off the docket and back it came from the ever helpful DND who nevertheless remarked that "DND is surprised that at this late stage the DNC should wish to make changes." It was a timely reminder; always remember that the other guy has problems, too.

One of the interesting events was the overload test of the prototype BH 5 catapult that was mounted on shore at the Royal Aircraft Establishment. The test required an aircraft to be loaded to something over 35,000 lbs and a twin engined Brigand or some such was fitted with housings for the launching bridle. When all was ready a cheerful young RAF pilot climbed in, started the engines, went through his checks and whoosh, the catapult fired and he was airborne. He stooged around a bit and then landed and taxied back to our side of the airfield. We had a close look at the aircraft and his smile faded a bit when we found small wrinkles in the aircraft's skin where the wings join the fuselage

Three ships of the class were being built, two at Harland and Wolff, Belfast and one at Swan Hunters, Wallsend. I had not up to this time been aware of the special circumstances obtaining in Northern Ireland and the cosseting of its industry but it was apparent even to me that in addition to that for HMS Eagle, these contracts had been continued for political reasons. Swans were producing a superior product at less than 90% of the Irish company's cost. Luncheon in the director's dining room at Harland's was a sombre affair presided over by Sir Frederick Rebbeck. During this time several promising directors and senior managers left. It was explained to me that Rebbeck saw them as a threat; not to himself but to the possibility of his son succeeding him. One of the things that helped to bring British shipbuilding down was poor management and in at least three companies we in the Admiralty watched with concern as promising managers were moved sideways or left in disgust as the chairman manipulated events to ensure that his son succeeded him.

The most dramatic and tragic event during my stewardship of the Hermes Class occurred when the Swan's ship, *Albion* was being towed to Rosyth Naval Dockyard for docking; there being no dock on the River Tyne capable of taking her. As she was being towed north in very bad weather conditions a collier on its way south to London collided with her and sank with the loss of over 20 men. It seems that the lightly loaded carrier with its large windage area had been towing at an oblique angle to the towrope and the collier had not seen her lights. I was at Rosyth by the time Albion arrived and for some time we indulged in my favourite pastime of pumping the ocean round and round while we endeavoured to establish the extent of her damage beyond the gaping hole in her side. We put her in the dock and divers went along her bottom to check that it was safe to put her down on the blocks. One of the sad lessons that I had learnt in the war was never believe a divers report without sending down one or two others to check it, for many people lose their orientation when under water and report port for starboard and forward for aft and so on. After listening to what they had to say I suggested to the dockyard officers to put her down. The flooding was quite extensive but the ship had remained upright and had never been in danger.

The chief constructor insisted that I should sleep at his residence in the Yard. The official residences in the southern yards were built in the 18th century and were spacious examples of their time. Those at Rosyth were made of corrugated iron in some less caring age but were comfortable nonetheless. His charming wife had gone back to her mother, again. We had some eggs and bacon and gin and for afters we had more gin. I was a sissy because I had water in mine and soon the first bottle was empty. When the conversation got around to the exquisite nature of pain, a topic suggested by him allowing his pet cat to scratch the back of his hand and draw blood I excused myself and went to bed. I got up at about 6.00 am, got myself some toast, gently opened the chief's door and found him still asleep and made my way down to the dock. When I got there the dockyard foreman said that the chief was about early, he had just phoned for a progress report. He had obviously phoned from his bed; I had learned another valuable management lesson.

The man who had reported the latecomers had been made my chief and after two years or so the man who had the *Ark Royal* design, Charles Penwill, relieved him. Charles told me that as part of the turnover, he had been told "You must watch young Daniel, he tends to make decisions and do things and tell you about it afterwards". Charles Penwill said to me "Be a good chap and continue doing just that ".

Lillicrap had retired and V.G. Shepherd had taken his place in Whitehall. H.S. Pengelley was now the senior man in the office in Bath and he wanted a personal staff office to 'filter' all the general papers and he wanted a man called Daniel for it. I was a little angry at leaving a splendid design job for what appeared to be a superior office boy's job, but I was given no choice.

There were no terms of reference for this new section other than to support the Principal Deputy Director Pengelly and to deal with design matters that did not fall within the scope of one of the existing design groups. There were only about six staff members including the assistant constructor Gus Gardner.

This was a potential non-job if there ever was one but there were things about the way the department operated that our sense of order suggested were in urgent need of improvement and here was the chance to do something about it.

H.S. Pengelly had a considerable reputation in the profession. He was the co-author of a standard textbook and an ex-professor of naval architecture in the RN College Greenwich. He had been Captain Bogie's predecessor on the Eastern Fleet staff and had until recently been seen by some as the potential successor to Lillicrap as the DNC and Head of the RCNC. This would have been a disaster, for it was quickly evident that he was a spent force who found it difficult to recognise new concepts and to make decisions. Like Shepherd the man who had beaten him to the top post, Pengelley had no children and spent most of his time alone in Bath while his wife continued her vocation in London as a senior executive with Dents, the glove people. On the few occasions that he saw my infant sons I sensed that he too would have liked to have had children. To his juniors he presented a forbidding manner. I like Marie Hancock's story. She and Norman had their first baby. One day just as she arrived home pushing her big perambulator, an unsmiling Pengelley came along the road and, to her horror, moved to assist her in manoeuvring the pram up the few steps to her front door, at the same time asking about the new baby. How relieved she was that he turned away without turning back the coverlet to reveal the pram's contents, not the baby, but a small barrel of cider!

He had difficulty in making up his mind and in consequence his 'pending' tray would get bigger and bigger until, with the connivance of his secretary when he was absent, I would deal with it. Much of it simply required 'Noted' and my signature 'for PDDNC' and for the rest of it I would have the answer typed-on ready for his signature. Whether he recognised the neatly typed minutes that his secretary placed before him on his return as the contents of his pending tray I never discovered but he signed them and that was that.

When I had to take something to him for decision he would reminisce, usually about battleship design and the Far East and raise all sorts of issues. Often I would emerge from his room after half an hour or so knowing that he had said "yes" or "no" but with only the vaguest idea which.

The first thing that we looked at was how the calculation work was done. Traditionally all calculations were recorded in Work Books and the more important extracted and put in a Book of Calculations for So and So Class and referenced back to the Work Book, such as 'see Daniel, WB 6'. The understanding was that the detailed calculations would be performed in the manner taught at Greenwich or in the latest textbooks but in many cases the calculation depended critically on the underlying data used and the assumptions made and in our experience different people made different assumptions and got slightly different answers; damaged stability and strength were good examples. Gardner suggested that we analyse the position across past and present designs, select the most reliable data and the best practice and embody this in a series of Design and Calculation Memoranda., the use of which would be mandatory.

The next thing was the absence of departmental wide instructions covering procedures, outputs and relationships. These were more general. We prepared drafts, consulted the most knowledgeable people and issued them as Standard Memoranda.

The third and biggest self-generated task was to produce a General Hull Specification. This was not an original idea for there were already General Electrical Specifications and General Engineering Specifications in our sister Departments and the Americans had a General Specification that covered everything. So why not a GHS. I had noticed in the war how many different types and sizes of hatch or watertight doors and other fittings there were in HM Ships and the nuisance that these variations were to those who were trying to repair ships quickly. Also, how the fitting-out of quite ordinary compartments differed in different types and classes of ships. Surely there was no reason why, say, a soap and tobacco store in a battleship should be fitted out differently from a soap and tobacco store in a cruiser, other than size. And of course this went for bathrooms, messes, storerooms in general, cabins and so on throughout the ships and their contents. A further need for standardisation was the recently agreed maximum size of electronics cabinets to be carried in HM Ships. Try getting those through some of the hatches fitted in earlier ships.

I proposed that we should review existing practice and make the best selections of types and sizes of all fittings and furniture used in HM Ships and also standardise the fittings and decor of compartments according to function and where necessary, type of warship. These would be embodied in a General Hull Specification, which would be issued to all design activities, HM Dockyards and the shipbuilders and would be mandatory. In future all would be singing to the same song sheet.

It would work like this. The DNC design Group would prepare the outline ship design and indicate the use and loading of all compartments .The shipbuilder would know from the General Hull Specification what should be fitted in each compartment and the preferred arrangement. Typically, that in the petty officers bathroom shown for 24 men, he must provide and fit items to the scale and arrangement shown in the GHS and this would include lighting, deck coverings, decor and services. And so on throughout the ship. The shipbuilder's proposed layouts would then be forwarded to Bath for approval and fitting-out would proceed in due course. Although I did not speak about it too loudly, my long-term aim was that the resident overseeing staff would approve most of these layouts locally.

Pengelly flatly rejected the idea of a General Hull Specification. Traditionally these things had been left to the individual naval constructor and that's how he thought it should remain. He was surprised to learn that there were more than thirty different patterns of watertight hatch in service and a similar number of doors and that, as specials, these items cost the earth.

Although he had refused to sanction the project I quietly put in hand the preparation of the general specification. The more we got into the thing, the more we realised its necessity. Some curious things emerged when we turned over some technical stones. I was and still am impressed at the efficient way my chaps went about the collection and analysis of hundreds of drawings and specifications and discussed the results with the experts. Gradually we completed the tens of chapters that I had sketched out. When the time came for me to move to my next post, the first edition of the Navy's General Hull Specification had been typed, and was being checked ready for printing.

The sort of design thing that came our way was the recommendation from the Naval Construction Research Establishment at Dunfermline that the sequence of filling the underwater side protection systems in major warships be changed. The anti-torpedo or mine protection systems consisted of a space between the outer hull and the important compartments within. This space was as big as possible, say 12 ft, and subdivided by longitudinal bulkheads to give three narrower spaces each about 4 ft wide extending from the ships bottom to above the waterline. Traditionally the centre space was filled with fuel oil, which was replaced by water as the fuel was used. The theory, supported by full-scale trials, was that this sequence was best able to absorb the energy of a torpedo or mine exploding against the hull. It was known as the air/water/air arrangement.

NCRE now proposed that the sequence be air/air/water. We pointed out that the structural integrity of the present system depended on the struts between the two middle bulkheads being in tension and that putting fluid on one side only might present problems. The battleship people said 'Let us do a trial filling but how will we know when to stop if there is a problem?' We did some sums based on the development of a plastic hinge at the bottom of the bulkhead frames (this was futuristic stuff in those days) and the trial took place in Portsmouth Dockyard. When we described what we were doing to a certain senior officer he went to his cupboard and took out the notes he had made at college a score or more years earlier and solemnly turned over page after page while Gus and I stood there wondering what on earth he was up to. At the end of which he said, "There's no mention of plastic hinges there" and closed the conversation. The subject was not worthy of discussion if it wasn't in Professor Haigh's notes.

When I had returned to Bath I had been instructed to lecture at the RN Leadership School at HMS Royal Arthur near to Bath. This required one or two morning's absence in each term and I found it a rewarding experience. I had continued to do this in my new post. I was now told that I was to be the department's liaison officer with a department of the Ministry of Defence called the Department of Administrative Planning. This was before the single services were combined into a single massive MoD and the Ministry that I liased with was a very small affair overlooking St James's Park. I felt that it had been created to provide a job where a noble minister could do little harm. The DAP staff consisted mainly of cheerful Lieutenant Commanders and their army and air force equivalents. My role was to think up real sounding yet spurious pieces of military information that would do no harm if they fell into the hands of suspected Soviet bloc agents. The day I joined the boys were taking it in turns to visit the Windmill Theatre. It seemed that the Polish military attaché had intimated to one of the girls that if she could obtain secrets by pillow talk with senior British officers, she would be richly rewarded. The Windmill girl had sped straight round to the Special Branch. The talk now was how could this patriotic young lady best serve the nation and many of the ideas had nothing to do with security but much to do with pillow-talk.

It was an interesting little sideshow and it did yield results. The same sort of job was done subsequently by the Foreign Office Information Research Department, set up to counter Soviet propaganda and disseminate information (and disinformation). This department was closed in 1977 by a Labour government that was moving rapidly to the left.

Sometime during this period the discussions on the Corps future position and salary structure vis-à-vis the civil service hierarchy came to a head. I was the secretary of the staff association and it was decided, much against the advice of senior officers who considered the whole thing to be infra-dig, to go to arbitration. The day came and we presented our case. Alistair Jaffray and Philip Moore represented officialdom, the opposition from the Admiralty and Treasury. At the end of the hearing we three adjourned to a local hostelry for a beer. I thought that we hadn't done badly and my friends from the other side joked that that was the end of their promising careers in the civil service. When the verdict was announced we had been awarded a very great increase in salaries and position. As for Alistair, he became a high official in the MoD and Philip became the private secretary to the Queen.

Shortly afterwards I was told that I was to move to the cruiser design section where the early problems were the introduction of new weapon systems into the fleet. Nevertheless, I reflected that my office boy's job had not been so bad after all.

The work of the Cruiser group was to look after the gunnery trials cruiser HMS *Cumberland* and the guided missile trials ship HMS *Girdleness* and to embody the results of the development work that these ships would perform in a new cruiser design of at present unknown size and shape.

HMS *Cumberland* was the trials ship for the Mark 26 6 inch turret, the 3 inch/70 anti aircraft gun mounting, various new radars and a multi-fin ship stabilisation system. HMS *Girdleness* was the trials ship for the Seaslug missile and the associated Types 901 and 992 radars.

The conversion work on Cumberland was largely complete and that on *Girdleness* just beginning. The equipment to be fitted for trial and the programme was supervised by a committee for each ship and the arrangement was that I was the secretary of each committee with gunnery officer chairmen from the Naval Ordnance Department – effectively, the users

Naval Ordnance Department was in transition. Traditionally the navy had been run by gunnery officers; their expertise was in handling men in basic marching and seamanship drills, leading to the team work in the handling of munitions, loading, directing and firing guns, from small arms to mighty 16 inch turrets. In many of these tasks an ability to shout loudly was not a disadvantage. In the mid-1950's many senior officers were still cast in that mould and only slowly coming to terms with the consequences for organisation and training of the technological revolution that was taking place. More and more they depend on officers of the weapons electrical specialisation and on civilian scientists and engineers. Furthermore, in two world wars the navy had found itself to be out gunned and out ranged by the enemy and had won through largely due to the bravery of its officers and men in closing the range to seize victory from potential defeat. In a future conflict the enemy would be far distant and bravery, of itself, would be of little avail.

The Department still had its characters; there was the commander whose choice language was such that only two of the forty or so typists would consent to enter his room. He went on to become Chief of the Defence Staff and was accepted as out swearing any labour minister of the Crown (and President Nixon). There was also the retired commander who acted as the department's blast pressure gauge. He would attend trials and stand on the forecastle deck or open bridge during live firings. One would see him flinch as the guns went off and their sharp blast wave passed by. I could never discover who, in DNO, ordered this man to do what he did or what were the criteria against which this human pressure gauge indicated acceptability or failure; if his nose bled?; if he died? or was simply blown into the sea?. He was known affectionately as "Deaffy" and he was, stone deaf. We had curves of the blast pressure versus distance for all the guns and we also knew to what pressure personnel could be exposed without physical damage and so I didn't know what useful function he performed; but he arrived up regularly at trials and did his stuff. There was clearly something in the training of the navy's gunnery officers that explained this sort of thing. At about this time I attended the navy's Gunnery Conference in HMS Excellent at Whale Island, Portsmouth. At breakfast, the wardroom Tv set, which was switched off, was struck by lightning, there was a loud bang, flames shot out followed by black smoke. I was facing the thing. No one took any notice. I would have run around and done something – I know not what – but my fellow officers and the stewards just carried on as if that thing in the corner always went bang and smoked gently at breakfast time.

As part of the turnover process I attended a trials committee meeting with my predecessor and nearly ended up in jail. It was like this. James had a Morris 8 car that today would not have passed any test. He loved his car, notwithstanding that when he turned to the left the passenger leant against him because the passenger seat securing bolts were missing. Mechanically it was 100%. We set off one morning for Devonport. It was long before there was a motorway. At Exeter we decided to go over Dartmoor and having gone a few miles were flagged down by two girls with large suitcases standing in a narrow section of the road. They were from New Zealand, working as nurses and now hitch hiking around Britain. They were put in the back of this small car with their suitcases on their knees. After some time the grim shape of Dartmoor prison loomed up. They would like to tell the folks back home that they had been to the infamous Dartmoor so we turned right and took them to the prison gates. They would like a photo so we stood them beneath a large sign saying 'Photography Forbidden' and took their picture whereupon a giant of a man in uniform with a flat hat came out and raged at us." Can't you see that photography is forbidden; come inside I should put you all under arrest for that" and so on. All that I could see was the headlines in the next day's papers. After a while he contented himself with ripping the film out of the girls camera and sending us on our way to buy pictures in the shop at Princetown. We dropped the girls at a round-about outside Plymouth, they were determined to make Penzance by tea-time and James Paffett and I couldn't decide whether standing on a round-about would be considered 'doing Plymouth' in the hitchhikers report of their travels.

An obvious difficulty in aiming a gun or a missile and the controlling radars at a target is the fact that for most of the time the ship is rolling or pitching. When naval battles were fought at long range using manual rangefinders, the gunner's art was deciding when to fire during the ships roll. A logical first assistance to this had been to stabilise the directors. It was concluded that it would be more cost effective to stabilise the ship, particularly since use could be made of the ships motion through the water to provide the forces to oppose the roll. HMS *Cumberland* was testing such a system. It had the considerable advantage that it could also be used in reverse, as it were, to roll the ship on a calm sea in order to do controlled rough-weather tests on some of the gunnery systems. It was not unusual to hear the pipe "The ship will be rolling in 10 minutes time". This gave the crew time to secure anything that might be loose and damaged during rolling, Thus it would be that this large warship would be seen in the English Channel, rolling at up to 15 degrees either way while sailing on a perfectly calm sea. What the passengers and crews of passing ships thought, can be imagined.

The systems trialled in Cumberland were very good. The problem child was the 3inch/70 mounting where the requirement was to fire 120 rounds a minute. The gun worked fine up to something like 80 rpm and the navy should have settled for that and then undertaken a slow improvement process using in-service experience. The Canadian Navy did just that and were generally satisfied after a somewhat shaky start. The RN spent too little money on system development and, wrongly, was seduced away by the thought that the future belonged only to missiles.

HMS *Girdleness* had been an auxiliary ship. When I took over she was in dock in Devonport, stripped down to her bare hull. The conversion was to provide a large magazine for missile stowage with a mechanical transfer system to move the missiles to a space for examination and testing and thence to a twin launcher on the ship's forecastle. Two major new radar systems were to be fitted, together with appropriate missile control rooms and so on. The ships original 2,500 bhp steam reciprocating engine and single boiler were retained and new turbo-alternators provided to give the quality and quantity of electrical supplies required by the new equipments.

The development of the Seaslug missile was the responsibility of the Ministry of Supply who had selected Messers Armstrong Whitworth as the prime contractor, supported by five or six main subcontractors each of whom took responsibility for a major system. The missile guidance system had to interface, of course, with the Type 901 radar.

From the naval constructors point of view the missile could not have been worse; its shape made it wildly uneconomic to stow and it was liquid fuelled. No one in their right mind would carry liquid fuelled missiles in a ship and when forced to do so, only with elaborate precautions. The Soviets did (in submarines as well) and had disaster after disaster. In *Girdleness* the magazine was given the most comprehensive and powerful spraying system I have ever seen. When initiated the spray was so intense that I doubt if a person 20 ft away from the exit, could have made it to that exit. The bottom of the magazine was shaped to carry the water quickly away and doubling plates provided because tests showed that the red fuming nitric acid missile fuel would burn through a half-inch steel plate in 10 minutes. Happily there was a good fairy called I.M.I. at Kidderminster who developed a solid fuel propulsion motor for the missile and saved the day.

There was no good fairy to change the shape of the missile. Most missiles require a booster to give the initial thrust to take them up to the speed at which the sustainer motor can take over. The elegant solution is to have a tandem booster at the rear of the missile from whence it simply falls behind when the main motor takes over. The very much second best is to have the booster wrapped round the missile, usually in the form of four small rockets, which peel off together (one hopes) when up to speed. Clearly stowing cylindrical missiles, cylindrical boosters and separate fins and bringing them smoothly together en-route to the launcher would allow the maximum number of missiles to be carried. However if one is told by the British missile designers that aerodynamically it is absolutely impossible to have fins that clip into position and that they must be riveted in place in the factory, giving a package to be stowed of about 20ft x 4ft x 4ft per missile, then the thought of having a second such lump for the tandem booster was just too much and wrap round boosters were adopted. I repeat, instead of handling smooth cylindrical units, we had to handle a large ungainly lump and the whole effect of missile, transport system and launcher was distinctly agricultural.

You can imagine my feelings when visiting the USS *Boston* shortly afterwards and seeing the tandem boosted Terrier missile's fins clipped into place in one deft movement as the missile moved from magazine to launcher. No wonder they could carry four times as many missiles as we could.

The missile development programme involved firings at the Ministry of Supply range at Aberporth. Each time they got ready for a firing one or other of the contractors had some cause for delay and it was not until we were well advanced with the ship that things started to improve due in large part to the appointment of Commander Charles Shepherd (later Rear Admiral) as the project coordinator for Seaslug.

The plan at that time was that Seaslug would be followed by an anti-ship version, code name Blueslug. Had this been done there might have been no need to buy the French Exocet.

Girdleness's officers were hand picked for their expertise and all went on to become captains or admirals. The commanding officer was Captain Maurice Greig who took snuff and had a lady friend called Peggy. Being simple, I thought that Peggy was the captain's wife; she was sweet. The commander had been in HMS *Ark Royal* and the sailors knew his good lady, Anne, as Ark Royal Annie. According to the ship's doctor, a specialist

126

in diving medicine (hence his appointment to a missile ship?) the current Kipling ditty on the mess decks went something like; "The captains fanny and Ark Royal Annie, are sisters under the skin."

The ship went on sea trials and inadvertently the magazine sprays went off. We found that the cause was a one-inch long piece of bare copper wire that a Devonport Dockyard electrician had cut off when wiring a relay and which had dropped into the box. When the ship rolled this had shorted the circuit and started the sprays.

The second disaster was much more serious. The ship had embarked the first six missiles and off went the spraying system. I sped down from Bath but all knew the cause. The boiler watch keeper had misread his gauges and the boiler had run out of steam, causing the turbo-alternator to slow down and hence the frequency of the ship's electricity to fall and off went the sprays and soaked six missiles.

Although the conversion of *Girdleness* was of great importance to the navy, to Devonport Dockyard it was a somewhat small thing, not to be compared with refitting an aircraft carrier or other major fleet unit. The section assigned to deal with the project in the Ship Drawing Office were not exactly world beaters and we soon came to recognise our own guidance drawings with our DNC number erased and a Devonport MCD number substituted, when returned to us for approval. So I took a hands-on approach to the actual work and had an excellent liaison with the dockyard foreman in charge. At the end of the conversion I learned that the leading draughtsman in charge of the *Girdleness* section in the ship drawing office had never been on board the ship in the years she was in the yard. That's dedication.

The day came when we sailed to Lyme Bay to fire the first unguided missile to prove the system. We sailed good and early but someone had been talking in a pub the night before because the Royal Corps of Transport yacht soon appeared and generally got in the way; sail before steam and all that sort of thing.

Hydraulic power is an efficient means of moving power and is used in gun turrets and other ordnance equipment, so it was not unnatural that the Seaslug handling and launching system developed by the Naval Ordnance Department should be powered in this way. This was not very clever. Although it was contained in the launcher cab, there was leakage in the form of a fine atomised spray from a component and we dare not engulf this in the missile efflux flames. It took all day to get the launcher sufficiently free from leaking hydraulic oil before we had the confidence for a missile to be fired.

We went to Guernsey for the weekend with the front of the bridge blackened with smoke and burnt paint. The Governor gave a small reception for the officers at his residence. The Captain wore his boat cloak. The story the next morning was that on leaving the party he made his way back to the barge that was waiting at the harbour steps but slipped at the bottom and fell into the water where in the dim illumination of the quay, his boat cloak spread out on the surface and with his white uniform cap in the middle he resembled a giant maritime bat. One can imagine the surprise of the ship's officer of the watch when the captain came over the side looking like Father Neptune.

The tragedy with the Seaslug missile and handling system was that although we were aware that the UK could do much better, we had to use the type of handling equipment used in *Girdleness* in our new cruiser concepts.

We embarked on studies of future ships with 6 inch Mark: 26 turrets forward and a Seaslug missile launcher aft. Analysis showed that from the ship-arrangement aspect, an arrangement with the missiles in two rows or more on the main deck was superior to a deep magazine. In parallel in the destroyer group, Herbert Chislett was looking into a destroyer with an as yet unspecified 5-inch gun.

Admiral Mountbatten was intensely interested and the cruiser got bigger and bigger until our preferred version was Study 85z at a displacement of 18,500 tons. I must confess that I added the Z to indicate to all that I thought that this was about as far as we should go.

Mountbatten was a markedly different First Sea Lord from those who had gone before. Usually a new First S.L. would visit Bath some months after taking up the post and shake one by the hand. He would be taken to a few design rooms and would at least be able to relate some of the names and faces to on-going work. Nearly three years later he would re-appear, just before retirement and shake one by the hand and that would be all that one would see of him. The classic occasion was when Admiral 'Wee' MacGregor came. Usually the "Wee" is a piece of Scottish under-statement and "Wee" McTavish turns out to be 6 feet 6 inches tall and built like an ox. Not the new First Sea Lord; he was made for midget submarines and the gold braid on his sleeve bid fair to reach the top of his arm. For his visit some genius had the bright idea of lining all the senior staff up in the long central corridor and have the visitor pass along the line shaking hands. He proceeded down the line shaking 250 hands in a somewhat stiff way, looked up into 250 faces and heard 250 names and what they did, none of which registered because there was no hook upon which to hang a recollection.

Not so my lord Mountbatten. At least once a month and usually more often, he would come to the department, perch his rear on the bosses' desk and send for the constructors dealing with the things that interested him. He was interested in missiles and cruisers and was very supportive but in the end budgetary pressure forced the abandonment of the big cruiser concepts and we looked at smaller versions. Eventually these were passed to the destroyer group and in due course became the rather nice looking, new, County Class Guided Missile Destroyer designed by Ken Purvis. Ken Purvis was the RCNC officer who had journeyed to Montevideo in the guise of a scrap merchant early in 1940 and examined the scuttled German pocket battleship *Graf Spee*. Several quite interesting and weighty bits of 'scrap iron' had arrived in Devonport Dockyard in due course.

I can recall being somewhat shaken one Monday morning; the Chancellor of the Exchequer, Peter Thornycroft and his two juniors at the Treasury, Nigel Birch and Enoch Powell, had resigned during the weekend over some question of fiscal policy; what Prime Minister Harold McMillan referred to as ' a little local difficulty' (Much later Enoch Powell was to describe the three as Thatcherites, long before Thatcher came to power.) Mountbatten breezed into the Bath office and said, "Now that I have got rid of Thornycroft, we can have a sensible defence policy". After the meeting I walked back to my room thinking what a cheek and then, well... he is the Oueen's uncle, he was the last Viceroy of India, he was the Supreme Commander in SEAC, so why shouldn't he get rid of a politician or two. One thing that was not in doubt was his devotion to the nation and to the navy.

Mountbatten was an inventive man and early in his naval career had produced a device by which a ship could tell how close it was to the ship in front. When he was in the Naval Staff he saw to it that it was specified for fitting in Daring Class and future destroyers.

When he came back as Fourth Sea Lord, he raised a rumpus by demanding to know who had removed the Mountbatten Station Keeping Device from the Daring Class. As Fourth S.L. he was responsible for victualling and he had strong views about the danger that oil-fired galleys presented in HM Ships. Statistics showed that most fires started in the galley in part because the cooks tried to force them to heat up too quickly (usually in the early morning) and overdid it. Although the small second-rate anti-submarine frigates of the Dundas Class were terribly short of electrical power, Mountbatten forced the introduction of electric galley ranges.

When he came back as First S.L. he raised a rumpus by demanding to know who had cancelled the electric galleys and substituted oil-fired ones in the Dundas Class. Obviously someone who had had to chose between power for weapons and power for the ships galley.

During this period we were diverted somewhat by the visits to Portsmouth by the Soviet cruisers *Sverdlov* and (later) *Ordonikidze*. These large ships had a formidable armament and speed and we were interested in learning as much as we could about them. We had been ordered by the Prime Minister that nothing was to be done that might cause embarrassment and so we contented ourselves with some interesting photographs from the South Jetty signal tower and attempting to measure the thickness of her side armour using Naval Construction Research Establishment's ultra sonic boat-hook. On one of the visits people were taken on a carefully conducted tour; the only thing that I learnt from this was that copies of Pravda, Red Fleet and Izvestia were carefully cut up into 5-inch squares and used as toilet paper. What a good idea. Obviously we knew nothing about Buster Crabbe and had I been asked at the time whether I wanted to know about the ships propellers and underwater fittings I would have expressed only lukewarm interest, a 'so what' sort of reaction to add to my general distrust of divers reports.

After leaving my previous staff job I had expected the General Hull Specification to be issued. I tackled Peter Lover, who had relieved me, to be told that it had been printed and 500 copies were in the storeroom but Pengelly would not allow it to be issued. I went and saw Pengelly and said that we proposed to issue it. He said not a word and the deed was done.

Sometime after this Pengelly retired and to most people's surprise, Chapman, the man who some years earlier had kept a record of the latecomers in Warminster Road, was promoted to Principal DDNC. He was not a person with whom one could relate. An incident that comes to mind concerned the annual spring meetings of the Royal Institution of Naval Architects. At these meetings papers are presented describing recent advances in Naval Architecture and Marine Engineering and other experts comment on them. Copies of the papers are available some weeks before to facilitate this. I had copies and Chapman sent for me and told me to prepare some learned remarks that he might stand up and make as his own views in contributing to the discussion on each of the ten papers. This I did. I then discovered that he was not going to be present on the third day and I was, so I said to him that I would use the remarks that I had prepared. "Oh no you will not" said he "I may wish to send in those remarks as my written contribution to the debate".

The Corps had its share of 'characters'. There were the Holt brothers, Neville and Bill. Both were keen yachtsmen. Neville had been Admiral Fraser's Staff Constructor Captain and was with him at the Battle of the North Cape. Bill was a small ship man and was responsible for motor torpedo boats and motor gunboats and so on. He suffered increasing deafness. Prior to the war some MTB's had been sent to the Mediterranean Fleet; they had made the journey as deck cargo on heavy lift ships of the day. Some time into the war there was the need to send some more. They couldn't be carried, so Brother Bill fitted them all out with large deck tanks full of petrol to give them enough range to get to Gibraltar and sailed there in one of the ships of the small flotilla. I understand that the weather in the Bay was terrible and that Captain Bill was the only one not badly seasick - perhaps because of his hearing problem. After the war he lived high on the Mendips at Green Ore and commuted in an ancient air-cooled Jowett car. Night after night in winter after people had gone home one would hear his self-starter grinding away as he strove to start the thing; he couldn't hear the sad noises it was making. He invested in a hearing aid. It represented the latest technology and was a box about 15cm square and 5cm thick, suspended round his neck with wires to an earpiece. One would be instructed to 'speak down here' while he fiddled with knobs on the front. Terrifying whistles would emerge from time to time and often he would simply switch off and rejoin the meeting later with some penetrating comment. It was not unknown for him to be two agenda items behind the others present. He was a fine man.

Another of the Corps characters was the man who used to dictate coded messages to his girl friend in Bath. He had been responsible for some of our best destroyer designs in the war He was brilliantly clever but odd. After he married her they took up ballroom dancing and I am told reached gold medal class - whatever that is, probably had a number on his back like a footballer. One would encounter him in the corridor and speak and he would do little dance steps around one while he spoke. In the middle of a technical chat he would suddenly say "tango, old boy". He usually had an official paper under his arm and he always carried a bulging briefcase. He was responsible for the measures to defend ships against attack by atomic, biological and chemical weapons and he told me one day that he had collected and condensed the information necessary to keep the Department running in support of the fleet and carried it with him always for use in a makeshift Admiralty in the event of a nuclear attack. Years later, in different jobs he always carried a small suitcase. No one ever saw what was in it, if he wanted something he would walk over to it, unclip the catches, raise the lid an inch or so and slide his hand in, grope around a bit and emerge with a packet of cigarettes or a notebook. His other idiosyncrasy was slipping down in his chair. He would start a discussion sitting normally at his desk and gradually one would realise that he seemed to be shorter. Eventually his chin would be level with his desktop like a sort of Kilroy, all the while having a perfectly normal discussion. Odd, but there was nothing wrong with his work.

Then there was the boss I had who would never, ever, write a final submission until five minutes before the absolute deadline. We would do all the spadework, gather the facts, do the calculations if required and draft the answers and he would then sit on it until the very, very last moment. If it was something that he alone could do he seemed not even to think about it until 'five to twelve' yet he always got away with it. There were many more!.

The Admiralty was much concerned with the problem of dealing with influence mines; mines that could recognise some characteristic of a passing ship. A steel ship passing through the earth's magnetic field will generate a signal. Similarly a ship makes a noise in passing through the water. We had ways of doing something about these. The difficult problem was how to disguise the pressure field generated in the sea for some distance around a ship due to her passage through the water. Such pressure fields are unique; an aircraft carrier moving at 20 knots is easily distinguishable from the signature of a destroyer at the same speed. And of course influence mines could combine all three types; so sweeping them would be hazardous if not impossible. The sort of thing that was looked into was the siting of huge wave generators at strategic locations; say along the Channel coast, to send various spectra waves along the sea-lanes. The powers required were phenomenal.

Another trick that was tried was to have destroyers make high speed turns across the line of advance of the Fleet to project pressure waves ahead. The trials were done in Lyme Bay and it appeared to work. The only problem was that it seemed to be unique to the depth and conditions in Lyme Bay and couldn't be repeated elsewhere.

I was sent for one day and told that some scientists at the Admiralty Research Laboratory at Teddington thought that they had the answer; a bluff form would push a wave ahead of itself. They had authority to do some trials on London's reservoirs and I was to liase with them and provide whatever they required. I went and talked with them and it seemed to me that they were talking about the rolling bow wave that we had observed in the first high block coefficient super tankers that were now entering service. I went back to Bath and reported that I didn't think that there was any prospect that this was the breakthrough that we were looking for and was told by Chapman to shut up and get on with it.

The plan was to move a Thames lighter, about 80 feet long and 14 feet beam, on to the reservoir at Staines where it would be pushed along at various speeds and its pressure field measured. Enquiry of the water authority established that reasonable pollution was no problem; the reservoir was considered to be part of the river and one could do all the things that one might decently do on the river itself. We selected a steel lighter and arranged for it to be grounded at Blackwall where it would be cut up transversely into bits that would be moved up river. Then we had to arrange a berth beside the reservoir on which the lighter would be reassembled ready for floating off. The water authority was quite willing to lower and raise water levels to facilitate this. Alas, no sooner had we got the paper work ready than ARL decided that it really wasn't an entirely new phenomena after all and the project was abandoned. Nothing is all loss; I made some new friends and they and others went on in the coming years to give us the novel breakthrough in submarine propulsion that we had been seeking.

It was during this time that Penney invited me to join his organisation at Aldermaston to design and produce nuclear weapons. At the time one million pounds was being spent each week on buildings and equipment and this seemed the place for a keen young man to be. I went there on a lovely sunny day, the birds sang and as I was driven through the leafy lanes I discovered that I had a conscience. Its OK to design things in which similarly equipped forces might oppose each other but killing and what's probably worse, maiming, hundreds of thousands of civilians didn't appeal to me, and that's what nuclear warfare would inevitably descend to. Also, I realised that I really enjoyed being a member of the Royal Corps. So I walked backwards out of Penney's job offer.

A few years later I was to design Britain's Polaris submarines, which I believe, with their US counterparts, deterred Soviet expansionism at the crucial time. Many people have asked me what good four submarines would be in countering the much bigger Soviet nuclear arsenal. My reply is to invite them to imagine that they are attacking Britain and allocate the 16 or 32 missiles available from one or two submarines to our major cities as targets. Each missile has three H bomb warheads (later reduced to two). One gets down to some quite small places. When asked a similar question, "How many H bombs would it take to knock Britain out" Penney had replied "I think five would finish us or shall we say eight to be on the safe side". I would not pretend that five would knock Russia out but thirty or so missiles could do much to reduce her ability to damage the western powers.

My cruiser design section shared a design room with that dealing with the Porpoise and Oberon Class submarine designs and the experimental HTP fuelled submarines *Excaliber* and *Explorer* (better known in the submarine service as HMS Exploder), which held the world record for speed on the surface of 26.25 knots.

I had for some time been privy to the work of a highly classified group at the Atomic Energy Research Establishment at Harwell known as the T party, which met to discuss the application of atomic power to naval propulsion. It was clear that the type of vessel for which such a power source would show most gain was the submarine but equally that no submarine could be configured to take the type of gas cooled reactor that AERE was working on for land power stations. A naval section was established at

Harwell in the mid 1950's and included representatives from industry. The senior MoD scientist was Jack Edwards who had been at school with me (and Charles Helps) when we were 11 years old. Jack was later to be the Professor of Nuclear Science and Technology at RNC Greenwich. It really is a small world.

I was not altogether surprised to be told in 1956 that all work on cruisers and missile ships had to stop and that my group would reform to undertake the design of Britain's first atomic submarine, preceded by a shore based reactor and machinery prototype.

I should perhaps admit that when I had been the Director of Naval Construction's professional secretary in Whitehall it had seemed to me that the staff in Bath was slow and not very bright. For a time after I had joined the aircraft carrier group in Bath it still seemed to me that they were slow and not very bright. Now I didn't notice it so much.

Chapter Seven

The world's first nuclear powered ship, the US submarine *Nautilus*, was already at sea when the decision was taken to design a British submarine and reactor system. Within the scope of known engineering technology only the pressurised water reactor as chosen by the US Navy had any promise of power to weight ratios that might be acceptable in a submarine and that would require much bigger submarines than had previously been built for the RN, in particular, much bigger diameters and, to compound it further, greater diving depths for safe operation.

Despite their name, prior to the introduction of nuclear power, submarines had been submersibles, vessels capable of submerging for many hours but which would have to come to, or close to, the surface to breathe if they wished to go anywhere. Their shape and propellers were designed to reflect the fact that if the submarine wished to make a fast passage she had to do so on the surface.

The possibility of nuclear propulsion would change all that; now we would be able to optimise the shape for submerged propulsion with one big propeller and achieve propulsive efficiencies we had previously only dreamed about. That would require a lot of research and development work, not only in the fields of nuclear engineering and radiological protection, but also in steel and welding and in systems to support life during weeks and months of completely submerged operation.

As Britain's premier submarine building and engineering company Vickers Ltd. were brought into the discussions and formed a new company Vickers Nuclear Engineering Ltd in which Messers Foster Wheeler, Babcocks and Rolls-Royce were participants. A naval/civil team was located at Harwell to liase with the Atomic Energy Authority and personnel from the companies and Naval Construction Department attended courses at Harwell. These courses reflected Harwell's preoccupation with gas cooled reactors and contained little about the more highly enriched pressurised water reactors. Indeed, those who attended reported that the AEA personnel were dismissive of Pressurised Water Reactor's and saw no future for them for civil power generation. The USA, France and Canada, to name but a few, had greater vision.

A stupidity in the early days was that, according to the captain leading the Harwell Naval Section, I was not supposed to let Commander Tony Kidd, the head of the submarine machinery section in Bath, know what was going on. Whether he was eventually to be involved in the work or not was a matter for the Engineer in Chief but it was to me unthinkable that the submarine engineer officer who got the DSO when Crap Miers got his VC in HMS *Torbay* should not share our confidence, so I kept him in the picture.

It was decided that we would need a shore prototype reactor and machinery set for research and training and that this would be located at Dounreay, in the very north of Scotland, immediately beside the AEA's fast breeder reactor establishment. There would be a wooden mock-up of the reactor compartment and components, which would be located at Southampton, in the very south of England. Although the need for secrecy was advanced as a reason for this perverse choice, it did not escape our notice that it provided a use for a surplus building that the aviation side of Vickers happened to have. The initial UK programme objectives were: Jan 1961 - Prototype critical at Dounreay; Mid 1962 - Submarine plant critical.

At this time it was difficult to know who was in charge. There were many meetings at which attendance seemed to be random and things happened at Southampton as the mock-up proceeded apace. Based on the designed output from the reactor a number of propulsion variants were decided upon; as the chap who had to get them all in the submarine it seemed to me that we had everything except rubber bands. The most far-reaching decision was to put the main propulsion machinery on a raft to isolate its vibration and hence its noise from the hull and the sea beyond. When in due course the US Admiral H.G. Rickover - the father of the nuclear submarine - learned of our methods during his third visit in 1962 he was dismissive of the concept and so years later when we finally got wholly British submarines to sea we had a noise advantage over our cousins as well as over the Soviets. It was several classes later that the US Navy started to raft mount its propulsion machinery.

The layout of the reactor compartment that was initially decided upon had a reactor pressure vessel in the centre and four steam generators (boilers) around it. The pipes from the reactor to the steam generators and from the latter out to the turbines wound round and round the reactor compartment to allow for their expansion when hot. It was a nightmare to design and it would have been a nightmare to build and maintain.

From what we now know about the Soviet's first nuclear submarine *K-3*, this was an even bigger nightmare with two reactors (presumably because of the ever present ice risk as well as extra power) and rows of small steam generators down each side of the reactors with steam and water pipes curving in all directions. The steam / water systems were probably not maintainable when built and any attempt at maintenance would have involved exposure to radiation. No wonder the Russian Navy had so many serious radiation casualties in the early days despite using condemned prisoners for the bulk of the nuclear work.

Looking at the thing in my design section in Bath one day in an endeavour to simplify it, one of my assistants said "if the pipes are a nuisance why don't we eliminate them?" This was so obvious now that he said it, so we put two short stub pipes from the reactor to two bigger steam generators and arranged the other things and sent it to the reactor team. Meanwhile a team led by Greg Mott, from the shipbuilding side of Vickers were teaching themselves to design shielding and devising computer programmes for this purpose. At the time the only available computer with sufficient capacity was at the Metal Box Company near Worcester. This involved much travel by car between Barrow and Worcester and regrettably some of the Vickers team were killed in a car crash when making this journey.

It will be appreciated that mankind's concept of size and the artefacts of our civilisation are all relative to the height of human beings; the height of rooms, of buses, of trains, the design of furniture and so on. This governs the height of houses; for each additional floor one adds 8 to 10 feet, not 4 and not 14 feet. Thus it is with submarines, as the number of decks is increased the submarine's diameter increases in discreet steps if the internal space is to be used to best advantage. All of our previous submarines had one internal deck. We were now designing a vessel with three decks. Thus we were able to spell out the allowable variants of diameter and allow the mock-up and the early construction work to proceed at Dounreay, where the reactor and a set of machinery would be placed in a simulated hull immersed in a water tank.

It is instructive to dwell upon the extent to which our thinking is influenced by our concept of size and scale and time. For example, the origin of what we call the universe and the 'Big Bang" for which several theories have been advanced. Perhaps the total matter in our universe was once concentrated in one star in an even greater universe and became a super-super nova tucked away in some corner of this even greater vastness.. Remember that it is only our concept of distance and time that tells us that a billion miles is a long way. Perhaps some of the more distant galaxies now being sensed really do belong elsewhere.

We were obsessed with safety; the shielding must be such that the crew would always be within safe limits The structure must be able to contain the consequences of a pipe leaking; the pressure and cooling arrangements must take account of the maximum credible accident, and so on.

Sometime in the piece, the Director of Naval Construction and the Engineer in Chief together invited the Atomic Energy Authority's Safety and Reliability Department to become our safety authority with the power of veto over our work on nuclear matters. We were furious. We had been designing submarines for years and always put safety first and we didn't need some smart-ass from Harwell or whatever to tell us our business. At one late evening meeting my chief leant across the table and pulled the SRD man's tie with a comment "Look, Mister, we have been in this game a long time and if we weren't safety minded we wouldn't be in submarines". It was really emotional stuff. When we designed any system it usually required two material or human failures in series to produce a problem. The SRD seemed to want four in a row before there was a problem. They were extremely nice and extremely persistent and gradually I realised that they were the best discipline that we could possibly have had. And of course they also helped to solve the problems. Since my underlying philosophy is that the man who thinks that he can't use help is a fool, this was good news.

There were little cameos in this. One of my chaps, Archie Reeves was dictating a particularly critical letter to one of the SRD men, with some rather uncomplimentary remarks on the side. When he got to the end he fumbled about looking for the address. "Don't bother" said the typist, "I have his address, he's my brother".

Admiral Rickover visited the UK nuclear activities for the first time at the end of August 1956 and again in May 1957. As the result of his interest, a UK team visited the US nuclear submarine related facilities. US officials and companies were severely limited as to what they could show and discuss with the UK visitors under the terms of the 1954 Atomic Energy Act and even then there was some criticism in the Congress that those concerned had transgressed this Act. They should have been told how zealously their interests were preserved at the Electric Boat Company, one of the firm's people giving a brief talk strayed into forbidden material and was literally pulled off the stage by two other men while in mid sentence!.

There was mounting concern in the USA and NATO at the possible rapid advance in Soviet technology and Prime Minister McMillan entered discussions with President Eisenhower and Secretary of Defence, Strauss, on possible pooling of nuclear research resources. The possibility of the UK being allowed to purchase a submarine reactor emerged. Admiral Mountbatten was keen that we should proceed quickly and he had a considerable part in the decision to seek to purchase a reactor from the US Navy. Legislation was introduced in Congress to amend the 1954 Act in respect of the provision of plant and know-how to the UK and set about with provisos to ensure that this should not become a launching pad for transfers to other nations. This Act, the 1958 Anglo – US Agreement was signed into law by President Eisenhower on 2nd July 1958.

This was not achieved without opposition in Congress and was much helped by Admiral Rickover's testimony before the Congressional Committee on 27th February in which he stated of the UK working alone, that "at the current rate of spend of 17 millions a year on submarine development it would be many, many, years before they are ready". He was adamant that the deal be between companies and not between navies.

The US government and in particular Admiral Rickover agreed to sell to the UK their latest S 5 W reactor and machinery. When we saw the layout of the S5W reactor compartment it was like the two steam generator arrangement that we had drawn, so much so in fact that the Rolls Royce man accused us of having had previous knowledge of the US arrangement.

The US has subsequently been approached by several other navies asking for access to naval nuclear technology and / or sales and has resolutely refused all such requests. Navies which asked us for information were earnestly advised to keep out of this costly business.

Admiral Mountbatten insisted that one man be put in charge of the British nuclear submarine project and by chance Roland Baker, who had been associated with the design of many of the most novel and successful landing ships and craft in the war when Mountbatten was the Chief of Combined Operations, was newly returned from Canada and was duly appointed. I was present when Mountbatten declared that the nuclear submarine was the capital ship of the future and would have as profound influence on naval warfare as had the battleship *Dreadnought* in 1909 and hence our submarine would be called *Dreadnought*. So Rolly Baker became DPT -the head of the Dreadnought Project Team. His forte was management. Some years later Norman Hancock was to remark that 'Bakers knowledge of submarine design would not cover half a sheet of foolscap but he, Hancock, had learned a hell of a lot about management from him'. We all did.

At this time my design work on the British submarine was well advanced and development of the machinery and equipment was proceeding as was the development of quenched and tempered steel in the thickness and sizes required for the hull plating and framing of a submarine more than 30 feet in diameter.

We had considerable trouble in getting the nationalised British Steel Corporation to take us seriously; they sent ex-navy salesmen to our meetings, not metallurgists, presumably under the impression that we would not be able to understand the technical terms. They told us that they saw their future in making vast quantities of strip steel for the automotive industry, not special steels for the Admiralty who in any case would only need a couple of thousand tons of the stuff each year. They could see no other use for such steels and why didn't we buy it from the USA? We pointed out that we were already buying American HY 80 quenched and tempered steel but considered that there should be a British supplier. Why should we spend a million pounds in giving employment overseas when we could be giving employment in the UK to the people who paid the taxes that made all this possible? We weren't at that stage talking about cost but simply asking the British Steel industry to make steel for the British Navy.

In the end British Steel came up with an arrangement by which ingots weighing tens of tons would be made in Sheffield and moved to near Manchester for rolling and heat treatment while a second stream would be at Ravenscraig in Scotland. The English stream was not successful but the Scottish plant produced acceptable plate thanks to the enthusiasm of the managing director, a keen yachtsman who only had one arm. It was unfortunate that at this stage none of us appreciated the need for standards of cleanliness previously undreamed of in structural steels.

Quite early in our design work we were allowed to visit USS *Nautilus* and, somewhat later, USS *Skate* when she arrived at Portland having made the first under surface passage of the Arctic Ocean and had completely altered the nature of future operations in northern waters. I can remember Lou Rydill's surprise when I dictated a 70-page report on what I had seen in walking through *Nautilus*. It was said that 95% of *Nautilus's* hand picked first crew were graduates, but in many cases this might have been college graduates rather than university graduates. Most went on to become officers in later submarines.

The decision to purchase an American reactor meant that the submarine design had to be altered to match the hull particulars for which the S5W had been configured. The arrangement and structural design of this British design was complete – it became the Valiant Class – but it was set aside for a time while I concentrated on the hybrid - UK Valiant front end / US S5W after end - arrangement of *Dreadnought*.

The bow of our submarine was shaped to embrace a giant sonar array designated Type 2001, positioned above six torpedo tubes. We had many arguments with the sonar experts from Portland because I thought that the sonar should be beneath the tubes for maximum sonar effectiveness and they wanted it above, principally for access in the lengthy proving trials. It was to be two designs later that we finally got the array in the chin position. What we were agreed on was the need for the smoothest achievable shape of the hull into which the sonar fitted in order to provide laminar flow of water over the delicate transducers. These instruments measure the miniscule differences in pressure in the water due to the presence of other bodies. An indication of the scale of these pressure differences is the human ear, which can easily detect fast, recurrent, pressure changes as slight as one billionth of a pound per square inch. The last thing we wanted was to surround the transducers with a mass of turbulence due to our own passage through the water. We emphasised this to the shipbuilder. In the early days it was an uphill struggle.

What obviously we didn't know at the time was that ex-navy Chief Petty Officer Houghton and female clerk Ethel Gee at Portland were passing detailed secret information on the Type 2001 sonar to the Soviets. They were caught and imprisoned together with their Soviet contact. It will be seen that the bows of Soviet submarines produced about that time bore a marked similarity to *Dreadnought's* bow. I wonder how smooth they were.

The purchase of the US reactor and machinery meant that we had to set up arrangements for the transfer of information to the UK. Admiral Rickover was adamant that Vickers Nuclear Engineering was not suitable to manage the nuclear project; he went further and stated that in the UK only Rolls Royce had the engineering standards and discipline necessary for the work. Accordingly, the companies performed a sort of musical chairs and formed Rolls Royce and Associates, located at Derby. In this Rickover was absolutely correct.

Stories about Admiral Rickover had preceded him across the Atlantic - dedicated, shrewd, awkward, ill mannered, rude and downright bloody-minded about everything and everyone except those whom he might use to his and therefore the United States' advantage. It should be remembered that Rickover had to overcome great disadvantages in birth, stature and character to succeed in the US Navy and these early experiences did much to shape his obduracy and stubbornness. He was single minded in pursuit of the difficult decisions that he had to make and knew that to make them last he often had to be brutal.

From the earliest days Rickover had no time for social chitchat. It is recorded that when ordered to attend a reception in the flagship, Lieutenant Rickover climbed up the ladder on the starboard side of the quarterdeck, was greeted by the Admiral host and left smartly by the port ladder to continue his studies. It is certainly true that when in 1939/40 the British navy sent to the US Navy information concerning shock damage to ships and equipment caused by German mines it was Commander Rickover who at once sent for all his electrical manufacturers and required them to redesign their equipment 'by next week' to meet new shock standards. However Rickover never learnt the cardinal rule for young officers-"Always smile when you tell your boss that he's a fool", and so he was not selected for promotion to flag rank. By the end of the war Rickover was a captain.

He had been quick to see the potential of controlled nuclear fission for ship propulsion and had worked himself into a new post in the Bureau of Ships as the head of the Naval Reactor Section, Code 1500. He had also had himself appointed the chief of the Naval Reactors Branch of the Reactor Development Division of the US Atomic Energy Commission, a position in which he was able to advise himself when in the other chair and where, more importantly, he was able to influence the spending of AEC money towards pressurised water reactor research and development. He was thus able to steer the development of US civil power reactors in the direction that he considered it should go and at the same time use this work (and AEC money) to benefit his naval programme.

The correctness of his vision is manifest in the adoption of pressurised water reactors for civil power generation by most leading nations of the world in preference to the wasteful gas cooled reactors on which the British AEA had concentrated its resources.

Rickover had also recognised the wish of the US Congress to be informed on nuclear matters and the part that Congress might play in advancing the application of nuclear power to ship propulsion and civil power generation. He was assiduous in his attendance on Senators and Representatives and played some part in the formation of the Joint Congressional Committee on Atomic Energy under the initial chairmanship of Senator Brien McMahon. Senator Stu Symington had the chairmanship now. This committee required a supporting staff and these were largely drawn from people who had served in Rickover's organisation in one way or another. The Joint Committee provided a splendid platform for Rickover to advance his ideas. Not always under his own name, of course. The method would be for Rick to suggest to one of the staffers that such and such should be considered, perhaps along the following lines. The staff would prepare a paper and discuss it with Rickover's office. The paper would then be sent by the Joint Committee Chairman to Rickover as the Chairman's proposal and Rick. would agree that it should be raised at the next committee meeting. At the meeting the Chairman would raise the matter and the Admiral would say something like "That subject was covered very extensively in your most perceptive letter reference so and so Mr Chairman, which was sent to all committee members and I know that it expresses what the members have been thinking. I move that it be placed in the record of this meeting, if the committee agrees". Of course the committee agreed and there it was, Rick had got his way and posterity would think what a clever chap the Chairman was.

Rickover used the committee to express his views on all sorts of things, like steel production, education (he compared the British system favourably with the US – but that was 35 years ago – I wonder what he would say today) and naval construction and policy as well as engineering. On general matters we felt that he was expressing ideas shared with his first wife who was highly gifted and much concerned with education. To those used to the sheer banality of the exchanges in the House of Commons and its Committees and in the House of Lords, the proceedings of the Joint Congressional Committee at that time provide a remarkable contrast.

His input to the Committee became less catholic after his first wife died. Some time later he, himself was seriously ill in Bethesda Naval Hospital and shortly thereafter he married the US Navy Commander nurse who had looked after him. It might have been a mad passionate affair, but knowing Rick, I am sure that getting a personal, trained, medical attendant played its part. He always, thereafter had an oxygen cylinder and mask in the corner of his room, and saw that his staff was instructed in its use.

He was exceedingly thorough in all that he did. His oft-repeated comment that nuclear work is 5% physics and 95% high quality engineering is only too true. He recognised the important part that the men selected to serve in the submarines and later the nuclear propelled surface ships, must play in the safe operation of the reactor systems and underlined this by acting as a one man selection board by personally interviewing all the officers nominated for service in nuclear ships. In the early days it was all submarines.

Everyone seemed to have a Rickover story. There was the chair in his office, which had one leg slightly shorter than the other three and which was the seat on which the officers were required to sit uncomfortably throughout the interview. Any initiative like changing it with a more stable chair was rudely rejected. Then there was the young Lieutenant Tombs. Rickover called him Toombs (as in cemetery) and the young man corrected him "Toms Sir" (as in cats) - "Rubbish" said the Admiral "your name is Tooombs'. Later in the interview, as was usual, he asked the young man whether he had any questions whereupon the Lieutenant asked Rickover for his views on 'Atomic Boombs'. He was not selected for nuclear submarine training. Eventually, as Rick got older, there was a certain cachet to being rejected for nuclear training.

The US Navy had steadfastly declined to promote Captain Rickover and he passed out of the zone of eligibility, whereupon Congress promoted him a Rear Admiral additional to the US Navy's authorised establishment, in order that he should continue his great work. In due time the Congress was to promote him Vice Admiral and then Admiral ~ thus the Vice Admiral Commander Sea Systems Command (as the Chief of the Bureau of Ships was now called) had a full Admiral, Rickover, as one of his Assistant Chiefs. Observing the personalities, not a restful situation, but history will show that the Congress had a better understanding of Rickover's greatness than did the US Navy that he served so well.

Returning to the British scene. In 1958 Rickover visited Britain for discussions concerning the commercial arrangements to follow the agreements that the UK and US governments had entered into concerning the sale and transfer of technology to the UK. As far as we could see he was willing to unbend slightly with only three people in the UK, the Queen, Prime Minister McMillan and Admiral Lord Mountbatten. To the few other people that it was necessary that he should deal with he was brusque and demanding. To the rest of us who attended the discussions he gave not a glance. That's not strictly true because he spoke to me, he grunted to me to get out of the way when he and I met in a doorway.

Roland Baker had an outgoing personality and would be at ease in most situations. He had served in Washington DC and in Ottawa. He escorted Rickover on visits to Derby and Barrow in Furness. They were taken by car to Euston station in silence. At Euston they boarded the train and entered the compartment in which the two window seats had been reserved for them. Rickover entered first and sat down. Baker went and sat opposite him, whereupon Rickover moved to the corridor seat as far as it was possible to be from Baker. All in total silence. Just before the train departed a little man got in and sat opposite Rickover, which the latter clearly didn't much care for. After some long while the little man caught Rickover's eye and said "Pardon me Sir, but aren't you Admiral Hyram G Rickover, the father of the nuclear submarine?" Rickover asked the man how it was that he recognised him to which he replied that he had seen his picture on the cover of Time magazine and had never forgotten the story of Rickover's achievement. Rickover was clearly pleased and according to Baker was almost civil for the rest of the day, he even nearly said sorry when he trod on Bakers foot getting out of the train at Derby. We couldn't decide whether the little man had been planted by some superior intelligence or public relations organisation.

I have already said that we were now producing a true submarine, capable of sustained operation at high-speed for months on end while totally submerged. No longer would we be groping around at 2 knots submerged with occasional bursts of up to15 knots for a few minutes, now we could move at speeds of about 30 knots for days on end.

This required a complete review of every design practice and I had my staff produce position papers covering every system and equipment used in submarines, with proposals for future development. Everything was examined.

It is perhaps not appreciated that the factors of safety used in the design of submarine pressure hulls are more akin to those of aircraft design than of surface ships, bridges and the like. Just as an aircraft designed to these more liberal safety factors would never leave the ground, so the submarine similarly designed would have no weight for machinery and weapons. That we are able to design, safely, to factors much less than two is not due to our great cleverness (although I would wish to claim this) but because we know to within close limits what the in-service loading on the structure will be due to the pressure of water at the submarines designed operational diving depth. This does not mean that the design process is simple, particularly if the shape changes towards the bow and stern and the various interruptions to the perfect cylinder due to hatches and other essential penetrations but we do at least know what the pressure is.

Modern submarines are immensely strong and the usual design criteria for surface ships, structural strains due to waves are no problem, but we did have to look fairly closely at what to us in the late 1950's was a new phenomena, the possibility of high stress / low cycle fatigue occurring late in the submarine's life due to a combination of the high yield strength coupled with the submarines ability to manoeuvre freely underwater - to change depth from shallow to deep a hundred times a day, if need be, and in consequence to load and unload the structure each time. Lou Rydill wrote the definitive paper on this in May 1958 (I think) and we sent a copy to our friends in the USN BuShips.

Nuclear submarines are best submerged; they fly underwater. In rough seas the best place to be is in a submerged submarine. The sailors (and Daniel) prefer it and if Horatio Nelson were alive today he would be a nuclear submariner. Normally the movement of water that causes surface waves degenerates quite rapidly the further one gets below the surface but sometimes the ocean plays a trick of its own. The sea is not uniform; differences in temperature and salinity of the water may result in layers and submarine commanders use these layers tactically. They might get below a layer to avoid accurate detection and location by an enemy's sonar or sit quietly on a layer for the same reason. Sometimes powerful wave systems develop between the layers some hundreds of feet below the surface and a submarine required to proceed on a given course at that depth might roll and roll for hours on end. Such was the case with HMS *Resolution* during one of her deterrent patrols.

With steam machinery we could provide as much fresh water as the crew would be likely to want and the three F's of wartime submarines would be a thing of the past. We must provide the means to maintain an acceptable environment within the vessel. This meant making oxygen and getting rid of carbon dioxide and all the other gasses produced by men and machines. We had lots of electric power and could make pure water from seawater. Pure water is two parts hydrogen and one part oxygen and electrolysis will separate them. Hydrogen is dangerous and a minor problem was how could it be discharged without being detected by the enemy or blowing up the submarine? The gasses to be got rid of include carbon dioxide, carbon monoxide, stibine, arsine, hydrogen and several others and hydrocarbons. The problem that we had was what percentages would be acceptable in the submarine's atmosphere. Most of the available industrial medical data was from the USA and based on an exposure of up to 8 hours per day; our exposure would be for 24 hours per day for day after day after day. We took the best medical advice and produced our systems. Some years later, analysis showed that the crews suffered with headaches and we halved the permitted carbon dioxide level (at some cost) and the problem disappeared.

The efficiency of fish propulsion was a subject of continuing interest. We had all seen dolphins playing happily around the bows of ships travelling at 20 knots or more and had been told by the experts that this was not possible. The RCNC experts at Haslar set out to find out. After some weeks of dashing about in the Channel in motor gunboats a dolphin was caught and put in the big tank. Its shape was accurately measured and models made and their resistance measured at various speeds. At the same time Professor Gray, at Cambridge, made measurements of the dolphins oxygen uptake and muscular weight to estimate the power they might develop. The measurements proved without doubt that dolphins could not swim faster than about 15 knots. But they did. The Hamburg tank did the same thing with pike, with the same result.

Full size models were coated with fish oil; no better and the same when we put in a system of ducts and holes to gently exude the oil. It was clear that the mammal had some means of controlling the thin layer of water close to its body to keep the flow laminar and hence much less resistant than if the flow was turbulent, which is the case a short distance from the bow of any ship. We speculated that the dolphin has some means of sensing infinitely small variations of pressure over its body and making small movements to prevent breakdown of the boundary layer, thus maintaining laminar flow. A second reason for our interest was that laminar flow is much more silent than turbulent flow.

My experience in the war was that submarine pipe work systems and valves were a major source of problems and of potential danger to the submarines. I decided to make all the systems from cupro-nickel and to weld the joints; for which we would have to develop shipyard techniques. Traditionally, the marine engineers dealt with the water systems in the diesel room and they said that they saw no reason to depart from traditional galvanised steel, – 'they were not aware of problems'. I suggested that they should ask Chatham Dockyard who replied that, because of corrosion; they renewed the entire galvanised steel water systems at each refit – about 3 years apart. Asked why they hadn't made a fuss about it the yard said that they had always done it and thought that the Admiralty knew. Some of us did. I should perhaps explain that with the change to nuclear propulsion there had arrived a number of engineering officers who were not submarine qualified but who were expert in steam machinery design and operation, and at that time they were still getting to know submarines.

We decided to use cupro-nickel for the systems and to weld all piping more than 1-inch diameter. With the decision to buy the US reactor and machinery we were surprised and somewhat horrified to see how extensively brazing was to be used on the systems associated with the S 5 W machinery. I proposed that we should weld them only to be told by Baker to do exactly what the Americans did. Vickers had endless trouble in making these joints and we had to develop ultra sonic methods of examining them. The US submarine builders did not admit to having the sort of brazing difficulties that we encountered, using identical materials. Meanwhile we also had to develop new ultra sonic and radiographic methods and techniques for examining the welding in the steel pressure hull plating and framing.

The step change in design that we had accomplished was nothing compared to the culture shock that industry had to undergo to come to terms with building and fitting out this new type of submarine. First there was security; to put a fence around the building berth and the fitting out dock into which only people who had been security checked were allowed access. Then there was improved material identification and quality control with what seemed to be endless documentation, quite apart from such things as building and maintaining circularity of hulls twice the diameter and twice the thickness of those previously built. There were new things to be done, and new technologies to apply.

One of these was radiological protection, to prevent dangerous radiation from the reactor harming the ships crew and also people outside the submarine when in harbour. We were concerned with two principal types of radiation, neutrons and gamma radiation. Neutrons are only present when the reactor is critical and can be stopped by light elements like water. Gamma is present when critical and when shut down and is attenuated by heavy materials like lead. One of the experts who came from the USA was the Colonel, complete with cowboy boots and a cigar, an adviser on the application of lead shielding to steel structures. He was insistent that we use St Joseph's lead and I assumed that this was because of high purity to avoid trace elements in the lead itself becoming radioactive under in-service neutron bombardment. The method of application was tedious and difficult and so time consuming as to threaten the construction programme. Half way through we could see how much quicker we could do it next time and when we learned that St Joseph's was the name of the lead mine in the US mid-west in which our adviser had a financial interest, our disenchantment with that part of technology transfer was complete.

The other feature that disturbed me was the inter-connection of sea water systems within the machinery package and the lack of isolating valves, which meant that in the event of a fault, many hull valves would need to be closed to secure the situation. In our design practice a maximum of two valves would require to be closed.

Although important these were peripheral to the reactor and machinery, which were splendid, were delivered to time and to cost and ran beautifully.

It was the practice to build full-scale wooden replicas of some important spaces like Operations Rooms and Control Rooms to enable equipment to be arranged to best advantage to those who will operate it or maintain it, in very congested conditions, in service. The practice arose of mocking-up the compartments in which the food is prepared and cooked -the galleys -in surface ships and submarines. No one would deny the importance of feeding the crew. In my experience, when on board, the sailors get better food with more choice, than they probably get at home. The real reason for the mock-up was the legion of people in the MoD departments and establishments, most of whom could not or would not, understand a drawing, who felt that they had the right and duty to comment upon the sailors victualling arrangements.

It was a source of some amusement to me that I could decide the arrangement of a new warships armament, machinery, protection, propellers, aircraft and so on, approve the drawings and get the ship built. Of course I had lots of experts in my teams and the drawings went to other departments but in reality, the buck stopped with me. But when it came to the galley, people who had a say in it emerged from the woodwork in all directions. Of course the Department of Victualling and the Naval Stores Department should be consulted and perhaps the RN School of Cookery but after that the floodgates seemed to open. For one submarine galley mock-up inspection no less than twenty-eight people attended. The floor area was about 2m by 3m. We went through all of this with the mock-up of the Valiant Class submarine's galley. We built the first submarine and the crew arrived. We found that the cook was about 5 feet tall and could barely lift the large saucepan over the worktop and ovens that had been the subject of profound debate by so many people.

It was accepted that we would require a mock-up of the new reactor compartment and machinery spaces. Special cases were then made for other compartments and I learned, with some horror, on his return from a visit to Barrow, that without any consultation, Baker had agreed that Vickers should build a full-scale wooden mock-up of the whole submarine.

Vickers Shipbuilders built surface warships and merchant ships as well as submarines at Barrow. Their labour resources reflected this. They had recently won a contract to build a passenger liner for a consortium of eight to nine hundred shareholders in Denmark and still had a force of nearly three hundred joiners whom the firm wished to retain. It seemed to me that their solution was to build the mock-up of the submarine. This seemed to be fun, to see everything exactly as it would be, but I quickly realised that its value as a design tool was strictly limited. The purpose of a mock-up is that one can move things to obtain an optimal arrangement. This is a fallacy in such spaces as machinery rooms because it's nearly as difficult and disruptive to move some giant component made of wood, as it would be to move the real thing.

Our US friends thought the whole thing a huge joke; they said quite seriously that they could not afford such luxuries since all their money went on building real submarines.

The brighter members of Vickers staff could see this and in due course we were able to phase out full-scale mock-ups in later designs in favour of scale model and computer techniques, developed by the company under Greg Mott and Tony Peake's leadership.

A decision that we were all to come to regret in the fullness of time was to put the work of building the prototype structure at Dounreay with a sub-contractor. All of the steel work and other material was prepared at Barrow and shipped to the site for erection by the subcontractor. The decision was absolutely correct in principle since the work on this remote site would be costly and if done by Barrow workers could be used to force up the rates for the entire Vickers labour force. What we didn't bargain for was the slowness and awkwardness of the sub-contract labour. Years later, under Greg Mott, Vickers adopted a novel way of building, transporting and installing the second prototype at Dounreay.

I was to do another job before *Dreadnought* went to sea. In 1958, following a major review, it was decided to combine the three major technical departments, naval construction, marine engineering and electrical engineering and the quaintly named naval equipment department together as Ship Department under a Director General. The new organisation would have a Project Group Constructive, which with engineering and electrical elements, would be directly responsible to the Director General for preliminary ship design studies. I was to be promoted and be the head of this new group.

Midway through 1958 I had been given the OBE.

The genesis of this project group post had something to do with Admiral Ralph Edwards remark to me many years earlier about Director of Naval Construction Lillicrap's lack of responsiveness to creative thinking about future warfare and ships. My job was to assist the DGS, Jack Sims, in putting concepts to the naval staff and in responding promptly to their proposals.

Sims, Baker and Victor Hall had been term-mates in the Naval College and had graduated in that order with Sims gaining a First. Because of the exigencies of wartime service, Baker had been promoted to Chief Constructor ahead of Sims but in 1947 when there was serious talk of reversions in rank, Lillicrap had told me that he would never revert Sims but would revert Baker if pushed. I had hinted at this to Baker when the Canadian job came up and urged him to accept it. He went and was a success as their Naval Constructor in Chief. Sims had continued his more academic career as professor at Greenwich and then a design post.

Victor Hall specialised on the dockyard side. One remembers silly things. When I was Lillicrap's secretary we received a complaint about Hall's facetious approach to serious matters. It appeared that the Head of General Finance Branch in the Admiralty Secretariat had telephoned Hall and asked him what he thought would be the cost of modernising such and such a ship. Hall had asked what work would be done and had been given a few facts.   After a few minutes Hall had said 4.6 million pounds. His questioner had said "That was quick, where did you get that answer from?" and the cheerful Hall had said "Off the ceiling", which was his shorthand for; "Considering the brief facts that you have been able to provide, my long experience of dockyard work and costing procedures indicates that he cost should be between 4.5 and 5.0 million pounds, say 4.6 millions." So this self-important man had sent his little note of complaint. Lillicrap signed the reply that told him in polite civil service English that we were surprised that he didn't have something more pressing to attend to than complain about one of our most experienced dockyard costing experts. This story would not be complete without remarking that when it was done. The ships modernisation did cost under £ 5 millions.

When I had first joined the submarine group in 1942 and had almost immediately been sent off to conduct a submarine trial, my chief, Pamplin had said "You may accept a dinner at the expense of the firm but that's all. Everything else you pay for". This was the pattern for the Corps throughout my career. I forgot, we were also allowed to accept a firm's pocket diary at Christmas, if offered. Imagine my surprise therefore at Christmas 1958 to find that the new combined DG Ships mail office and the corridor opposite to my office was knee deep in parcels all containing presents from firms for the electrical engineers. This might be the usual practice in the electrical contracting industry but Sims rightly stopped the practice the next year. As the Chinese proverb puts it "The acceptance of a gift should not be undertaken lightly" or as the Americans would say "There is no such thing as a free lunch".

DG Ships had a number of Directors heading technical divisions. The electrical side seemed to generate characters and not always loveable ones. An earlier one used to show his dis-pleasure if an officer of junior rank entered the lift when he was using it. His successor who served Sims was a Scotsman who had a deserved reputation for meanness.   Stories about him abounded; how he would use every possible excuse to avoid buying any colleague a drink, how on a duty trip he always took sandwiches and ate them outside the car to avoid getting crumbs in his car and (sic) how he would switch off his car radio to save his battery when going under a bridge.   He cycled to the office in pouring rain because it was not worth getting the car wet. He was a dour and unhelpful man. His successors were better.

Although we made many studies of surface warships in the group, I always felt that we were marking-time awaiting the resolution of a problem as yet not properly defined. The problem was to do with the future need for, and the cost, of aircraft carriers and their aircraft, bedevilled as far as the aviators were concerned by the fact that a nuclear submarine programme was already under way and taking big money - £18m in the case of *Dreadnought*.

Nevertheless we provided the quick response that Sims wanted, so that promising concepts could be pursued and non-runners discarded. He would come back from London, send for me and say something like "The Vice Chief of Naval Staff is thinking of a ship with this missile, this or these guns, this aircraft and this speed and range to do this. How big do you think it would be, what size crew and what cost and when could it be an service?" By the end of the day he would have a weather deck plan and elevation of a possible ship, a statement of its size and cost and how long to design in detail and build.   He would also have, not for Whitehall, an additional statement of the make up of the weights, stability intact and damaged and strength. And yes, it would be in a glossy folder to make it look professional.

This was all done, of course, by means of a whole range of data, graphs and non-dimensional plots that I had created in my earlier appointments and I had some excellent draughtsmen who would take something that I had sketched out on squared paper and quickly make a small scale drawing fit for a king.

Twenty years later, using an extensive suite of interactive computer programmes, Ship Department was taking four days to do the same thing. At the time the young men persuaded me that their answers were better than my one-day jobs or at least they were auditable. I remain firmly of the view that, more often than not, a 90% answer today is of more assistance to the naval staff than a 98% answer in one week's time.

I mention elsewhere the considerable problems that the universities are laying-up for themselves through their emphasis on published work as a criterion for advancement or preference. Thus Associate Professor Smith, who received praise for his paper on 'How to come in out of the rain' is now to be found publishing the sequel 'Rain, how to come in from it' and rumoured to have 'Should we come in, that is the question' in the early stages of preparation. In my own profession I note the number of papers analysing the warship design process. Of course there always had to be method in the design process and the introduction of computers made it necessary to set them out in some detail but now it's papers-for-papers sake with copious references to other peoples equally vacuous work. The result is to enable mediocre people to produce mediocre designs. What Jack Sims was kind enough to refer to publicly as the mark of genius, has gone.

The most important design investigation that we undertook was the proposed new aircraft carrier to operate hypothetical new naval aircraft, aircraft that would be faster and heavier than the navy had previously operated. Needless to say they would take-off and land faster as well. Every design study that we made told us that we couldn't meet the requirement on less than 75,000 tons and a length of over 1,000 ft. Such a ship could not be built for the 60 million pounds 'order of cost' included in the forward plans. Perhaps more seriously such a ship would be unable to enter Portsmouth or Devonport harbours and Dockyards due to insufficient depth of water. This is why, today, when a US Navy monster carrier visits Portsmouth, they do not enter the base and come alongside; there isn't sufficient depth of water and so they anchor in Spithead.

I really became aware of the geographical constraints that our harbours place on warship development. Slightly bigger ships could enter Devonport than Portsmouth but I concluded that even here the maximum displacement that could be accepted was not greater than 55,000 tons and such ships would not be able to be as long as good hydrodynamic practice would suggest, nor would they be long enough to operate the high performance aircraft then under discussion.

There was the problem of new catapults to launch the new aircraft. A slotted tube catapult committee was formed to guide its development. The most important question was -what is the required performance: and here we rather went to town by calling for an ability to launch 40 ton aircraft at 200 knots to get people thinking big. The next question was where will the power come from. There were three possibilities; steam, cordite and a liquid fuel. Notwithstanding the successful steam catapults in HMS's *Ark Royal* and *Eagle*, steam was the least attractive because the steam demand would require a boiler room as big as those needed to drive the ship and also vast, heavy steam reservoirs high up in the ship. Next, we calculated that we would have to carry many hundred tons of cordite to operate the catapults. In action there would be many tons in the supply chain between the magazine and the catapult 'breech' and it would be difficult and costly in top weight to protect this against enemy weapons. Liquid fuels seemed to provide an acceptable solution, particularly mono-fuels, which would be stowed deep in the ship and piped to the catapult in metered quantities. The catapult committee visited the Rocket Propulsion Establishment at Westcott to discuss fuels. Iso-propyl-nitrate sounded just right. Exploring possible stowage arrangements in ships I asked whether it was corrosive, "Oh yes" replied the rocket people, "we have to stow it in aluminium drums" My spirits sank as I thought of the added problems of getting big aluminium tanks into the forward ends of the carrier and then preventing them from corroding in the salt laden sea air.

In the afternoon we visited the test site to witness the behaviour of the fuel. There was an aluminium milk churn nearby and in passing, our guide removed the lid, put his finger in, licked it and said "Yes, that's Iso-propyl-nitrate". I said "I thought that you said that it was corrosive?" to which he replied "Yes it is, like sea water". I recount this story to point out how important it is to ask that extra question at meetings to ensure that you fully understand the information given. I should add that it is equally important to make ones requirements absolutely clear to those to whom one is giving instructions. Brokensha's story is a good example. He was the Constructor Commander on the staff of the Admiral commanding our naval forces in the 1953 Korean War. One of our destroyers had its depth charge thrower damaged. The massive securing bolts were bent. Brokensha took one of the bent bolts into the Kobe Japanese yard and asked for four new ones by Monday. On the Monday morning he was presented with four bolts meticulously bent to match the sample provided. Luckily they could provide straight ones from stock so the ship still sailed on time.

I sometimes wonder whether even well informed members of the public appreciate what a marvel of naval architecture and engineering an aircraft carrier really is. Imagine an Air Force base to take two squadrons of fighters or strike aircraft, say 30 aircraft. There would be at least two runways one mile long, hangars, workshops, magazines, opps rooms and living quarters for the station and squadron staffs. The whole would extend over several square miles of land and perhaps more if the base had to make its own electricity and fresh water.

Now put all of that in a ship's hull about 800 ft long and 100 ft beam. Not 30 aircraft but over 60 and an ability to move the whole airfield and its personnel at about 30 mph and over distances of thousands of miles. And defend it with guns and missiles and design the hull to remain afloat and stable after enemy attack. That's an aircraft carrier.

The great concern in carrier design is to prevent free water reaching the hangar deck consequent upon flooding due to battle damage, with resulting loss of stability due to the 'free surface effect'. It was cardinal in design in my days that the ship would have to be practically sunk before water got through to the hangar deck. From the 1950's onwards I watched in horror as British and overseas designers of vehicle and passenger ferries ignored this basic principle and introduced craft with vehicle decks vulnerable to flooding. This was part of the message that we had tried to put over to the Department of Transport officials in preparation for the 1948 Safety of Life at Sea conference and subsequently, to no avail and it has taken a tragic loss of life to finally move those responsible to force the operators to make their craft intrinsically safe. Even now, in the UK, it has been ex-members of the RCNC who have largely taken the lead in this.

A warship design concept that I rather liked was a helicopter carrier with a powerful missile armament forward, a high bridge structure and a big wide deck aft with a hangar under for many helicopters. The naval staff could see no need for such ships ; their eyes were firmly fixed on the future aircraft carrier to operate high performance aircraft and the last thing they wanted was some smart Alec in DNC Bath diverting ministers attention to other ship concepts.

In 1963 the soviets laid down two ships, the *Moskva* and *Lenningrad*, which bore a striking resemblance in size and shape to our helicopter carrier concept. An advantage the Soviets had over us, apart from an ability to spend money on their navy, was that they had some decent weapons to put on them.

In this job I was required to attend NATO Headquarters as a UK delegate to the Information Exchange Group concerned with naval materiel. I confess to being a little confused concerning the venue of the first meeting that I attended; I am sure that it was in the building near the Bois de Boulogne in Paris. Of the subsequent meetings I am absolutely sure; General de Gaulle had kicked NATO out of Paris and we were in Brussels. I was mildly surprised at three things. The Chairman of the naval steering group was Italian ex-Rear Admiral Cioppa, the secretary was a German who was as silent as Cioppa was voluble, and the French who had resigned military membership of NATO were there large as life absorbing knowledge like mad. There was tremendous goodwill towards Britain and a joint resolve that the future depended on collective security. Admiral Cioppa was a charmer. In discussing anything that happened during the war years he invariably opened with "I remember it clearly, at the time we were being bombed by the British (or the Americans)."

At the meetings we sat around the four side of an open table an alphabetical order, which resulted in the UK and the US sitting side by side. Since relations between the two navies on ship research and development were very close this was a good arrangement, The subject matter was kept at 'Confidential' level and all nations understood that there were things at a higher classified level that we were not able or ready to discuss with our allies. There was one Canadian officer, a naval constructor commander who was a thoroughgoing nuisance. Because of the closeness of their relationship with the USN and the RN, the Canadians were privy to a lot of what was going on although they played no part in it. This Canadian frequently embarrassed the USN delegate and me. Something would be discussed in which we would participate, say describing our results up to confidential level or keeping quiet, when suddenly the Canadian would lean forward and say something like "Oh, come on, what about the trials you are doing with xyz," or "What about your research programme opq". All of which would be classified Secret. I was surprised many years later to find him a Rear Admiral.

The Italians were a constant delight to me. It could be guaranteed that if anyone felt it necessary to use the blackboard to explain a point, the Italian delegate Captain D'Alesandro would also find it necessary to use the blackboard. They even produced a Commander Bernouli who, believe at or not, talked about fluid dynamics. I was aware from my days with Lillicrap that although a part of the Italian naval organisation, the Italian naval constructors hold military rank, not naval. Thus their top man is a General, not an Admiral. One day the resident technical man in their delegation in Brussels, an electrical specialist called Captain Lupo, took me confidentially aside and pointed to D'Alesandro and said "Him not really Capitano, him Colonelo".

The Americans were their usual selves. They were responsible for a most embarrassing incident, which I still believe they did not realise, had occurred. I was walking across the Grand Place one evening when I met the two US delegates. "Come on lets have a drink, we found a nice bar here last night, come on" and I was ushered through the door of the end house on the corner. At that moment I realised that this was not a select little bar but was the Royal Aero Club of Belgium. The steward was splendid; he sat us down at a small table just inside the door and took our orders. We chatted among the mounted propellers and other memorabilia and in due course we left. I said, "Did you know that bar was the Aero Club of Belgium" and they said, "Yes, it was OK wasn't it".

British officialdom does not change. The per-diem subsistence rate that we were allowed by the British Treasury was only sufficient for accommodation at the smallest hotels in Brussels and then only at a special discount for NATO. This was the source of some good-natured amusement on the part of NATO colleagues from allegedly less prosperous nations who were permitted a higher standard.

Occasionally, a big, bearded, weapons electrical commander would be part of the UK team and in the evening we would repair to a particular restaurant on the Bvd Adolf Max where my friend would demand "the two litre glass". Perhaps all the bars had them but this was the only one that I ever saw and it looked enormous, much more than four times the half-litre glasses that we lesser mortals favoured. It took both hands to lift it and the curve of the rim was more suited to wide mouths if dribbling was to be avoided.

Some time later the naval staff had concluded that sea skimming missiles launched by hostile aircraft and ships would constitute a threat and that perhaps the ships of the Royal Navy should have some to deter potential enemies. None of the proposals made by British industry in earlier years for such a missile had been acceptable and the usual UK weapons procurement scenario now unfolded, overnight the requirement was urgent, there was no acceptable UK system available, development of a UK system would take too long and cost more than buying from overseas and to hell with the UK's technology base. Perhaps an overseas manufacturer would let us manufacture some bits to keep the patriots quiet?

The search was on. Missiles that might be suitable 'on paper.' were in an advanced state of development in France, the USA, Italy, Norway, Sweden and Israel. Although it seemed that half of the chiefs of British business were donating millions of pounds to having a building or park named after them in Tel Aviv or Jerusalem, the Foreign Office was concerned that we should not upset the Arabs by an open show of interest in anything Israeli. Eventually it was agreed that a British officer should make a very low key plain clothes visit to Israel for discussions. The bearded commander was selected. He emerged from the aircraft at Tel Aviv airport to be blinded by television lights and a reporter welcoming "Our guest from the British Navy who has come, we hope, to buy our Gabriel missile". He need not have worried, next day he found that representatives of most of the European navies were also present.

During my tenure in the project group the senior man in the marine engineering section was promoted to the rank of Captain. There was no job to which he could be appointed for two months and he was told to continue in his present position. He argued strongly that this was not for Captains, Captains didn't work, they commanded shore establishments and walked round with a silver topped walking stick and a spaniel dog at their heels. He really declined to work and as far as I could judge the productivity of the group went up.

It was during this period that I was asked to give a talk to the Birmingham Electronics Society. Lectures at the Naval Architects or Marine Engineers seldom attracted an audience of more than forty and sometimes press-gang methods were required to raise a quorum for the Annual General Meeting's. Imagine my surprise when I found that I had an audience of three hundred and fifty. After the lecture and question period I was taken to dinner at the Midland Hotel. It was late and shortly after we were seated, a Danish couple called Nina and Frederick who were topping the bill at the adjacent Midland Theatre entered and were seated at the next table. They proceeded to have a very public row – in English.

A battle that I fought and lost was to have a computer installed in Ship Department. That computers were big, costly and unreliable in 1959 was true but the reason that I was given was that the local powers-that-be could see no use for a computer in our work.

At about this time all sorts of special teams emerged from Whitehall and elsewhere with the stated aim of making us all more efficient. Most of the ideas and methods they peddled would have been described by my mother as logic and by my father as applied common sense. One that had a high profile was 'Work Study' and the Work Study Team led by a Paymaster Captain visited all naval activities to spread the message, which appeared to be Think about what you are doing. When I attended one of their sessions they presented two examples that they had studied, the Main Signal Office in the Portsmouth Command and the Mobilisation Plan for the Reserve Fleet in time of war.

They showed a viewgraph of the MSO with its telex and cipher machines around the four sides and then showed a mass of crisscross lines, which were the movements of the personnel across the room as they collected and distributed the signal traffic. They then showed how a rearrangement of the equipment would reduce the movement of people. Jackie Fisher would have remarked "movement kept the buggers awake". The fleet mobilisation example was more dramatic in so far as they sought to demonstrate on the wildest of assumptions that no less than 70% of the fleet would be sunk en-route to its war station. This was so silly that I suggested that if this was so they should shoot the officers who had prepared the mobilisation plan because they were obviously enemy agents.

Our US Navy liaison officer, Commander Hal Kaufman, was enormously taken with the work-study idea and wrote several reports to the folk back home in Bu Ships. His tour of duty ended quite soon thereafter and when I next visited Washington DC I found that he had been promoted to captain and Head of the US Navy's Work Study Project.

It was Hal Kaufman who sought advice on what he should see in Scotland during his forthcoming two weeks leave. He was told that in two weeks his family would barely have time to scratch the surface of Edinburgh, let alone the beautiful and historic places in the Highlands. Ten days later they returned to Bath, having 'done' Scotland, Wales and Cornwall.

A resignation in 1960 caused my rapid return as the Chief Constructor of the nuclear submarine design group. The Dounreay prototype was in the early stages of construction as was HMS *Dreadnought* and the contract for the first all-British submarine HMS *Valiant*, would be placed before the end of the year.

We were already determined that the method of build adopted at Dounreay would never be repeated. Construction at this remote site would always present difficulties with all skilled and semi-skilled labour being brought from afar and paid accordingly. The installation was a partial submarine hull containing the reactor compartment and machinery with a large brake to load the propeller shaft. The part of the hull around the reactor was in a circular swimming bath as a further precaution against radiation - remember, we had still to prove the accuracy of our shielding calculation methods. Everything that could go wrong seemed to go wrong. As the months passed, the project developed a receding completion date as woe piled on woe.

When we plotted the predicted date against time to completion the curve said 'never", but we kept a stiff upper lip and patience won but it took time and money. Both the MoD and Vickers resolved that if we were ever to have another prototype at Dounreay, we would build the thing ourselves and get it there somehow.

These were the years of hard work, getting the detail right, bringing UK manufacturers in and getting things made to nuclear standards, as well as getting the submarines built.

There were two companies on the Barrow site, Vickers Shipbuilders and Vickers Engineers. They shared certain common yard facilities, including the Directors dining room where they faced each other across the table.

Barrow, isolated on the Furness peninsular is a one-industry town that lives or dies with Vickers. Barrow was conceived as a port to rival Liverpool in the carriage of Irish immigrants in the 1860's. The port had spawned the Barrow Shipbuilding Works, which underwent a series of ownership changes with famous names like Maxim, Armstrong and Vickers to emerge as the raison d'etre for Barrow when the immigrant trade ceased. Even in the lean years, VickersArmstrong's survived and since the mid-1930's the area had enjoyed continued prosperity. I used to walk around the mean streets downtown with their little houses built of crumbling soft red bricks and wonder where the hundreds of millions of pounds provided in shipyard workers wages had gone. In the south it would have been evident in housing but not in Barrow town.

It is not given for humans to be grateful; to lend a needy friend money is often to make an enemy. So it was with the elected representatives on the Barrow council and the local trade union officials, ever keen to bite the hand that fed them. There were two ex-Vickers employees whose names would always come up whenever the conversation turned in this direction, Montgomerie, the union man and Booth, the politician.

Montgomerie was a thorn in Redshaw's side for years until his ambition took him away to be a full time union official. Some years later he came back seeking employment, which the firm was pleased not to provide. Albert Booth, the ex-draughtsman became a Labour Member of Parliament and (unbelievably) Secretary of State for Employment in Wilson's government.

In the mid-1970's I was sitting next to Len Redshaw at the Royal Aeronautical Society dinner at the Dorchester Hotel. We were at the top table, opposite to and a few places to the left of the president. Albert Booth was on the president's immediate left and hence even closer to us. He had a pasty face with bright red cheeks. Suddenly I realised that Len Redshaw was gesturing dismissively across the table and saying to those around us in a most audible stage whisper in a Lancashire accent "Look at him, some minister, looks more like a bloody ventriloquists dummy". And you know, he did.

Sir Len Redshaw was a remarkably gifted man, a giant in an industry populated by pigmies. Yet he was curiously naive in some ways. National Service - a euphemism for conscription - was still in operation when we started building *Dreadnought*. Redshaw came to Bath one day and suggested that work on such an important national project should excuse Vickers young men from doing national service. So far so good, nice try Len. He then added that it was a curious thing that very few of the young men who had left Vickers to do their national service had ever come back to Vickers, Barrow. He couldn't understand why we fell about on the floor laughing. They had caught a glimpse of the great big world outside the Furness peninsular.

His father, J.S, was the Vickers naval architect during the war years. Len was proud of his relationship with the workforce; he was one of them, an ex-apprentice who had become the boss via Liverpool University, Blohm and Voss in Hamburg and much hard work. He believed that it was because of this empathy that he could settle disputes in the yard. There was a dwindling element of truth in this but the shop stewards and local union officials were not slow to exploit it. They realised that the clever thing to do was never to settle at a lower level but to force things up to the Managing Director (later

Chairman) from whom they always emerged with something, not all that they asked for, but something.

Each two weeks there was a meeting at Barrow to review progress. I would take two or three people from Bath and the principal naval overseer and two of his staff would attend, making six or seven on our side of the table. On the other side would be Len Redshaw and all the Vickers local directors and behind them, in two or three additional rows, about forty design and production staff. I would sit there wondering how the management could allow their staff to spend their time in this way when they could have been building the submarines but the firm strongly resisted any suggestion that they should reduce their representation. It quickly became evident that my Admiralty meeting was the occasion on which the underlings were briefing Redshaw and Co. It was usually a very laboured process and on several occasions I had to privately warn the Principal Naval Overseer to keep quiet when, to hurry things along, he started answering extensively on behalf of the firm.

The firm never seemed to realise why it was that I was always so well informed on the state of the work. Perhaps they thought that it was the PNO's briefing. In those early days we travelled to Barrow by sleeper train, arriving at about 6.00am. Since I did not eat breakfast, I would walk down to the shipyard and have a good two-hour crawl around the submarine before the meeting started. The firm's report of the state of the boat did not always tally with what I had seen earlier that morning.

I went to the slipway one morning and inspected the way the streamlined shape around the sonar had been done. It will be recalled that we impressed on the firm that we had to have the smoothest transition possible. What I found was that the starboard side had a gumboil. Let me be clear, it was no easy task to mount the big castings for the sonar accurately in position and the firm had done this well but above it was the bump. At the meeting I said that it would have to be changed and the firm denied all knowledge of a bump. Bill Richardson, Redshaw's deputy could not disagree when, after the progress meeting, he came down to the boat with me to see what I was talking about. There were all sorts of things that seemed to miss the routine inspection process.

After the start of machinery installation there was one man who certainly knew that I had been on board because he was always there. It seemed that whenever I visited, morning or night, weekday or weekend, George Standen, the manager responsible for the reactor and machinery, would be there. No matter when, it seemed George would emerge from a hatch looking pale and drawn but always in complete control of the situation.

About each quarter there would be a big meeting chaired by Rowland Baker with a correspondingly higher noise level.

The nuclear project required much more extensive procedural and test documentation than we had haltingly started to use in building the Oberon Class. The documentation and test teams were of vital importance and without them and the discipline they instilled we would never have completed the submarine — well not safely.

An important part of the review of all design practices that I had initiated a few years earlier when we started the design had been resistance to underwater shock. Large sections and panels of structure were being tested in full scale at the Naval Construction Research Establishment in Fife against the shock waves from underwater explosions while model sections were being tested in pressure chambers for their resistance to collapse under static underwater pressure. I wanted all components tested. Hull valves were traditionally made from gunmetal. Indeed so convinced had generations of naval constructors been of the soundness of this metal that submarine conning towers in all the non-welded submarines that went to sea in the war were made of it. I had found the records of earlier tests of gunmetal valves to be unsatisfactory and had commissioned an entirely new series. The results were not good, gunmetal was not the nice, flaw-free material that we had always assumed it to be.

We began a search for a stronger, more homogeneous material that could be cast in intricate shapes, examined radiographically, and would have high corrosion, erosion and shock resistance. With Keith Foulger's help, I selected Nickel Aluminium Bronze, a metal alloy with remarkable strength and shock resistance. The only problem was making satisfactory castings so we called together all of the top firms. I had heard much about the specialist suppliers to the aviation and weapons industries and so we brought them in and gave them development contracts. The idea that the high duty aviation makers would be able to make satisfactory castings in nickel aluminium bronze could not have been further from the truth -firms that had grown fat and famous making cast components for aircraft were quickly eliminated, followed by firms like Weirs until we were left, believe it or not, with Vickers Engineers. Vickers had problems, in the beginning they made about five castings for each one that met our X-ray and sonic tests, but they persevered (and we paid), and finally it was OK. HMS *Valiant* still went to sea with a few castings that we replaced at the first refit but the one thing that I could absolutely guarantee was that these were much, much stronger and shock-resistant than the gunmetal ones that otherwise would have been fitted. However, late in the year 2000, I learned that it had been found that these NAB components were subject to complex corrosion mechanisms which could not be detected by any of our non-destructive tests in situ and that as a sensible precaution, they were being replaced by new NAB components each ten years or so.

The small-scale models of sections of the 30ft plus pressure hulls were about 2 ft in diameter, with frames to scale welded in place – really highly skilled work. They were tested in one of the NCRE mechanical testing laboratories. For several years I went into and out of the laboratories without noticing except in a most perfunctory manner, the coat of arms and motto over the door. One day I read the motto – U. MACUM. V. BRACUM. Get it?

In the week that the reactor core was to be loaded into the *Dreadnought* - a procedure requiring all sorts of cranes, rigs and fittings — a Rumanian merchant ship decided to call at Barrow Docks to unload cargo. This had seldom, if ever, occurred before. Someone had a quiet word with the docks people and the stevedores worked like Trojans and the ship was made to sail before the interesting things happened on the Vickers side of the basin.

Excitement mounted as the reactor went through its setting to work procedures and finally criticality, power range testing and fast cruise for which the submarine was completely sealed as if submerged for some days while performing propulsion exercises.

Rolls Royce and Associates were fully associated with the task of installing and setting to work the reactor and nuclear systems and the exacting standards set by the AEA's Safety and Reliability Department had been a powerful discipline for excellence. Some of these standards had seemed to us at first glance, quite unachievable. Who would expect to build structures, pierced by more than two hundred pipe runs and electric cables and only have a leakage rate from the compartment, when under pressure, equivalent to a drop of water a day. The question of what pressure caused much debate. The nuclear reactor and its systems were contained in a section of the submarine through which was a tunnel at the top to connect the forward and after parts of the boat. The tunnel and end bulkheads were heavily shielded against gamma radiation and neutrons. The reactor people postulated various defect conditions resulting in the release of super-heated reactor water into the compartment and the resulting pressure, the worst of which was designated the maximum credible accident pressure, was what we had to deal with –

with no leakage.. And the pressure kept going up. In the end Vickers had met the standards and the reactor was allowed to go critical.

Finally in mid-December 1962 we embarked for sea trials. The weather was foul and we all took our sea-sickness pills, at which point due to a quite minor communications failure caused by a CPO pulling out, and hence disconnecting, a drawer in an electronics cabinet (why, oh why must people feel that they have to be doing something) we were delayed sufficiently long in the Barrow dock entrance to miss the tide in the difficult Walney Channel.

Dreadnought's CO Peter Samborne having read the riot act, we sailed the next morning into a very stormy Irish Sea. The safety tug that was supposed to accompany us was unable to sail out of Heysham Harbour and the only ship we saw was an Eastern Bloc ship that was too busy worrying about her own safety to pay much attention to us. HMS *Dreadnought* behaved splendidly.

Clever though we pretend to be, we could not say with certainty how fast *Dreadnought* would go on the surface. Her shape was optimised for submerged propulsion and we knew full well how fast she should go submerged but the surface speed depended on whether she would get over a particular hump in her surface resistance characteristics. We knew that she would do 15 knots or was it 20? so evenly were her hydrodynamic factors balanced. She went like a racehorse, through her resistance hump and away, swept along on a great wave at about 20 knots with her bow casing dry and her stern well down. I was on the bridge when it happened and could hardly believe my eyes when suddenly the bow came up and the forward deck was dry.

We had received exemplary service from the US Navy, the Electric Boat Company and Westinghouse in supplying *Dreadnought's* nuclear machinery plant and invaluable advice. Looking back in today's inflated world, it does not seem credible that the total cost of the US package was something over 8 million pounds and the total cost of the submarine (including the US costs) was just 18 millions.

It was not to be until 1965 that the first UK manufactured reactor went critical at Dounreay, in time to provide operating experience and burn-up before the reactor in the first all British submarine, HMS *Valiant*, went critical in 1966. We were still able to achieve our designed aim of taking a core through its whole life cycle under closely instrumented conditions in the prototype before the submarine burnt up its core.

We were pleased with ourselves for completing HMS *Dreadnought* to time and cost and eventually the all-British HMS *Valiant*, but here, even with the US know-how we were four years later than the original dates assumed in 1955 for criticality at Dounreay (January 1961) and criticality for the submarine (mid-1962) Although much of the delay was due to the problems encountered by the sub-contractor responsible for building the prototype at Dounreay, it demonstrated how little the Naval Section set up at Harwell in the early days really understood of the problems of engineering and commissioning a compact, no leakage allowed, reactor system and how right Rickover had been in his high-handed approach to British industry and his insistence that Rolls Royce should be made responsible for the RN's reactor systems.

With *Dreadnought* completing, *Valiant* in build and *Warspite* about to be ordered, I had already started, in the second half of 1962, with my team, to think about the next generation of submarines and the lessons learned from our work thus far. In particular the shape of the pressure hull to avoid stress concentrations and the design of the internal water systems and hull penetrations to preserve safety.

Both earlier classes had parts of their pressure hull forward and aft of less diameter than amidships to provide space for the main ballast tanks. The transition from one diameter to the other and conical shapes generally, were regions of stress concentration which we had been at pains to reduce with torospherical units, but which were best avoided if possible. Water piping under pressure in a submarine must be treated with respect; the force from a jet of water an inch in diameter at a pressure of 500psi and the resulting spray when it hits things within the sub-marine are difficult to imagine; its unbelievable. Wherever less pressure will suffice this should be used.

Hull valves and their connection to the hull were, I thought, a weak point particularly under shock loading from enemy weapons. There was little point in fitting back-up valves (which we did) if the connection of the valve to the hull should fail. US steel makers had begun to make large cast billets of their HY 80 steel, which were as strong and ductile as the plate, confounding all of our dogma that 'castings are brittle'. It seemed to me that here was scope for change. The other worry I had about hull valves was the time and difficulty of closing them by winding a hand-wheel round and round, even if we could mechanise the process. I wanted valves that would close with one simple stroke - ball valves, in fact. I could see how this could all be done in an elegant, unstepped hull, with unpressurised water systems and steel bodies welded integral into the hull to take ball valves. This was the shape of the future.

However at the end of 1962 I was told that I was to leave the submarine group in the early summer of 1963 to become the Professor of Naval Architecture in the Royal Naval College, at Greenwich and someone else would have to develop these ideas.

Post script~

Admiral Rickover was retired by order of President Reagan in 1982 having been in charge of the US Navy's nuclear propulsion programme for 30 years. As the years have passed I have come more and more to appreciate how great was his achievement and its contribution to the preservation of the free world. In the end, as the years took their toll, he was probably resisting all change. If I had to pen an epitaph it would be "The US nation can never repay him for his great achievements (but he went on doing it for too long)".

Chapter Eight

At Christmas 1962 I was told that my appointment as professor at Greenwich would not proceed and that I was to form a new submarine group to design the UK Polaris submarine and look after its construction within the DPT organisation.

In the late 1950's we had learned of the US Navy's proposal to launch ballistic missiles from submerged submarines to give the deterrent forces a degree of invisibility not achievable with land silos or aircraft. We had received information concerning the submarine aspects of the system and more general information about the missile and the on-board systems required to define the submarine's position precisely at launch, discharge the missile and programme it to reach its target. At the beginning of 1958 we learned that some of the US Skipjack Class were to have 130 ft added to their length to take two rows of eight missile tubes, fire control and navigation equipment. The ships would initially be armed with the Polaris A-1 missile with a range of 1200 nautical miles. Such was the urgency that the first ship, USS George Washington was commissioned 26 months after laying down and accomplished the first underwater launch in July 1960.

Within Ship Department I had informally looked at the design options for a Royal Navy ballistic missile submarine based on the Valiant SSN design. Problems foreseen were the maintenance of constant depth when launching 16 missiles weighing 20 tons apiece in rapid succession and the maintenance of secure communications with the UK government ashore. And of course maximum silence at all times to meet the three criteria, constant readiness, maintain secure communications and remain undetected.

In the post war era the V-Bomber force of some 325 aircraft equipped with free-fall bombs had constituted the British nuclear deterrent. The development of anti-aircraft defences made this force vulnerable and in 1960 the UK government contracted to buy the Skybolt missile from the US to be launched from the V bombers. To some extent this decision by the British Conservative government was meant to be some redemption for the cancellation of Britain's ICBM, Blue Streak. When the Skybolt project had cost half a billion dollars and was predicted to cost a further two billions, President Kennedy cancelled it. The US had land-based missiles and sea based missiles to take its place but the British were out on a limb. This opened the door to the acquisition of the Polaris system and at the end of 1962 conjecture became reality. Prime Minister MacMillan met President Kennedy at Nassau and the UK Polaris submarine project was born.

In January 1963 I led the Deep Technical Mission to the US Navy in Washington DC to obtain definitive information on the systems to enable the UK to design the British Polaris submarine with confidence. Pat Jarvis, destined one day to be Director General Ships was the weapons-electrical member of the team. We met the Special Project Director, Admiral Pete Galantin and his deputy Captain Levering Smith (the brain behind the US navy's strategic missile programme), and the Captains responsible for the missile, fire control, navigation and ship sub-systems. It came as a cultural shock to me to find that the submarine was regarded as a sub-system but I soon got used to it. What's in a name?

Vice Admiral Levering Smith is now retired. He was a true friend who followed the spirit as well as the letter of the Nassau Agreement. He clearly had no use for the flag officers shouting and bullying course. One's first meeting with Levering was, well, unusual. Our staff officer in Washington, had warned me in advance "Ask your question and wait, don't repeat it, just wait". But it was still a little unnerving to sit opposite a man and ask a question and wait 30 seconds, 60 seconds and sometimes more with his bright blue eyes fixed on one but doubtless far away, until he spoke and then out would come the complete answer arranged chronologically with all the relevant facts that also answered the three or so follow up questions that one had in mind.

The first week in Washington was more than unpleasant for me because I had influenza. Each day I would drag myself down to the Navy Department and each evening go miserably to bed. My bed was very hard and uncomfortable but one of my team assured me that American beds are much harder than we are used to in the UK. By the Saturday I felt sufficiently well to look at the bed and discovered that I had been sleeping on a board covered by just a sheet. I told the chambermaid that in future I would sleep in the other bed in the room. "You want that ah should move that board to that bed?" she asked.

Captain Bob Zeller who headed the ship desk arranged our briefings; It became clear to us that although these were good, the SP organisation did not have the information that we required and would need in great detail as our design progressed on how these missile sub-systems interfaced with the rest of the submarine's systems. We asked to visit the Electric Boat Co, shipyard at Groton NH, the lead yard for the US Navy's SSBN's and after some debate, which clearly had involved persuading Admiral Rickover, we were given permission.

The journey to Groton was by train. It was made the more interesting by the antics of the US Navy commander who was our escort. At each station he rushed to the telephone. We speculated on the reason. I could tell which members of my team spent most time at the movies. We discovered that he was in fact ringing his boss, Captain Bob Zeller to report progress. I am sure that was not Zeller's idea.

The Electric Boat Company made us welcome. They were already under contract to support the UK on the purchase and installation of the S5W reactor system in HMS *Dreadnought* and they co-operated fully in supplying the outline information that we required. We found that there were about 30,000 line items of shipbuilders supply equipment necessary for the installation of the Polaris weapon system in an SSBN and which had received no mention during our briefing in Washington. EBCo were, of course, providing these for their own boats and given US government approval would be pleased to give design support and provide equipment for the UK programme, thus giving the UK the benefit of the lower prices obtainable by being added to the already large and keenly priced orders for the US boats.

Mercifully we were not entertained to lunch by the EBCo senior management. I mention this because when I had visited the company at the outset of the *Dreadnought* contract I had been so entertained. A guide who wished to stress the British connection with the area had showed me around the yard. Unfortunately most of what he could recall involved wars in which we had been on opposite sides. He related how the commander of the garrison had surrendered to the commander of the British force who had promptly run him through with his own sword and how the British had then burnt the town 'just as they had burnt the White House in 1812.' When the time came for lunch I was invited to say a few words; almost as soon as I stood up the fire alarms sounded and fire engines rushed through the yard. All I had to say was "The British are coming".

From Groton we went north to Boston by train and were then driven further north to Portsmouth NH. It was evening; the countryside was white with snow and we were lodged in a rather nice hotel. I was struck by the contrast between night and day. At night we passed exciting looking places with bright coloured neon signs announcing their name and purpose. In contrast to Britain it looked exciting, like seeing Los Angeles from the air at night. Seen in daylight, however the signs were seen to belong to drab single storey wooden buildings with dirt parking areas and garbage out-back or used-car lots. There were power and telephone poles everywhere.

In Portsmouth Navy Yard the shipyard basin was covered with ice and we learned that here the submarines were built and launched bow first. We visited the SSBN, *Charles Adams* and met Captain Bill Heronemus USN who later in the year was to come to Bath as the SP ship (as distinct from weapons systems) representative. He told us that the practice for the senior living descendant of the president after whom the SSBN is named to be invited to sponsor the vessel can sometimes have embarrassing results. The US Navy had identified the lady and confessed to her in passing that they had had some trouble finding the Adams's. No problem said the gracious lady and come the day of the launch one couldn't move for members of the Adams family; there were nearly a hundred present.

Heronemus was the yard Repair Superintendent. USS *Thresher* was in dock following refit and I walked along her deck and met some of her officers and the yard officers responsible for the refit. A few weeks later she was to be lost with her crew and many yard personnel while carrying out a post-refit deep dive. When Bill Heronemus joined us in Bath he was still a very distressed officer obsessed with personal guilt that as the man responsible for her refit he should have been on board (and died) with those other splendid men.

A detail that I recall with some embarrassment was calling on the Rear Admiral Shipyard Commander at about 5.45 o'clock in the afternoon. He asked me if I would like something to drink and I didn't know what to say. In Britain, if it were getting on for 6 o'clock you would know that the admiral hardly meant tea but I didn't have a clue what was the done thing in US Navy yards. So I said lamely," Perhaps a glass of sherry" and in due course a steward brought me a tall glass filled with ice cubes over which a little sherry had been poured. To my horror the shipyard commander had nothing and doubtless went home that night and told his wife about the dissolute British.

On return to the UK we recommended strongly that the UK should opt for the latest US systems, the A-3 missile and the 640 Class submarine missile arrangement. Design work was already well advanced at EBCo on the SSBN 640 Class, six vessels of which were authorised in the fiscal year 1963 programme. These would deploy the A-3 missile having nearly twice the range and a greater payload capacity than its predecessors, which would be phased out as stocks were built up, and shipyard conversion capacity allowed. The US commitment to the successful development of the A-3 system was total and its timescale was compatible with the UK programme; it was clear that the UK should purchase this system, not only because of its superior military qualities and availability from current production, but also to avoid the possibility of early uniqueness of the British deterrent system. There were a few high ranking officials in Whitehall and Bath who felt that we should 'play safe' and go for the earlier and proven A-2 / 616 Class arrangement to whom I had to point out in words of one syllable that the UK would become the only user of that missile system when the USN updated its earlier boats and anyway they had a far greater and more urgent reason for making the A-3 system a success than the UK had.

We started the design in March and released the structural drawings to Vickers in April-May to enable them to order the steel. Deliveries commenced in September and fabrication began. The Resolution Class design was approved by the Board of Admiralty in December; a quite remarkable achievement.

The decisions that were made seem obvious now but at the time they required much thought. We adopted the US 640 Class missile section and to this added forward and after section's based on the Valiant arrangement, modified to take the electronics

157

associated with the A-3 system, and adjusted in diameter to align with the missile section diameter. It was of course a new structural and hydrodynamic design but this was the genesis. I was determined to keep to the British methods of fabrication of welded pressure systems with which our shipyards were now familiar. I also made all hull valves, ball valves, capable of rapid closure by a simple linear ram movement, the whole to be welded integrally in the pressure hull. All hull valves above a given (small) size would be capable of instant closure from a single control in the submarines control room and from the reactor/ machinery control room.

We decided to design our own hovering system on lines suggested by Roy Burcher.

A feature of the US Navy's Special Project organisation was the Management Meeting held every Monday morning at 8.00am at which the admiral and his captains were present together with the managing directors of the major contractors. This meant that a goodly number of those present spent every Sunday in an aeroplane or took the 'red eye' overnight flight, flying in from the West coast. The project was extensively documented with milestones for progress on every item and sub-item and corresponding financial projections. Reporting was usually at commander's level and against agreed milestones for progress and cost. There were other subjective reports with four headings of increasing intensity; the third one indicated that the reporting officer had a problem and the fourth indicated that, you, admiral, you have a problem. Rather like if you owe the bank 10,000 pounds you have a problem but if you owe them 10 million then they have a problem. The commanders reported against a three-month period, the amount of money obligated and progress achieved. The good guys had obligated over 90% of funds.

We were invited to attend this meeting whenever we were in Washington DC and I did so regularly; it was one of the most valuable management lessons of my career. We adopted the same management tools and indicators to manage the UK Polaris project. I devoted a lot of effort to making Vickers place orders at the earliest possible date - to spend money as fast as they could - a total reversal of the usual government practice.

Years later as Director General Ships, I would sit through high level presentations in which ship or weapons or dockyard project officers would present their progress curves showing expenditure in the first six months well below the planned level while claiming that the planned completion date would be kept. I would be disbelieved and somewhat resented for predicting that the project end date was already lost.

Another thing that I learnt was that the word "failed" was never used in SP. Remember that they were not only designing and developing the submarine systems but also the missiles themselves and all the things to make sure that they landed within a few metres of their target 2,500 miles away. It was a really gigantic achievement. The programme involved numerous missile firings to test various components and not all performed correctly the first (or the second or the third or the) time. We saw the reports and they never mentioned the word 'failed'. A missile might blow up 2 seconds after launch, this would be described as 'a non-success from which valuable lessons were learned'. And of course they were right.

The reason why we, the British, parade our failures so publicly might be because we always have inadequate funding for development of new systems and have to plead in each years estimates for money to carry on, usually with ministers and treasury officials who have little comprehension of technology and, regrettably, sometimes even less interest. The reason why we were able to succeed with the Polaris programme and complete it to time and cost was that we had the Prime Minister and Secretary of State Carrington firmly behind us from the outset.

With the Dreadnought project we had entered into the era of mega-documentation, with quality control, material's identification, planning and design, construction and support documents and handbooks orders of magnitude more detailed and numerous than before. The Polaris programme brought even more detailed documents and procedures and we began to believe the US quip that the weight of the documentation would equal the weight of the submarine by the time the first vessel was completed. We had all been much amused (and warned) by the LPH project's experience. This was the project to acquire a class of assault carriers to carry US Marines, their weapons and vehicles, their command and control, their helicopters and their landing craft. Because of shortage of space in the Pentagon and elsewhere, the project, under its Ship Acquisition Programme Manager would be accommodated in a disused brewery in downtown Washington DC. The great day came when the US corporations who had each spent some millions of dollars responding to the invitation to make proposals for the design and build of these useful vessels, delivered their responses to the project. Each set of the documentation weighed about seven tons and no sooner had they been wheeled in than the brewery floor collapsed.

The announced UK programme was for four or five submarines to be sure of always having two on patrol (and three for most of the time). It was evident that Vickers, Barrow had insufficient capacity to construct this number in the time available. Another builder was required. We were also much concerned about the problem of moving these large deep vessels through the shallow Walney Channel and also the possible dangers in the busy River Mersey, should Cammell Lairds be the second builder. This led us to privately consider whether it might not be better to build a new facility adjacent to Devonport Naval Dockyard to construct the SSBN's and to use this also for refitting them afterwards instead of Rosyth. It is interesting to speculate what would have been the long-term effect on the four yards had this decision been taken. The conclusion was that the work must be placed where the specialised submarine skills already existed and orders for two SSBN's each were placed with Vickers and Cammell Lairds with the former responsible for the programme as a whole and Len Redshaw as Builders Chief Executive. Six other firms were brought in as steelwork sub-contractors. The procurement of the missiles and the ship's missile associated sub-systems from the USA was handled directly between the two navies.

We had Vickers set up an office to handle the purchase of materials from the USA via The Electric Boat Co at Groton. We monitored the proposals closely, especially after we found that they had a tendency to 'go over the top' and buy everything from America presumably on the argument that, should anything be wrong, we couldn't blame Barrow. I even found them considering ordering and air freighting to Britain, aluminium ventilation trunking from America -the sort of thing a back street workshop in Wigan could make, given the chance.

Within DPT a deep study was made of the likely life-time spares requirements to support the British SSBN's since we would have to make the necessary US purchases while the US production lines were still open. Our boats would be identical for US equipment and elsewhere, as far as possible, would have the same equipments as our attack nuclear submarines to give us a greater population of applicable equipments and reduce the logistic task. As was usual with British warships, no deviation would be allowed. This was in contrast to the US Navy at that time where shipbuilders could fit their choice, provided it met the specification. We were allowed to visit the US submarine base at Holy Loch in Scotland where the true cost of non-standardisation was all too evident, the number of auxiliary vessels and lighters attached to the depot ship USS

Hunley, to carry the spares for all the attached submarines, was already a supply officers nightmare.

We had had an office at EBCo Groton for the Dreadnought contract and we arranged for it to continue. This time, however, we were not allowed to be within the company but had to be just outside. Admiral Rickover also dictated, not unreasonably, that the British were to be escorted whenever they went into the yard.

This question of secrets was a funny one. Admiral Rickover became more paranoid as the years passed. As part of the Agreement which authorised the purchase of the S5W machinery, Code 1500 was committed to keeping the UK informed on any problems with the plant. I rather assumed that we would receive periodic bulletins but we received not a word. The shutters came down when *Dreadnought* was completed and Rickover insisted that we should stand on our own. When many years later we did ask a question through the tortuous channel that he insisted on, the helpful reply was something like "If that's all that's troubling you, you're lucky"

Notwithstanding Rickover's prohibition, I was not in total ignorance of the general situation regarding US submarines in service and building. The US government and public press is a valuable source of information and really all that the Soviet had to do was to cross reference the information in various publications to get a fair picture of what the US forces were doing. No need for false beards. In my case the last item at SP's Monday morning management meeting was the ship sub-system that covered ships building and being refitted. I would sit at the back and listen to the officers making their reports about delays with machinery and reactor problems and other things in named submarines. I never made a note or mentioned what I had learned to others in the UK, but I was, as a result, that much more reassured that our experience was typical and Levering Smith knew how valuable that was.

In an SSBN the missiles are carried in launch tubes mounted vertically in the hull. The way in which the missile launch tube passed through the pressure hull and the means of ensuring that the basic strength of the hull was not impaired was crucial. The ability to make large strong castings with the strength and ductility of high strength steel plate could not have come at a better time. I approached British Steel and asked them for proposals for making five submarine sets - a total of eighty castings or forgings. We gave them a small development contract but they weren't enthusiastic. They attempted a forging but in a short while they said that the job was beyond them - not in those exact words - and we would be well advised to buy them from the US supplier. I ordered five ship sets through EBCo from General Steel, St Louis.

The missile is carried in a tube supported within the submarine's launch tube. In the system that we used this inner tube was moulded closely to the submarines tube but for the earlier A-1 missile system, the inner tube was freely supported by shock absorbing hydraulic cylinders. During my first visit I was shown this system being installed. I looked at the small space between the tubes and at the shock absorbers and remarked, "Who do you employ to fit those shock absorbers, dwarfs?". My guide said 'Yes, and here is one" as a midget emerged from the tube manhole.

Every three months I would visit Groton and review the status of every line item that we were purchasing against the 'required in UK' dates. The first time I did this I found that I was booked to fly from Kennedy to Groton and to check in at the United terminal. When we reached the terminal and looked about we found a small card which said 'Back at 4. 00 leave your bags here'. At about 3.50 a cheerful young man in shirtsleeves arrived and said, "lets take the baggage out". This sounded democratic so we followed this porter who, to my surprise, climbed into the pilots seat and said, "Lets go". I was sitting beside him as he taxied out into the maelstrom of voices and static that came over the cockpit speaker but soon we were speeding over the rooftops of Long Island on our short trip north. It is somewhat unnerving, however, when the pilot pulls a knob and out of the window one sees what looks like a piece of string move and a flap move, especially when the cheerful young man asks you to. I should point out that this was not a United Airlines flight.

Another flight that sticks in my mind was on Thanksgiving Eve. I was to take the evening RAF flight from New York and our staff in Washington had said "No problem in getting to New York. You take the shuttle on the hour, every hour". So I turned up at National airport and joined a milling mob, all of whom wanted the 6.00pm shuttle to New York. The shuttle promise was that even if one extra passenger arrived and found the aircraft full, an additional aircraft would be put on. Of course in the real world it takes so long to arrange, that the passenger finds himself on the 7.00 flight. I was on the third aircraft of the so-called 6.00pm shuttle — it was about 7.15 pm and we were airborne. From my seat I could observe the blue flames emerging from the two starboard engines of the Super Constellation. The scene on board was chaotic with the flight attendants pushing trolleys along the aisles collecting fares and so on. When I took stock of my neighbours I found that I was the only layman in about four solid rows of priests, most of whom were massaging their rosaries like mad. My immediate neighbour confessed that he was terrified. It had been bad enough waiting that extra hour at the airport and now the engines seemed to be on fire. I felt like singing "Nearer my God to thee". The thing that he found particularly depressing was that he would have to go through the entire process in reverse the following Monday because they had a reduced price block booking.

Groton, across the River Thames from New London, was a pleasant New England town in which someone in the early years of the century had placed a submarine builder and the Mohican Hotel. The hotel was remarkable; someone, perhaps in the first world war had built this large, square, red brick box, about 10 floors high and with more than a hundred rooms, in this small town in which all the other buildings were of two floors. The plumbing fixtures might still have been the originals but they worked and the per diem rate in 1958 was affordable to British government employees. A good number of Vickers staff and workmen visited Groton for training or otherwise in connection with the MoD's submarine contract. They declined to stay in the Mohican on the grounds that it was not of a sufficiently high standard and stayed at the more modern and considerably more expensive motel. The bill for all these Vickers costs was, of course, eventually paid by the British taxpayer as part of the submarine contracts..

From the upper floors of the hotel, trees stretched to the horizon as an unbroken carpet to the north, west and south. In places if one wandered into the woods, were the remains of dry stone walls placed there by the early settlers when they felled the forest and cleared the land of stones for cultivation. When the settlers moved on westwards to better farmland, the trees had grown back again. Up the coast was the historic harbour of Mystic.

One of the most pleasant afternoons at EBCo was being taken, with Pat Jarvis, to one of the northernmost of the Long islands, Block Island, by one of the EBCo missile system engineers who was an officer in the US Coastguard Auxiliary. His boat positively bristled with electronic aids to navigation. The island was the summer home of many exclusive New York families and in 1964 the public could not go more than a hundred yards or so from the landing place. We tied up to a private dock and were permitted to land and walk along lanes heavy with the scent of large privet trees that met above ones head. It was like being back in the quiet of old Dorset lanes. We hadn't walked far when we were overtaken by an elderly lady in her chauffeur driven Cadillac and the bucket of herrings between her feet in the back made us realise that it was she and her driver whom we had seen fishing out in the sound in a very small boat. She loved the British and had been a frequent visitor to London in her younger days.

There was a problem with the missile tube castings being made by General Steel and the inspecting authority, which happened to be the US Army, would not pass them. Both the US and UK deliveries were held up. After asking what the US Navy was doing about it and finding that there was some sort of inter-service hands-off understanding, I asked to see for myself. Commander (later Rear Admiral, USN) Kenny Wilson gave me a lift from Groton to New York in his early Volkswagen that seemed to have very light steering and to wander about the highway while he instructed me in the mysteries of baseball.

The castings were lined up in the hot sunshine. If one looked very closely there was some surface craze cracking, with none of these minute things deeper than a millimetre. I looked at all of the massive castings and said that they were acceptable to the Royal Navy. The reason that the plant was under US Army inspection was that its principal government product was cast tank bodies. In the plant were large moulds for the bottom and top halves of the tank body and a third mould for the gun turret. Cast in thick steel, quenched and tempered afterwards, these things were better than those made of welded steel plate and about half the cost. When I asked about the army inspection they told me that they counted the tanks as they rolled out of the gate, that's how reliable the process had become. Remember this is the steel for which British Steel could see no use when we went to them at the start of our nuclear submarine programme.

The steel was made in open-hearth furnaces and the firm's escort asked Kenny if he would like to go in one. Like an idiot he said, "Yes" and we were taken through the space where the hot gasses circulate to heat the furnace. This furnace had only recently been shut down and it was very, very hot and outside the summers day was sweltering.

That night the company entertained us to dinner in Stan Musials restaurant and took us to the ball game afterwards. This was a memorable occasion. I had expected something like a 1960's football crowd and instead the supporters were in summer frocks and jeans sitting on comfortable benches three tiers high on two sides of the diamond, itself green and brightly lit. The St Louis Cardinals were playing the Pittsburgh Pirates and each side displayed high skill. The Cardinals ace pitcher didn't do too well and his manager took him off, meaning that he couldn't pitch again in that game, without realising (or so it seemed to me) that he didn't have another pitcher worth a damn that night. So the Pirates won 13 to 2, which I was told was a quite remarkable score. Occasionally the ball would be miss-hit over our heads and out of the stadium and I would hear someone's windscreen shattering somewhere in Missouri behind me.

In the earlier SSBN's, before the introduction of the massive castings, the missile tube was connected to the hull by a huge weld, at least 20cm thick at the throat. One day, when crawling around one of the US submarines being built at Groton, I spoke with one of the EBCo welders who was making some of the hundreds of runs that made up such a weld. He was an athletic looking coloured man who told me how pleased he was to be back at work at the EBCo He produced his welders card which had his photograph and the types of welding he was qualified to perform on USN submarines and the dates on which he had last been checked out on these procedures for HY 80 steel, stainless steel and monel. He chatted quite freely and was proud to be working on SSBN's. I was reminded of the time that I had spent in US Navy ships. It was not unusual for an enlisted man to come up to me and say something like "Hi Commander, where are you from in England?" and then strike up a conversation on something of interest as we leant, side by side, say, on the bridge rail. No awkwardness or embarrassment about rank, simply two people talking.

Compare this with the same situation in a British shipyard or ship. There is an immediate and almost unbridgeable gap in which the welder or sailor answers in monosyllables and patently wishes that you would go away. The reaction is that you are checking up on them because you are a boss, you are one of 'them' and not one of 'us'. What other reason could you possibly have for talking with them? Stand fast the Chief PO's. It is perhaps only by observing such relationships in other countries that one realises how divided British society remains despite all that has been done to open up higher education and job opportunities. Alan Clark's Diaries illustrate how wide the gap is between those who feel they were born to govern and the rest.

At my quarterly progress meetings at EBCo I noticed that a set of electronic cabinets had been shown as 60% complete for several months and this time I demanded that our man on the spot, Constructor Commander John Cameron RCNC should see them. He returned to the meeting to say that they were not 60% complete, they didn't appear to exist at all and neither did those for the US Navy's boats. This triggered a great review of the entire situation and urgent recovery action by the company. Deliveries were rescheduled and we planned around them to avoid delays to our submarines. To their great credit, although they were in programme trouble themselves, the USN kept the UK in the same place in the delivery queue as before, we didn't go to the bottom of the list as I fear might have happened in a comparable situation elsewhere.

Such evidence as was available indicated that the flooding that had overwhelmed USS *Thresher* had been due to a hull valve failing at its bolted connection to the pressure hull. We had already developed the welded integral hull valve and all of our systems were welded, so we were OK. The US Navy took urgent action to develop sub-safe modifications, which delayed the completion of some of their submarines and thus eased the problem that the shortfall in other equipment deliveries would otherwise have presented. I was filled with admiration at the speed with which they moved once they were convinced that it was necessary. I believe that it was beneficial to them to have someone who was not of their navy with whom they could discuss these things informally, a relationship from which we, in turn, derived great benefit but which alas no longer seems to exist.

We were extremely fortunate in the US Navy officers and the US contractor's representatives who were seconded to work on the British project in the US and in the UK. Their encyclopaedic knowledge, good humour and dedication to the task was a constant inspiration that some of the British personnel found it difficult to equal. This example came from the very top, from Admiral Levering Smith and his captains whom we saw every six months at the Joint Steering Task Group meetings held alternately in the US and UK. The most memorable JSTG socially was held in Bath at the time of the Bath Festival when, for once and once only swimming would be allowed in the Roman Bath during a "Roman Orgy" that someone had dreamed up. Commander Stu Roy USN secured the tickets. Some visitors from the US entered into the spirit of the thing and came in togas, which got wet and stained yellow by the sulphurous waters of the bath. Their hotel was not amused when they took their sheets (sorry, togas) back.

Among the many visitors from the US Navy whom we got to know well was Commander "Chuck" Slonim but no matter what contribution Chuck may have made to the advancement of the UK programme, the thing for which he will be remembered, was losing his uniform trousers. It was like this. Chuck was staying at the Royal York Hotel and it was bitterly cold. We were gathered in one of the lounges and Chuck, in uniform was standing with his back as close as possible to the gas fire. He suddenly became aware that the back of his legs was hot and brushed at his right calf with his hand, whereupon the back of his trouser leg fell off.

The earlier mention of dedication to the task reminds me of the occasion when I emerged from my office into the corridor of C Block at Foxhill at about 5.30pm and was almost submerged by a tide of junior engineers and draughtsmen going home. It had not really occurred to me until then that, whereas what I did between 8.00am when I arrived in the office and 8.00pm when I went home was the most important thing in my life, to those draughtsmen what they did between 5.30 pm and 8.30 am the next morning was what really mattered.

Sometimes one got a new view on sporting events. I suggested to John Schilling a US commander on our London staff that we should go to Lords to see the Test Match and learn something of cricket. It transpired that he knew about cricket and gave me a new perspective by saying " Gee, Jack, how can you play a game for three days and then call it a tie?". I didn't like to stress that rain is our faithful ally in turning imminent defeat into a honourable draw. When it rains at a baseball game they give you a rain check. On another occasion we took Captain Joe Sneider to dinner in the pub at the far end of Walney Island at Barrow. We took a bus to its terminus at Walney and set out to walk in total darkness with the sea pounding on one side and marshland on the other. Joe kept up a barrage of complaints about the distance "Its only four miles" lied big Commander John Hughes, "when did you last walk four miles, Joe" to which the reply was "I have never in my life walked four miles". And he meant it. Joe was a retired officer whose other claims to fame were that he had been the unsuccessful Democrat candidate for mayor in New London and he had eleven children.

To operate a deterrent missile system it is essential to have continuous communication from Whitehall to the SSBN. This is especially difficult since radio waves will only penetrate a few tens of feet through water and the submarine can't spend its patrols at such shallow depths. Low frequency waves penetrate best and much effort has gone in developing extra low frequency transmitting systems. It was said at one time that half the state of Maine was the baseline for one ELF aerial system. When Resolution Class was being built we had to find a way to have the aerial close to the surface while the submarine was deeply submerged. The solution was to tow a buoy from the submarine, a buoy that could control its own depth beneath the rough Atlantic Ocean. When not in use the buoy would retract into the submarine's casing. We designed the system and addressed the mathematics of the buoy's self control system. Under advice we placed a small contract with an eminent professor at Cambridge to propose a solution or at least some equations of motion. Some time later he came to Bath and told us that we had a difficult problem. Yes, we said, forbearing to add that that was why we had consulted him. We waited expectantly but beyond telling us what we already knew he had nothing to offer. Thus began my lifetime's disenchantment with consultants, a view that a further 30 years of hard experience has done little to change.

I was reminded of an occasion some years before at the RINA when the control of submerged bodies was being discussed. A retired RCNC officer called Lloyd Woollard was present. He had written textbooks and had a reputation as a mathematician. To help people spell his name he would introduce himself as a "two commodity man". He stood up and said;

"The equations of motion of an oblate spheroid moving through a fluid beneath an oscillating surface are very complex and difficult to formulate".

We waited; he sat down. I can remember thinking if that's the way to build up a reputation; I can be hailed as a genius at the age of forty. Woollard had been the Personnel Officer when I had joined the department in Bath in 1942 and even then the years were beginning to tell. One could say of him as was said of Espinesse that "He only heard half of what was being said and reported on the other half'.

164

We made extensive model tests and trials of buoys and things at sea from submarines. One of the final trials of the first system was from an Oberon Class submarine sailing from Lerwick in the Shetlands. I had not been to Lerwick before – this was before the oil boom – and had been surprised at the readiness with which the sole hotel, the Victoria, took my telephone booking. When I arrived there I found that the hotel occupied the upper floors of the building with the public bars beneath. I climbed the stairs to reception and was told "Yeer we Mrs MacPherson to sleep an ye cum doon here to breakfast". I was given careful directions up the hill to Mrs MacPherson's cottage where I was made most welcome. The only problem was that it didn't get dark. It seemed to me at first glance that those who had planned Lerwick's main street had been odd. It went, say, north to south but it would turn right for about the length of a house go along for a few houses and then a left turn and a right turn would bring it back to its original line. One felt that the planners had been quite mad and then one reached the end of the street and the wind blew one flat on one's back.

For the trial a Ship Department electrical engineer, an expert in cables, accompanied me. We prepared the submarine and sailed for the trials at 06.00 the following morning. It was not dark and not light and from the bridge of the submarine as we drew away I suddenly realised that the figure standing placidly on the dockside was the electrical engineer who I had last seen, safely down below, nursing his instruments. No one had told me that wild horses wouldn't get him under the water in a submarine, the hell with promotion prospects.

The contract had been placed with Cammell Lairds to build two of the SSBN's. Notwithstanding a loyal bunch of good workers the firm did not have a good reputation for labour relations and we wondered whether we had delivered a hostage to fortune. I had a side bet with myself that Len Redshaw would manipulate things so that both the Barrow boats would be delivered before the first Cammells boat. At both firms we funded the construction of Polaris offices and other real estate to push the project along. Cammells, or rather Merseyside, lived up to their reputation. The first consignment of valuable bronze metal castings and fittings was delivered on a Friday and lodged in a secure store just inside the wall. On Monday the store was found to be empty.

US personnel liked visiting Cammell Lairds because of its proximity to Liverpool, the home of the Beatles. Each had seemingly been instructed by his daughter to bring back John Lennon or, failing that, a piece of the stage of the Cavern, the small Club/theatre where the boys had first achieved fame. This 'pieces of the stage' business proved lucrative for the shipwrights in Cammells rather in the way that pieces of timber allegedly from Nelson's flagship Victory had supplemented the wages of a few shipwrights in Portsmouth Dockyard in the pre-war years.

In 1965 President Kennedy gave a substantial increase in pay to US civil servants but not to the US servicemen with whom relativity in pay had hitherto existed. Our resident US Navy representative, Captain Bill Heronemus concluded with great regret that his salary was not sufficient to put his sons through college and that he would have to leave the navy and seek an academic career. This he did. Quite soon, Professor Heronemus was recognised for his work on the generation of power by windmills and was featured in Time Magazine.

Two journeys with Bill stick in my mind. It was my practice to travel to the shipyard at Barrow by day-train on a Sunday if required to be there on the Monday. The trains were slow and un-crowded and usually went via the Severn Tunnel to a mysterious place called Pontypool Road and then North through the delightful Welsh border country through Hereford and Craven Arms before rejoining the main line to Scotland. On this occasion the train went via Worcester. There beside the station was a factory, which announced to the world in large letters that this was the home of Lea & Perrins Worcestershire Sauce. I drew Bill's attention to this and he said "Gee, that's diary material" and duly recorded the fact.

The second journey was by car, one Saturday afternoon, from New London to Sturbridge in southern Massachusetts which was styled to show what life was like in late 18th Century / early 19th century USA. It was a hot afternoon and we followed the tracks around the village and saw people in authentic costume doing all (well, nearly all) the things they did in those days, working in the fields, spinning, weaving, sewing, milking, baking, working at the forge and so on. It was most interesting. It was also a long, slow, dusty, hot way round and I was secretly pleased when we got back to the starting place and could sit down with a cup of coffee. Bill had repeatedly remarked on the important role such realistic demonstrations played in reminding young people of the way the people who had built their nation had lived in the dim and distant past. In the end I could not resist pointing out to him that the house that he currently occupied in Bath UK had been built many years earlier than the period depicted here. All things are relative. The other thing I recall about that afternoon was how his driving had evidently been affected by two years of driving on the wrong side of the road in the UK!. It is a great honour to have known him.

Heronemus was a 'ship' man. The 'weapons' man with us was Commander Stu Roy US Navy. Stu was a tower of strength in all ways and paid Britain the ultimate compliment of marrying a Scottish girl, Lorna. His early death was a profound shock.

There was much speculation at the possible outcome of the general election to be held in Britain in 1964. The Labour party, under Harold Wilson, was generally considered by the media to be the likely winner. The party executive was opposed to the retention of nuclear weapons and committed to the cancellation of the UK Polaris programme but important personalities in the shadow cabinet were thought to be somewhat ambivalent on the issue. Ever mindful of the employment opportunities, there was talk of turning the Polaris submarines into attack nuclear submarines.

To satisfy my curiosity I took the Polaris design and removed the missile system and re-jigged the remainder to produce a balanced SSN design with the minimum waste of ordered materials and equipment. The resulting design was about 30 ft longer than Valiant Class. A profile and plans were drawn and given the title HMS *Harold Wilson*. It was shown to a few friends in the Naval Staff and put away. In the current political climate we thought it to be a good joke. Imagine my feelings when, one day, the First Sea Lord asked to see the Harold Wilson design.

I pressed on with equipment orders and I committed funds. The five ship sets of sixteen missile tube castings were delivered from America and put in a field somewhere in the Lake District and we generally stocked up for life.

Labour won the election and decided that work was too far committed for cancellation of the four submarines now building to be possible but the fifth SSBN would not be ordered. The postscript is that the fifth boat set of castings were sold back to the US Navy for use in updating an earlier SSBN to take the A-3 missile, without loss to the British taxpayer.

I left the project in January 1966, was promoted and went to the Imperial Defence College for a year's study, which was followed by a research appointment. During this time I witnessed the minor drama of the launch of HMS *Repulse* at Barrow when tugs were unable to secure her quickly enough and the hull grounded on a falling tide, eventually to be seen high and dry on the Walney Channel sands. It so happened that we had some time earlier looked into the stability of grounded submarines, would they roll over as the crew flooded compartments and attempted to escape for example and I knew that she would sit there safely upright until the next tide floated her off. She was a splendid sight; this was the one occasion on which I saw the whole beauty of the shape of an SSBN. I quite enjoyed the launch lunch but there were many empty chairs.

I returned to DPT in 1970 by which time the first three missile submarines were in the patrol cycle and the fourth working-up in readiness for her missile firing trials.

This is not the place for a technical dissertation, but the Resolution Class SSBN's were really splendid submarines.

Chapter Nine

I was the first naval constructor officer appointed to the Imperial Defence College where senior officers of the armed forces, diplomatic corps and home civil service, destined for higher rank were brought together for an updating on world affairs. The concept of the IDC had been Winston Churchill's in the 1920's reasoning that generals appointed, say, C in C Middle East could be expected to know all about the forces in the area but their duties would require that they should have an understanding of the politico-economic factors and personalities, as well.

The 1966 course had ten officers each from the navy, army, air force and civil service and twenty-eight similar officers from Commonwealth nations. The latter included five from the USA. They were an impressive bunch, particularly the soldiers. I had seen soldiers do all sorts of brave things in the war, like rushing up beaches while someone shot at them or being landed from submarines and disappearing into the jungle and had thought them to be very brave but not very clever. After all, if they were clever they wouldn't be rushing up beaches etc.

The IDC altered all that. Like their air force colleagues, these soldiers had passed qualifying examinations for advancement and many had taken time out for university. Most of the naval contingent had only their cadet training and sub-lieutenants examination and of course had taken naval specialist courses: thereafter they had been promoted on the basis of their annual reports, a system that, no matter what correcting factors were applied by the Second Sea Lords department, inevitably clones officers in the mould of those who have gone before and, in time, breeds mediocrity. There were two naval students who, in the whole year, did not ask a single question of any of the distinguished personalities who came to lecture in the college and there was another who asked every lecturer whether they deplored the recently announced decision of the British Labour government that the Royal Navy should have no new aircraft carriers, irrespective of the subject on which the lecturer had addressed us, be it Transport Policy or the economics of Outer Mongolia.

The civil servants had their characters; the scientist who sat at the back of the lecture hall with a long woollen scarf around his neck like a prototype Dr Who of TV fame, and the administrator who always asked very profound three part questions each part of which had two or more sub-parts, you could see the lecturers eyes become glazed. There was also the Treasury man whose impish sense of humour was never far below the surface, yet who could say "No" most charmingly and finally.

The Commandant was General Sir John Anderson, a delightful Ulsterman. He attended most lectures and thanked the lecturers afterwards. One quickly learnt that his use of superlatives was quite different from one's own and much more sensible. If he thanked the speaker for a splendid lecture, that meant that it was about average. And so on upwards. He shared this trait with the eminent Danish physicist, Nils Bohr who, it is said, greeted new pieces of work from his students with the comment "Magnificent", meaning average; thereafter they went down, "Very, very interesting" meant not much good at all. For the first month we all wore badges with our forenames; thereafter we were expected to remember them. On Day 32 Sir John passed me in the cloakroom "Morning Peter" said he "Jack, Sir" I replied to a departing back. Round the corner "Morning Peter " "Ted, Sir" said a New Zealand voice, "Morning Peter", "Morning Sir" a voice replied. By now the Commandant was on his way back; he passed me with a grin and said "I knew I would get one in the end".

1966 was a General Election year. A Conservative political agent from Smith Square was resident in the Belgravia hotel in which I stayed during the week. George Wigg, a member of Harold Wilson's government had an apartment in nearby Eccleston Square. He was nominally the Paymaster General but, according to Whitehall insiders, seemed to have a more sinister role as Wilson's spy on his own cabinet. At this time it was suspected that Wigg was orchestrating 'spontaneous' heckling and worse at Conservative party election meetings and my friend the agent was interested in the number of young men who were constantly in and out of George Wigg's apartment. It was all good political fun. Today, regrettably, an entirely different construction would probably be put on this.

Ministers, ambassadors and service chiefs all addressed us. For the first time the Soviet ambassador was numbered among them. Two grey men who sat in the front row accompanied him. He opened his talk by reminding us of the great size of the Soviet Union, from Poland in the west to Vladivostok in the east, ten time zones "In fact" he said, "it might be said that the sun never sets on the Soviet Union". That brought the house down and thereafter he had a captive audience. He spoke brilliantly for about forty minutes and concluded with five minutes of political dogma, presumably for the benefit of the two men in the front row.

In the first term we were concerned with economics and communism. I read Karl Marx for the first time and found that I did not disagree with much of it. I would read communist books in the train to Bath on Friday evenings, sometimes to the concern of little old ladies sitting opposite. The supporting programme of visits was to city institutions such as the stock exchange, the Baltic Exchange, Lloyds and so on.

At Easter we broke into a number of groups and visited industry in a part of Britain. My group went to the North East; we visited a coalmine, a chipboard factory, a brewery, a chocolate factory and a shipyard. Only in the nationalised coalmine did we find any real rapport between management and men and evidence of planning. The chipboard people were doing a good job using waste wood from the Kielder forest. The brewery was making money but should have been making a good deal more. I looked at the pipe systems where aluminium, copper and stainless steel pipes were joined together and asked the chief engineer if he had corrosion problems? Did he have corrosion problems! He said that they poured away hundreds of gallons of beer each morning and after the lunchtime break because the beer lying in the pipes was tainted by corrosion. I wondered whether the company paid excise duty on this wasted beer and what sort of supervision they had to prevent some of this beer being diverted by enterprising employees.

The chocolate company was famous for its chocolate biscuits; we wondered for how much longer because, it seemed, the chocolate was made up there in one building and then carried across the road and taken up there to where the biscuits were in another building. The shipyard had just had a 4 million pound modernisation and the management methods were still in the ark. What was most interesting was that the other IDC members with no industrial experience whatever unerringly picked out the shipyard management as the worst of the set.

The coalmine was interesting. The air commodore in our small party might have flown missions over Berlin but he had to be persuaded that the honour of the air force was at stake before he would come underground. While we were being briefed I asked whether the holes created by the removal of the coal remained or fell and caused surface subsidence in later years. I was told that the roof comes down and fills the space 'in due course'. A thousand feet down and more than a mile out under the North Sea we reached the coalfaces. About 25 men out of a pit strength of 1,800 were actually operating the machinery on this, one of two faces. I crouched between the steel props as the rotary cutter made its cutting way across the face to where a large recess had been cut into which it would advance, ready for the return cutting run. The foreman shouted to me to stay within the steel pit-propped frame while the whole lot moved forward about 3 ft. ready for the return run - and the now un-propped roof beside me promptly fell down with a tremendous roar. So much for 'in due course'

A lecturer during the year was the Minister of Transport, the motorway network was a subject of interest and she told us that her ministry estimated the cost of completing the country links at £ 1.5 billions and the urban parts at £2.5 billions. These were heady sums in 1966. I suggested to her that the major reason for providing the motorway network was the carriage of goods from factories to ports and retail outlets and the general stimulation of trade and hence such carriers might be expected to bear the major part of these costs. I asked her what was her ministry's estimate of the increase in cost per ton mile of goods carried, necessary to yield £4 billions over a reasonable number of years, say, ten? She replied that the ministry had never looked at it in that way.

The second term was concerned with the world and global politics and the armed forces. We spent a day at sea with the navy and a day climbing in and out of aircraft at an RAF station in East Anglia. We went to Germany to visit the Army of the Rhine and Berlin. We drove tanks and other army vehicles and once was enough for me. We slept in a panzer barracks but our Treasury man was billeted with the CO of a cavalry regiment. He arrived early and was entertained by the colonel's wife who explained that they did quite nicely, living on their allowances and banking her husband's salary in England. And no, they didn't have anything to do with the Germans. When the husband arrived home and learned what had been said and that their guest was the man in the Treasury who might deal with their allowances the shock was so profound that his spur came off and shot under the settee. Well, that's Bernard's story.

We did the usual things in Berlin, like lining up with our toecaps on the border at Checkpoint Charlie and being photographed by the East German guards. As an occupying power the IDC went for a tour of East Berlin, all except the Treasury man and I because of the nature of our jobs, mine because of Polaris and Bernard because of certain funds that he handled. It's a rum world isn't it. We visited the HQ of the British forces, Berlin, in the Olympic stadium where Hitler had refused to recognise Jesse Owens the great US sprinter because he was black. We gathered, chatting, in the lecture theatre that had rows of hinged seats all tilted up. Suddenly a stentorian voice shouted "Sit down" and various Brigadiers, Air commodores and Civil Servants tried to sit on seats that were not there only to find that the GOC Berlin was talking to his dog.

In the evening Bernard and I went to a Bier Keller. It was vast and had a bandstand complete with brass band. It was all very jolly. The bandleader invited people to come up and conduct the band. We did not know, and obviously neither did the unfortunate man who was at the centre of the resulting scene, that at the conclusion of his number, the fledgling conductor is asked to buy each of the band members a drink "or should we say, settle by giving the band DM 100" for the privilege of conducting. When we left the last amateur conductor was still arguing.

For the visit to Germany we were transported in an RAF Britannia aircraft from Lyneham. On arrival back at Gatwick and clearing customs I rejoined the aircraft for a lift back to Lyneham since I lived in nearby Bath. The cabin staff was busy mustering the crockery glasses and cutlery with which the plane had been provided for the visit to Germany. From my seat in the middle of the cabin of this "whispering giant" aircraft I could hear them chanting "one spoon, officers" "one knife, air marshals" and so on. There was mention of an unopened bottle of white wine; apparently the air force had supplied wine for the Commandant and his two-star directors sitting at the front of the cabin. No one suggested that the surplus bottle of wine should be returned to the RAF station supply organisation. When I stood up to leave the aircraft I remarked on the quietness of the cabin environment. The warrant officer had the grace to look sheepish.

The RAF officers on the course were an enigma. Their training or something seemed to have made them nitpickers, more at home in the detail than in the big scenario. There was one exception a rather splendid Air Commodore from High Wickham who had himself left the air force and had been invited back. One senior man's contribution to any syndicate's work was to ensure that the paragraphs were correctly numbered according to the latest NATO standard. They were a source of innocent delight to the RAAF Air Commodore on the course, an engineer pilot. I spent a lot of time trying to persuade them that the Air Staff were wrong in stating requirements for faster and bigger aircraft. Since the aircraft of the future would be the launching vehicle for autonomous target seeking missiles, it didn't really matter if it went at Mach 1 or the Mach 2 plus they kept specifying. The burden of my message was the absence of numbers of RAF aircraft from the skies of Britain; far better to purchase a hundred souped-up Hawks to fly about and let the great British public see that we still had an air force, than to buy twenty precious Mach two plus planes that have to operate over the sea. All the public sees are Hercules C 130's doing things for the army. Who needs an air force?. They were just as receptive as the Chief of Naval. Staff was, many years later, when I tried to persuade him that what the future navy would require was large numbers of moderate speed patrol ships of about 1,800 tons with a sonar, a helicopter and a close-in defence system to work in concert with the nuclear attack submarines and the army in war and the fishing fleet in peacetime.

In days gone by, people going overseas or for a holiday trip round the bay, would see warships in or near the ports – Britain's sure shield and jolly Jack and all that. Nowadays more and more people go overseas but they go to an airport, they never see a ship and there is no longer an instinctive pride in the navy in the population at large.

One of the more interesting days was the day we were told that we were the Soviet General Staff and invited to view the world scene from that staff's viewpoint. The thing that I recall most graphically was a view westwards from the Kremlin, across Russia, then Poland, then East Germany, then West Germany, then the low countries to the Channel and across there, lost in the misty distance, was a smallish island.. As a Soviet General my reaction was "Why should I bother about what the British might think". NATO was a different proposition.

In the summer the IDC went further afield in groups to various parts of the world. I volunteered to go to southern Africa but this was cancelled because of the political climate at the time and we went to South America instead. We had our own Comet 2 b aircraft. There were about twelve IDC students and, we found, an aircrew of fourteen, all sorts of squadron bods had come along for the ride plus three tons of spare parts, of which only one rubber "0" ring was required on the six week tour. The squadron bods included two fitters to do any repair work. I gathered from the RAAF Air Commodore member of the group that the fitters were disgruntled because they were not eligible for flying pay, it having been ruled that they were only doing what they would have done in the UK where they might be flown to a grounded aircraft to do a repair. Looking at the wing commander and squadron leaders who had come simply for the ride and who spent all day lounging around hotel swimming pools but who were getting flying pay, I had some sympathy with the aircraftmen.

The pilot and captain of our RAF Comet was a pilot officer called John Tulip. His co–pilot and navigator were both squadron leaders, a situation that I had only encountered before in a Russian submarine where time in submarines determined seniority of command and not the number of rings one wore on ones sleeve. Tulip and Co. had not flown to South America before and always flew over an airport at which we were about to land to have a good look at it before landing. At Brasilia we flew over the airfield several times before landing; the reason was that the Brazilians had moved a radio beacon a week earlier and had not yet published the fact. It was still transmitting and inviting aircraft to fly into an adjacent hill. The Brazilian government was in process of moving the centre of government to Brasilia and away from Rio where most ministers, civil servants and the whole diplomatic corps would prefer to remain. I thought that it was an exciting concept designed to remind Brazilians of the size and wealth of a great country awaiting development.

A concept that I believe would greatly benefit Britain would be to move Parliament to Manchester for some months each year and thus force our many MP's who seem to have gone straight from Oxbridge to Westminster to recognise that the real industrial wealth of Britain, in which jobs are as important as profits, is located somewhat further north than Watford.

By way of contrast the British Motor Corporation was in process of closing its manufacturing and assembly plant in Brazil because it was not profitable while Volkswagen was taking a longer view and expanding its plant in a nation who's population was expected to grow to 100 millions by the year 2,000. Actually it reached 164 millions by 2000 and Volkswagen are selling cars like hotcakes. In similar vein, we were taken for a boat trip around Santos harbour. This was, and probably still is, Brazil's busiest port yet there was not a single ship flying the British Red Ensign among the fifty or so ships present. French, German, Spanish, Russian, Dutch, Panamanian and US flags but no Brits. Surely there should be some remnant of national pride somewhere?

At a reception in Sao Paulo some of the expatriates complained a little about the time that it took to get a new service such as a telephone installed in their homes in the suburbs and the poor surface of some suburban roads. This was not to be wondered at because, at the time, there was considerable migration from the countryside into the city whose population was growing by about 250,000 each year. Imagine how long it would take to get a telephone in Bristol if it doubled in size each two years. Sao Paulo's population reached 16.5 millions by 1995.

Flying down from Brasilia to Montevideo we passed over a city called Frey Bentos. I had always imagined this to be an obscure translation of corned beef! Uruguay is a vast country, which at the time had a population of two and three quarter millions of whom one and three quarter millions lived in Montevideo. I don't remember the size of the army but at one reception given in our honour there were over a hundred generals and colonels present. The idea that I advanced to their naval chief's that they could use hovercraft to patrol the shallow but wide estuary of the River Plate foundered on the fact that the crew needed would be less than 20. What they wanted was something that would have two or more funnels and justify a Captain, several commanders, a couple of hundred men and perhaps even an admiral.

On arrival in Buenos Aires we were given a motorcycle police escort along the motorway into BA. We passed under the concrete bridge upon which someone had daubed "Go home Yankees" and someone else had daubed below "Via Pan Am". Our helmeted police escort had dark blue uniforms and black jackboots. If a car did not move to the side quickly enough they rode up beside it and kicked the drivers door, at 60 mph. One little old man was driven right off the road as we swept past.

The worst event of my time at the IDC was in Argentina where some genius arranged a visit to an abattoir. To our mounting horror we were shown the sickening whole works, from the Judas donkey to the packaged product. The one impressive thing was the special cleanliness and hygiene feature the firm had been forced to introduce to win a contract from the Campbells soup company. What we, the students, never forgave was that our Rear Admiral team leader and the naval attaché BA who had arranged this ghastly visit, did not appear until the visit was over.

We flew to Cordoba to visit the aircraft works and see a small missile fired; there was no guidance system. We were the weekend guests of prominent families. Brigadier Glyn Gilbert and I were the guests of the Roca's in their town house and briefly at their hacienda in the foothills of the Andes. Senora Roca was a noted landscape artist of whose work I had, quite by chance, seen examples in the hotel in Buenos Aires. On the Friday evening they took us to a reception given by their son-in-law the Governor of Cordoba province. The mayor of Cordoba City was present; he was married to their other daughter. Driving home afterwards Senora Roca suddenly said, "I would like my sister to meet you, we will call at her palace". We did and it was.. Externally it looked like the British Museum; we mounted the steps and entered through Doric columns. The vast reception room had galleries on all four sides above, giving access to the upper rooms. We sipped sherry with her young lady companion and after a while were joined by our elderly hostess for a short while before she re-entered the lift and disappeared upstairs again. The next morning we went to the hacienda.

We flew south from Cordoba before turning west into Chilean airspace and then north to Puerto Montt where the people spoke German. On the second day we went by bus for miles along dusty roads, past Lago Llanquihue, and La Ensenada, past a volcano called Osorno that had last erupted four years earlier and up into the Andes to the border of Chile and Argentina where we stopped at the poor looking tavern that was our destination. The proprietors were an elderly Scotsman and his Chilean wife. I do not know what grapevine had told the IDC that he was there but our leader had brought with him a bottle of Johnnie Walker whisky and we all sang 'I belong to Glasgow' and the old man wept.

Perhaps the most amusing thing about our arrival in downtown Lima was that we found our way impeded by a procession to which our cars added themselves for a mile or so, until they could cut away to the right while the procession went round the square outside our hotel. Only then did we realise that the procession was anti-American and anti-British. It got rowdy later on and the riot-police who we had spotted waiting in their vans up side streets, duly intervened.

It is remarkable how British governments had neglected this great continent. In 1966 a British Foreign Secretary visited South America for the first time to meet with the ambassadors who came to Lima for the occasion. The only embassy that Canada had in the continent was in Lima. When we arrived there not only a British diplomat but also a Canadian diplomat met us since we had a Canadian brigadier in the IDC party. The Canadian diplomat was a very attractive young lady. At a reception the following evening they were at different ends of the room. Someone asked her what was wrong with the brigadier and she said that he had started to behave foolishly last night and she had told him that he reminded her of her father.

South American navies had a long history of buying their warships from the UK but in the post-war period the market was to a certain extent satisfied with surplus US ships. Not so Peru. To visit Callao was like visiting Portland. In the bay were two ex-RN Colony Class cruisers and four Daring Class destroyers. Fast patrol boats crossed the harbour, powered by Napier Deltic engines. Knowing the problems that we had with these engines, I asked how they got on. "Oh" they said, "we had to strip them down and change some of the clearances and they are alright now". The RN's problem could have been that we kept shipping them back to the manufacturer who kept putting new components in, instead of letting some of the RN's artificers have a go at adjusting the tolerances as had the Peruvians. The C in C of the navy did not speak English but he had a German wife so I spoke German to the wife and she translated it into Spanish for her husband. No wonder that he looked puzzled.

There was little foreign currency for the importation of new cars and models that had long disappeared from the streets of the USA and UK were common. Most cars were battered, indeed at the time I described the average Peruvian as a man who could reduce a new car to matchwood in six months and then keep it running for the next twenty years by sheer mechanical genius.

We went to the heavily guarded Gold Museum and to several others that seemed to be filled with shelf upon shelf of rather ordinary looking Inca pots. I was not then aware of the duplicity and cruelty of the Spanish conquerors who came in 1532 and my thought at the time that the reason the Inca's were overcome was that they were too busy making pots, now has a rather sick ring to it.

South America throbbed with music and colour despite the real poverty that was only too apparent away from the city centres. I was filled with admiration for the Roman Catholic priests who lived as well as worked among the shantytowns and who in the end were censured by the Vatican for their too close involvement with the plight of the people.

The Columbian armed forces transported us from Bogota to Cali. The first leg was in a C-46 cargo plane to the foothills of the Andes where we got into a bus. We drove in tropical heat through fields of flowering trees and bushes and gradually started to climb. After a while I realised that at each corner there were little groups of soldiers who got into their transport and started down the mountain after we had passed. We learned afterwards that these were there to prevent us being robbed or kidnapped by brigands. Soon we were freezing as we crossed the divide and started the long descent to another airfield where our RAF Comet waited to take us on the final leg to Cali.

No sooner had we arrived in our hotel than we were off again to a reception by the Governor of the province. We hadn't eaten since breakfast and it was now 7.OOpm. We were taken to an enclosed estate - it was pitch black - where there were lots of people and drink but no Governor and no food. At about 9.00 he arrived accompanied by a most beautiful girl in a black gown, whom he introduced to us as his mistress. Somehow the other guests drifted away and we were taken to an adjacent room for a buffet meal at about 10.00 pm, quite early by Cali standards we learned.

We flew from Cali over endless jungle to the airport for Caracas, situated near to the Caribbean coast. The drive to the capital was through a long tunnel beneath the coastal mountain range. Benito Mussolini might have built the government buildings, with huge columns fronting buildings and vast parade grounds for ceremonial parades. We stayed at the closely guarded Military Club; this did not prevent one of our Canadian officers having his wristwatch stolen off his wrist as he mounted a flight of steps between club buildings. The British Embassy was on the seventh floor of a downtown office block. When I remarked on this, and 'Why?' the ambassador asked whether I had ever tried to throw a brick through a seventh storey window?. The other unexpected thing, at the time, were the light aircraft that flew close past the window en-route to landing at a small airfield within the city limits.

Guyana seemed to be an exercise in man's futility. The coastal strip about 10 miles wide is below sea level and is protected by a sea wall which it took a goodly part of the annual budget to maintain. In case the wall should fail the houses were built on stilts. The population was equally divided between Amero-Indians and Indian-Indians brought in by the British as indentured labour when the Amero-Indians declined to work hard in the sugar cane plantations. These two ethnic groups did not like each other   The sugar cane was transported by small iron barges in canals, which seemed to surround all the fields. We were told that there were piranha fish in the canals. I didn't put my hand in to find out. We stayed in what seemed to be the only hotel in Georgetown whose end wall on close inspection was found to be covered with flattened 5-gallon gasoline cans nailed in place like tiles.

Sugar and Bauxite were the major export products and we were flown inland along the brown-sugar coloured Demerara River to the vast bauxite plant. There were two aircraft, a seaplane and a landplane. For obvious reasons I chose the landplane flown by a British army air-corps pilot; after all, to crash is one thing but to crash and be eaten by piranha fish would be inexcusable.

But our final night was memorable. We were guests at a reception in what had six months earlier — before independence— been the Governors residence. The party was on the upper floor with all the windows wide open to attract a breeze. The sisters of two of the famous three 'W's' of test match fame were present and beneath on the lawn the Guyanan Police steel drum band played in the starlight.

This tour had been the experience to end all experiences; we never passed through customs or immigration in any country and Presidents and Ministers lectured us wherever we went. Our route was the Azores, Cape Verde Islands, Recife, Rio de Janeiro, Sao Paulo, Santos, Brasilia, Montevideo, Buenos Aires, Cordoba, Puerto Montt, Santiago, Lima, Bogota, Cali, Caracas, Georgetown, Bermuda, and home. It was extremely tiring and after 24 hours rest at home we would all have cheerfully repeated the whole thing.

At the start of the final term each overseas tour team made a presentation of the highlights of their tour. As might be expected the soldiers took charge and stage-managed excellent reports. The team that had visited the USA had been to Lockheed's and had seen plans for their aircraft to out-jumbo the 747 jumbo. I have no recollection of its dimensions or power but it would have had 28 toilets and that must be a big aircraft.

The third and final term at the IDC was full of interest on current world issues but it was evident to me that the thoughts of many of my friends were on their next appointments.

There was a considerable social content during the course including weekly movies (at which I saw my first coloured film, The Pink Panther) to which wives were invited. We all had our stories. I was introduced to an Australian officer's sister-in- law. "I'm Glaad" said she, "Yes" I replied "I'm happy, too" " Naw", she said "Me names Glaad". A really nice lady who told me her entire life story between soup and coffee. Then there was the wife from the sub-continent who confessed that she was fed up with being expected to be a sophisticated western wife in public and then go back to Putney and behave like an eastern slave. Everything was done discreetly; it was some time before I learned that the reason that I no longer saw a certain officer's wife to talk with at the weekly reception was that she had run away with a Swiss banker.

Two years later the college was renamed The Royal College of Defence Studies and the student body was no longer restricted to the old Commonwealth (and the USA). I am grateful to have been there while the shades of Empire were still discernable.

It was perhaps typical that of all the people attending the 1966 course at the Imperial Defence College, the only one who left not knowing his next posting was myself. In late December I called on Sir Jack Sims and he asked me where I would like to go. I said "Ship Production" which clearly surprised him. He said "Why on earth should you wish to do that? Those jobs aren't for people with Firsts" I said that at the end of the day we were judged by the ships as they entered the fleet and I felt that the builders could do with a good deal of sharpening up. He said that would have to wait a bit and that I was to become the Assistant Director responsible for research. I thought Hydrodynamics and he said "No, Materials".

This was a job in which one could do much or simply swim with the tide. I was now responsible for everything from waste bins to the materials from which ships were built and perhaps equally importantly how those materials were joined together and examined.

The day I joined one of my constructors invited me to visit Thornycroft's at Southampton the next day when a two-thirds scale section of the proposed new plastic mine- sweeper would be launched ready for testing. I duly attended and examined the thing, which was built from thousands of plastic boxes covered with an inner and an outer skin, all glued together with epoxy resin. I was told that this sort of box-core construction was used for protecting RAF aircraft deployed in NATO. Now of all the ships in a navy, the type most likely to be exposed to underwater shock is the minesweeper or as the new ones were to be styled, the mine counter-measures vessels. It is their job to detect enemy mines and make them harmless; in some cases by counter-mining and when things go bang under-water, there is shock.

In my submarine world, large panels representing proposed hull units and fittings were built and exposed to increasingly severe underwater shock levels as a matter of routine, so as the test section slipped down the launch ways I turned to my young man and asked to see the shock test results for this egg-box sort of structure when we returned to Bath. I was astonished to be told that shock resistance had not been considered. I told him to have the company in Bristol, who had encouraged him to adopt their boxes, manufacture some flat panels for explosion testing at the Naval Construction Research Establishment at Rosyth and at the same time manufacture some panels of the same weight per square foot without the box-cores, for comparison.

The company, which was used to dealing with the Ministry at Supply on aviation projects, adopted a hostile attitude and questioned the right of this new man to ask questions about their product. They flatly refused to make the non-box core panels and spoke of taking legal action if I went ahead and shock tested panels made with their box-cores. I told them to stop being stupid and ordered some panels from English Electric in Preston..

The panels went to NCRE for testing. They were mounted on massive steel chambers and lowered into the sea and explosive charges set off at calculated distances from them to subject the air-backed panels to shock loads of increasing severity. Since each test panel is tested separately at a series of shock levels and brought to the surface for examination between shots until serious damage is registered, this is time consuming and costly. As I expected, the box-core panels failed at a ridiculously low shock factor. I banned their future use on the ship project and set out to develop the single skin structure that common sense dictated. The responsible constructor was moved to other duties.

Thornycroft's were taken over by Vospers to become Vosper-Thornycroft and it was on this company that we relied to develop the techniques to manufacture ships hulls out of plastics. This was by no means an easy task and the measure of their success is the ships at sea. The British navy was the pioneer in this work, which attracted lively interest on the part of our NATO allies. They all wanted to come and see the work in progress and we had to agree that NATO military representatives (but not people like industrialists) could visit. One day we received a panic call from Vospers to say that of the team of four from the Italian navy who had arrived for a scheduled visit that day, three were from their competitor dressed up in naval uniform for the occasion - doubtless instant reservists.

Another of my responsibilities was paint. At first glance not very exciting perhaps but think a little; if properly applied it protects the steel ship from corrosion, if it fails and has to be renewed it adds to the top weight of ships and reduces stability and it occupies a great deal of the sailors' time in cleaning-off and repainting. Then there is the paint that we put on the bottom of ships to stop weeds and barnacles growing, which would reduce the ship's speed and degrade sonar performance.

I collected a great deal of data. It appeared that frigates were painting themselves overall eight times a year. Tons and tons of paint were being sloshed on. Investigation showed that ships did not paint themselves because the paint had failed as a protective, but because it had become dull. Closer questioning showed that the dullness was apparent when the paint nearby had had to be touched up because it had suffered local damage, like being struck hard when coming along- side, in which case the new paint was shiny and the good old paint wasn't. Furthermore, the navy was convinced that Brand X paint was better than the battleship grey paint ('pussers' paint) supplied through the Naval Stores organisation..

Weather deck painting and preparation was another disaster area.

The anti-fouling paint applied to ships bottoms works by gently leeching out poison into the water to kill the things that would settle there. The current formulation would be effective for two years and someone had raised a research item for one that would last for four years.   In my experience ships didn't stay in the water this long, how realistic was it? We examined the record of the fleet's frigates; on average each ship had to be docked for one reason or another at least twice a year and often more frequently. Most dockings lasted more than a week and the duration of the docking was set more by dockyard work practice than by the defect - such as a damaged sonar dome - that had caused the docking.   I also learnt that the anti-fouling paint would quickly oxidise when exposed to the air and would lose much of its effectiveness if not immersed in seawater within five days of application.

Clearly there was much to be done. With the responsible Chief Constructor Cas Palmer I set up a series of trials.

Frigates were forbidden to paint themselves without seeking our permission. We gave them better cleaners for washing down their paintwork and matt finish paint for touching up damaged areas, which made the re-paint less prominent. In a two year period each ship painted overall three times compared with the sixteen or so times in the preceding two years.

We took three frigates and painted one side with 'pussers' battleship grey paint and the other side with a proprietary paint. After two years only one of the proprietary paints showed up a little better than pussers paint, the other two were not as good. The paint that was better cost about eight times the price of our old-faithful paint and was more difficult to apply. Having regard to the conditions of use of warships, such expense could not be justified and so we kept with our Admiralty paint.

The derivation of this paint is interesting. Way back when Britain had a mighty navy, the annual order for battleship grey paint was perhaps the biggest single order placed with the paint industry. A genius had the idea of awarding the contract for a five-year period on condition that the formula and process information became the property of the Admiralty. After five years this became the benchmark that the companies had to beat and in this way the Admiralty evolved a highly satisfactory and sailor-proof paint.

Tests established that the paint had a shelf life (a-use-by-date) of two years. I found that the Stores Officer in one of the Dockyard's that kept the Fleet supplied with paint was proud of always having not less than two and a half years supply of paint in his store.

Corrosion of the inside of ship's bottom plating was a problem in the machinery spaces brought on by the hot moist conditions and the different metals present. The Royal Navy seemed to have a perennial problem in keeping fluids in pipes without leakage. We had it in submarines and, oh boy, we had it in surface ships. .I. would visit the ships of the US and other navies and squint down at their beautifully dry and clean bilges and then I would visit an RN ship and ugh, what a wet mess. We had done most of the things that we could do in design to obviate this problem but somehow it still occurred. I concluded that we couldn't change a national culture and that we must provide a technical solution. This was to zinc spray the inner bottom and this would require planning on the scale practiced in the submarine group. There was fierce opposition from the guided missile destroyer group but the directorate stood firm and zinc spraying was integrated into the building sequence — by no means an easy matter since it necessitated grit blasting first.

The problem that we saw with anti--fouling paint was not with the paint but with the system for painting and undocking- to get it into the water without delay. It quickly emerged that the fly in the ointment was the practice of rigging staging around the hull for the painters to work from. It took the riggers in the Royal Dockyards five days to dismantle the staging around a frigate and since this usually included a weekend it was a useful source of overtime. To have some idiot in Bath urging the dockyard management to invest in scaffolding towers, which could be put into and removed from a dock in a few hours by crane, was a matter for their trade union and much hot air. Since they wanted to argue I also threw into the discussion the proposal that we should have no staging or scaffolding at all and should arrange our docks to use mobile platforms from which the hulls would be spray-painted and otherwise serviced.

During this period the nuclear submarine HMS *Dreadnought* was docked at Chatham. To match our enthusiasm in designing the vessel and to ensure the best possible speed, the scientists of the RNSS had developed a new anti-fouling paint known as ACC 655. When *Dreadnought* was docked she was absolutely clean, after more than three years in service. The dockyard gave her a brisk rub down prior to repainting and in accordance with regulations the dockyard's Surgeon Commander took dust samples adjacent to the hull. He immediately prohibited all further work on the grounds that the dust had high mercury content which was hazardous and that was the end of that paint. No wonder the hull was clean.

Weather decks were a big problem. In the end after trying various coverings we had been driven back to painting them. The problem was that where things were welded to a deck the paint system would fail and rust would appear. The sailors would then have to clean away the rust before repainting and since the rust was usually in pokey corners this was seldom effective. We noticed that in Singapore, Australian navy ships similar to British ships didn't seem to have this problem. Not for them the rows of boot faced sailors chipping away with their pointed hammers (and incidentally doing more harm than the rust would do if left alone), Aussie sailors could get a run ashore while their rust-less decks sweltered in the sun. The answer (as if we didn't already know it) was coating the deck plating with another metal. So I then started the battle to have the weather decks zinc sprayed followed by aluminium spray. Just as with the zinc spraying of inner bottoms there was loud opposition from the ship design sections and from some of the ship- builders, largely on the grounds of the interruption in construction schedules and the need to plan work in more detail. But we prevailed and in future the labour and noise of chipping away on the weather decks would be much reduced in the ships of the fleet.

The bulk of the experimental work on paints was done in the Central Dockyard Laboratory at Portsmouth. The title was historic and the laboratory had an independent role outside the dockyard organisation. Under the new order it was being rationalised as an outpost of the Admiralty Materials Laboratory at Holton Heath itself a legacy of the days when the most important quality was the strength of gunpowder. I was lucky that the enthusiastic team was still there in my time and their major interest was still their work for the navy.

Under Chief Constructor Arthur Weekes we were still devilling away with NQ 1 steel, its welding and the examination procedures and we were developing a machine that would crawl around a circular hull while ultra sonically inspecting peripheral welds - someone had copied the boyhood stories of Spiderman or some such character who could crawl up vertical walls and over ceilings using suckers. We were deep into automated welding processes and the development of all the peripherals that go with it.

There was a problem in one frigate due to rudder vibration. I looked at the rules governing rudder-bearing clearances and concluded that they needed tightening up. I caused a revised Admiralty Fleet Order to be issued instructing the ships to take the clearances and if not in accord with the new order to have the bearings changed at the next opportunity. Some time later I was in Portsmouth Dockyard and the foreman of ship fitters explained that he was unable to do neither something that we wanted nor any of his normal work because all of his men were engaged in replacing Leander Class rudder bearings. All other work had stopped. I slunk back to Bath and made the rules less stringent.

Recruitment into the Admiralty service was traditionally through the Royal dockyards by competitive examination. Young men would enter and be trained in the various trades required to build, refit and support HM Ships. Many of the 'trades' were small in numbers of workpeople and many had lost the importance they had in the days of wooden walls and sail. The promotion opportunities for these minor trades were limited but their top man in the Admiralty service was graded at Senior Foreman or Examiner of Work level and I had several on my staff. The thing that I remember about the paint man was the strict injunction from the other members of my staff that I should never, but never, ride in his car. His most obvious fault when at the wheel was to turn his head and body when talking to his passenger and it got worse from then on. One day he took his front axle off on one of those small switch levers on the dockyard railway. I learned that I had an office in Bradford, Yorkshire in which was the navy's textile man who had started his career as a sail maker. I dropped in on him one day and learned most fascinating things about the industry and its products. It seems that it was a long time since any senior officer had visited the textile offices and yet there they were working away as if the empire depended on them.

It was while in this post that I was asked by Clive Whitmore, the Head of the Secretariat Materials Branch, to contribute to a brief that Prime Minister Harold Wilson might use during his forthcoming visit to Southampton. I felt that Vosper-Thornycroft's work on the development of plastic ships was clearly noteworthy and so I enlarged upon this. There was an election shortly afterwards. It was no part of our duties to assist candidates by supplying election material and I was just a little surprised sometime after Mr Wilson had been re-elected to read a piece in 'The Times' accusing him of having uttered the most utterly banal and boring statement of the whole election campaign. For the record, my breathless prose, all ten or twelve lines about epoxy resins and such like, was reproduced in full.

I had much enjoyed the variety and scope for improvement possible in the research job and was most reluctant to leave but Jack Sims had decided to bring all the project work, including submarine concepts, under one functional head answerable only to himself, to be called the Forward Design Group and I was ordered to form the group and be its first head.

This took place a little while after the responsibility for making feasibility studies of the proposed Type 42 destroyer had been placed with the destroyer group. The navy needed a new air-defence destroyer; after a great deal of discussion and pressure, the Chancellor had agreed that the navy could have a new class of destroyer provided that the cost of each ship did not exceed £11.25 millions. The naval staff had spelt out their requirements and someone had equated this and the cost to a displacement of 3,500 tons. This had come to my old Project Group Constructive, now headed by Chief Constructor Tony Austin, who had said that the requirements could not be met on less than 4,100 tons. The Controller of the Navy, Admiral Law, did not welcome this and there was considerable argument but Austin stood firm. So higher authority did the equivalent of shooting the messenger and moved the design responsibility to the destroyer design group, which was making 'can do' noises. All sort of weight and cost saving measures were introduced by the destroyer people such as deleting one of the two bow anchors, reducing the number of boats and fittings and so on. The most serious measure was to reduce the length of the fore-body of the ship. One cannot help wondering if the determined effort to reduce weight and cost by eliminating system duplication did not contribute in some way to the unhappy loss of HMS *Sheffield* in the Falklands War.

When I took up the new forward design post, DG Ships asked me to have a look at the Type 42 and I had to tell him that the requirements could not be met on 3,500 tons. I suggested that we were having the wrong debate, we should be discussing cost with ministers and here I was sure that we could find an answer, which would be acceptable. I strongly advised against the reduction in ships length; this would make the ship uncomfortable at sea and propulsion less efficient. I pointed out that the cost saving would be much less than 1% of the cost of the ship. I suggested that we should build the biggest possible ship and say in good faith that the longer and heavier ship could be built for £ 11.25 millions with all the usual weasel words about the cost of radar and weapons systems still under development. The first ship would not enter service for another five years, there would be changes in the rate of inflation and labour costs and furthermore there would be a general election and ministerial changes if not a change in government in that time.

Privately, I considered that it was scandalous that we should allow such a ship to be built to save a sum of money which would be less than a bookkeeping error.

The chickens came home to roost several years later. The Type 42's were certainly not as fast as they might have been and were not good sea boats. The first of class, HMS *Sheffield* commanded by Captain Robin Heath damaged her hull plating due to slamming badly in the Channel en route from a visit to France and all subsequent ships were reinforced while being built, and, yes, after all the 'can do' assurances, when completed, the Type 42 destroyer had a displacement over 4,000 tons. Some years later, when Director General Ships, I was able to increase the length of the second batch of ships to make HMS *Manchester* and her sisters the excellent ships they are.

There had been an increased interest in the real costs of ownership of HM Ships which would include the cost of design, building, stores, crew, maintenance, refitting, fuel, armaments and modernisation and, if a class required a special sort of facility or stores (such as special fuel or weapons) a part of the cost of running that facility. The crew, men, were doubly expensive because they had to be fed and paid and ships had to be that much bigger for each man carried. He also had a pension. So we were automating everything possible while realising that although we might be eliminating three ordinary seamen whom it cost us £10,000 each to train, the petty officer required to maintain the automated equipment might cost us £50,000. The most expensive man to train in the whole navy at that time was a helicopter pilot.

A Life Cycle Costing Working Party was set up of which I became the Chairman and Professor Ken Rawson the Secretary and driving force. We found that for each man in a seagoing ship there was another one and a half men ashore, thus each complement billet cost two and a half men, plus the cost of their accommodation and support ashore.

We developed a whole host of possible life cycles using different periods between, and lengths of, refits and we looked long and hard at the need for mid-life modernisation. It will be realised that from the moment a ship enters service its equipment becomes obsolescent vis-à-vis the potential enemy as his equipment is improved. Thus the curve of a ships military worth declines with time and the clever thing is to know at what stage the improvement in a potential enemies equipment capability makes it essential to upgrade ones own ships equipment to restore the balance. This means an extensive (and expensive) modernisation. Using discounted cash flow procedures we recommended that provided that the cost of modernisation did not exceed 70% of the cost of a new ship, it was worth doing. This was using the Bank Rate current at the time.

We looked at the 'short life frigate'; a ship designed for a life of about 12 years and then scrapped or otherwise disposed of. We concluded that when established, such a system would show cost savings and a slightly more modern fleet. The problem was getting there; how to phase out the long life ships and get into the short life fleet without a substantial increase in cost over the transition years. There was no chance under the British method of defence funding that any minister would accept an increase in expenditure in the next few years or even next year alone, for the certainty of saving more money in, say, five years and thereafter. The span of ministerial attention is strictly the duration of the present parliament (if one is lucky) and more usually simply next years estimates.

When all-important projects, be they military or civil, take more than the length of one parliament and frequently two or more parliaments to pass through the planning and execution stages, the British system is hardly a recipe for dynamic progress.

There was intense private lobbying by the principals of Vosper-Thornycroft and Yarrows that they should be allowed to design warships for the navy instead of simply developing designs prepared by the RCNC. This lobbying fell upon receptive ears with the naval staff and the Controller of the Navy, Admiral Law. An outline staff requirement for a light frigate had been prepared and circulated which DG Ships had been unable to deal with due to pressure of other work. The firms had been invited to make proposals and eventually prepared a joint proposal, which was an enlarged version of the Mark 5 small frigate that Vospers were building for Iran. They were given a contract to develop the design. When I started the Forward Design Group the Controller sent for me and said that he relied on me "to ensure that the firm's designers were given a fair chance to produce a small frigate acceptable to the Royal Navy and that the Royal Corps did not frustrate this aim". The Controller visited the firm about once a month to chair a meeting to discuss the Type 21 design and any problems arising. This was a quite extraordinary thing for a Controller to do and equally singular was the fact that his Naval Assistant did not accompany him. Peter Usher and Tony Dorey represented Vospers and the Controller and I were the MoD. Surprisingly, Yarrows were never represented at these design meetings.

It was a requirement that the ship should be capable at being back-fitted with the Seawolf missile system when this became available and for which space and weight was to be allowed. The design proposed was on the lines of the craft featured in the Usher-Dorey paper 'A Family of Warships' presented at the Royal Institution of Naval Architects, and most recently the frigates for Iran and Brazil, racy looking with an aluminium superstructure and bridges. I argued strongly against the use of aluminium because of its loss of strength and eventual combustion in a fire; [aluminium particles are used as propellant in space rocket booster motors]. The designers argued that the entire ethos of their design and its stability depended on its use and stability was marginal (by navy standards) anyway. The firm discounted the possibility of fire, then one of the frigates that they were building for Iran caught fire while in dock at Southampton and its aluminium superstructure burnt and was destroyed. The firm's designers did still not accept this as a sufficient reason to revert to the steel structure that I wanted in the Type 21; they had already had to make the ship some 18 ft longer than originally intended to provide acceptable stability. They proposed lining the aluminium with thermal lagging and the Controller, despite my objections, ruled in their favour.

There were all sorts of questions where the firm's proposals were a departure from established naval standards, for example, having bunks four high in sleeping spaces which the navy had vetoed in other ships; most were accepted. Where there were problems they were discussed at the meetings with the Controller. Usually the decision would not invite total disaster and in such cases he would smile sympathetically at me, and side with the firm. How else could we try out new ideas?.

What did happen, of course, was that making the ships acceptable for service in the British navy, made the ships tighter and heavier than the firms initial proposals and in the end there was no possibility of back-fitting the class with the Seawolf missile system. Thus these nice looking ships would have an armament of a 4.5-inch gun, two 20mm oerlikon guns and a helicopter, hardly a world-shaking outfit. Later they were given some French Exocet missiles.

Of course, the Board of Admiralty was tackling the wrong shortcoming. What we required was not racy looking hulls, but modern, world-class British weapons systems and electronics that the majority of other nations would be happy to buy.

In due course the design was approved and three ships were ordered from Vospers and five from Yarrows. The lead ship, HMS *Amazon* would be built by Vospers who were contracted to provide 'lead yard services' to Yarrows. The dispute that Vospers and Yarrows got into in building the Type 21 frigates comes later.

Two ships of the class were sunk in the Falklands war; HMS *Ardent* was struck by rockets and was abandoned with her aluminium superstructure burning, losing twenty-two dead and HMS *Antelope* similarly became a burning hulk after being struck by a delayed action 500-pound bomb. On Monday 24th May 1982, following a statement by Mr John Nott in the House of Commons on the progress of the war, disquiet was expressed about the use of aluminium – 'a known fire hazard' - in Britain's frigates. I suppose they blamed the RCNC.

The British were keen to sell Rolls Royce marine gas turbines to other navies and the Dutch navy was keen to have them. The Dutch wanted a quid-pro-quo and eventually we agreed to explore the possibility of producing a common frigate design, the Anglo-Dutch frigate. There was tremendous good will on both sides as we embarked on the proposal. The Dutch Prime Minister had commanded a Free-Dutch submarine during the war and regularly attended the submariner reunion at Fort Blockhouse in company with many of his officers. Many Dutch naval aviators cross trained in RN ships and flew British planes and having a common frigate seemed a Good Idea to make the best use of each nations potential at least cost while advancing standardisation within NATO. The Dutch were if anything more determined than the UK to limit the size of the ship. They specified the maximum acceptable beam and draught and hull factors which defined a rather round bilge shape. This was puzzling until one day I was browsing in a bookshop in the Hague when I found an old print of the brick lined graving dock at Den Helder and, you guessed it, it was the cross-sectional shape they had stipulated for the common frigate.

The actual design of the anti-submarine frigate would present not too many problems; the interest was in industrial participation. Each nation would build and fit-out its own ships. There was remarkable agreement in the schedules that each nation prepared detailing the many hundreds of feet of electric cables and piping and numbers of fittings and equipment and the order of cost.

The machinery, equipment and armament items would be shared in the ratio of the number of ships to be built. Thus if the Dutch bought five ship sets of gas turbines from the UK, we would spend the equivalent amount on buying equipment from Holland. Since at that time we still prided ourselves on our manufacturing industry and were totally self sufficient in naval materiel, collaboration became a question of selection of who should be put out of work in the UK in order that, for example, Rolls Royce should sell their gas turbines to the Dutch. Since the Dutch industry was active at the upper end of technology and could offer high value products such as electronics and gearing, someone in Britain was going to be hurt, in short, we would reduce employment in Leicester in order to keep employment in Derby.

The thing that really shook me was when we were comparing the cost of building. I was gratified to find that our estimate was substantially the same as the Dutch. I then discovered that the Dutch hourly cost per man was exactly twice what we allowed, meaning that they would take about half the man-hours that we would. This was the first time that I had really faced up to Britain's low productivity / low wage economy and started to realise the massive investment required to update and expand our manufacturing base if we were to survive into the next century without massive long term unemployment. The whole sequence, education, research and development and manufacturing would require funding on a scale only possible by government. The Dutch had survived over the centuries and particularly in the post-war era by doing just this.

During my earlier visits to the Netherlands I had been made aware by some naval officers that they blamed Britain for the loss of their far eastern possessions. The argument was that if the British had not been so lily-livered in the face of Indian intransigence and had refused them independence, they, the Dutch would have been able to resist similar claims in Indonesia. The East Indies was the jewel in the Dutch crown. They had separate colleges for the armed services and virtually a separate navy out there. At Independence, the officers were given the choice of coming back to the Netherlands or taking their chance in the free Indonesian navy. At the time of the Anglo-Dutch negotiations, the Dutch Controller was an officer from the Indies (literally) . A gifted and charming man who I sensed was conscious of subtle reminders in Navy HQ of the difference between his culture and that of the European staff. We had dinner together on several occasions at the sea front Spa restaurant at Scheveningen with the angry North Sea lashing spray outside the windows. In discussing the frigate negotiations one evening he reminded me of an old Indonesian proverb "When you shake hands with a Dutchman, count your fingers afterwards".

As the discussions advanced differences began to emerge. The British requirement was for an anti-submarine ship to combat the growing threat from high performance Soviet nuclear submarines. To British defence planners this commitment was absolute; to make the major European contribution to the preservation of the sea-bridge from the USA to Europe in time of war. The Dutch had the same commitment, well, nearly, except they knew that their contribution would be marginal compared with the US Navy and to a lesser extent, the British Navy. They also felt that their ships should be more 'general purpose' and in this I began to sense that they had the requirements of other navies in mind and of potential sales to those navies.

These arguments were put to ministers by both nations. I got the impression that British ministers were realising for the first time that sharing production internationally meant that difficult choices would have to be made, choices that would affect not only the industrial base in the longer term but also local employment and arguments with the trade unions and votes at the next election. Furthermore, the industrial planning and cost sharing arrangements would require that they would have to commit the UK at the outset to buy a minimum number of ships of the class instead of the usual drip-feed of orders, one or two ships at a time.

There had already been a significant transfer of technology to the Dutch in the discussions on sharing manufacture and such things as hydrodynamics, noise and shock resistance. For years it was not possible to visit the hydrodynamics laboratory at Haslar without running into a Dutch visitor, usually a man called Dirksweger whose real claim to fame (with us) was that his wife owned a Gin distillery in Holland. Why any man whose wife owned a gin factory should prefer to spend his time messing about at Haslar we couldn't imagine.

Discussion of the pro's and cons went on for some time but eventually we found that the Dutch were developing their own frigate just as we were developing ours, the Type 22, free from the dimensional and equipment constraints sought by the Dutch.

The most difficult decision to be made in any post-war warship design is what level of anti-air defence to provide. In the second world war we had perforce to rely on gunfire but our ships could not carry sufficient AA shells to withstand repeated air attacks – a County Class cruiser carried enough 4-inch ammunition for only 10 minutes of continuous fire by all the guns. The battleships *Prince of Wales* and *Repulse* had been sunk off the east coast of Malaysia by a force of 72 Japanese torpedo bombers. The British force had simply run out of ammunition. The Japanese lost only 2 of these land-based aircraft in inflicting this stunning defeat.

To render a modern warship ineffective it is not necessary to sink it; knocking out its electronic aerials by blast and fragments is usually enough and starting a serious fire inboard is also a killer. Air attack on ships can be with missiles or bombs fired from the air or missiles launched from other ships or land. The ideal defence is to destroy the enemy aircraft or ship before it can launch its weapons but each time a longer-range defensive missile is developed, the attacking formations deploy missiles that can be launched from a greater range. When the attacking air formation is a score or more aircraft, each carrying four to six missiles and supported by electronic warfare aircraft jamming the fleet's long range warning, target acquisition and missile control radars, the size and nature of the air-defence problem becomes clear.

What is needed to give the ships half a chance of survival are fire -and – forget missiles that can be launched in numbers and seek out and destroy the enemy. In 1968 there was no such system. There were the area defence missiles SeaSlug and the much newer SeaDart and under development, the Small Ships Guided Weapon, SeaWolf. The Type 22 frigate would be the first class to carry the latter.

For some extraordinary reason we all accepted the idea that this SSGW system would be small. Certainly the missile and its launcher would be smaller than SeaDart but the missile electronics to detect an incoming missile, align the launcher, fire a missile and guide it to intercept the target within one or two seconds were formidable. Understandably, the systems designer's estimate of the size of compartments and the power and cooling requirements grew and grew and the in-service date went back and back.

The staff requirements for the Type 22 specified a SeaWolf system forward and aft and two helicopters. I was concerned at the absence of a simple weapon that would go bang. How else would the ship deal with, say, an Arab dhow or a revolutionary guard launch? I added a 40 mm gun on each side of the bridge and it was legitimised in later editions of the Staff Requirement. Subsequently a battery of launchers for the French Exocet missile was added forward to give this valuable design some anti-surface ship capability. Incidentally the protection fitted to the sides of these launchers was not for war but to guard against hostile acts by terrorists when the ships were in harbour. Some years later, when we produced the lengthened Type 42 design we also introduced a lengthened Type 22 design with a 4.5-inch gun added forward.

Perhaps I was old fashioned but I regarded the provision of guns to go bang as psychologically important. I can vouch for my own reaction in ships when we were being attacked. The sailors would be tense and then visibly relax when our own anti-aircraft guns opened up. Tremendous!. It was, of course, the same in the London blitz. The intense barrage of gunfire that went up every night had as much to do with the maintenance of civilian and military morale as with shooting down enemy aircraft.

We did a great deal of detailed design work on the Type 22 design before it went to Alan Bull in the Destroyer and Frigate Group to supervise the development of the shipyard working plans and the actual building. The ships as built are unchanged from that prepared in the Forward Design Group and I was extremely proud when the Admiralty Board invited my wife, Liz, to launch the third ship of the class, HMS *Brilliant*. The one thing for which I was not responsible was the funnel in the first two ships of the class. When I was appointed Director General Ships and assumed responsibility for surface ships as well as submarines, I was astounded to find that the funnel shape that I had given to the design of Type 22' s and which was similar to that already at sea in the Type 42 destroyers (which had the same gas turbine propulsion machinery) had been changed to give a peculiar shape at the top. For some reason this rather clumsy shape was the source of considerable amusement among my marine engineers. I sent for the head of the design section, it was now Alan Creighton, and required him to return to sanity; he couldn't alter the first two ships but the third, *Brilliant* was completed with an orthodox funnel and went just as fast.

The Board was intent on getting fixed wing aircraft back in the fleet. The Labour government of Harold Wilson and Defence Secretary Dennis Healey had ruled that the navy should have no more fixed wing aircraft carriers. They were absolutely right. As a nation we could not have afforded the cost of operating monster carriers and their aircraft. We were not allowed to mention the words aircraft carrier but we could talk about 'through deck cruisers' that were ships with a big flat upper deck with the bridge and funnels offset to the starboard side and a hangar underneath. All this became possible because of the development of the Harrier Jump-jet aircraft. We did a number of studies of through deck cruisers to establish the order of what was possible and acceptable to the aircraft designer for operating this remarkable aircraft. With the aircraft designer we looked at a number of other quite novel proposals for getting Harriers to sea.

In the submarine group, DPT, Valiant Class attack submarines and Resolution Class ballistic missile submarines were being built and design work had restarted on the next class of attack boats, the Swiftsure Class. It was necessary to take a long look ahead at the sort of equipment that should be under development to meet the likely threats of the 1990's and beyond and to do this we had to envision the submarine of the future. The Future Generation Submarine studies were an attempt to set aside previous constraints and judge the extent to which material and engineering developments might support this aim.

The latter would embrace the development of advanced detection and communication systems, machinery and silencing, and weapons systems without anticipating unreasonable advances in materials. Two working parties were set up, I chaired the one dealing with the material aspects and a senior scientist, Stuart Reid chaired that dealing with operational analysis.

We now had a small mainframe computer in Ship Department. It seemed to me that of all ship types, the submarine must be the one most easily modelled and that such a model would be of the greatest value in our future submarine material studies. So Chris Stonehouse prepared a submarine design program. The input data was largely based on the Valiant Class and when he inputted the Valiant operational requirements his program faithfully printed out the correct design data for Valiant. The problem with this first effort was that when we put in the Swiftsure Class operational requirements, the program gave us rubbish. We had much to learn about computer programming.

The material team reviewed possible advances in all fields. My declared position was that everything was up for grabs, for example if the weapons and sonar people demanded a nearly spherical shape then I was prepared to design and build nearly spherical hulls but the navy would have to accept that in most other respects such hulls would be a disaster. Would the operational studies give such boats an acceptable survival rate? The weapons people had nagged on and on about firing torpedoes aft, clearly a difficult thing to arrange in a streamlined hull with a big propeller or, failing that, at the very least to fire them broadside. I said splendid, I could arrange this and would be interested to learn how they would give their weapons the speed that launching astern would demand and / or the increased lateral strength to prevent them being bent as they emerged from the hull when fired broadside. What about firing when practically stopped in the quiet mode?, but then firing would give away the submarines position and she would be unable to gain sufficient speed to avoid the enemy counter attack which the noise of her torpedo running would undoubtedly trigger. Thus there would be a good chance of both attacker and attacked being sunk. And so on.

We examined all the possible propulsion plants and hull materials, high strength steel, aluminium, titanium and glass and the problems that fabrication would entail in the yards. Remember we are speaking of operational submarines, not research vehicles in which 60% of their weight is devoted to structure. Our studies showed that we could produce military submarines in steel with diving depths approaching 2,000 ft. Beyond that, titanium looked good but there were problems in producing the thickness we required and in welding them. The metal could not be welded in air and shielding the welding process well nigh impossible. My solution would be to build the hulls in a sealed hall filled with, say, argon gas and have the men wear space suits (or perhaps face masks would do.) to weld the hulls. The cost would be horrendous. And what about refitting?

There was hardly a field in which we did not find good logic behind the principles already embodied in the Swiftsure design and the need for truly massive investment if we were to go much further. Perhaps the available funds would be better spent on developing effective long-range autonomous weapons?. The operational value of significantly increasing the performance envelope of future submarines would be assessed by the operational studies; would the benefit justify the cost of getting there?

Substantially increased diving depth is not necessarily advantageous because seawater bends and refracts sound waves according to its salinity and temperature. If someone was attacking me with depth bombs I would prefer to be closer to the surface than deep but on the other hand if attacked with target seeking torpedoes an ability to go deep would give the enemy weapon a three-dimensional search problem and increase the possibility that it would run out of power before hitting.

The importance of the operational studies is apparent. They were to play war games, to postulate various tactical scenarios and make computer simulations with the submarine characteristics systematically varied to assess their effect on the outcome. Unfortunately Stuart Reid was not provided with a sufficient staff to prepare his programs and he was dependent on the Operational Research Establishment at West Byfleet for assistance and for time on their computers. Neither was willingly given. He never got beyond single ship versus single ship engagements during the time that I was head of Forward Design. Stuart bore all of this with a sad smile. He was remarkably tolerant.

I had been responsible for British nuclear submarine design development for about 15 years by now and could predict the outcome; short of developing titanium hulls at enormous cost we were limited to those steels for which we could develop shockproof welding processes if we were to build military submarines. Speed wise we had to learn how to control the boundary layer since we were already in the region where hydrodynamic noise - the noise of water swishing along the hull and into the propeller and its avoidance- was a determining factor and he who made a noise was likely to be sunk. We were back in square one, inching forward along familiar technical paths.

Until this time in naval design we had been the equal of the US Navy. They had admitted that British inventions like the steam catapult, arresting gear, angled deck and the deck landing sight had 'kept them in the carrier business'. In several respects the work that we had done in the submarine group and at NCRE had materially assisted their submarine design but now I was only too conscious of a growing gap between the two navies, particularly in surface ships and weapons.

My own experience was typical. There would be a requirement. We would see five lines of research which might solve the problem and hence meet the requirement. After a lot of discussion we would decide to put our effort on, say, line two. Meanwhile the US people would research all five lines. Line two would prove to be the right one and we would feel mighty pleased with ourselves for getting it right. The next problem might be on line three. We would start from first base but our US friends would already have the results of the earlier exercise from which to start, say, second base. For the next problem they would start from third base and the British wouldn't start at all

I was aware that the French were doing better than this sort of logic would suggest and slowly realised that we and more importantly the US defence industry were, or had been, the target of the French intelligence service. When he had come to power the General had turned the security service around from spying on the Russians to collecting information on the allied missile, electronics, nuclear and submarine research programmes. As the Soviets were to show, reading US journals, appropriations, invitations to tender, university grants, theses and the press gets you most of the way without breaking the law. In marked contrast to the British, the French then formulated a long-term development and naval construction, missile and nuclear programme, which has enjoyed the support of successive governments to the present time.

We were under some pressure to exploit the hovercraft as a naval weapon and also conscious of the US work on hydrofoils. These were portrayed as alternatives to give the forces a high-speed craft but really they were horses-for-courses, the hovercraft would provide an amphibious capability but was not good in ocean waves whereas the hydrofoil was a small ship, which by means of its foils could operate in ocean waves but not run up beaches! Hovercraft were on our doorstep and hydrofoils were in Seattle. We recognised the role for hovercraft in littoral operations, the transfer of personnel and goods across water, ice, mud and desert. The obvious suggested main mission was putting forces ashore but the helicopter was a powerful alternative, which would provide a wider choice of landing sites for the troops. The big SRN 4 operating across the Channel was the jewel in the hovercraft crown; it was the perfect example of a vessel best suited for its operating scenario, the journey length, the premium passenger density and the year round sea-states combined to make success possible.

Hydrofoils, if workable, gave promise of using advanced technology to enable small craft to operate in ocean waves at high speeds. Such craft would be riding the waves and difficult to detect; armed with surface-to-surface missiles they could pose a serious threat to superior surface forces. The Soviet navy was known to be giving considerable development effort to these and similar unorthodox craft.

Rear Admiral Brian Straker and I went to Washington DC for meetings in the Pentagon and thence to Seattle, now accompanied by the Commander of the British Naval Staff in Washington, Rear Admiral Jim Jungius. We flew to Chicago on a Saturday and took the Union Pacific Railroad express for Seattle. The big attraction was to see something of the Rocky Mountains. In the early evening of Sunday the train was well into the mountains when it stopped at a place called Whitefish. We got out to look around and to our surprise saw a small diesel engine shunting our coach away from the rest of the train. We walked beside the engine and the driver told us that he was adding an extra saloon car.   He then asked if we were Canadian and when we said "No, British" he invited us up to join him in his roomy cab. He continued his shunting operation with his head partly out of the cab window while he told us that the Union Pacific Railroad was the best railroad in the USA and that Whitefish was a prosperous town with many residential and factory sites available at reasonable prices and he would be pleased to show us round and introduce us to likely people or forward particulars to us in England. By this time he had parked our sleeping car on a siding, collected another saloon car and connected it to the train and returned to collect our car to reconnect it to the rear of the train. It would be difficult to envisage the driver of a shunting engine in the UK having the assurance to invite three Americans on to his footplate and singing British Rail's praises while trying to sell them local real estate.

We soon saw the reason for the added coach as the weekend's quota of skiing casualties were variously carried or assisted on board with arms in slings, legs in splints and turbans of bandages.

The railway leaves the western foothills of the Rockies somewhere to the north of Seattle and runs south along the shore of Puget Sound.   In discussions with Boeings, the protagonists and manufacturers of hydrofoils, they had repeatedly used 'hitting a log' as an example of the sort of accident that a hydrofoil might encounter at high speed and survive. This preoccupation seemed odd since the number of logs that I have seen in British offshore waters could be counted on the fingers of one hand.   But now all became clear, the shores of the Puget Sound were literally covered with logs, logs that had escaped from the giant logging rafts on the Canadian and US rivers to the north. In the early morning mist small seals were reclining on the logs.

After a tour of some of Boeings facilities we were taken to the dock. It is inevitable on such occasions that the latest, all singing, all dancing, hydrofoil that we had come so far to ride in was not available so we rode in a larger, older craft which behaved very serenely in the sheltered sound but really proved nothing to us. During the trip a prototype 747 flew over, its vast bulk, seen for the first time, making it seem to move slowly in the sky.   The trial trip took us close to the west shore of the sound where Mount Olympus was clear in the distant sky. Like British Colombia to the north, the state of Washington is a paradise. Boeing was the biggest single company whose employees peaked at something over 130, 000 attracting designers and skilled workers from Europe as well as all parts of North America. Significantly, when aircraft orders fell and the workforce was more than halved there was no general exodus from the Seattle area. Presumably today they all work for Bill Gates.

The US Secretary for Defence, McNamara, was a keen advocate of Total Package Procurement, the sort of procedure under which USAF aircraft and weapons systems were produced in which a contractor chosen by competition is made responsible for the specification, design, construction and support of the entire system. He wished to apply the process to naval orders with a corresponding reduction in government employees. The DD963 Class would be the first large naval project contracted in this way. Three companies had each spent many millions of dollars assembling design teams and preparing proposals and keeping those teams together through submission, resubmission and the selection processes. For the two companies not selected this was all lost cash and management effort. Littons had set up a design office with about 500 staff at El Segundo and won the contract.

It should be noted, however, that the companies that were not successful were not so keen to invest substantially in subsequent procurement exercises and that even Littons found it not cost-effective to keep large numbers of staff in the design offices against the possibility of winning future competitions and so naval design continuity was being lost.

Companies will not participate in such a scheme unless there is a guaranteed programme and a known number of ships to be built. The halfway house of using a design agency divorced from shipbuilding will spell long-term trouble. US experience is that non-successful companies lose interest while the successful bidder seeks additional funds to keep the team together.

We were interested in the Total Package Procurement method and accordingly we went from Seattle to Los Angeles to talk with the team who were designing the Spruance Class and then to New Orleans en route for Pascagoula to see the new shipyard that Littons were building for the rapid construction of these ships. That night, for the sum of one dollar, we sat on a wooden floor in Bourbon Street and listened to real jazz.

We flew back to the UK in an RAF VC 10, assembling in the British Airways (or was it still BOAC?) terminal in New York. We were very pleased to be flying RAF and not commercial. It was at the time of the 2,000 years anniversary celebrations in Israel. The liner Queen Elizabeth 2 had been chartered to take several thousand pilgrims from the United States to Israel and there was a story that Libya was trying to buy a submarine to sink the ship as she passed through the Mediterranean. Thousands more were travelling by air. This was when the threat and actuality of highjacking and bombing was at its peak and airline security was a major problem. That night the British air terminal was a seething mass of rabbi's, black suits, black hats, black beards and bibles everywhere. The BA flight should have left before our RAF flight but as we boarded they were about to unload all the baggage to search it for the third time.

In RAF passenger aircraft the passengers are seated facing the rear for added safety, with the most senior people nearest the nose and the more junior people towards the tail. That night, the British Ambassador was in the first row and we were in the second and thus it proceeded through the aircraft to a score or so of junior naval ratings in the tail. There were several female passengers some of whom had small babies for whom a sort of small hammock was suspended from the luggage racks.

The RAF cabin staff consisted of a warrant officer, a female sergeant and a tall curly headed corporal. The warrant officer was visible when we embarked and during take-off but was not seen again. . The lady sergeant was a blonde who looked as if her hobby might be tearing telephone directories in half. She very occasionally walked through the aircraft and gave orders o the corporal. The corporal did all the work. This did not seem to be too onerous since the scale of refreshment provided to passengers during the entire flight was one cup of coffee, served in a paper cup. . Protocol dictated that he should bring the full tray to the front of the aircraft and serve the senior passengers first. The sight of the corporal weaving an unsteady path along the aircraft aisle with about 50 filled paper cups on a tray was calculated to keep all the people in the aisle seats awake lest he should spill the lot on them.

All very unimportant no doubt but what the passengers remembered and spoke about afterwards was not the RAF's superb flying, faultless navigation and reliable engineering but the pantomime of the sergeant and the corporal.

Back to work but all too soon I was promoted and returned to the submarine directorate, at first as the Deputy director and then Director, Submarine Project Team, a title contrived to keep alive the acronym, DPT, of the original Dreadnought Project team.

Chapter Ten

In 1970 Sir Michael Carey, the Permanent Secretary of the MoD had a word with me about my succeeding Vice Admiral Raper as DG Ships when he retired some four years hence. Meanwhile I would be promoted and in due course become the Director of the submarine project organisation, which was still unique in the MoD in bringing all activities together. The major tasks were trials of the remaining SSBN, *HMS Revenge*, getting all four boats into the patrol and maintenance cycle, building the Valiant and Swiftsure Classes of attack submarines, and the new design to follow.

A decision that had caused us some thought in 1963 at the outset of the Polaris programme had been whether to continue with HMS *Warspite*, the second ship of the Valiant Class on which work had just started or whether to stop her and use the materials already ordered for the SSBN programme. Rowland Baker tended towards deferment but I argued in favour of pressing on so that we would have three SSN's available by the time the first SSBN went on deterrent patrol. The SSN's would be useful in training the two crews for each SSBN but most importantly in my view would be available to sweep our exit routes clear when our SSBNs sailed from the Clyde and make sure that Soviet submarines that had been lying in wait were not trailing them, a process that the submariners quickly dubbed delousing.

The record of industrial relations in the Liverpool area was very bad and a problem that we had faced early in the game had been the possibility of industrial action at Cammell Lairds delaying the delivery of their second SSBN ; the last ship syndrome. The answer was to make *HMS Revenge* not the last ship by ordering an SSN to follow, so there were three Valiant class SSNs under construction at Barrow and one at Cammell Lairds. The correctness of this decision was underlined when the SSN was approaching completion and some Birkenhead patriot put a handful of metal objects in her gearbox, delaying completion by many months and costing the taxpayer a million pounds.

Design work had proceeded under Norman Hancock on the submarine to follow the Valiant Class embodying the ideas that had been set down at about the time the SSBN's were started. The first two ships of this, Swiftsure Class, were under construction at Barrow with a further three ships planned to follow. Hancock had now left the submarine group to become Director of Warship Design and design work had already started on the 'T Class under his successor. As Deputy Director my responsibility was with the SSBN's and in accordance with precedent, the Director dealt with the new design. I argued strongly that the T' s should be a logical derivative of the Swiftsure class of which the first boat was still about three years from entering service, but the retiring Director was not strong and the young men were allowed to start with a clean sheet of paper on what was called the SSN OY design.

Meanwhile the Polaris construction programme which comprised not only the submarines but also a large missile depot and a submarine base and school, all carved out of Scottish hillsides,, and the preparation of Rosyth dockyard to refit the submarines, had been completed to cost and to time.

Revenge was working-up in readiness for sailing to Florida for her DASO — Demonstration and Shakedown Operation — and the other three boats were in the operational cycle. Plans were already afoot to sail the first ship, HMS *Resolution* to Rosyth to start her first refit somewhat earlier than material and nuclear fuel usage considerations would require but necessary to establish the pattern and timing to suit the force as a whole.

Much thought had been given to maintenance and repair in the design. I had put a 3ft diameter hatch in the pressure hull adjacent to the machinery spaces to facilitate the removal and replacement of equipment and this was proving invaluable during inter-patrol periods at the Clyde submarine base. US Admiral Levering Smith told me that the big hatch was one of the five design features he envied in our SSBN s. The others were the hovering system, the welded hull valves, the standardisation of valves and the raft mounted propulsion machinery.

Deep study had been given to the numerical basis for spares provisioning; mean time between failures; mean time to repair and bathtub curves were the jargon. I found that it had been calculated that there were nearly 200 equipments in each boat that would be refitted by repair-by-replacement. Someone had decided that it would be advantageous to exchange some 14 of these equipments at each inter-patrol period at the base at Faslane, from whence they would be forwarded to Rosyth for maintenance and return to the spare equipment inventory. When I took over it was quickly evident to me that damage was being done to equipments and to the submarine in general by sailors moving heavy items in and out, notwithstanding the planned equipment removal routes. So I stopped the circus and issued instructions to the effect that if equipment is running OK and not making a noise, leave it alone.

Equipment removal and handling seemed to be a particularly British problem. The UK had contracts with US activities for assistance with the in-service support of the missile system. This included an arrangement with the EBCo for the repair of missile-associated ship items under which such items were included with those from US submarines for refurbishment at prices negotiated by the US Navy. Some years into this arrangement a friend at EBCo remarked that they could always recognise a fitting from a British submarine. I suppose that I assumed that he was about to pay a small compliment but he went on to say, "They always look as if they had been maintained by agricultural engineers". I was frankly not surprised at this because I had been appalled at Faslane and in the Dockyards to witness sailors emerge from submarine hatches clutching something like an electro-hydraulic servo valve costing several thousands of pounds and throw it the few feet to the concrete dockside instead of carrying it ; a practice that seldom raised a protest from their officers. The US Navy did not have this problem; their officers and enlisted men seemed to have a different sense of responsibility and cost consciousness.

HMS Revenge arrived at Port Canaveral for her DASO and various VIP's flew in at the last moment to witness the firing of her first missile down the Atlantic Missile Range. I had flown to Washington DC and an admiral friend had flown directly to Miami. No sooner had I arrived in Crystal City, near the Pentagon, than our resident 'Polaris' Captain telephoned from Canaveral to say that they had almost had to carry the admiral off the aircraft at Miami and he thought that he should be taken to the nearest US Army or Navy hospital for treatment. He seemed to be very ill. I said "No, take him to his quarters at the US Navy base and put him to bed and I'll come down as soon as I can". I had flown the Atlantic with my friend on many occasions. On a recent flight, when he had drunk his way across the Atlantic, the usually oh so discreet BAOC chief steward had muttered to me as we disembarked "I think that he's got hollow legs, Sir." I knew his habits and that at the present time he was very overworked and tired and the last thing that he would want was for a US service doctor to see him as he was.

The next morning I flew to Canaveral and we gently brought things back to normality; just before the First Sea Lord and the Permanent Secretary flew in. The weather in sunny Florida was atrocious with days of cold rain, driven by near gale force winds. I walked alone on the wet, wind swept beach and the locals thought, correctly, that I was mad.

It is perhaps worth describing the missile preparation and launching process. Contrary to popular belief the missiles do not come on board already designated with an intended target, in fact the missile is never given the actual geographical location of its target, it is simply given an angle and speed that it must achieve at a given altitude after launching. The theory of ballistics does the rest. The submarine has an elaborate inertial navigation system that accurately computes its position throughout the patrol and the ship's fire control computers have all the information on the geographical co-ordinates of possible targets. In the moments before launch the computers are told that missile X is designated to impact target Y and that the submarines present position is Z. The computers then calculate the angle and velocity that the missile must achieve to hit the target and transfer these data to the missiles own computers, which will control the on-board guidance and power functions. At the moment of launch the missile is blown out of its launch tube and rises in its bubble of gas until it breaks surface when the propulsion motor ignites, the missile stabilises and commences its flight. Every metre of error in the submarines position at launch is a potential metre error at the delivery end.

The big unknown at the commencement of the missile programme was the precise location of the possible targets, not hidden things like secret factories and command bunkers but obvious things like where precisely is Omsk. We all know that its a little black dot on a map but that's hardly good enough when you have to impact a missile within a few hundred metres of the centre and you have no idea give or take ten kilometres where that centre is. Hence the U2 spy planes and today's satellites.

At the time of launch the submarines depth must be accurately maintained by the hovering system and by the missile compensating system to instantly enter a weight of water into the missile tube equal to the weight of the missile that has just been fired, in order that the next missile may be launched at the correct depth and so on until all sixteen missiles have been launched.

It is vital that the missiles be launched as quickly as possible. The public is generally aware that the army has target-locating radars, which compute the trajectory of incoming shells and mortar rounds to pinpoint where the enemy guns or mortars are. This is why the artillery no longer gallop up on their horses, fire a few shells and then have a cup of tea before firing a few more and settling down for the night. Nowadays they drive up, fire a few rounds and then depart with all speed before any enemy counter fire can arrive.

Thus it is with the SSBNs, the moment the first missile appears above the enemy's radar horizon his radars will detect it and compute the position of launch and the probable position of impact. Depending on a number of factors, his first counter-fire missile could impact in the vicinity of the submarine at about the time the submarine's sixteenth missile is being launched. The reality of the situation would be that a number of SSBN's would be launching missiles and the enemy radars and counter-fire directors would have considerable target discrimination problems. Furthermore, would it be worthwhile wasting a missile on a submarine that had already launched its missiles when it might better be aimed at the enemy's capital?. One does not know and so the launch sequence had to be made as rapid as possible so that the launching submarine could leave the area with dispatch.

On the day of the DASO we embarked in the submarine and sailed for the exercise area accompanied by a US Navy tender in which some VIP's were embarked. When the submarine was in position and the all clear signal given by the range controller ashore, the missile was set up, all system checks run through once more and the missile was launched. Within the submarine there was a slight judder, like going over a bump in the road in a car, accompanied by a low rumble of water flooding into the vacated tube.

Radio reported that we had ignition and the missile was climbing beautifully. After about 50 seconds, however, shore control reported that they had destroyed the missile by their command signal because it was heading for New York instead of south towards Ascension Island. We had a "non-success".

Analysis of the telemetry records showed that our malfunction was due to a unique combination not previously encountered and the test and maintenance routines were amended as a result; thus 'non-success' was probably a fair description since 'valuable lessons were learned'. Two days later *HMS Revenge* fired her standby missile, which flew perfectly down range and impacted in the target area. This time I was in the support vessel. The February weather that had been so cold and rainy for days had cleared and was sunny and calm. To see the missile emerge from the sea with flames belching from the tail, stabilise and then lift away into the stratosphere was much more impressive than the slight bump and rumble that those inside the submarine would experience.

Before returning to the UK, Michael Carey and I went to Disney World at Orlando. At Disney World we parked our hire-car in Line 54 of car park J, made like the notice said and double checked the line number and the car-park letter and boarded the tractor drawn open sided trolley - all painted brightly like Noddy toys - to be transported to the turnstiles. Now the problems began because we were in a line of people and had to pick which exhibits we wished to visit from a wall display, while having no idea what the titles meant. One didn't simply pay to go in, one had to pay for each bit, in advance. Not having taken the Walt Disney World pre-entry acquaintance course we had no idea what we could do in the time available (or whether we would wish to) so we compromised and picked about 6 dollars worth in the middle. Actually it didn't seem to matter much because the moment one went through the bat-wing doors of the Lucky Chance Saloon or some such title on main Street USA one was faced with the same copper and china and leather nick-nacks for sale as one found behind the portcullis of the Magic Castle. It should also be remarked that no matter what the setting, New England Seaport or what have you, the food was the same and uniformly terrible.

The big event was the parade down Main Street at mid-day led by a band and Walt Disney characters. It was quite mechanical, straight down the road, waving etc, to the assembled onlookers, straight through the private passage at the end and back to their other tasks or lunch. The parade was concluded by a high school brass band, which halted at the end of Main Street and gave a quite delightful concert for over half an hour.

The impressive thing about Disney World as I saw it in 1970 was the concept and execution of the engineering, the lake, the overhead railway and the services. All the supplies were brought in and the rubbish taken out through miles of underground tunnels. I had not realised it before, although it should have been obvious to me, Disney World was meant for adults since they are the ones with the money.

The big moment came as we were travelling to Orlando when out of the morning mist a long low building appeared with rows of seats arranged in the forecourt beneath a tall flagstaff and the proud legend, 'World Headquarters -Tupperware".

We in DPT had purchased sufficient spare items to support the submarine forces in all reasonable circumstances by means of repair-by-replacement; by usual navy standards the provision was lavish. In many cases the spare items were common to both SSBN s and SSNs. All schedules of spare equipments and components had low stock alarms to trigger action for replenishment. We found that these levels were being reached far sooner than we had anticipated because my staff was authorising the issue of new items when they could not get repaired items.

Things came to a head one Friday afternoon when a bilge pump destined for a Polaris submarine at Faslane that was due to sail on patrol on the following Monday, failed its noise and vibration test. My chaps called up the standby spare which also exceeded its noise and vibration limits. I am a trifle vague about the various permutations we tried to get a satisfactory pump but we found that there were no less than seven of these big and costly items in the repair cycle. Late on the Saturday I asked Vickers to take out a brand new noise tested pump recently installed in one of the SSN's building at Barrow and rush it to Faslane and the Polaris submarine sailed as programmed on the Monday.

Enquiry showed the problem to be the failure of Rosyth dockyard to repair or to have repaired by the manufacturer, those items that for the past year and more had been removed from the submarines under the repair-by-replacement policy. I went to Rosyth to see for myself and was astonished to find many, many items that had been reported to DPT progress meetings as   under repair were standing untouched, still in the state in which they had been removed from the submarine and not yet opened up for inspection. From the General manager down, Rosyth senior officers seemed not to be overly concerned at this failure but I was concerned that our monitoring system appeared to have failed As a result we negotiated our own contracts with the manufacturers and with Vickers for the repair of equipment and preinstalation testing and took the dockyard out of the loop.

This was a salutary experience; it wasn't as if the dockyard was short of labour. One couldn't enter a Dunfermline pub without hearing envious remarks about the wages of the people working inside the SSBN security fence or meeting a man who's brother was on the night shift and slept most of the time. Several workpeople were caught doing just that and were dismissed.

I was now the Director — DPT for short; with the job I inherited the redoubtable Miss Bullock as my secretary. She had been secretary to all the occupants of the post from Baker onwards. She was a tall serious woman who kept strictly to the office hours. Although she might be in her room she would not unlock the communicating door until 08.30 each morning and at 17.45, even in the middle of dictation, she would close her book, stand up and walk out, locking our communicating door behind her. There would be a sort of metallic noise for many minutes thereafter before silence suggested that she had actually gone. Sometimes it would start all over again and I finally realised that it was the noise of the combination dials on the filing cabinets being repeatedly spun and shaken to make sure that they were shut. It was not until after I had left the DPT post that I learned, through my wife, Liz, that Betty Bullock had an 84-year-old mother whom she had to 'see to' every morning before she came to work and each evening on leaving work. Not a word of this was ever mentioned in the office. Many, many of the senior secretaries in the civil service in my time were the sole support and comfort of elderly mothers and this brief paragraph is my tribute to them for their loyalty.

I remarked earlier that meeting US Admiral Levering Smith for the first time one had to get used to the pause that occurred between asking him a question and his always complete and comprehensive reply. My predecessor as DPT, Harold Tabb, was the complete opposite, asked a question he would immediately start talking while he thought out the answer, thus one learnt to ignore the first few paragraphs that he spoke because they were nearly always rubbish.   An event that still gives me some amusement was when I found myself in a train compartment with the Chief of Fleet Support, Admiral Alan Trewby, the Chief of the Polaris Executive, Rear Admiral Charles Shepheard and Harold Tabb. The conversation got around to golf. "What is your handicap Charles" asked Sir Alan? As quick as light I said "Harold Tabb". Harold was one of the nicest people but he was a trifle distant for the next few days.

Although the S5W reactor and machinery supplied by the US Navy had operated superbly in HMS *Dreadnought*, I had continued to be concerned at the amount of brazing used in connecting pipe work and the extent to which water systems were interconnected which would make isolation difficult should a problem develop. In service the ship had had minor problems with leaks from brazed joints, probably because we hadn't been able to make them as well as the US builders did, and the incidence of leaks was becoming more frequent. I decided to renew all the major salt water piping systems in the boat with pipe welded to our latest standards. Vickers manufactured the systems and they were installed at Chatham during her mid-life refit. I slept a lot more soundly when this was done.

A matter of concern was the problem of rescuing the crews of deep diving submarines should there be an accident, such as a collision with another vessel. These submarine's hulls would remain intact at depths far deeper than those from which free ascent was possible and there would be the possibility of a submarine and its crew being stranded on the bottom and unable to bring the boat to the surface but with its reactor and life support systems working to provide a live-in-able atmosphere for several months and an ability to communicate with the outside world. The US Navy recognised the problem and developed the Deep Submergence Rescue Vessel (DSRV), which would be capable of being air freighted to the vicinity of a sub-marine disaster anywhere in the world. They volunteered that their vessel would be available should an RN submarine be lost and we made the small changes that would enable the DSRV to mate with our nuclear submarines. In due course we would have our own rescue submersible.

I started to think about what we would do when a nuclear submarine came to the end of her useful life. Normally she would be sold and reduced to scrap iron but even after removing her nuclear core *Dreadnought's* reactor components would have some residual radioactivity due to having been bombarded with trillions of neutrons each hour that her reactor was critical during 20 years of service. I happened to see Bill Penney at some gathering in 1973 and asked him what the AEA planned to do with their reactors. He said that they hadn't really given the matter much thought; they would probably just take out the hot bits and then cover them with earth. He added cheerfully that "they won't be very big hills, you'll hardly notice them". Thirty years on, the cost of decommissioning these civil nuclear power stations is a matter of public concern. When interviewed on the subject on 24th May 2,000, Mr Wedgwood Benn said that he had been the Minister who had approved the construction of the Magnox reactor stations on the advice of the nuclear experts. At the time no one had mentioned the likely problem and cost of their eventual decommissioning and in the event the power had always cost three times more to generate than coal fired stations. He added, "I now realise that I was wrong. I have learned that one cannot trust the nuclear people".

The uncaring solution would be to sink the submarine in the deepest part of the Atlantic Ocean but this was unthinkable for environmental reasons. Next we thought of cutting out the reactor section of the hull and embalming it at a remote site and finally of just tying her up somewhere while the environmentalists had their say. The US Navy would meet the problem before we did so the next time that I was in Washington DC I raised the question informally with friends. I was told somewhat unconvincingly that they hadn't thought about it yet. I did know that they had boats tied up and inactive so perhaps they were in the same position that we were heading for. What I did learn some years later was that the armed forces were responsible for a great deal of nuclear contamination at many remote sites in the USA and that Secretary for Energy (Admiral) Watkins severest problem in the late 1980's was cleaning them up.

By mentioning this topic at all I was skating on thin ice because Admiral Rickover had decreed that all communication with his organisation should be through the MoD's Chief Scientific Adviser, Sir Solly Zuckerman, and this arrangement persisted long after Zuckerman had gone elsewhere. Actually, on this occasion I did not consider that I was 'communicating with his organisation'. We used the channel perhaps once a year and then usually to report, as we were bound by the 1958 Agreement to do, something to do with the S5W plant. We would inform CSA's office; they would tell Zuckerman; he would then tell a man called Wagner in Rickover's organisation and Wagner would presumably tell Rickover. Any reply would follow the same path.

An incident that gave me some satisfaction was when HMS *Dreadnought* developed a small problem while deployed in the Far East. We asked Australia, New Zealand and Singapore if she could enter their waters to sort things out and each nation refused. We told Admiral Rickover who said that she could go to Guam and his people said that the job would take a shipyard six weeks. We flew a Submarine Maintenance Team under Commander Tom Brinkley out to Guam and they completed the job in less than two days and came home.

During my earlier time as chief constructor in the submarine group we had looked at the possibility of saving shipyard effort and cost by using extruded pressure hull frames instead of fabrications. The US Cameron Iron Co experimented with possible frames at its plant in Scotland but concluded that its machines were not adequate to press such massive sections in high strength steel. This had not been entirely unwelcome news to me since I was concerned at the presence of residual stresses in the frame as extruded and then when bent to a circular arc and welded to the pressure hull plating. When I left to attend the Imperial Defence College, I had placed a cautionary note in the records that extruded frames should be annealed after bending. I was much concerned to find, on return, that a small number of non-annealed extruded frames had been used in one submarine. After much study, the appropriate action was taken with the help of the Naval Construction Research Establishment at Dunfermline / Rosyth but it was an extremely worrying time for me. Annealing facilities were commissioned at Barrow for future use.

My predecessor had allowed the SSN OY submarine design to go ahead as a completely new venture and the design had received Admiralty Board approval. I had argued that we should build on our design experience with Swiftsure Class the first of which was still some years from completion and represented a substantial development in submarine design philosophy and innovation. It was now my responsibility and I had a gut feeling about it. Professor Lou Rydill was the new Assistant Director SSN's and I instructed him to make a thorough review of the design and report. After a most painstaking review he reported that it did not reach certain vital and quite fundamental design criteria.

I informed the Controller of the Navy that I had no alternative but to withdraw the SSN OY design and we discussed whether a sixth Swiftsure Class boat should be ordered instead of the first "T" Class. This was done.

The "T" Class design now went ahead under Lou Rydill, in the way I wanted and produced a superlative submarine. Seven were built. This was probably the last UK submarine type that matched and in some respects, bettered the USN submarines being built at the same time. But of course we still lacked good, state of the art, British weapons.

One day I received a letter from New York, from a man called Florsheim or something similar informing me of his intention to sue me personally and the UK MoD generally for using Crane valves in our submarines. He claimed that following the sale of the company that owned the Crane Valve Company in the USA; he owned all the rights to these valves. I took advice from the government's lawyers and replied that the UK MoD purchased its valves from the UK Crane manufacturing company and that if he had a problem with ownership or patent rights he should discuss it with that company. My chaps spoke with the UK company who said that they had title to manufacture the valves. We quietly ordered all the valves we required for the submarines in the programme — better be safe than sorry. There were one or two follow-up letters from the US man to which I made much the same reply. Eventually he wrote to say that he would be in the UK and wanted a meeting. I replied that we would await him in Room "X" of the MoD Whitehall at 2.30 pm on the day that he had suggested, where officials would be available to hear his case. I added that failure on his part to attend would be taken as confirmation that he had no claim on the Ministry or its servants. We waited for an hour after the appointed time and then dispersed. He did not appear, we never heard from him again and the UK Crane Co continued to supply the valves that the navy wanted. I could not help wondering if he had meant to come and had been run over by a bus because in my experience real odd-balls (with names like his) do not give up that easily.

I should explain that within the secure, constantly patrolled Admiralty site at Foxhill, Bath, the submarine block, Block C, had even more fences and security guards and different passes depending which area of the block the holder was allowed to visit. We held the most sensitive missile and nuclear data. This was where I was sitting one day when my deputy director for weapons brought a man from Post office Telephones Security to see me. He explained that there had been a great amount of cheating in the use of telephones, 'phone freaking' I think he called it. He mentioned, for example, that the revenue being received from calls to Australia fell far short of what the logged duration of the calls should have brought in. They had found Bath to be one of the worst places for originating fraudulent calls and had for several months been monitoring calls to and from certain numbers. He had to tell me that some of the calls were originating from a number in this, one of the most secure Admiralty buildings. Could he have my permission to interview Mr X?

Mr. X admitted the offence, he had been mostly calling his mother in Aberdeen, To my intense relief I learned that he was a British Aerospace man employed under contract and so we were able to ban him from the site immediately and return him to his parent employer in Bristol that same afternoon. We then looked at our own security arrangements and whether they should have picked this up.

I was asked to accompany Sir Herman Bondi, the Chief Scientific Advisor on a visit to a nuclear submarine. We joined the Valiant Class vessel in Cardiff docks and soon we were somewhere south of Ireland while the CO and his crew demonstrated the boat's capabilities to their distinguished guest. Late the following afternoon we surfaced and rendezvoused with a naval helicopter. We were given flying helmets and told to climb up the inside of the sail to the top where the helicopter would lower a noose which we were to put under our arms for winching up. The message was "you must on no account raise your arms". I followed Bondi banging my head on bits of structure that I had probably put there. Down came the noose and through it went my head and arms and up I went. Wild horses wouldn't have got me to raise my arms. When I reached the top they had to pull me in and virtually prise my arms away from my sides to get their noose back.

We flew to the naval air station at Culdrose where an RAF communications aircraft was waiting. This small twin engined plane had three rows of two seats, the front two occupied by two grey haired squadron leaders. Off we went over Cornwall to Exeter and beyond. After a while I noticed that the main railway line was down there to the right and that when the railway line changed direction, we changed direction. I taxed the co-pilot and he said "Yes, we call it the iron compass, the rule of the road is to always fly 300 yards to the left of the railway lines otherwise you might collide with another member of the air force coming the other way. So that's how they do it but I confess that I might have got my left and right mixed up.

No sooner had the Polaris submarines settled down into their patrol cycle than we began to consider how the effectiveness of the missile system and hence the national deterrent might be maintained in the light of the development of giant Soviet radar installations and the known deployment of an anti-ballistic missile system around Moscow. The US Navy was introducing the Poseidon Missile and MIRV's, Multiple Independently Targeted Re-entry Vehicles, intended to increase the area of devastation from each missile but most of all to confuse the defensive system by presenting up to fourteen small targets from each missile fired by an SSBN.

The Polaris missile systems for the UK had been among the last of this system to be produced and the US production lines were now phased out. The UK would have to fund their reopening should additional items, such as replacement propulsion motors (these were time limited) be required. Thus for two reasons, the possibility of reduced effectiveness and possible UK uniqueness, we had to give consideration to the longer-term future.

This gave rise to a remarkable power struggle between the central scientists and the navy within the Ministry of Defence. The navy argued that we should plan to upgrade the system by buying the US Navy's Poseidon missile at the end of the US Navy's production run to give the advantage of longer range (and hence a greater area of ocean to hide in), bigger weapons load and longevity. The Poseidon missiles would fit within the existing missile tubes of our Polaris submarines and would require only minor changes to the on-shore missile arsenal. The nuclear policy scientists wished to keep the Polaris missile with a redesigned weapons package comprising two warheads (instead of three) and decoys to confuse the Soviet radars. Much was made of the role that Farnborough and Aldermaston would play in this development, which was given the code name, Chevaline.

Throughout the whole saga no one was prepared to explain how two warheads and a few decoys would be more capable of penetrating the Soviet anti-ballistic missile systems than fourteen warheads or various combinations of warheads and decoys up to fourteen. With their huge 'Hen-house' radars, the Soviets would detect the incoming missiles the moment the missiles appeared above their radar horizon and would then detect the deployment of the missile payload. They would then compute from whence the missiles had been launched and prepare their own intercontinental missiles for counter-fire and also track the warheads as targets for the anti-missile defences and to predict the probable strike area for those that penetrated those defences. To be useful the decoys must be indistinguishable from real warheads as far as the enemy radar is concerned; it is not simply a case for releasing acres of 'chaf' hundreds of miles out in space! One can conceive really clever active decoys but why not simply swamp the missile defence radars with real warheads 'so that everything that gets through goes bang' as one of my USN friends said. If one hinted at this, the reply was that if the US ever had to launch its missiles there would be so many in the air at once that all the Soviet defences would be saturated and so all payloads could be warheads whereas if the UK launched its missiles the payloads would be few and capable of interception. The idea of the UK going it alone against a power sophisticated enough to have anti-ICBM missile defences does stretch the imagination.

President Nixon had expressed his willingness for the British to acquire Poseidon but with some reservations concerning the release of the US MIRV technology. We had firm costs for purchasing the Poseidon missile system from the US Navy. I recall a figure of about £ 280 millions to which would be added the relatively small cost of modifying the submarines by ex-changing the Polaris equipments for Poseidon equipments just as the USN was doing. In his book, "Inside Story", Chapman Pincher pours scorn on the navy's cost figure of £ 250 millions for equipping the RN Polaris force with the US Poseidon missile system and quotes an unnamed US source for claiming that the cost would have been double that figure. Pincher was misinformed: the cost figures that we were providing came directly from Admiral Levering Smith, the Commander of the US Navy's Strategic Missile programme, who already had submarines at sea equipped with Poseidon missiles and knew the cost down to the last cent. To date everything that we had purchased from the US Navy for our submarines, notably the reactor and machinery for *HMS Dreadnought* and the Polaris systems for the Resolution Class had been supplied to time and at, or below, the cost quoted at the outset. There was and is no reason to doubt that this would have been the case if the UK had purchased the Poseidon missile system. This does not include the warheads and other things in the re-entry package to be made in British establishments, of course.

The Chevaline programme held a considerable element of risk. All of the components would require extensive environmental testing as well as functional testing on missiles. The environmental testing would include exposure to moderate heat, extreme cold and then extreme heat coupled with various spectra of vibration and shock, culminating in test firings. The Polaris missile system would be largely unchanged except for the re-entry vehicle and some electronics. At the time that £280 was quoted for the fully proven Poseidon solution, the alternative was quoted at under £260 millions.

We maintained that the estimated timescale was wildly optimistic and pointed out that the continued retention of the Polaris missile would require a purchase of replacement second stage missile motors at the UK's considerable expense since it would entail reopening the US Hercules company's production facility and that this cost should be included in the Chevaline costs. This cost would be over £ 30 millions. To no avail..

I had several meetings with the First Sea Lord, Admiral Sir Eric Ashmore, and advised him that in my view the Chevaline solution would cost at least twice the present estimate and would take twice as long to develop. Ashmore asked for proof, "How can I go to ministers to contest these figures if you can't give me positive proof?" All that I could say was that the whole of my professional experience was that people (and particularly those who are new to the game) planning projects were always over-optimistic; they would claim that they had included for contingencies, such as allowing three spare Skylark missile shots and so on, but in the real world they would find that the fix-it solution that flew on the second spare missile didn't work for some reason and the schedule is delayed and unforeseen costs mount while a new fix-it is designed and tried. I instanced our 4 year delay in getting the Dounreay reactor to criticality and on a more modest level, the trouble we still had with aircraft and warship completion dates and cost overruns — if British industry still couldn't get that right after all this time, Ministers should be very wary of accepting the estimates for the Chevaline project. I cited the escalating cost of Blue Streak, which had led to its cancellation. In comparison, the Poseidon estimate was firm and we would be in the mainstream of US development.

Admiral Ashmore said that this was not good enough and he wanted hard facts. I said that for the life of me I couldn't see how I could provide the sort of facts he appeared to want without actually making Chevaline and looking at the fiasco afterwards. The British aircraft and missile industry was a saga of cost and time overruns.

The Chevaline project was approved. The programme went ahead and as we had predicted, safety considerations made it essential that the Polaris missile second stage motors be replaced, requiring the facility in the US to be restarted at the UK's expense.

The only reason that I could see for the Chief Scientific Adviser going ahead might be to preserve the future of Farnborough and Aldermaston. Little did I suspect at the time amid all the argument and bluster by those responsible for nuclear weapon matters that they had been receiving copies of secret US drawings of nuclear weapons provided under an unpublished provision of the 1958 Anglo – US Agreement, and virtually copying them.

In his Biography, "The time of Life', Denis Healey wrote; "I regard it as one of my mistakes as Chancellor (of the Exchequer) not to get Chevaline cancelled after 1974 when the following Labour government found that its costs had escalated beyond control".

By the time it entered service, the cost of the Chevaline project had quadrupled to over £1,000 millions and taken four times longer to develop than the central scientific staff had predicted.

Let there be no doubt that, perhaps with the exception of some rather fast footwork by one or two people in Whitehall, this programme was executed by able, dedicated and talented people who were doing their best. The trouble was that they were out of their depth. It was, as we in DPT strove so hard to point out from the outset, a far bigger task than Whitehall ever realised.

The process of rationalisation of research establishments would only be advanced with much pain and grief. I was asked to sit on a committee to consider the possible amalgamation of the establishments concerned with explosives (among other things). The chairman was Tom Kerr, a senior member of the scientific service. The directors of the places under consideration attended. I learnt the value of patience from Tom. He would ask the directors to examine a reduction of some sort and report. At the next meeting no one would have done it, all for very good reasons. I would have raged like a US General but Tom smiled gently and said he knew how difficult it all was and then produced another set of requests. After two or three such sessions as we crept slowly forward, more and more data was assembled which rather put the reluctant directors on the spot. A typical log-breaking ploy was to consider what would be the effect of increasing their staff by 5%, decreasing their staff by 5% and decreasing by 10%. At the next meeting they all knew what they would do with a 5% increase, a few hazarded a guess at what disasters would follow a 5% decrease and to all of them, except one, a 10% reduction was unthinkable, Tom fastened on the one director who had thought about the unthinkable and we kicked around various scenarios into which discussion the others were drawn and so on. At the next meeting we had some idea of the things that would suffer and ideas of how to get round it. We turned to sites and machinery and I realised why our one director had been so helpful at the beginning; it appeared that if we wished to shut his explosives factory we would have to remove some top soil that had become permeated with nitro-glycerine and similar substances over the past century. Just to a depth of a few metres over a few hundred hectares or so!. And still Tom Kerr smiled and jollied them along.

Perhaps at this point I should mention the Vickers Flights. Very early in the nuclear submarine project it was evident that the only sensible means of travel between Southampton, Bath, Barrow and Dounreay was by air. Initially British United Airways provided the occasional service. The first time that I flew to Wick (for Dounreay), the small four engined Heron aircraft landed and taxied straight into a hangar for us to disembark. I remarked to the stewardess, in her black velour schoolgirls hat, that this was unusual and she explained that if they stopped outside the wind would blow the unladen aircraft over on its back. En route by road to Dounreay one noted the diminutive haystacks each covered by heavy rope netting for the same reason.

There is a small landing strip on Walney island adjacent to the Vickers facility at Barrow from which the Chairman of the company, Len Redshaw, flew with the local gliding club. The Heron aircraft could not use this strip and so we used Blackpool for passengers from and to, Barrow. This was not efficient and eventually the decision was taken that Vickers would hire or purchase two 12-seater aircraft and operate the service themselves between Bath and Barrow twice daily with flights to Wick once or twice each week. The Southampton office was closed.

There was an operational RAF airfield at Colerne, literally on the outskirts of Bath but they refused to entertain the idea that a company aircraft flying solely on Admiralty business to convey personnel employed on the nuclear project, could use this airfield. So Bristol airport was used. The Vickers pilots were ex-RAF and we soon learned that the main reason for refusing the nuclear submarine project's request to be allowed to use Colerne was that the late afternoon flight bringing people back to Bath from Barrow arrived at about 6.00pm and the air force at Colerne shut down everything except for the public telephone at 5.30pm. It was a trifle tedious getting to and from Bristol airport but the airside service was very good.

Then one day the RAF made overtures for the Vickers flights to use Colerne. Please would we use the local air-station? The naval grapevine discovered that RAF Colerne was on the short list of stations to be closed for economy reasons and someone was now trying to play the Admiralty card - too late.

The flights were then moved to the RAF's principal air transport base at Lyneham. Lyneham is the RAF's big, busy centre for all C-130 Hercules squadrons and open 24 hours a day. The pilots of the Vickers aircraft approaching the field would sometimes find that they would be asked to join a stick of three C..130's circling the airport and participate for a few minutes in the air direction, marshalling and landing exercise taking place. If I was sitting in the co-pilots seat — for there was only the pilot — I would notice the change in how he responded to commands from the air traffic controllers and in the way that he handled the aircraft. To the ex RAF pilots it was just like old times.

With the ever-present terrorist threat, security was tight at RAF Lyneham. Past the armed guards, those without station passes were directed to the guardhouse to identify themselves, state the purpose of their visit and receive temporary passes, with or without an escort. This was done with the minimum of fuss as far as we were concerned because we had MoD passes but as I stood there waiting my turn to be processed I could not help reflecting on what a poor public relations image of the RAF the guardhouse presented. To most of the drivers of delivery vehicles, contractors and the like seeking authorisation to enter, this would be their closest encounter with RAF organisation. They would have parked their vehicle between some ill arranged cones and now at about 7.30am, were in a queue, which advanced very slowly towards the counter at which a young RAF person was entering their particulars in a register. The RAF person had obviously never seen the register before and seemed to be incapable of remembering the column headings between entries; thus entering each visitor was new adventure in 'pick the column'. Visitors got impatient at the slowness, particularly since through the open door to the room behind were to be seen at least three RAF Police sergeants lounging, smoking and drinking tea.   Never in the 20 or so years in which I passed through did I see a sergeant who was not smoking or who came out to help the 'erk' at the desk. If one was lucky the young RAF person on duty at the counter was a girl and they seemed always to be more intelligent than the men.

When I was with British Shipbuilders and later VSEL, Liz used to meet me off the plane. She was being processed at the guardhouse one evening so that she could drive right up to the arrivals terminal to meet "her husband who was on the Vickers flight". The man looked a little puzzled and said " I didn't know they had flights for vicars. Is he Church of England or Roman Catholic?" Liz regretted later that she didn't say that she was a catholic priests wife.

The aircraft were so useful in reducing time away from the office that MoD personnel on other projects building at Barrow were carried at a substantial cost saving to the Crown. Among other things it avoided overnight absences. Under British Shipbuilders and later VSEL, the aircraft often flew to London usually to RAF Northolt but occasionally to Heathrow. The HS 125 jet that BS had hired in the early days had no problems with Heathrow but the Vickers pilots did not much like going there in their propeller planes for a very simple reason. The commercial jets had slowed from their 500 plus knots and were hanging in the air on their wings and flaps at something over 200 knots on final approach prior to touch down whereas the Vickers flight would have to go flat out at its top speed of 230 knots to stop itself being overrun by a Boeing 747.closing from astern.

In the spring of 1974 I was promoted to the rank between Second Permanent Secretary and Deputy Secretary, (called Higher Intermediary, would you believe) and became Director General Ships. In order of seniority I was now the fourth most senior career civilian officer in the UK Ministry of Defence.

With a team of gifted colleagues, I had been responsible for the design and construction of two generations of British nuclear submarines, five Classes, that were better and orders of magnitude safer than any submarines that had gone before in the Royal Navy. I suppose that it would have been un-British for anyone in authority to say Thank You.

Chapter Eleven

I had been appointed Head of the Royal Corps of Naval Constructors early in 1974 and succeeded Vice Admiral Sir George Raper as DG Ships and deputy to the Controller of the Navy in May. The post of DG Ships was created in 1958 and I was the third occupant. The title had been chosen without thought to its relationship to people occupying the same sort of posts in the army and air divisions who were Deputy Controllers. The development of the Procurement Executive brought this into sharper relief and the Ships title was subsequently changed to Deputy Controller Warships, with corresponding changes to the ranks below.

During my time as DG Ships I served under two Controllers of the Navy, Admiral Sir Anthony Griffin and Admiral Sir Richard Clayton. Griffin was an officer who had benefited, in career terms, from the untimely death of Michael Le Fanu. He was a worrier who was at his desk 'til late in the evening, clearing his In-tray. He claimed to be the only Captain who had collided with a lighthouse and still made flag rank – his aircraft carrier's overhanging flight deck had hit the light on the mole at the entrance to Beirut harbour. He left to be the first chairman of British Shipbuilders. Dick Clayton was a bachelor, highly intelligent, a clear incisive thinker, who regularly cleared his In-tray by 6.00pm and did the "Times" crossword while his staff got rid of it all, ready for the next day. It was a matter of great regret to all who had served with him that he did not become the First Sea Lord.

My responsibilities as Head of the RCNC took me into the Dockyards, the research establishments and overseeing as well as Ship Department, in fact wherever members of the Corps were serving. In Ship Department I had a staff approaching three thousand, the senior members being my 8 civilian and naval divisional directors and deputy directors of 2 star (rear admiral or civilian equivalent) rank. In addition as the senior MoD officer, I had certain responsibilities for all six thousand or so staff in the Bath area.

The Foxhill site consisted of seven large single storey buildings arranged as drawing offices, conference rooms and offices together with ancillary buildings such as security control (at the main entrance), boiler rooms, model shop and canteen. They were designated Block A, Block B, etc up to Block G, located closest to the main entrance. With time and usage, the public house across the road outside the main entrance became known as Block H and indeed so proclaimed itself by a sign affixed to its wall.

Some years before I became DG Ships it had been decided that the new Headquarters offices for the MoD's Procurement Executive would be located at the Foxhill site. The buildings would house 4,000 staff. They would be four storey's high and trials with tethered balloons were used to assure the City fathers that the buildings would not be visible from the city centre. To allow the Department to continue to function during the several years of building work, the present blocks would be demolished one by one as new office space was completed, commencing with Block E. To accommodate the production staff, book writers, and costing people dislodged from Block E, a new two storey block was built between Blocks A and B. Block H having already been pre-empted by the pub opposite, the new block became Block J.

In accordance with this plan Block E was empty and whichever government department was responsible for such civil engineering projects had removed the internal fittings such as central heating systems and wash places to prevent the block creeping back into temporary use.

Meanwhile people elsewhere were developing their proposals; the buildings were now required to house 6,000 staff and be six storeys high, including one or two mainframe computers.

Thus it was when I took over, Block E had stood empty for several years, we were short of space and what was worse all requests for repair to the other blocks were met with a polite refusal, or at the very best, questioning as to whether it could not await the completion of the new HQ building. Little seemed to have taken place to advance the new project for some years. I found that there had been problems. Two outstanding issues that had seemingly disappeared into the sands of time, were the extent of the underground quarries beneath Foxhill from which Ralph Allen had mined the Bath-stone from which Bath is built and the matter of access from and to the site and who should pay for the proposed new access scheme. The local authority was not being as helpful as one might have thought it should be in consolidating its future hold upon what was, at the time, the city's largest employer.

Looking at the situation, it seemed to me that there was little prospect that the new HQ complex would ever be built at the Foxhill site and I proposed that this be recognised by bringing Block E back into use. This was agreed with no argument and the new HQ has since been built in a much better location in South Gloucestershire.

With the post of DG Ships I inherited the senior RN driver (a civilian) as my driver. I viewed this as a mixed blessing. When he drove me I arrived quickly but was most surprised to arrive in one piece at all. I discovered that his nickname among the other drivers was Fangio, which says it all. He was the driver that Admiral Vian had been looking for all those years ago in 1947/48. It was with mixed emotions that I learned one morning that he had been killed the previous night when his private car had failed to negotiate a bend in the country road when returning from a local village pub.

There had been two major changes in the post-war organisation of the Defence departments in Whitehall; the amalgamation of the three separate service ministries into a combined Ministry of Defence with a Chief of Defence Staff and, subsequently, the absorption of the Ministry of Supply into the MoD with the creation of the Procurement Executive.

In theory this put a number of senior appointments in the melting pot. There were posts that clearly should be filled by a sailor or a soldier or an airman and there were a whole lot more that were not single service and for which the best man available might be chosen, even a civilian. Of course he wasn't; the services shared them out or took them in turn, but always they were watching their backs and one found admirals so busy with self-preservation that the interests of their subordinates and to that extent the nation, became a secondary concern. This particularly affected the RCNC, which had hitherto been the creature of the Board of Admiralty and to whom the Corps looked to preserve its interests.

With the creation of the Procurement Executive the senior staff from the MoS appeared smiling and virtually took over the materiel functions of the MoD, except for ships. Ministers and the Permanent Secretary welcomed the change for it gave them a bigger command with a much bigger budget and in consequence a louder voice in the Cabinet and its committees. For their part, the Prime Minister and Chancellor would be pleased to see all defence funds in one basket and more visible for cuts in the future

The mainspring of the Procurement Executive set up within the MoD to bring together the procurement functions of the 'old' MoD and the Ministry of Supply were the Sea, Land, and Air Systems Controllers. This brought into sharp focus the differences in procurement practice between the services. Since Pepys, the Admiralty had had its own organisation to design and build its ships, guns and ammunition. The ships of the Line were designed and built in the Royal Dockyards by the Master Shipwrights from whom the Royal Corps evolved. In the heyday of Britain's power the line of 'firsts' from this Corps was impressive and why in the absence of corresponding skills elsewhere, the Corps was entrusted with the design of the early British airships and radio masts and the first land ships, better known today as tanks, as well as HM Ships and Auxiliaries.

The Ministry of Supply did research but most development and design of aircraft, missiles, electronics and land vehicles was usually contracted-out to industry, which would manage and run the projects. Thus significant parts of establishments like Farnborough, NGTE Pyestock, Fort Halstead, Malvern and so on were in effect working under the direction of managers employed by defence contractors and who were often less well qualified than the civil servants in the establishments and far less good at controlling expenditure. Why should they when the purpose of the exercise (for many of them) was to enhance their company's earnings?

The fact that we remained among the world leaders in submarine and surface warship design right up to the 1980's while our weapons and electronics systems were surpassed by so many other nations from the 1960's onwards might itself be indicative of the relative merit of the Admiralty and MoS design and procurement arrangements over that period

It must be appreciated that although the MoD took over the duties and staff of the MoS, the number of scientists and engineers in the latter far exceeded the numbers in the Royal Naval Scientific Service. One could not help feeling sorry for the people in the RNSS. Created after the war by bringing together the small groups of staff working on sonar, radar, explosives, materials, communications and the like into what became an affective research and development organisation operating mainly within the naval environment, they were now to be merged into, and lost, within a mass of different talents.

The MoS brought with them the Royal Ordnance Factories where armoured fighting vehicles were made and repaired. My mindset on tanks and those responsible for them was formed by Liddell Hart in the pre-war years when as part of the debate on the tactical use of tanks, there was considerable discussion concerning the most important feature of what, today, we would call Main Battle Tanks. The French favoured high speed and the British would sacrifice speed for heavier armour. To my schoolboy mind the most important thing to me would be to have a big enough gun to destroy the enemy before he could fire at me, but no one seemed to discuss this in the press, it was speed versus armour. Came the day in 1940 and the German big gun tanks blew our lot to kingdom come.

There was some reallocation of responsibilities in the interests of organisational neatness. That which affected me most was the transfer of my seven research establishments into a Research Controllerate, while still manned by officers of the Royal Corps of Naval Constructors (RCNC) and the Royal Naval Scientific Service' (RNSS). We still ran them professionally but they were 'owned' by the ex-MoS scientists in Whitehall.

In my previous posts I had dealt usually with RNSS scientists whom I had known for years, but now I was much more conscious of the number of people I didn't know who would arrive at meetings with a folder under their arm, declare that they representing Assistant Chief Scientific Adviser (ACSA) Something or other, play no constructive part in the proceedings, insist at the end that some other scientific staff office should be consulted and depart, having effectively delayed a decision by another month or two One recalls that in 1945 US Senator Tydings had declared that 'an atomic scientist is one of the few persons whose intellectual development in many respects bears the same relation to that of the rest of us as a range of mountains bears to a molehill'. This mantle had somewhat been assumed by lesser, non-atomic, fry.

It was many years before the secretariat and the service operational requirement divisions realised that these chaps were not people of infinite knowledge on all things and by that time there were about 320 of them swanning around the Main Building. As Private Eye was to remark more than 20 years later - "Such conceit has always been around in one form or another. Bishops used to have it, and Lords. Now, however, it's a speciality of a certain sort of scientist. Although their individual contributions to the advancement of science may have been tiny or non-existent, they assume all the credit of the discipline as a whole. For the most part secretly they believe that the opinions of non-scientists are pointless, not worth considering any more, utterly abolished by progress ".

It was particularly disheartening to the many real scientists in the establishments - the people capable of original work - to accept that the way to advancement and recognition was to move to Whitehall and shuffle pieces of paper about. There developed so much dissatisfaction that 'merit' promotions were introduced in the research establishments to try to redress the balance.

It has to be remembered that the acceptance of scientists and engineers in such numbers and high ranks in the government service represented a substantial change. From its early days the Higher Civil Service and Armed Services at home and abroad had been staffed largely by arts graduates and their service college equivalents. This was natural in the late 19th Century   The Royal Navy, as the most technical service at the turn of the century, treated its engineering officers as an inferior class, they had separate messes and slightly different uniform. It was not until after the First World War that they were given the 'executive curl' and not until well after the Second World War that an engineer officer was made a member of the hitherto exclusively-executive-officer-manned Admiralty Board. As for the civil service, even after the Fulton Report on the Civil Service had been adopted as government policy requiring all senior posts to be open to the best man for the job, people with special professional skills were still sidelined as 'specialists' in favour of generalist arts graduates when top posts had to be filled. Modern Britain is the result.

The US Navy woke up many years ago to the need that those who are to command ships and fleets should understand the technology of those ships and aircraft and made it mandatory that all officers should earn an engineering degree at Annapolis or elsewhere and should serve as an engineering officer in a warship or aviation squadron. Their service has gone from strength to strength. A similar change in the Royal Navy is long overdue.

There is considerable career planning to ensure that the officers destined to fill the highest appointments occupy the right posts on the way up. I recall that when John Treacher was the Controller of the Navy's naval assistant he explained to me the narrowness of the field from which the future Chief of Naval Staff would be selected and the favourable position that he occupied in that field. In the event Admiral Sir John Treacher was C in C Fleet and left the navy from that post.

When something happens and the man being groomed is unable to take up the post, the consequences reverberate fairly widely. When, as has happened, the post in question is the Chief of Defence Staff, the situation is very serious. The remarkably gifted Admiral Sir Michael Le Fanu fell mortally ill some months before taking up the Chief of Defence Staff post. At first glance the solution would appear to be to appoint the soldier or airman whom it was planned would have followed him as CDS some three years later under the buggins turn arrangement   but this would have disrupted the career planning of all three services and meant officers missing operational commands judged to be important before reaching the top. The solution was that the navy had to appoint another officer to fill the CDS billet to see through the navy's turn and the effects of this went down the navy's command structure. At least one officer who had been destined to leave the navy as a rear admiral ended up a full admiral.

The same sort of confusion, only more so, followed Mrs Thatcher's insistence that John Fieldhouse, the C in C Fleet at the time of the Falklands campaign and the sinking of the *Belgrano*, should be appointed CDS when it was not the navy's turn. In this case the career planning of all three services was disrupted.

The Committee of Enquiry gambit is played by a Minister or Permanent Secretary when the pressures on him to make some evident change to which he and the Treasury are opposed, can be resisted no longer. Perhaps questions are being asked in the House. The procedure then is to set up a high level committee to inquire into the matter, chaired preferably by a retired judge who has not quite reached his dotage and comprising members who know not much about the real issues at stake. The Committee secretary must be an administrator from the fast stream who knows that his personal future depends on his writing the committee's report to include in its recommendations what the 'establishment' can accept.

The Permanent Secretary has further safeguards. When the committee has reported, its recommendations must be considered by the appropriate government departments before, if necessary, going to ministers. This is a good time to feed in additional material that has just come to light, preferably material that blurs those recommendations that officialdom doesn't like. Meanwhile, there will have been some organisational changes or reallocation of responsibilities in an area bordering on the thing that the committee was considering, making it possible, should ministers inquire, to implement a few of the minor recommendations as an interim step while stalling on the major ones 'due to changed circumstances'.

Implicit in all of this is the knowledge that somewhere in the process time-scale, there is bound to be a crisis of some sort, with or without a general election and perhaps a change of government or at the very least, a change of minister. Sometimes a determined minister will ensure that a major report is approved. It then falls to the service or civil service chief to implement it. Those recommendations that are liked will be acted upon while those that are not liked will be discussed ad-nauseam until there is a change of minister and then quietly forgotten. There is a more than evens chance that the incoming minister will not wish to pursue hares started by his predecessor. I am not condemning the process out of hand; there is a lot to be said for keeping a certain amount of inertia in the decision making process.

I fail to understand why a committee to inquire into some army matter should always be chaired by a general; even when far removed from actual warfare and tactics; and similarly for the navy and air force - an essay in how to preserve vested interests. I would always have appointed a non-service chairman; a good lateral thinking woman might remove a few sacred cows. Indeed the whole subject of committees set up to inquire into something is worthy of study.

It might be felt that Parliament was slow in questioning the entire rationale of service complements and structures. To me, the most telling example was the US Air Force base at Bentwaters in Essex where a 2 star US Major General personally commanded more aircraft than there were in the entire British air force. A reason often advanced for the military top-weight is the need to be able to expand in war. It cannot be too strongly put that the officers who have reached the top in peacetime will mostly be those who have the skills for the paper battles of Whitehall and these are not the skills for actual field command in war. Two world wars have demonstrated this.

The principal reason for the number of service and civilian officers with 2 stars and above, is the need to pay the going rate for expertise that does not exist elsewhere and which it would take a great time to create elsewhere Creating quasi-official agencies only indirectly answerable to parliament in which higher rewards can be offered without the need for ranks or embarrassing titles and, in theory, no long term commitment to employment, will eventually present Ministers with longer term funding decisions that an in-house arrangement would avoid.

There would have been substantial changes in the top management at Vickers Shipbuilders if Sir Michael Carey had not died when he did. He was strongly of the view that British industry was performing badly because of inadequate management and that promotion to the post of Managing Director or Chief Executive from within a company should only take place when the internal candidate was exceptionally well qualified and never as a matter of routine and never twice in succession. MD's sons and 'favourite sons' were to be frowned upon. He was concerned that the succession at Vickers shipbuilders, the man to follow Sir Len Redshaw, should break the mould and he approached Sir Peter Matthews, the Chairman of Vickers asking that the post should be filled by an external candidate. The Controller of the Navy and I accompanied Michael Carey to Millbank on two occasions and received a firm assurance that the position would be filled by external recruitment. Michael died and I heard nothing more until I read in the Times one morning that Redshaw's deputy, Bill Richardson, would succeed him when he retired. Whether the Controller of the Navy was consulted or simply told, I do not know. Richardson was in turn succeeded by his deputy, Greg Mott and Greg Mott by Tony Peake, both from within the firm but neither had spent his entire career with the firm. Tony Peake came from Rolls Royce. Both were good managers in a very complex technology.

With the return of a Labour government in 1997, occupying the middle ground of political opinion, it is difficult to remember how far to the left the Labour party had moved in the 1950's to 1977's, as exemplified by the policies espoused by the party National Executive and the Trades Union Congress. These bodies were strongly anti-establishment, pro-disarmament and stridently anti-nuclear deterrent. Since the political pecking order and the prospect of future cabinet posts depended to some extent on the elections to the National Executive, which dictated party policy, the parliamentary labour party mouthed the same slogans. The more intelligent – and honest – of the senior labour people knew that the realities were very different from the dogma preached by their militant members, and had to steer a course around this, particularly as regards nuclear disarmament. Dennis Healey has written extensively on this dilemma and commented that the arguments of his party members were too often confined to theories of Socialist doctrine and not upon the formidable realities that a Labour government would face when in office – " they were concerned too much with how to present our policies   so as to cause least offence to the Party's power   brokers in the trade unions or the constituencies".

For the six years prior to 1974, Dennis Healey had been the Secretary of State for Defence. He made a thorough and much overdue review of Britain's defence commitments and the forces necessary to meet them. His appointment to the MoD was not without comment; he had been a member of the communist party when at Cambridge and later had adopted some pretty far left postures. Our US friends were puzzled at a situation in which we would not have been allowed to be employed on sensitive defence work had we even so much as hinted at a sympathy with the communists, yet we could have a Minister who had actually been a party member.

The 1974 election saw Labour returned to power and the appointment of Roy Mason as Secretary of State for Defence. He was a lightweight, whose main concern seemed to me to be that he should be liked. He was much dependent upon his officials, a situation that we felt, all things considered, was in the nations (and the Prime Minister's) best interests. He was followed in turn by Fred Mulley. Mr Mulley's ministers were John Gilbert and Patrick Duffy. Mr Mulley would tell how as a private soldier he had been captured by the Germans and had studied while a prisoner to earn a degree. He was a fellow of St. Catharine's Cambridge and was subsequently made a life Peer. Sadly, he will always best be remembered for the fact that at the RAF's display to celebrate the queens silver jubilee he was photographed asleep at her side while jet fighter planes roared past, a few hundred feet above his head. Mr Mulley used to chat with me about ships. A joke we shared was when he repeated something that someone had suggested to him and which was technologically not possible and I said "Why is it, Secretary of State, when you have this vast organisation feeding you with the true facts, why is it that if someone stands next to you in the House of Commons lavatory and tells you something daft, you believe them?"

We discussed the nationalised British Shipbuilders. I expressed the hope that public ownership would be used to raise the overall standards as it already had in mining, steel and the utilities. One way would be to raise the technological level by recruiting better managers and specialists. He was surprised to learn that one of the reasons why Japan was outstripping the UK in merchant shipbuilding was their superior technology, brought about in part by the large numbers of graduate engineers employed in their yards, in many cases starting at the bottom as welders to gain practical experience. In one yard alone there were nearly nine hundred graduates. I compared this with the British yards in which one would be lucky to find twenty and more usually less than ten in a yard. The warship builders were little better but were controlled fairly closely by the RCNC officers of the MoD who were responsible for the design and oversight of the building of HM Ships. About 80% of the graduates in the industry were in the RCNC. To change this round would require time and effort but could benefit the industry in the longer term.

We had tried to do something in a very modest way with Vickers Shipbuilders at the beginning of the nuclear submarine programme. Their number of graduates was laughable and we insisted that as a start the company should recruit a further 12_ graduate naval architects. This was done. At the end of two years only 2 remained, the others had been frozen out by the 'born in Barrow' boys — quite simply by not being included in the distribution of documents, not told of meetings and generally ignored. The second tier of management at Barrow — the people who actually ran the show — had reasoned correctly that by then the RCNC officers would be too busy with problems about building the submarine to do anything about it.

Mr Mulley commented "Why don't you join British Shipbuilders and help make the industry more efficient?"

Two recollections of Mr Mulley concern the launch of the first 'through deck cruiser' *HMS Invincible* at Messers Vickers Shipbuilders at Barrow. Some time before, he asked how much the launching would cost and was told about half a million pounds. He mulled it over and said that with all the wood and tugs and things he supposed that was reasonable. "Oh no," I said "this half a million is for the actual ceremony. There is a separate clause in the contract to cover the cost of the band, luncheon, flags and so on and for the special train from London and overnight accommodation for VIP guests". Mr Mulley said that he could not and would not wish to justify such expenditure to parliament and instructed me that the scale of entertainment be reduced. I pointed out

210

that we could not really have less guests than for the previous royal launch at Barrow and we agreed that this should be the scale, without the pre-launch dinner and overnight accommodation. This was confirmed in a letter from Patrick Duffy which stated that the number of guests should be limited to 150 couples of whom only 50 should be from the MoD, that trade unionists were to be included in the total and given prominent positions on the launching platform and that his mother should be invited.

I was in Barrow some days later and informed the Managing Director, Bill Richardson, of the S of S's directive. Bill Richardson immediately said "No, that is not acceptable. We have always been justifiably proud of the standard of hospitality provided at Vickers launches and that standard would be maintained for the launch of HMS *Invincible*". I said that I was most pleased to hear this and I was sure that Ministers would be, to learn that Vickers would themselves meet the additional cost of entertainment over and above the limit that the Secretary of State had set. Bill Richardson said that he hadn't exactly meant that.

The day of the launch it teemed with rain. We were driven to the shipyard through streets wet with rain but lined with small macintoshed children waving union flags, shepherded by patient teachers. The plan was that the senior Vickers staff would be presented to her majesty in the foyer by Lord Robens, the firm's Chairman, followed by Mr Mulley presenting the senior MoD staff. Mr Mulley would then escort the queen up the stairs where the wives would be presented.

The royal car pulled up outside and the queen and prince Philip entered. They had returned from an overseas tour only the previous day and the queen did not appear to be happy as she advanced along the line. When it came to Mr Mulley's turn he forgot all the names so he invented them. Prince Philip with whom I had been briefly in a destroyer in the war and had met on several occasions subsequently, most recently at the Royal Academy of Engineering, stopped in front of me and made some comment about changing names but the queen was already on her way, alone, up the stairs. According to Liz, the queen appeared, put her head round the door grinned and said "Am I in the right place" to which the irrepressible Eve Robens replied "Come on in your majesty and meet the front row of the chorus".

We assembled on the Launching platform. I didn't notice whether Mr Mulley checked up on where the trade union leaders were. Her Majesty duly performed the naming ceremony, the band played Rule Britannia and the ship slid down the ways and completed the dangerous translation from land to water. The queen promptly turned on her heel and marched off the platform. Officials ran to bring her back to watch the fly-past of naval aircraft and helicopters and, in particular, the Sea Harrier which hovered in front of the launch platform before standing on its tail and roaring away vertically upwards into the clouds. It was still raining.

Perhaps someone had set a very tight budget for the lunch. It was the worst meal that has been served at any ceremony that I have attended. How the Palace could have agreed that the queen should be served trout complete with all the bones followed by mutton (yes, they called it mutton on the menu) with rather cold potato and peas, I do not know. We were immediately opposite the queen and prince and they ate even less than we did. But the chocolate basket sweet was nice. A brief speech and they were off to their next engagement in Lancaster.

One lesson that Socialist Ministers learned loud and clear was that the quickest way to revive a community like the Clyde and Tyneside by providing jobs was to order warships. We usually could order a repeat of the last class that they had built or an updated version thereof to get the show on the road and, of course, twice as many jobs would be assured elsewhere in industry, manufacturing the equipment and machinery to go into the ships.

Submarine launches are like reunions. In 1976, a few months before we married, Liz came with me to the launch of HMS *Sceptre* at Barrow. This was before Mr Mulley asked his questions about costs. Vickers could be justifiably proud of their hospitality; luncheon was served on the special train from London, a reception, dinner and a night at the Old England Hotel at Windermere and a fleet of cars the next morning for the trip beside the lake to Barrow for the launch of the submarine. One of the groups whose pay and conditions of service Liz looked after in her MoD job were the Admiralty Regional Officers and three of these retired captains were ex-submariners and were present. They had recently had a substantial increase in pay and so she was among friends that evening. When we went to our rooms we followed a trail of wet footprints and espied the back of a large naked man who had been for a swim in the lake, at 1am in November. The next morning, as the submarine slid down the ways, this same Captain Jack Bishop stood at the salute with tears running down his cheek, he looked at Liz and said "There are only two things that make me cry Ma'm and launching submarines is one of them". I know exactly what he meant. To appreciate this story one had to know this large jovial, fearless submarine engineer officer whose courage and strength in his job and on the rugby field for the Royal Navy were legend.

The launch was different in that the gracious lady performing the ceremony forgot to say the bit about "and may God bless all who sail in her" and did so at the lunch afterwards.

Marriage to Liz brought many changes; I stopped going to the office Saturdays and Sundays (I took it home instead) and I learned much about how the staff felt. I had always regarded myself as one of the boys, did I not play in the annual Staff v RCNC soccer and cricket matches until I was over 40? Bill Locke opened my eyes just a little. We had been students together at the RNEC. He had retired from the navy as a Commander and had joined the Royal Naval Engineering Service to work in Ship Department. Now, following a medical problem, he was to retire for good. I said that I thought him to be wise, I had recently married and now realised that there was much more to life than slaving away in Ship Department. I was shattered when he replied "and aren't we grateful, you were bloody insufferable". Perhaps I still am.

Princess Margaret launched HMS *Illustrious* at Swan Hunters. For some reason the tabloid press had been giving her a bad time; if they could publish an unflattering picture or put the wrong construction on something that she said or did, they did so. At the launch she was closely escorted by Admiral Mountbatten, she was elegant, beautiful and charming. At the reception they spoke with us briefly and Mountbatten took her away with a laughing comment like "you won't want to talk with him, he designs warships in Bath". Some minutes later the princess came back, saying, "Come on lets talk about Bath". Many years earlier the princess had been a frequent visitor at Widcombe Manor and more recently had dined privately and shopped incognito in Bath; a pattern followed for many years by several of the young royals.

My single recollection of the day we met Princess Anne is of the princess standing directly in front of Liz and looking her up and down in the realisation that they were dressed in identical suits, in the same colour and with the same accessories. It was reported that Mrs Thatcher once approached the palace and suggested that on those occasions on which they would be together in public, the Queen and Mrs Thatcher should exchange information on what they intended to wear. The palace is reported to have informed her that the Queen does not notice what other people are wearing. Princess Anne most certainly did; perhaps she should have a word with her mum.

Iceland had unilaterally declared an exclusion zone to preserve the stock of fish in the waters around her coast. Most people in the UK had some sympathy with the inhabitants of this barren island and their wish to preserve their most valuable source of export earnings but in those days the UK fishing lobby was loud in its claims that the sea and the fish in it must be free to everyone. The Royal Navy was ordered to protect the fishing fleet. The Icelandic Coast Guard ships ignored RN fishery protection ships. Small frigates were sent and were bumped broadside on and damaged by the rugged Iceland ships. Ocean greyhounds are not designed for maritime bumps-a-daisy so we decided — sympathy or no sympathy — to better equip our ships for this 'cod war'.

The nice peaceful solution that I favoured was to weld railway lines across the frigates deck with the ends sticking out about a metre on either side of the ship. Bump that if you dare. Despite protests that the rails were entirely passive and of no danger to anyone who kept their distance, Ministers vetoed this solution as too hostile. Another frigate was quietly being made less visibly rugged, but very rugged none the less, in Chatham but happily a political solution was reached before she could again reach Icelandic waters.

In 1978 a delegation from the Peoples Republic of China Navy visited the UK and spent 24 hours in Bath before going to Vosper-Thornycroft at Southampton to see the plastic mine-countermeasures vessels being built. It was our usual practice to have visiting VIP's home for dinner but there were about 24 in the Chinese party and one didn't know their social habits so I took them to dinner at the Francis Hotel. Liz who knew a few words of Chinese said that she would like to meet them and was in the hotel foyer looking a million dollars when we came out from dinner. Relations were good because their leader, who told me that he was the Commander of the Chinese Northern Fleet, had learnt that I had been in the British Pacific Fleet 'attacking our common Japanese enemy' in the war. I introduced Liz and she tried her few words of Chinese which they promptly declared to be Cantonese and hence unworthy but she met them all and we chatted for about twenty minutes. On the way home she was highly amused; it seems that the Chinese leader had said to her, or rather the Chinese interpreter had said that the admiral had asked "Do all beautiful English girls marry old men?" That should teach me not to marry a girl 20 years younger than myself.

At 8.00 am the following morning they were all in my room at the MoD Foxhill. The first question was "Where in the British Ministry of Defence organisation is British Shipbuilders". I explained that British Shipbuilders was not part of the MoD. The day wore on with questions and answers; I became fascinated by the nature of their interpreter's replies; they might ask a question to which the reply was simply "No". The interpreter would then turn to his colleagues and speak for at least a minute and frequently longer. I began to wonder whether he was having a separate meeting, or rehearsing possible follow up questions to test the veracity of my replies. Since the members of the team wrote down my answers as I spoke, I reasoned that most of the silent Chinese team could speak English and probably had degrees from western universities. I supposed that they had their own internal checks and balances. Perhaps there just is no word for "No" in mandarin. If so it might explain why China has such a big population.

On a domestic note, we showed them where the men's toilets were and late in the day realised that at least two of the visitors might be female. They all dressed the same, kept their Mao hats on and, to me, looked alike.

They were programmed to depart at 16.45, en route to Southampton. They were still asking questions and eventually finished at 18.45. The last question that they asked was "Where in the British Ministry of Defence organisation is British Shipbuilders?"

I simply report what occurred to point up the differences in culture and the real language comprehension barrier. A story that illustrates this was when relations between China and the USSR were at low ebb and large Soviet forces were massed along their common frontier. There was a recognised unity of purpose with NATO in confronting a common threat. During a discussion with western military staff, the Chinese Chief of Staff conceded that the Chinese army would not be able to stop a Soviet advance and would have to fall back to draw the Soviets further into mother China. "But surely that would involve your suffering large casualties" suggested his western counterpart,' "Oh no", was the reply "only about a hundred million".

It was the practice to stop all office heating in April/May and have contractors dismantle, clean and repair the large boiler systems that provided the hot water for office heating. Each of the blocks occupied by Ship Department at Foxhill, Bath had a boiler and they were all stripped down when we had a particularly cold spell in June. After some days of working in overcoats and gloves (it really was that cold) the representatives of the draughtsmen and clerical staff came and saw me and asked that the office heating be switched on or failing that, the office be closed and the staff sent home. We all stood in my office; it was too cold to sit down. I said that I could grant neither of their requests. Even if it was possible to put the boilers together in time to do any good in this short cold spell, it could not be allowed because it would put the completion of the maintenance back into November when they would expect the offices to be heated and as for shutting the office, there was a navy somewhere out there that it was our duty to support. I was sorry but we would all have to put up with it but if anyone found that they could not stand the cold conditions then they must make a personal decision to go home; they had my assurance that it would not count against them or their leave entitlement in any way. They departed. Not one of the several thousand staff went home although the bitter weather lasted a further week or so.

The Queens Jubilee naval review took place on 28th June 1977 in Spithead. I was asked to join the RFA *Sir Bedivere* in Southampton Docks and to help host the members of the Diplomatic Corps who would view the event from this ship. The day dawned wet and misty. We were due to sail through the assembled lines of warships to where the Royal Yacht was waiting and then follow her through the lines under review and back to her station at the head of the lines. Whereupon, we would go back through the lines to Southampton. In short, Her Majesty went up and back again and we did this twice over. For the occasion, the large tank deck of the *Sir Bedivere* was fitted with tables and chairs and made as comfortable as possible for what was expected (by some supreme optimist) to be the few moments that the ambassadors would be able to tear themselves away from the riveting sight of a hundred or so grey, wet ships in the mist. There were also a number of television screens on which the event might be seen.

It was at a time when the US and China were not on speaking terms. A new Chinese ambassador to the Court of St James had just arrived and met his US counterpart for the first time that day in RFA *Sir Bedivere*. A number of the crew of the ship were citizens of Hong Kong. It was suggested that the Chinese ambassador might wish to address a few words to them over the ships internal loudspeakers but he declined, explaining (as they always do) that he spoke only mandarin.

Sir Bedivere proceeded down Southampton water and a few brave souls paraded on the weather deck seeking a first sight of the assembled armada. The brave souls at that time included the US and Chinese ambassadors and indeed this is when they met!. After a while I realised that I was practically alone on deck and found that the ship's stewards were serving drinks to the diplomats down below. A few did reappear momentarily when *Sir Bedivere* joined the Royal Yacht *Britannia* but then someone discovered that the television screens in the tank deck "lounge' could be made to show the tennis from Wimbledon and all was lost as far as looking at warships participating in an historic occasion was concerned.

One thing that I do recall about the final return trip that we made through the lines of warships was the several sailors caps floating in the water, lost either to a freak gust of wind or an over-enthusiastic waving when invited to give three cheers for her Majesty Queen Elizabeth the Second. My mind went instantly to the emphasis that our professor had given to the need for care in siting saluting guns in HM Ships; it seems that sometime before the first world war, a visiting archduke and his companions had had their hats (and wigs?) blown into the Adriatic Sea, due to the saluting guns in a visiting British warship being placed too close to the quarter deck.

A few years later, when the Chinese were waving their little red books and barely speaking to the British, Liz and I were invited to a reception in the Chinese embassy at Blackheath. That's another story.

Warships entering service for the first time or after a refit need a period to 'work-up' in which to familiarise the crew with each other and with the ship. This had always been centralised for submarines and the surface navy came into line under Flag Officer Sea Training, based at Portland. FOST and his team of sea-riders would put ships companies through a most rigorous sequence of trials, inspections and exercises lasting several weeks, most of which were recorded in some way and analysed afterwards with the ship's staff. In my time, the FOST experience was well recognised in NATO and ships from other navies, notably the Netherlands and Germany, came to Portland for the treatment. At FOST's invitation I attended his 'summer war' in which the ships working-up proceeded to sea attended by the NATO minesweeping force. The crews were dressed in their anti- flash clothing and the force was almost immediately attacked by aircraft and later by submarines. The young men of the Fleet Air Arm seemed to vie with each other to fly closest to our masts and the waves; there had been a force 9 all night and the waves were not small.

Parliament's watchdog over public expenditure, or rather over the way the funds authorised by parliament are spent, is the Comptroller and Auditor General. His small department has access to all the activities that spend money voted by parliament and can ask to see all official papers. They study the periodic reports of expenditure versus progress on important projects and will ask questions of the responsible department should these depart substantially from plan. In cases where the department's reasons seem to indicate a possible weakness of the system or individuals, the CAG reports the facts to the Public Expenditure Committee of parliament, which might then summon the department to appear and explain itself. In serious cases the PAC might censure the department as a result and heads roll.

Mr Gladstone introduced the Public Accounts Committee in the 1860's. He was the Chancellor of the Exchequer (for the third time) and had yet to be Prime Minister. In a farsighted decision he set up the committee and ruled that it should always be chaired by a member of the parliamentary opposition.

Being summoned to appear before the PAC is not to be taken lightly and we always went to considerable pains to prepare our case. The early exchanges between the MoD and the CAG at officials level would show the reasons for the reference to parliament and on the old-boy net we might receive an indication of the CAG brief and the suggested lines of questioning provided to the chairman and members of the committee. This was accepted as sensible by both sides to help extract the most value from the time allocated; it did not prevent the committee members from raising other items.

I found that I had an ambivalent attitude to the PAC. When it was some unfortunate man in, say, Transport being told that he was an inefficient crumb because his motorway contractor was 20 million pounds over budget and 2 years late, I applauded parliamentary democracy at work. When it was one of my ships that was over budget and a year late and it was indicated that I was an inefficient crumb, I felt how unfair the whole procedure was; how could I have prevented the shipyard welders go-slow or the engineers strike in an equipment manufacturers factory miles away from the sea that had disrupted the programme. And so on.

The PAC hearings took place in a committee room in the Houses of Parliament, opening off a long corridor in which one stood about or perched on benches until summoned to appear. Within the room the committee sat around a horseshoe shaped table with the chairman at its apex and we sat facing him with a stenographer or two in between. High in the corners of the room were closed circuit TV screens, which showed the name of whoever was speaking on the floor of the Commons, the name of the Bill under discussion and the time. The time was very important to us. We were usually summoned to appear in the afternoon and I quickly learned that the Chairman and members of the Committee liked to finish with a subject and close the meeting by 7pm to go to dinner. So one kept an eye on the clock and prayed that the division bells would not ring to call them away to vote on the bill that was under debate, thus losing valuable time which might mean coming back on another day. In an unobtrusive way one encouraged the members of the committee to speak rather than us. Always remember that people like to speak rather than to listen and that this is particularly so with politicians, so don't interrupt, indicate that that is a good question and sit back and watch the minutes tick away.

The MoD team on shipbuilding questions was usually the Controller of the Navy, myself and the Under Secretary Material supported by one or two of our officers who would have prepared our excellent and substantial briefing pack.

The last subject on which I was summoned to appear before the PAC to explain my actions was HMS *Cardiff*. *Cardiff*, a Type 42 guided missile destroyer had been ordered from Vickers Shipbuilders, Barrow. Vickers, by virtue of the large white collar technical staff built up for the nuclear and missile submarine programmes, was the only company with the resources to develop the Ship Department's design of the through deck cruiser and sensibly were awarded the contract to build the first ship of the class, *HMS Invincible*. As work progressed, it became clear that their blue-collar labour force in certain critical trades was not big enough to meet the programme dates for their nuclear submarines, HMS *Cardiff* and HMS *Invincible*. *Cardiff* seemed to be starved of labour and we in Ship Department were showing our displeasure. One day Len Redshaw told me that he had been talking to Swan Hunters and they were prepared to take a sub-contract from Vickers to complete *HMS Cardiff* on the Tyne. Vickers would remain responsible. My whole experience of Swans had been good, good workmanship, good cost control, good management and above all the truly splendid dedication of the people of Tyneside to the Royal Navy.

I said OK and *Cardiff* was towed round the North of Scotland to the Tyne. Of course there were problems in getting a new company's workpeople to finish work that others had started, not for doctrinaire reasons but questions of accuracy and eventual responsibility. It was also at the time when strikes were fashionable and in a vast building and assembly industry' like warship building in which twice as many people are employed elsewhere in the UK making things to go into the ship as are employed in the actual shipyard, quite small stoppages could affect the programme. But in the end she joined the Fleet far earlier than if she had remained at Barrow.

The post-war industrial and social climate had resulted in the inclusion of liberal force majeure clauses in government contracts. Starting with the premise that a labour dispute in a subcontractors works that delayed the completion of a ship should not invoke the ship contract's penalty clauses on late completion, force majeure had come to excuse everything except deliberate wilful acts by the firm's directors. One did not have to be a genius to realise that a shipbuilder who was behind with, say, his electrical work and likely to suffer penalty clauses, could provoke a strike of, say, the plumbers by some device as an unfair dismissal or hiring a non-union man, while the electricians worked like mad (on overtime, of course) to catch up. When the 'strike' was settled the ship was still delayed but the delay was now put down to force majeure and the consequent added cost paid by the taxpayer. The other side of the coin, of course, was the realisation by the more unscrupulous workpeople that they could threaten to delay completion, say by going slow, to wring concessions from their employer, which he would have difficulty in attributing to force majeure.

Cardiff's delayed completion and force majeure costs were the reason for the referral to the PAC. The burden of the questioning was " Why had I acquiesced in the transfer to Swans" The answer was that the delay and cost would have been greater if the ship had been left at Barrow to interfere with the other programmes and this was in part due to the hand to mouth, one ship at a time ordering policy adopted by successive governments, Labour and Conservative, which made companies reluctant to invest in, and maintain, the men and material resources for modern engineering manufacturing.

Whenever the questioning became drawn out, one particular labour MP would say something like, "Since I represent a Cardiff constituency, I suppose that I should say something " whereupon he would summarise the reasons for the referral and the nature of the reply that the MoD had given, comment on the problems of management and labour in industry and generally show that this was really all for the best in democratic Britain. This would be interspersed with short questions, which presented the MoD in the best light and probably prevented other members of the committee putting the same points in a more hostile manner. He would manage 10 minutes or so while out of the corner of my eye (and I am sure, his) the hands of the clock moved inexorably towards seven o'clock. I always enjoyed his interventions.

The PAC Chairman and Mr Geoffrey Pattie visited Ship Department to see something of its work and, at their request, I arranged for them to visit Swan Hunters at Newcastle. When I asked the firm's Managing Director, John Steele, what they had thought of the firm, he said that he had no idea; he said that they seemed more concerned with whose Rolls Royce they should use for a visit to some sort of local political function. There are, apparently, greater priorities than shipbuilding.

The Chairman Edward Du Cann and the committee while remaining aware that this was not a routine rubber-stamping exercise always treated us with consideration. The value of the reference to the PAC was in the internal reviews that it set off within the government department concerned and this, the Chairman and the Comptroller and Auditor General knew full well.

An example of the genuine troubles that can threaten a shipbuilder's programme was the *Invincible's* gearbox. The two huge, heavy gearboxes were fitted before launch. One was found to be defective and removed from the hull, loaded on a road vehicle and taken back to the manufacturer. It was returned to Barrow, put back in the hull and was still not right; out it came and back it went to the manufacturer. Building the ship continued on the slipway with a huge gaping hole in the side through which Vickers skilfully entered (and removed!) the gearbox. This happened so often that I feared that its weight would make grooves in the M6 motorway. Meanwhile the unhappy Vickers management carried on building the rest of the ship as best they could.

An event that gave me considerable personal satisfaction was to do with the clutches that connect the propulsion gas turbines to the propeller shafts. These unique, high precision, clutches were manufactured by the small SSS company in the Home Counties. Prime Minister Callaghan was caught in a spiral of mounting inflation caused by malcontents in the trade union movement and had brought in his wages standstill policy. It was decreed that as a condition of getting a government contract, a company must sign an undertaking not to increase their employee's wages and also to ensure that their subcontractors and suppliers entered into the same undertaking. To most companies it was a matter of give us the order, we will sign your piece of paper, worthless though it will prove to be when faced with the demands of trade unions inflated with years of getting their own way (as well as beer and sandwiches in No 10 Downing Street) in Harold Wilson's time.

My production director had ordered some SSS clutches for 4,000 tonne frigates and sent the firm the no-wage-increase forms to sign. Back came all of our documents with a polite letter saying that SSS could not give Callaghan's undertaking. So I wrote to the managing director asking him to be a good chap and sign the forms. Back came the documents and a letter saying that his workpeople were highly skilled and deserved to be rewarded. Furthermore, in all honesty, he could not ask his suppliers etc, etc. We wanted our clutches so I got the Minister, Dr. John Gilbert to write to him. This was now big stuff. Back came the reply drawing attention to the previous correspondence and reminding the MoD that at least 80% of SSS work was for US, Dutch and other foreign navies. In these circumstances the company respectfully suggested that the Royal Navy should take its orders elsewhere.

Without reference to anyone, I had my chaps place the order for our clutches, excluding any reference to Mr Callaghan's wages-freeze. A year or so later I met the SSS chief and found that his refusal had nothing to do with politics, he had throughout been governed by his sincere Christian beliefs — he just would not tell what seemed to him, a barefaced lie.

The Controller of the Navy had a series of six-monthly or annual discussions with his opposite numbers in some other NATO navies.

The exchanges with the USN's Chief of Naval Material were always an uphill struggle because the Americans had so much and could do it all. British inventions that had done so much to enhance these exchanges, like the steam catapult and the Harrier, need a fertile and ongoing research and production environment in which to blossom and even in my time the UK's was drying up. The inward visit that I recall most was that of Admiral Ike Kidd USN during which we tried to interest him in our new torpedo being developed by GEC Marconi and the Lynx helicopter for both of which we were in the Portsmouth area. Admiral Kidd was a square shape with crew cut grey hair and had clearly passed the US flag rank shouting and bullying course.

When the time came for the Lynx demonstration we gathered on the outside platform of the control tower of Lee on Solent naval air station. There was a loud noise and the prototype Lynx helicopter suddenly appeared about 40 feet above us — but upside down. This was the first time that any of us had seen a helicopter flying upside down and it was quite a shock. It flew around the airfield, turned the right way up and landed. Controller's naval assistant Captain (later Rear Admiral) Ron Holley produced a white flying suit and helmet and said "Now, Admiral, we are sure that you will want to take a ride." I swear that Admiral Kidd went white. He said that he would only get into that thing provided that it would stay the right way up - my sentiments exactly. Eventually he went for a dignified triangular ride over Spithead.

The US Chief of the Bureau of Ships visited me in Bath. This was my long time friend Bob Gooding who had been the captain in charge of SP-24 responsible for the navigation sub-system of the Polaris SSBN programme in 1963 when the UK had purchased the Polaris A-3 missile system from the USN. But Vice Admiral Bob Gooding had since taken the shouting and bullying course. The reason for the visit was to discuss with us our experience with controllable pitch propellers. The US administration had announced its intention of building fifty frigates each of which would cost 50 million dollars and one of the cost cutting features was to be a single shaft propulsion arrangement. Because of the ship's size and speed, the shaft would have to deliver about twice the power that we had on each of our (two) shafts but we assured him that we saw little problem in this. In discussion I learned that the proposed FFG 7 Class would be, in effect, a 200 ft long, 16ft high aluminium box on top of a 450 ft long steel hull. As politely as I could I remarked that in my experience it would be difficult, indeed, impossible, to prevent a large structure of this sort taking longitudinal loads, notwithstanding expansion joints and the like and the result could be extensive cracking. Bob Gooding said that the US Bureau of Ships had confidence that the expansion joints and changes of width would take care of this and clearly resented any suggestion that there could be any question concerning the proposed structural design of the FFG 7 Class. He made it quite clear that he did not really welcome my views and I got the impression that they were too far committed to do anything about it.

There was nothing particularly clever in my observations about the dangers of putting large aluminium structures on steel hulls. Unless such structures are properly integrated and sized accordingly, they will break. There were countless instances where this had occurred prior to my comments to the Chief of the Bureau of Ships recorded above. There are now many more.

The early vessels of the FFG 7 Class went to sea and developed cracks measuring several feet in length going inboard across the top and down the sides of the aluminium box. In the case of one ship, the USS *Duncan*, the cracks went right across the top, some 4Oft in length. The Australian Navy was buying four ships of the class and when I was there in 1980 had taken delivery of the first two. One of the ships that I visited in Sydney already had cracks about 3 ft long on both sides of the aluminium top deck. The other had a crumpled bow as testimony to the problem of learning how to control single screw ships.

Following the NFR90 NATO Frigate studies, the US Navy's NAVSEA and the RN's Sea Systems Controllerate made joint studies of a frigate to meet the same military requirement, to investigate the reasons why the US design criteria produced a larger ship than the RN criteria The results were reported in a paper presented to the Society of Naval Architects and Marine Engineers in New York in 1991 by messers L.D. Ferreiro (US) and M.H. Stonehouse (UK). In discussing the Deckhouse Structure they comment: 'both the US and the UK use steel deckhouses. While this has been the norm in the UK for many years, it represents a considerable change for the US which for 30 years has used aluminium as a means of saving weight (it may be worthwhile to note that the reason for switching back to steel has less to do with fire protection than with maintenance i.e. less cracking.)'

Admiral Clayton had a half share in a chateau in France to which he went whenever his duties allowed; he confessed to me that if he had great wealth his only extravagance would be to have his own aeroplane to make this journey easier. I was surprised therefore to find that given a choice he would always fly in commercial airliners rather than the naval communications aircraft to which his rank entitled him. That is, until we visited Germany.

We boarded our twin engined naval communications aircraft at Northholt. They wound up the propellers and we were off over Essex and the North Sea at all of 120 miles an hour. Sometime after noon and a cup of coffee poured into a paper cup by a wren, we landed at Hamburg. Following meetings with the redoubtable Karl Heinz Otto of the BVD and a visit to Blohm and Voss, we were driven to Bremen for presentations by Atlas on sonar concepts. It was nice for me to be back in Bremen where I had spent several happy months as an exchange schoolboy in 1935. As a small intensely patriotic 'Englander' brought up on Clive of India, General Wolfe and Cecil Rhodes, I was amazed and hurt to learn that the colloquial German expression for stealing was 'To buy British'. All these years later, the few of my German classmates in the Bremmer Realschule who survived the war must have grinned wryly when they learnt that in 1997 Britain had a foreign minister called Robbing Crook and B.Liar for prime Minister.

The next day we boarded a Luftwaffe small passenger jet for a flight to Friedrichshafen on the Bodensee. For much of the flight I could look down to port, past the wing with its iron cross insignia and down into East Germany where, in those days, the potential enemy lurked and where, if it came to war, the future of mankind would probably be decided. Throughout all those years of confrontation I never ceased to be impressed at the steadfastness and loyalty of the German people to the western alliance. From Friedrichshafen we were taken by road at breakneck speed to Ravensburg and thence to Ulm to visit the MTU diesel engine plant. For the last part of the journey the sun shone and we travelled through picture-book country. The hotel in which we spent the night was equally picturesque both inside and out; I suddenly realised as I lay in bed, that the ornate striped wallpaper went up the walls and across the ceiling and all over the wardrobe and the room door. It was somewhat overpowering in a small room.

We did not really need to visit the factory to know that MTU diesels are among the best in the world. The return journey was an interesting experience. We boarded a Chinook helicopter, which flew us to an airfield where the jet waited to fly us to Bonn and the British Airways flight to London. The Chinook flight lasted less than an hour but it seemed much longer.. For the entire flight the helicopter had a large bow-up angle and the tail was less than 10 metres above the ground except when we lumbered up to go over electric power cables or a farm barn. The pilots were up there somewhere, demonstrating their ground hugging techniques for avoiding detection by an enemy. I was conscious, as we stood in the middle of the fuselage looking out of the small portholes, that the tail was down there somewhere, nearly dragging on the ground. But the Luftwaffe delivered us safely.

The visit to the USA with Dick Clayton and his naval assistant provided a Sunday in San Diego following visits to the vast fleet of warships alongside in the naval base and to the Underwater Research Laboratory on the promontory to the north with its monument to the first Spanish explorers who had come up from the south in the 16th century while the British and the French were busy colonising the continent's eastern seaboard.

On the Sunday we hired a car and drove south across the border to Tijuana in Mexico. Leaving the USA in company with thousands of other cars was no problem, we were waved through, but re-entering was an entirely different matter. We joined one of about eight queues and inched our way forward to the immigration post where we cheerfully presented our British passports. There were no welcoming smiles; it was OK for the locals to stream back with the minimum of formalities but three Britons sneaking-in was a different matter. We directed the inspectors attention to the entry stamp from

Dulles airport some days earlier and the hire car documents from a San Diego firm, dated that day, and were admitted, not without a reminder that as non-US citizens we should have checked out properly that morning. He was absolutely right.   Perhaps the impatience of the drivers of the cars stuck behind us in the queue had something to do with it, but we were not delayed as long as we probably would have been in similar circumstances in Europe.

We called on Ambassador Peter Jay in Washington.

A personal complication on the visits to the French DCN was Dick Clayton's command of the French language. In deference to our hosts (who must get very tired of Englishmen who display no knowledge of their language) the Admiral conducted his part of the meetings in French and I contributed a few oui's and non's.   DCN was commissioning a new facility in their Ship towing tank at Bvd Victor by which submarine models would be towed from below. I would much have liked to compare the results with the more usual method and with the full scale at full speeds. At Lorient I was shown the new derrick and winch system fitted at the stern of their frigates to handle their variable depth sonar – sonar set in a streamlined body that could be towed behind the ship at depth to increase its detection capability. There was a gap between the drive winch and the cable drum and I made some comment about the gearing to go between. "Oh no", said my guide "no gearing, just a rubber belt, if its good enough for Renault then its good enough for us". I found this a very perceptive comment.

I did not go on the visit to Toulon, which was concerned with torpedoes. The French navy's underwater weapons facility is close to St Tropez. Controller and his new naval assistant Captain (later Rear Admiral) John Burgess stayed at St Tropez. I understand that the visit was the more interesting because topless sunbathing was just becoming fashionable.

In my time, one of the 'ploys' used by skilled Chief Executives who wish to depart in some way from the terms of their contract or other undertaking – and usually cost the taxpayer additional expense – was the 'Controller of the Navy ploy ', namely, if you want to get away with something, tell the Controller, don't go near to the professional directors in Ship or Contracts Departments because they will screw you to the floor by reciting the conditions of contracts. Go to the Controller and say your piece; if you can get out of the door without the Controller saying "NO" very loudly, you've got away with it. Go ahead. This ploy was based on an awareness of the psychology of senior uniformed officers, (a) that they wish to be seen to be in charge, and (b) that they will never admit that they do not know or understand, something.   When some time later the people in Bath find that the programme is not on track, the contractor will say, "The Controller agreed". Now (a) and (b) operate in reverse as the Controller strives to justify that with which he is said to have agreed.

John Rix of Vosper-Thornycroft had informed the previous Controller that he would progress the lead ship of the Type 21 Class but not the following two ships whose completion would have to follow the completion of the four frigates for Brazil, in effect, priority would be given to the Brazilian ships. This reached me as a fait accompli ("The Controller agreed") and was to cost the unfortunate taxpayer some tens of millions of pounds in due course. When questioned, Admiral Griffin said that Rix had said that he saw his company's future in warship exports and not in building for the Royal Navy, partly because the MoD interfered too much. Yet within two years VT was soliciting RN orders to keep their workforce busy and received the order for HMS *Southampton*.

Yarrow's had contracts for five Type 21 frigates and these would be the main source of employment in the Scottish yard. Vosper-Thornycroft as the lead shipbuilder were required by contract to provide lead-yard services to Yarrows and a most important part of this was the supply of drawings for use in the shipyard to build and equip the ships. The whole purpose of giving the order for the lead ship of the class to VT was so that VT would have demonstrated the accuracy of these drawings in its construction.

Soon, Yarrows complaints were brought to my attention. The supply of detailed shipbuilding drawings received from VT was behind programme and, increasingly, no sooner were the drawings received and the shipyard work started than a 'stop' notice would be received from VT saying that the drawing would be modified and re-issued. We told Yarrows to be patient but as the months passed the situation got worse instead of better with many drawings being stopped and re-issued several times over. Ignoring manufacturers equipment and component drawings, a shipbuilder would have prepared about 4,500 individual drawings to build and commission a Leander Class frigate. With the more rigorous standards that modern technology now required, the lead shipbuilder had to produce about 19,000 drawings to build and commission a Type 21 frigate. Of these, more than 16,000 of those issued by VT were then stopped, revised and re-issued, in several thousand cases more than once. Each revision stopped or changed some work at Yarrows.

In the end Yarrows were in deep trouble; their workforce was not being efficiently employed, dates were slipping and they were not receiving instalment cash payments from the MoD because the work that would have triggered such payments was not completed. Something had to be done. We produced the argument that the ships as designed had turned out to be much more complex than Yarrows had been led to believe when they had tendered for the contract and we proposed that the firm be paid a 'design complexity allowance' of several million pounds per ship.

This really was the tongue in cheek proposal to end all tongue in cheek proposals. I expected the Treasury to reply, correctly, pointing out that Yarrows and VT had jointly lobbied to be given the contract to design the Type 21 frigate. Their case had been pushed by the then Controller of the Navy, Admiral Sir Horace Law, they had been given the design contract and they had been well paid for this work. Since they were the co-designers how could they be surprised at its complexity? And as for the delay, under the rather generous MoD contracts the companies would be reimbursed for the effects of inflation and delays beyond their management's control. So why propose to give Yarrows an extra 20 million pounds of the taxpayers money?.

To my great surprise the finance people said no such thing. They said that they would wish to be represented at the meeting at which I would put this proposal to Yarrows. The meeting was held in my room at Foxhill on 7th May 1975. Ernie Norton, the Deputy Managing Director led for the company, accompanied by a man with reddish hair who I did not recall meeting previously. I had forewarned Ernie Norton of what would be proposed and he was delighted. I opened the meeting and explained that the complex nature of the design as it had developed was giving Yarrows some problems compounded by the frequent changes made by VT for the same reason and so on. The man with red hair was clearly unhappy with my references to Yarrows not understanding things and kept muttering. His body language conveyed the message that this was all a big exaggeration. I could see my chaps getting concerned so I called an early break and took Ernie Norton to one side and told him that if he wanted to receive these pennies from heaven he had better tell his companion to cool it.

A pleasant duty for the head of the Royal Corps was membership of the Victory Technical Advisory Committee, whose responsibility it was to monitor and advise on the material state of Nelson's flagship. In true British fashion there was no separate budget for upkeep work on HMS *Victory* and we had to depend on the good offices of the General Manager of Portsmouth Dockyard, a senior member of the RCNC, to get things done. And things certainly needed doing; after 220 years in service the oak planking and frames were rotten and the rate of decay was increasing each year.

The ship was in her permanent home, a dry dock near to the main gate of the yard. The wooden masts had been replaced by steel plate ones which were stepped on the concrete floor of the dock because the wooden hull could no longer support them. For the same reason the halyards from the masts were brought down to the dock walls and not the wooden ships side. On either beam were the rows of cannon, wooden replicas since the decks would no longer support the weight of iron ones. Nelson's gig still sat on the mid-ships boat beams now made of aluminium with a wooden veneer. The gig is a copy, of course. Standing in the bow, looking aft, I sometimes had the feeling that we were turning Victory into some sort of Disney creation and would then recall the hundreds of men and boys (and women, too) who had lived and fought and all too frequently died, for King and Country, in her.

There was a loyal band of about fourteen shipwrights working away rebuilding the ship from the after end, forwards. She was being rebuilt in teak. This came in a thickness of about 5cm and the thick bits of ship were made from multiple thicknesses glued together and then shaped with an adze. The workmanship was probably better than that of the Chatham Dockyard shipwrights in 1750. The constant worry was whether the fore end would collapse before the re-builders got there. Despite our efforts to pull up on the forestay, the huge bowsprit was already pressing down on the figurehead.

The rigging was a recurring problem and expense. It had been renewed in sisal in the 1960's and was again in need of replacement thanks to the acid pollution borne by the west winds from the oil refineries on Southampton Water. Our choice was polypropylene. In reaching this conclusion we had to take account not only of its resistance to corrosion, but also its weight and strength and elasticity wet and dry.

Inboard, one can walk along the top of the massive keel for the whole length of the ship. The timber is under constant attack by brown and purple death-watch beetles. Victory's naval crew collect the dead beetles daily; the total weekly number is interesting but the ratio of brown to purple is critical since this indicates the likely severity of the beetle attack. HMS Victory has a commanding officer and a navy and marine crew who show visitors around with evident pride. Nelson's quarters are lovingly preserved, as indeed is the whole of the ship as far as they are able.

In my time Victory flew the flag of the C in C Home and if one was particularly honoured one might be invited to dine with the Admiral in Nelson's great cabin. On one occasion I was present when C in C's Royal Marine band beat the retreat on the dockside against a backcloth of a floodlit HMS Victory. I confess that at that moment, I would have faced the hordes of Tuscany, alone, with my bare hands.

MoD Whitehall was a hothouse of committees. In the old days we would meet with our friends in the Naval Staff and Secretariat and decide what the navy required and what we would do about it. The place hummed with activity well into the evening as we argued the pros and cons and we would then go away and prepare the paperwork for our chiefs to approve. The Procurement Executive changed all that; there were now many more people who insisted that they should be aware of what was going on in case it had some relevance to something else. Committees were formed at which these representatives of the central mafia might appear. I was particularly involved with the Naval Projects Committee, the Naval Weapons Project Committee and two more senior Committees. The two more senior committees were central committees with representation from all three services whose deliberations were intended to determine whether the military aim might be achieved in another way and to balance the requirement for new equipment against the needs of the other services and the funds available.

The NPC was not really required except for matters of internal ministry politics. Ship department designed the warships, got them built and looked after them for the rest of their lives. We looked after their safety, stability and strength, their machinery, electrics and everything that went into them. We had budgets within which we were required to work and the Navy and the Secretariat set the policy and priorities and monitored our programmes. We had the nations experts within our ranks and there was always a naval constructor, marine engineer or electrical engineer officer or group to whom responsibility was assigned. What could be simpler?.

The Naval Weapons Project Committee betrayed the organisational problem that beset the naval weapons world in the post-war years. In the beginning there had been guns and torpedoes which were looked after by naval officers assisted by some civilian engineers and draughtsmen with the powerful support of companies like Vickers, Armstrong's and Whiteheads for whom the mighty British navy and the other navies of the world provided a steady stream of large orders. The 1939-45 war brought rapid change and a need for dedicated expertise in electronics and other fields. The RNSS had been created to provide an umbrella for the many centres of expertise, which had grown up. Groups that had worked under a Captain RN now had a chief scientist or civilian equivalent rank but the navy insisted that the captain remain. In many cases an officer of the new naval electrical specialisation filled the post most ably. This was patently inefficient but no matter how the weapons and electronics establishments and HQ Departments were divided or re-arranged this duality persisted. The naval scientific staffs were further affected by the arrival of the ex-Ministry of Supply people in Whitehall and the latter's increasing ability to direct effort from science to the administration of science and the share of the navy's weapons budget that went on such items. The underwater weapons and detection experts maintained their cohesion longer than most, in part because of the special nature of their expertise and the closeness of their relationship with the submarine service and also because they had some splendid directors who fought their corner. Perhaps this is why in the submarine application and detection fields the UK was second to none in the world for so long.

The same could not be claimed in the surface and anti-air warfare fields. How we envied our US and Soviet counterparts who seemed to be able to get the sort of systems that we were discussing into production in the same time as it took us to get approval to start.

The gradual realisation that advancement was more easily earned by moving to non-productive quasi-administrative posts and the transfer of decision making away from those best qualified for the task and, later, the insistence of Conservative Ministers that the work should be put out to industry gradually sapped the real enthusiasm there had been for naval weapons systems development, the missionary zeal was gone; it became just a job.

The thing that gave me the greatest satisfaction was the decision to produce a lengthened version of the Type 42 destroyer and then, but not for the same reasons, a lengthened Type 22 frigate. The story of how the length of the original Type 42 destroyer had been curtailed in order to keep within the ceiling price of £ 11.25 millions has been told already as has the fact that, as predicted, the sea-keeping characteristics as built were not as good as one would have liked. Controller Dick Clayton and I decided to do something about it. We had approval to order more Type 42 destroyers; furthermore we did not need to seek central committee approval to introduce (modest) alterations. So what about an alteration making the next batch of Type 42's longer for only a very small increase in price?. Not only would the ship's sea keeping be improved but also the ship would go faster for the same power as its length was increased. It was decided to make the ship 42 ft longer at the waterline [50ft overall] and 2 ft broader and since these were mere alterations to an already approved design there was no need for reference elsewhere. The same reasoning led to the Batch 3 Type 22's being made some 50 ft longer and given a 4.5inch gun. I ordered that both designs be given racy looking bows to make them look like ocean greyhounds.

I contrasted this with the three-funnelled County Class cruiser designed by Lillicrap in the 1920's where every variant of the basic Kent Class design was given a new class name. None of the variants was as different from the original as HMS *Manchester* was from the original HMS *Sheffield* design, but, of course they did build more ships in those days. Incidentally, it had been proposed to name the Type 42 ordered from Messers Cammell Laird of Birkenhead, HMS *Manchester*, but we bowed to the urgent representations of the company that such was the rivalry between the supporters of the Liverpool and the Manchester football clubs that their Lordships would be well advised to select a different name for the Birkenhead ship.

The design of the Invincible Class aircraft carriers – called through deck cruisers – gave the Department much concern. The requirement was for the biggest possible hull and flight deck length to carry and operate Harriers and helicopters while limiting the cost and the displacement to about 17,000 tonnes. The result was a big hull built of thinner steel than our predecessors would have recommended. Norman Hancock was now the Director of Warship Design and I shared a concern that we might, perhaps, be moving into a new area of hull vibration problems and the like. Great credit is due to all those who produced this design. As the design progressed it was evident that there would be considerable military advantage if the Harrier aircraft could make a running take-off rather than rise vertically and it was decided to ramp the fore-end of the deck to literally throw the aircraft up. The angle of ramp was governed by what the aircraft nose wheel could take. In the first ship this was less than 10 degrees but was doubled in the next ships when aircraft had their nose-wheel strengthened.

One day I was asked if I could make arrangements to see US Admiral Levering Smith who was on a cruising holiday on the Thames and particularly wanted a private chat. I was due to visit NCRE in Scotland and agreed to drive there via Goring-on-Thames. Levering had two cabin cruisers to accommodate himself and his wife, Boots, her two sisters and their third husbands, his deputy in Special Projects Rear Admiral Bob Wertheim and his wife Barbara and his indefatigable liaison officer in Bath, Commander Stu Roy and his wife Lorna. We found Lorna barely able to hide her irritation. Everything nautical (except steering) was being left to Stu and everything domestic was being left to her. The sisters were there on holiday and that did not include cooking, cleaning or making beds. The previous evening Stu had fallen down between the boat and the dock wall and they had spent a good deal of the night at the Reading General Hospital checking for broken bones; he was there to greet us but was clearly in pain and also concerned that there was no food on board. "No problem" said Liz and produced the picnic hamper that she had prepared for our trip north to Scotland. There was enough for all of us.

What Levering wanted to see me about was Cruise missiles and to give me some advice on the advisability or otherwise of the UK adopting them. He told me that there was an undercurrent of propaganda to suggest that the British should adopt the cruise missile as its deterrent weapon instead of, or to follow Polaris, Solly Zuckerman was known to favour this and was thought to have persuaded David Owen that such a system would be good enough and cheaper. We discussed the probability of the number of UK missiles that might be able to penetrate Soviet air space in the face of the massive Soviet defensive gun and missile systems. Much of the subject matter of our private chat that lunchtime was included in a briefing paper that I prepared for the House of Commons Defence Committee a few years later when a member of British Shipbuilders Board and was also part of the private briefing that I gave to David Owen at the time of the Liberal-SDP alliance when he had the difficult task of reconciling his own view that the UK should maintain its independent nuclear deterrent with the anti-nuclear stance of the Liberal leadership.

The Chief Scientific Adviser to the Secretary of State for Defence was always an academic brought in on a 5 year contract to bring to the MoD a greater awareness of what was going on in all disciplines in the universities. Ron Mason had succeeded Herman Bondi in this post. One day he asked me in for a chat about the future of the UK's independent nuclear deterrent. I remarked that we had had no indication from Labour ministers that they contemplated retaining this capability when the Polaris submarines reached the end of their effective lives and he reminded me that we nevertheless had a duty to the nation to consider these matters. We agreed that the UK should continue to have a submarine based system to provide a second strike capability and that the missiles should have a greater range than the Polaris A-3 to give the launching submarines many more thousands of miles of ocean to hide themselves in. Experience with the 'Chevaline thing' was demonstrating that a future British government would not be willing to devote the necessary financial resources to enable the UK to go it alone and develop a really independent deterrent and so we would have to seek to use a US missile and in the given time-scale, this would be Trident. I assured him that given a modest sum to equip a shipbuilder, we could design and build these large submarines in the UK. It had been for precisely this reason that I had required that the navy's new nuclear reactor be given the highest possible power rating.

I know now that at the meeting of western heads of government called by President Carter in Guadelope in January 1979, Prime minister Callaghan spoke with the president informally about the possibility of the UK having the Trident C-4 missile system to follow Polaris and that Carter's response had been favourable.

Recalling the purpose for which these scientific advisers are brought in I am puzzled that it would seem, from Ministerial statements, that no-one within the scientific establishment, and particularly the CSA, looked into the cocktail of chemical substances with which our troops and equipments were treated in the Gulf, nor the possible harmful effects of using weapons containing depleted uranium, notwithstanding the mass of publicity attending the subject in the British and US press. This I simply cannot believe. When I was the submarine director I had been approached by the Atomic Energy Authority to use depleted uranium for ballast in submarines and for obvious reasons had declined the proposal.

During this long period the British electronics / weapons industry did not rush to produce private venture systems of any size to meet foreseen requirements. Those with cash mountains simply sat on their cash and waited for a benevolent government to provide some more. An example was the replacement of the navy's long-range warning radar. It had long been appreciated that the radar widely fitted in the Fleet could be easily jammed, if not by the proverbial cigarette lighter then certainly by a well equipped adversary like the Soviet naval air force. New more agile equipment was required for HM Ships. A dynamic electronics company would have seized the bull by the horns and produced one while the argument about the need and the desirable characteristics and the cost went on. Two or more years later it was still going on when the Dutch firm HSA walked in the door with exactly the equipment that the navy now realised that it wanted. Doubtless I have made it sound simpler than it really was.

It is typical of organisations that if required to make changes or reductions in staff, it is always the junior posts that go. In the end they are all Chiefs and no Indians. The services and the civil service will fight on the beaches and in the by-ways before they will give up senior posts. The duplication of posts in the naval weapons field already described was just a small example. I accept absolutely that my Royal Corps of Naval Constructors was no exception to the rule that it's easier to shed junior posts than senior posts, even though the junior chaps are probably more useful to have.

Many years ago a committee set up under a Labour government recommended that the Royal Dockyards should be given greater autonomy under a civilian General Manager and that there was no requirement for an Admiral Superintendent. This was implemented but the naval flag officer reappeared as the Port Admiral to coordinate the naval aspects of the activities in the port, in a short while it was just like old times.

Historically, the coordination of finance and programmes in the Royal Dockyards was. the responsibility of the Constructive Manager , a senior member of the RCNC and a lineal descendant of the Master Shipwrights of old. Soon there was naval pressure for a re-organisation of the dockyards on functional lines with planning, production, finance and resources managers under a general manager instead of the constructive, engineering and electrical professional departments as hitherto. Engineering and electrical admirals, or ex-admirals, would be eligible to be general managers. Soon it would be simply jobs for the boys.

The argument was that this would make the dockyards more efficient and more accountable. Since at that time the dockyards employed about 28,000 people, as many as were employed in the private shipyards in building warships, this was clearly a laudable aim but it did require that the other side of the coin be accepted, namely that the navy's refitting and modernisation programmes must be fixed well in advance to enable new equipment to be purchased and available before the ships arrived for refit and that the programmes be rigidly adhered to. To make it possible to plan the refit work on any sort of realistic basis, it was planned that teams from the dockyards would ride in the ships making surveys for some months before the refit started, since experience is that 60% of the work in a warship refit is discovered on 'opening up' equipment for inspection. Given firm programmes, the dockyards would be able to increase their cost-effectiveness and reduce their labour force, given the political will.

In practice the navy could do no such thing. The refitting and modernisation work of major fleet units could be planned and pretty well kept to, but the refitting programme for destroyers, frigates and smaller ships was subject to disruption due to the random loading caused by ships requiring emergency repairs and docking following incidents like colliding with other ships or with dock walls, going aground ever so slightly but enough to damage the sonar dome, getting wires around their propellers, galley fires, random flooding incidents and so on. This defies logical planning and disrupts the planned allocation of resources such as graving docks and skilled men. This affects the base load ships as well unless some contingency margin is allowed and of course, putting a contingency back in the programme brings things back to how they had run when the Constructive Manager was primus inter pares, save of course, that the yard now has to carry the costs of the multitude of planners and senior and junior managers passing pieces of paper around.

The naval fleet planners had parallel problems because ships would have to be switched round to do the job of a ship now undergoing emergency repairs. Frequently it meant that a ship would not now be available to come into a yard for its planned refit on the date set. This might be at another dockyard which would then complain that it had under-utilised resources and men. I recall Admiral Ray Lygo, when Vice Chief of Naval Staff, telling me rather plaintively that he sometimes felt that the Royal Navy existed solely to provide work for the Royal Dockyards. He had a point.

Which is simply to point out that notwithstanding the sincere efforts of a large number of people, you can't make a complex jobbing engineering business like warship repairing run as efficiently as a Jaguar production line.

An obviously sensible measure that was taken was to allocate ship classes and types to yards, thus Polaris submarines went to Rosyth, nuclear attack submarines to Chatham and Devonport, Leander Class Frigates to Devonport and so on. The work to be undertaken during a refit would be the repair of Defects (putting things back the way they were) and Alterations and Additions (making something different). When the A and A work was very substantial the refit would become a Modernisation.

The system worked something like this. The Fleet would report defects and the real extent of the work required would not be known until the items were opened up in the yard. A policy of repair by replacement was introduced to make the dockyard work quantifiable, with the actual component repair taking place outside the refit time-scale and frequently back at the manufacturers works. A's and As would be proposed by the Fleet and by the MoD, investigated and costed by the Ship and Weapons Departments and other specialists where appropriate and either approved or rejected for the Class. Approved items would then be designed in detail and equipment prepared and earmarked. A set of such items would be assembled and forwarded to the selected dockyard in preparation for the ship's arrival for refit. The dockyard would then prepare the detailed working drawings and schedules. I had begun to notice as early as the late 1950's that the dockyards were simply copying our naval construction guidance drawings, giving them a yard number and sending them back for our approval. All very flattering but not what they were being paid to do which was at the least to adjust the plans to reflect the small differences that exist between ships of the same class built by different shipbuilders.

As the head of the profession I was concerned to note that the drawing offices in the royal dockyards no longer had a professional engineer in direct charge and were run by chief draughtsmen. The professional engineers were 'managing' but were remote from the day-to-day work. This was fashionable — the age of the manager. The management bug had particularly seized the naval engineering officers. I suggested to the Chief Executive Dockyards, a senior member of the RCNC, that while Ship Department as the overall design authority for HM Ships, would still carry out the initial investigation of A's and A's and obtain approval, and watch over the ship's stability and strength, all of the detailed design work thereafter should be done by the dockyard drawing offices, since they would have to prepare the detailed plans for use in doing the work at the ship. In this way I intended to put young professional officers back in to run his dockyard design offices and reverse what I found to be a depressing downward trend in the competence and output of those offices. If he agreed I would prepare the documents to make this official; I could expect some opposition from my own chaps who would see this as a diminution of their own task and eventually a threat to drawing office jobs in Bath.

To my regret, but not to my surprise, the Chief Executive Dockyards declined to take on this extra responsibility. The reason given to me was because it would require an extra 28 staff. He had something like 28,000 staff and workpeople at the time.

I have mentioned elsewhere that some of us were unhappy with the academic standards in the RN College Greenwich from the late 1940's onwards and that this led eventually to the transfer of the academic training of the officers entering the RCNC to

University College London. Although my officers belonged to the appropriate professional learned societies I was conscious that many of them were content to rest upon the 'Masters' qualification that they had achieved at the age of 22/23 and to pay not too much attention to more recent theoretical work that was not of immediate concern in their job. I arranged that they should go to University College London for a months mid-career updating. They would at least learn something of what the recent graduates — who they would have working under them — were talking about!. It was a demanding month. Those officers who were destined for higher rank made the best of it and others clearly enjoyed their stay in London.

I had been made an Honorary Research Fellow in University College London in 1974.

Between 29th March and 2 April 1976, University College London was the venue for the 11th Symposium on Naval Hydrodynamics sponsored by the US Office of Naval Research, UCL and others and attended by a powerful international gathering of mathematicians and hydrodynamicists. The theme was the "Unsteady Hydrodynamics of Marine Vehicles". I was asked (told!) to make an opening address, a chore that I would share with a US Assistant Secretary for Defence. Being a swat and a former lecturer in hydrodynamics, I read all of the papers to be presented. On the day, I stood up and welcomed the delegates and gave them a ten-minute overview of what they were to hear in the coming days. When it was his turn, my American co-opener stood up and said something like "Hi guys and girls, we sure are glad to have you all attend this symposium here in UCL London and I hope you have useful discussions". He then walked off the stage and I did not see him again at the symposium. Nevertheless the official report of the symposium carried a record of what he apparently was supposed to say and not the few words that he actually uttered. Between meetings in Whitehall I attended several sessions and the more abstruse the mathematics became, the more convinced I became that my co-opener had the right idea.

The paper that I and I am sure the rest of the audience remember best was a piece of mathematics entitled "Velocity potentials of submerged bodies near a free surface — application to wave-excited forces and motions" presented by M.S. Chang and P.C. Pien from the David Taylor Basin at Bethesda, USA. This is a very demanding subject. The mathematics is formidable and relevant to our long-standing problem with submarine communications. The authors provided many slides of mathematical symbols projected on a large screen. When the time came for questions there were many and it finally occurred to me that they nearly all required the presenter, the diminutive Miss Chang, to reach up to point to the equation at the top of the screen, whereupon her mini-skirt went up and showed her knickers. It really was a most happy circumstance; Miss Chang had never had a more receptive audience and we all learnt something.

She certainly eclipsed a young man at the Admiralty Experiment Works at Haslar who lectured to a VIP audience with the front of his trousers gaping open. His audience was transfixed while the young man himself could not understand why his boss, Peter Lover, sitting in the front row, was mouthing words at him and making what seemed to be obscene gestures.

Making speeches, giving lectures and attending those made by others, filled a tidy portion of my duty and off-duty hours. I had found it to be most difficult to persuade myself when young and now to persuade my younger officers, that they must be ruthlessly selective in the points they wish to make and to hammer those few points home when making presentations. I have sat through countless sessions during which a speaker has tried to tell all that he knows within 30 minutes, with viewgraphs flashing on and off the screen so quickly that none present can comprehend their content, to leave the audience with but the vaguest notion of the intended message.

At the other end of the spectrum one of my directors would sit through my weekly management board meetings without saying a word until right at the end he would summarise the difficulties. Finally I took him to one side and pointed out that I could hire hundreds of people who could tell me how difficult it all is; I expected my directors to produce solutions, not problems. I was, however, reminded of the need to keep a sense of proportion in such matters by Charles Shepherd. One day I was moaning generally along these lines when he said, "Look it's no good moaning that so and so doesn't think the way that you do. If he did he'd be a bloody admiral, wouldn't he"?

I was approached by a friend one day and asked if I would speak on the potential for the use of computers in warship design and construction as a guest speaker at the Sperry-Univac centre in St Paul du Vance just north of Nice. The participants would be from many nations. I took Liz. It was raining when we landed in Nice.

We were housed in an isolated hotel about two miles from the Centre. The hotel had once been a splendid mansion with marble decor and large public rooms. Each day there was a painting on display on an easel in the foyer and if there were more than ten other guests we did not see them. Dining alone in the vast dark dining room was a little spooky. On the first day the session ended in mid-afternoon and I decided to walk back to the hotel along the pleasant country road with its gated entrances to houses nestling on the wooded hillside above. Half way along the road I was aware of dogs barking and to my horror two Dobermans burst through the hedge beside me and came up snarling viciously. They accompanied me, snarling, for about 60 metres until there was a great whistling from the rear and they turned and went back. Liz said that I was as white as a sheet when I arrived at the hotel; there was dog saliva on my trouser legs, they had been that close. When I described my experience, the locals said that only a fool would walk along "that road, did I not realise that those chateaux were the retreats of film stars and financiers from Paris, the sort of people who get robbed, raped, kidnapped or murdered ?. Only last week at the place I described the caretaker had been murdered by robbers".

The freedom to seek employment anywhere within the European Community had brought a need for recognition of acceptable professional standards across the nations. For example, if an engineer is to certify the safety standard of, say, a bridge, his professional qualifications must be acceptable to the nation whose bridge it is. This highlighted the long running problem caused by the wide spread misuse of the designation 'engineer' in the UK and led to the creation of the Engineering Council, which alone can authorize the designation Chartered Engineer, C Eng, to those having the appropriate academic and practical qualifications.

Although not directly related, but similarly, it had long been accepted that election to membership of the UK's most prestigious scientific institution, The Royal Society, was an honour much less frequently accorded engineers than pure scientists. In 1976, with the strong support of Prince Philip, Admiral Mountbatten, and The Royal Society, the Fellowship of Engineering was created to provide a parallel body for engineers, with an initial membership of fifty Fellows judged to be eminent in their disciplines. I was one of these Founding Fellows. With the passage of time the Fellowship has become The Royal Academy of Engineering with a membership of about one thousand spread across all fields of engineering.

Sometime in the late summer of 1978 I attended a meeting with the Permanent Secretary, his Deputy and the Controller of the Navy. The subject was who was to succeed me when I reached the age of 60 in February 1980. In the normal order this would be a vice admiral of the engineering specialisation but the powers-that-be had concluded that there was no one suitable who would be available at that time. The rear admirals now in Ship Department would retire and a new man might be available in 1982. This would also affect the succession as head of the Royal Corps and enable authority to appoint a design man, which was the Board's wish. Asked, I said that I would be willing to continue in service. They didn't make any commitment. It was all remarkably casual, so casual in fact that I didn't give it another thought. It was this undertaking that I was to break to join British Shipbuilders, where-upon the MoD did not proceed with the knighthood that I was told (informally, of course) I would receive in the 1979 New Years Honours List. Those who deleted this award did not tell all those who had been privy to the earlier decision and so in January 1979 I received several letters from Mr Patrick Duffy, MP, a Member of the Navy Board, addressed to Sir Jack Daniel. The only people to benefit were a rear admiral who unexpectedly became a vice admiral and a civilian who became head of the Royal Corps.

Part Three

THE WASTED YEARS

Chapter Twelve

The second most stupid thing that I ever did in my life was to allow myself to be persuaded to resign from the Ministry of Defence to become the Board Member for Warshipbuilding in the recently nationalised state shipbuilding corporation, British Shipbuilders. A decision made quite absurd within a month by the Labour government's defeat by the Conservatives led by Margaret Thatcher. Had this not happened, we may have been able to nurse some of the merchant shipbuilding industry through the bad years.

The rot in British industry had started in the early years of the century. The Empire no longer bought everything from Britain and manufacturing was no longer the dominant sphere for investment; short-termism was increasingly the order of the day and why bother to modernise heavy industry and deal with those dreadful trade union people when one could make twice the profit making potato crisps or selling-off valuable sites?. Public ownership had been seen as one way of taking a grip on industries that had once been vital to the nation's prosperity and of managing their run down in manpower, re-organisation and modernisation to fit them for a continuing role in the future.

Socialist ministers had some intellectual sympathy and understanding of the need to maintain a sound technology base in the UK and could be persuaded that one day the rising living standards and wages in the Far East and modernisation and rationalisation under EEC rules at home, could make Britain's engineering industries competitive and would provide thousands of technology jobs across the nation. The Japanese government had kick-started their industries with massive loans at 3%, repayable over 50 years. Why not the UK?

On the other side of the coin was the behaviour of the Trade Unions whose leaders were incapable of curbing their extremist elements and who had brought down the Labour government. For a stable industrial and social future, the power of the unions had to be curbed.

Today, there is little public awareness of how close to anarchy the UK was brought by communist activists within the trade union movement. The unemployment and hardship of the 1929-31 depression had brought a widespread desire for change among blue-collar workers and through the 1930's the communist party built up a hard core of shop floor activists to follow the lead of the intellectuals like Pitt, Haldane, Smollett and Cockburn and their newspapers The Daily Worker and The Week. The outbreak of war in 1939 brought no change. Until June 1941, the Communist Party of Great Britain was opposed to the British war effort; they saw the war as a means to destroy Imperialism and the 1939 Nazi-Soviet Pact put them on the side of the enemy. The pretext was the 'Cause for peace' and a 'Peoples Democracy'. After Dunkirk they called for a 'Peoples Peace' and went so far as to organise a revolutionary assembly in London with delegates claiming to represent over a million people. This Convention Movement was supported and reported by both Soviet and Nazi radio broadcasts, often in identical language. The channel was, of course, the Soviet embassy in London. Not much known at the time were the strikes they caused in the aircraft and armaments factories, even during the Battle of Britain. In many cases the activists were dealt with summarily by their fellow workers, most of who had sons or brothers (and daughters too) in the forces, but the moles were always there, digging away.

There was some embarrassment following the Nazi attack on Russia on 21 June 1941. The Convention Movement was wound-up on the 22nd but the propaganda for peace and a people's democracy continued whilst covertly, the CPGB spied upon and undermined the 'free' governments in exile of countries like Poland to ensure that after the war the Moscow variant should govern.

The end of the war saw a powerful nucleus of communists embedded in the trade union movement as left wing labour supporters. Their aim was the destruction of the British parliamentary system through industrial unrest. The immediate post war prime minister Clem Attlee and his Minister of Labour, Ernie Bevin were aware of this and held the line but weak political leadership of both major political parties in the next 20 years, lack of foresight and drive in managing the changes in industrial production from heavy engineering to electronics and automotive and aviation products and accompanying social changes, nearly allowed the communists to succeed. They did succeed in undermining the motorcar builders. It was evident what was happening – I wrote a thesis on the need for trade union reform when I was at the Imperial Defence College in 1966.

The slide towards anarchy continued, the trade unions stopped industrial production at utilities and factories not part of a dispute by secondary picketing, tabled double figure wage demands, brought about a three day working week due to shortages of power and essential supplies and generally behaved as if the law of the land did not apply to them. They brought down the Heath government and Callaghan only survived by giving-in to most of their demands until even he could not survive the 1978/79 'winter of discontent'. It wasn't until Margaret Thatcher had the courage to 'take the unions on' and confront the militant miners with the forces of law and order and then to pass the necessary legislation to restore democracy to the trade union movement, that order was restored. Historians will doubtless record the part that US agencies played in the war and afterwards in identifying and helping to curb the communist threat to Britain.

Wartime shipping losses had been catastrophic and European shipyards badly damaged. There was an urgent need for replacement tonnage and extra tonnage to meet the expansion in world trade of the 1950's and 1960's. The British shipbuilding industry had survived intact from the war. . There had been little need for the shipbuilders to solicit orders while ship-owners were beating a path to their doors asking for ships. More than one UK yard had an open order book from the big oil-tanker companies who 'would take all the ships you can build'. Management and men believed that it would go on for ever ; the workforce could demand annual pay increases, the general unions could press for the employment of extra semi-skilled and unskilled workers and management could pass the costs on to the customer, so why struggle to improve productivity, reorganise the trade structure or bring in new practices'?. And risk strikes. Inexorably management had ceased to manage, costs rose and productivity fell.

However, giving the unions what they asked for with only a token resistance did not prevent strikes. The wage structure in the industry had been set in the days of simple riveted hulls when those who built the hulls and boilers were king and were paid a few pence an hour more than the other trades, like joiners and painters and those new electricians. The powerful Boilermakers Union ensured that this state should continue through the years while the introduction of welded hulls and prefabrication totally altered the nature of the work and their membership numbers of platers, riveters and caulkers declined. By the 1960's the engineers and electricians could see no good reason why they should be paid at a lesser rate than the boilermakers and asked for parity. Strikes, go-slows, refusals to work with other trades and so on resulted. Most managers tried to buy themselves out of trouble but by the 1970's the customers could go elsewhere

We in the MoD watched this with horror. The workers building warships were members of the same trade unions as those building merchant ships, in many cases warships and merchant ships were built in the same yard and the increased costs due to poor management, wage increases and labour problems were passed on to the taxpayer via the force majeure clauses in warship contracts.

In 1950 the UK had produced 50% of the worlds new merchant tonnage. The Japanese entered the lists in 1953 and by 1970 the UK was producing less than 5% of an admittedly larger overall, world tonnage. Government, the financial institutions and the unions share the blame for the failure to preserve Britain's place in shipbuilding and of these only the first had the authority to structure the environment in which the other two must perform by such devices as tax incentives and trade union reform. I would not pretend that this would have been easy but government could have placed orders at prices to drive the thing through. Already, by the late 1960's when I conducted the negotiations on the proposed Anglo-Dutch frigate, productivity and wage rates in Dutch yards building warships were twice those in British yards.

It was pointless to rely on the shipyard management to pull the industry round, management's mindset had been corrupted by the easy order books of the 1950's just as much as the trade union's mindset was still redolent of the 1929 Jarrow marches.

Most of the measures taken by government before 1976 were trivial. Some were absurd.

The Edward Heath government even provided a subsidy to British ship-owners to buy new tonnage and allowed it to be spent on orders from foreign yards and then allowed them to register the ships under foreign flags. In fact, until the Labour government attempted to take the shipbuilding industry into public ownership, successive governments and city institutions of this island nation had manifestly failed to foster industries that today could still be a significant source of employment and earnings.

This then was the industry that was nationalised in 1977 with nearly 90,000 direct employees of who about 30,000 were employed on warship building and hence, in my view, already subsidised by the British taxpayer.

By 1970, there was already an element of public ownership of the shipbuilding industry as a result of the financial collapse of the Court Line and the problems at Fairfield on the Clyde. There had been a number of closures of shipyards on the Clyde, companies without the financial resources, space or management ability to survive. Most had survived thus far on small warship or naval auxiliary orders and had adjusted their programmes to share mobile teams of workers such as electricians, joiners and outfitters who moved up and down the river as the work required. When ships became orders of magnitude more complex, there was a need for more permanent skilled workpeople and facilities, and firms such as Dennys and Stephens closed.

Fairfields were similarly in trouble. They were effectively insolvent and still had some important ships to complete for the Royal Navy. After much wringing of hands and intense pressure from Scottish MP's, trade unions and Glasgow civic leaders, the government guaranteed funds to support a consortium of Clyde yards, which included Yarrows initially, to be called Upper Clyde Shipbuilders and appointed an MD who was chosen to bring modern commercial management practices to the industry. Prominent in the negotiations for the workpeople were Jimmy Neil and his sidekick, Sammy Gilmour.

Despite government assistance the venture did not prosper and UCS was effectively bankrupt and ripe for closure when nationalisation took place.

Clause 4 of the Labour Party constitution required that the means of manufacture and production should be owned by the people and in pursuit of this doctrine the major utilities such as gas and electricity production, distribution and supply, water, coal mining, steel making, railways and road transport had been taken into public ownership. An appointed Board answerable to parliament through a minister governed each.

Shipbuilding and aircraft production, both of which were effectively subsidised by defence work and suffering from foreign competition, were on the list of industries to be taken into public ownership.

The Ministry of Defence as the biggest single customer of shipbuilding and the department of state with the strongest knowledge of shipbuilding, marine engineering and aeronautical engineering was kept informed and consulted about both proposed nationalisations. The MoD had its own design organisation in the Royal Corps of Naval Constructors and ran the Royal Dockyards with nearly 30,000 employees. Work on the construction of warships gave employment to about 30,000 people in private shipyards and to more than twice that number in industry across the land manufacturing equipment to go into those ships. Discussions about the form and extent of nationalisation looked at several alternatives, such as including the Royal Dockyards in British Shipbuilders, or creating a separate corporation for warship building and repair, (a sort of British Warship builders) or excluding the private warship building yards altogether and so on.

Thus in the mid-1970's, ministers saw the industry in some trouble and prepared draft legislation to take over the rest of it. Civil servants in the Department of Industry had noted the quality of management in the shipyards that they had inherited and some of them decided that they could do better themselves, given the chance. In most cases they had little comprehension of industrial management or the amount of management effort that went into dealing with workforce trade disputes, bolshy shop stewards and trade union officials.

Draft proposals were made and provoked loud opposition from the Tories and from business and industry, the former for political reasons and the latter in the main because the terms of financial compensation were not generous enough. The first attempt to pass the necessary legislation through parliament had to be abandoned because of some problem with ship-repair companies and it was not until 1977 that the Shipbuilding and Aircraft Industries Act received Royal Assent and British Shipbuilders and British Aerospace were formed.

The driving force behind the nationalisation of these industries was the Secretary of State for Industry, Tony Wedgwood Benn, supported by his minister, the 'sinisterly smiling' Gerald Kaufman. As the senior shipbuilding professional in the MoD, I attended one or two of the meetings chaired by one or other of these ministers. I formed a considerable regard for Benn's intellect and respect for him personally, in part because of the honesty of his position. He saw public ownership as the one way of modernising the industry and preserving the jobs and the skills therein. He believed passionately that a person who had acquired skills to do work should not be summarily sacked at the whim of someone sitting in a city office, without being given the opportunity to acquire new skills and fitness for employment elsewhere. He believed that there is good in everyone. He was also a strong advocate of introducing new technology.

The problem with Benn was that he tended to develop his arguments further and further as he warmed to his theme and sometimes reached infinity, but his officials hauled him back. I rather like the later description of Tony Benn as 'the perpetual voice of opposition within the Opposition'. In all the years there has hardly been a single anti-war, anti-nuclear or peacenik campaign that has not seen Benn addressing the assembled gathering. As a leader of the left wing of the Labour party he is alleged to have attracted the attention of the KGB who tried to cultivate him as an unwitting source of intelligence. I would have much liked to sit in on any such discussion from which the KGB man must have emerged totally confused. According to the defector, Gorievski, the Soviet ambassador in London was to report later to his Moscow superiors "Looking back, I see that all his (Benn's) assessments were wrong and that none of his predictions has come true".

The story that I liked most about Kaufman was when Graham Day, then the Deputy Chairman Designate, developed a complicated argument about how something should be done. Kaufman listened patiently. "Very well' he said when Day was done, and then proceeded to summarise the reverse of what Day had suggested. "OK Minister" said Day "you want to do it with mirrors".

Representatives of the Shipbuilders and Ship-repairers National Association conducted the negotiations on behalf of the industry. It was clear that the warship-builders with their bread and butter workload provided by the Navy, had no interest in nationalisation, they just wanted to be left alone, and it was largely their interests that had fuelled the resistance in parliament. From my observation, and irrespective of what their shareholders might be saying in the City (to drive up the share price), the managers of the merchant shipbuilders couldn't become nationalised quickly enough. One of the negotiators was from a company concerning who's financial stability the naval contracts organisation had expressed serious doubts when we proposed to place an order for a naval auxiliary with them in the mid-1970's.   They were right - this Scottish company went on to cost British Shipbuilders and hence the taxpayer, the best part of many tens of million pounds in losses on merchant ship and offshore contracts.

British Shipbuilders was intended to be an autonomous corporation, given powers by government to stand-alone and run the enterprise free from interference. Under the Conservatives nothing could have been further from the truth, interference by ministers and DTI officials was on a daily basis. Being the Member for Warshipbuilding I suffered less from DTI than my colleagues but of course the amount of investment in the yards and eventually the sale of yards was reason for official interest. Discussion with the Ministry of Defence was usually constructive because I was on their wavelength. All of this meant that Board members spent most of their time in London

The message that we kept drumming home was that within the next 20 years, all of the tonnage pouring out of Japanese and Korean yards would need replacing. The early Tory ministers like Adam Butler could see this but quickly fell out at favour with the Prime Minister and were replaced by ministers who did not argue with her. A greater economic vision was needed. When would UK ministers start to appreciate that the most important duty of a government is the provision of education, stable employment and a safe environment for its people.

Two things of importance to be settled were the location of the British Shipbuilders headquarters and who was to be the first Chairman.

Newcastle was selected for the headquarters with a sub-office in London. The headquarters building was Benton House. It would have better been named Jude House after the saint of lost causes.

The selection of the Chairman was much more fun. To Labour ministers, the key was to make the labour force part of the team and how better than by having a prominent trade union leader as chairman? Alf Robens had been a good chairman of British Coal, so why not Hugh Scanlon at British Shipbuilders? Departments concerned with Industry, Defence and Security looked at his extreme left wing stance on most subjects. They were aware that the Czech defector Frolic had named Scanlon and three or four other trade union leaders as prime targets for Soviet Bloc intelligence. There was no suggestion that he had been recruited but the fact that he was considered by the Soviets to be sufficiently close to their camp to be worth a try was sufficient for him to be black balled. Departments worked their way down a list of trade union leaders who had dominated the news in the 1970's with the same result. Danny McGarvey the Boilermakers leader was one of the first ten. It seems that he was sounded out informally, perhaps by the Secretary of State himself, and interpreted this as assurance that the job was his for the asking. He went public locally in Newcastle and Eric Varley made a rapid night journey north to shut him up.   He, too, was not acceptable to other ministries and was given a knighthood in compensation for the mix-up. He died before he could be dubbed but a special case was made for his wife to receive the honour. What odd people the British are.

According to Admiral Sir Anthony Griffin, who was the Controller of the Navy at the time, Eric Varley and his advisers went down the list of possibles until they came to an admiral and Varley said "The MoD won't be able to object to him".   There was however, the curious story that surfaced in the Department of Industry a good time later, that when asked for background information about Admiral Griffin, the MoD had sent across the C V of Rear Admiral Mike Griffin who, being an engineer with considerable industrial experience, looked to have the sort of background the job required.   I cannot vouch for its accuracy.

The lengthy gestation period provided ample time for discussion and prevarication, too much in some cases, leading to the departure of the first Deputy Chairman Designate and so Admiral Tony Griffin became the first chairman of British Shipbuilders and Michael Casey, a senior civil servant in the shipbuilding policy division of the Department of Trade & Industry, left the civil service and became the Chief Executive.

The Board had eight executive members and the Secretary - the Chairman, Deputy Chairman/ Chief Executive, second Deputy Chairman and members for Merchant shipbuilding, Warship building, Engineering, Finance and Personnel.   When I joined, this team, less the warship building and engineering members, had been in existence for about 16 months.   The Chairman sat in his room on the fourth floor, puffed his pipe, worried and was largely ignored by everyone. The Chief Executive ignored the Chairman completely. The second Deputy Chairman was the political nominee nominated by Benn who was supposed to reassure the trade unions. His expense account was such as to excite comment. And when he joined the Engineering member had extreme difficulty in keeping up with events.

Board meetings had a semblance of order because the excellent Secretary managed them. Executive Committee meetings were for the most part unstructured because the Chief Executive refused to have an agenda and liked to discuss what was currently on his mind.   This might sound all right, but most times degenerated into a quite enlightening school for scandal.

It was some time before I realised that the second Deputy Chairman, the trade union man, seldom stayed until the end of a meeting. He would arrive at his usual seat, spread out his papers and exchange cheerful greetings, usually about the Welsh national rugby side or Swansea's most recent performance.   The meeting would have been under way for some time when one would notice that his seat was empty. Perhaps an urgent telephone call?. He would never re-appear and at the close of the meeting his secretary would come and gather up his papers.

Mercifully Maurice Elderfield the Member for Finance and his team were professionals and at least the books were kept and presented in proper form.   When we were preparing the Annual Report one day, Reg Arnell, the Director of Finance, remarked on the change in fortunes of Auditors. When he had qualified, all good accountants had gone into companies and only those who were not good enough to attract company offers became auditors. Now, with the growth of companies in public ownership, the auditor was riding high and Ministers regarded them as some sort of surety that public funds were not being misapplied. It seemed to me anomalous that a company should be responsible for selecting and paying the watchdog on its financial behaviour. Any chairman worth his salt would see that others replaced auditors who were becoming difficult in the fullness of time. As far as I was concerned, each year they would draw attention to a number of minor points in the warship building yards' accounts and each year they would seemingly provide reasons justifying why the yards had ignored what they had said the previous year. When I proposed stern action they went into reverse. I put auditors in the same category as I put consultants.

Beneath the Board members were a number of Directors at HQ and the Managing Directors and staffs of the yards and works. I was well supported by two divisional Directors, Marketing and Operations. The former was Captain Ian Wright RN (rtd). Ian Wright had been in the same term as Anthony Griffin at Dartmouth and had won the sword of honour; he was navy of the old school and truly blue.

One of Ian's last naval appointments had been as the British Navy Liaison Officer with the Nigerian Navy. Notwithstanding the chaos of Lagos and the rawness of the personnel, he seemed to have enjoyed this posting. One piece of information that he provided was that the Vice Admiral C in C of the navy occupied one of the few houses in Lagos that had a WC (where the effluent went to afterwards was anyone's guess.) The ships of the Nigerian Navy seldom went to sea. It is perhaps difficult to fully comprehend the difficulty of training recruits in such developing nations at that time. I recall that in his annual report, the captain doing the same sort of job in Kenya remarked "Let me put it this way, if you asked one of these sailors the difference between a nail and a screw, he would say that it is much more difficult to hammer in a screw than a nail".

The Operations director's post was filled by secondment from one or other of the yards and provided valuable experience for men destined for higher rank. Yarrows declined absolutely to nominate a candidate; the several young potential managing directors who left the firm at about this time could hazard a guess why this was so. Officers from the other companies who filled the post did live up to their potential; Clive Benton became the Managing Director of Brooke Marine, Tony Peake became Chief Executive of VSEL and Walter Brown became VSEL's Armaments Director. All were absolutely splendid people.

The general impression of British Shipbuilders can be judged from the fact that the managing director responsible for the ship repair division was permitted to keep his own ship repair yard on the Tyne, outside the British Shipbuilders organisation. This must have placed him under intense pressure in allocating the work between his own and the BS yards.

The shipyards had been vested in British Shipbuilders with their existing management structure and workforce. The principle warship builders did not wish to be nationalised while most of the merchant yards were not displeased, even though some presented a public image to the contrary. They all resented interference from BSHQ; their philosophy was best summarised by Robert Atkinson, who succeeded Tony Griffin as Chairman, as "Please go away and leave us alone, just leave the subsidy cheque outside the door each month".

Some of the top men bowed out rather than become public servants, once removed. In my division, John Rix of Vosper-Thornycroft and Eric Yarrow of Yarrows had resigned. I felt a particular sorrow for the latter whose grandfather had started the firm on the Thames before 1900 and later moved it to Glasgow where it continued to flourish under the second Sir Harold and then Sir Eric. Nationalisation made little difference to Vickers Shipbuilding & Engineering, they were used to doing their own thing while paying lip service to a main board at Millbank and could see no reason why a change of owner-ship at the London end should affect the way they behaved.

In the first years of public ownership Conservative MP's, in opposition, took every opportunity to question and to criticise the shipbuilding industry and those who ran it. Some of the questioning in parliament was inane and spiteful. I recall that the number of cars parked outside the British Shipbuilders London Office was the subject on more than one occasion. Vosper-Thornycroft had been the most outspoken opponent of nationalisation and a great deal of the material used in criticism bore their stamp. Some MP's were persistent in their questioning; one of these was Michael Grylls. In the mid-1990's it became public that some Conservative MP's had been accepting gifts for exercising parliamentary privileges. What the press dubbed 'cash for questions'. The matter was reported upon by the Parliamentary Standards Commissioner and considered by the Standards and Privileges Committee of the House of Commons in July 1997. It coincided with a general election. For accepting gifts, five MP's or ex-MP's were singled out for censure, such that they would have been suspended from the House. Sir Michael Grylls was publicly named by the Committee as one of the most serious offenders. Early in 2,000 in a Channel 4 TV programme 'Sleaze' it was stated that Grylls had received over £ 100,000 from lobbyists, holidays from British Airways and so on and that his former secretary is the wife of the ex-Tory MP Neil Hamilton, himself disgraced for allegedly accepting money in brown envelopes from the owner of Harrods store.

An aspect of this 'cash for questions' scandal that did not receive much media comment was the fact that the internal self- regulation procedures of Parliament failed to stop the practice; it was brought to public notice by a private citizen (admittedly one who claimed that he had paid for questions to be asked). Observing the nature of the daily life in the Commons, no one can doubt that the practice had been going on for many years and that the Whips must have known it. To those of us who were in British Shipbuilders and Ship Department in the early 1980's it might perhaps explain statements that were made to us several times by a person who was being publicly critical of the Ministry's officials, that he "Could have a question asked in parliament in a weeks time", and that "He had access to the Prime Minister" and more in the same vein. And how does an MP who has been the recipient of 'brown envelopes' or exceptional hospitality behave when he becomes a Minister? There was one minister in the MoD in Thatcher's government who was dubbed privately by the Contracts officials as ' the Minister for British Aerospace'. The great tragedy of these revelations is that it has struck deeply and irreversibly at the very image of the British parliament.

Both Rix and Yarrow had appointed their successors before I arrived. In the 1960/70's Vosper Thornycroft had been very successful in obtaining orders for warships from Iran, Brazil, Nigeria, Egypt, Oman and elsewhere and, perhaps reflecting this, Rix's nominee was from the sales side. This man promptly asked BSHQ for a 'slush fund' of several tens of millions of pounds with which to secure overseas orders, claiming that without such a fund his firm would not be able to win further orders. Otherwise he would resign.

He was told firmly by the Chairman that no such funds would be allowed and his resignation was accepted. There was a rapid reappraisal of the senior staff at Vosper Thorneycroft, no one was thought suitable at that time to be Chairman and in a quite remarkable action Admiral Griffin appointed Bill Richardson, the Chairman of Vickers Shipbuilders to be additionally chairman and executive boss of Vosper Thornycroft, flying between Barrow and Southampton in midweek in the Vickers aircraft. When I arrived the result of this mix of alien cultures was already apparent. In October 1979 we discovered that Govern shipyard had been paying its workforce a productivity bonus of several pounds a week although the yard had no worthwhile work. There were some management changes.

Subsidies were available but limited to levels set by the EEC and the subsidised costs in our yards were still more than the price at which comparable ships were being offered by Japan and Korea. We discussed closing the Govern yard on several occasions but were told by the Department of Trade and Industry not to pursue this in view of Scottish sensitivity. We even had a message from Whitehall that some committee of Chief Constables had said that they would not wish to be held responsible for the maintenance of law and order on the streets of Glasgow in such an eventuality. We reflected that if the Chief Constables of Newcastle or Hartlepool or Merseyside had said the same thing they would have been sharply reminded by the Home Secretary that that was what they were paid for.

It is a sad reflection that in the British Isles it does not pay to be English. There is always ministerial concern for the Scots or the Welsh or the Northern Irish but not over-much concern for the English. In the early 1980's there was a problem getting work for Vosper Thornycroft and a Tory minister said to me " This government will not die in the ditches to save Vosper Thornycroft".

The Northern Irish had it made. The classic case was Harland and Wolff in Belfast. I had dealt with them when building the Hermes Class aircraft carriers in the early 1950's. They had two ships and Swan Hunter at Newcastle had one; Harland's hull group cost was £9 million per ship and Swan's was £8 millions. They had been excluded from nationalisation of the British industry but had continued to receive massive and sometimes hidden, subsidies. To add insult to injury some of the warship orders, which were 'placed there' in recent years, have had to be brought to mainland Britain for satisfactory completion. All the while that British Shipbuilders was being pilloried by Conservative ministers and MP's in parliament and elsewhere for requiring an annual subsidy of over £100 millions, to provide employment for some 50,000 people in the merchant shipyards and a further 100,000 in the supporting industries manufacturing machinery and equipment, the same government was giving sums of this order to keep Harland and Wolff and Shorts in business in Northern Ireland. As a senior official said to me "They can't afford to have another 6,000 unemployed Protestants roaming the streets of Belfast". I learnt that for decades there had been an understanding that Roman Catholics would not be employed in the yard. I wondered why the Chairman and Board of the company had not been prosecuted for religious discrimination?. There would have been an outcry if a similar situation had occurred in England. It was Edmund Burke who said "the only thing necessary for the triumph of evil would be for good men to do nothing"

In London we shared a British Shipbuilders apartment in the Brompton Road. An ageing Sloane Ranger who preferred socialising to hoovering looked after us. The only noteworthy thing about the apartment was the fact that from one of the apartments in the block opposite, a young girl would emerge each weekday morning, dressed always in a 'twin set', skirt and flat heeled shoes and make her way, we understood, to a toddlers crèche where she helped out. She was indistinguishable from the thousands of other girls one saw each day in central London and it was a matter of some surprise one morning to find the pavement seething with photographers and reporters and to learn that this seemingly very ordinary girl was betrothed to Prince Charles and would be the future Queen. The apartment that Lady Diana Spencer shared with two other girls went on the market the same day.

The Sloane who I remember most vividly was the one who applied for the post of secretary to Bill Richardson. She was beautifully made up and exquisitely dressed. She could type a little but shorthand, No. She saw her role more as a personal assistant to put visitors at their ease and there would be other girls to do the typing. Her husband, the

Colonel, was over the road with the Horse Guards and it seemed that in every second sentence she referred to the Colonel. It transpired that she would only accept the post (if offered) if she was given a 24 hour parking space in British Shipbuilders small car park because it was almost impossible to park the family car near their place in Knightsbridge.

Later we moved to Devonshire Place, next to Harley Street, in a building that consisted of medical consulting rooms on the lower floors and apartments on the upper floors. My driver, George Rodgers would collect me at 8.00am each morning. One morning I emerged to find no George but a very large London policeman who volunteered, "Your car's up the road, Sir". As I started down the five or six steps to pavement level, a black Jaguar car stopped outside and some young men stepped out followed by Prime Minister Margaret Thatcher, dressed in black. She swept past me and the bobbie without a glance. This went on for about six weeks. On the first occasion I turned my head as she reached the top and, man like, noted that although she might have had all the best beauty treatments, she had old woman's legs when seen from the rear. Shame really, when one recalls that, according to Carol Thatcher's excellent book about her father, he was first attracted to Margaret by her legs.

George Rogers objected to the fact that as a chauffeur he was required to wear a seat belt whereas taxi drivers were not. So he sat in the car with his seat belt tucked down between his legs instead of safely housed in its anchor point. It is said that the hallmark of good driving is always to be in the right gear in the right position in the road. George never was. Typically he would enter, say, Hyde Park corner in the outside lane, wishing to cross four lanes of traffic and exit by the first turning to the left, and he would make it! Asked how he did it he said, " Never look at them, Sir. Never make eye contact with the other drivers". He had married a German girl during his national service and sometimes, when he had to take me out at night to some function he would bring her along for company for both of them as he waited to bring me home. I believe that she still missed her homeland, even after many years.

George's uniform was a smart grey suit and peaked cap with a cockade at the front. One day the Chairman, Robert Atkinson, asked him why he had this cockade. "Because I used to drive a Baronet, Sir ". That same afternoon the Chairman decided that George (with his baronet cap) should become his driver and I should have the man displaced. George was never reconciled to this. He particularly resented being shouted at and his driving criticised from the back seat and on one such occasion was involved in an accident for which he was, of course, loudly blamed. He used to sit morosely in my secretary's room and would break the golden rule of all chauffeurs of never talking about his bosses business. As a result I found that I, rather unwillingly, learned a great deal more of the Chairman and his wife's private affairs than perhaps they realised.

It was suggested that the tax position as regards the use of company flats in London would best be regularised by Board Members acquiring a 'main residence' in Newcastle, the city with British Shipbuilders HQ. Liz and I journeyed to Newcastle, had dinner in the hotel and studied the local evening paper. There was a fully furnished two bedroom apartment and garage for sale; we went and looked at it in the dark, and bought it on the spot. The young woman owner was emigrating to Canada, following her boss who had moved from Proctor and Gamble, Newcastle to Proctor and Gamble, Toronto. Privately we wondered whether he would be pleased. The apartment was the upper, left, of a block of four with magnificent views to the north and west, with the racecourse and the main railway line and road to Scotland in the far distance. On the other side of the coin was its exposure to the northerly gales.

When I told my colleagues that I had bought an apartment in Killingworth you could have heard a pin drop. This was evidently a non-U suburb. There was admittedly a grey concrete block of council flats way over there somewhere (.it has since been pulled down) and many of the shops in the small shopping centre were closed but we were in a green area of small houses and flats occupied mostly by young married couples struggling to survive decently in an area of high unemployment. Colleagues seemed to have missed the point that the objective was to have a Newcastle address; I suppose that I slept there less than a hundred times in three years and Liz less than fifty, but we liked the flat and the people around us. Her arrival with the little dogs was always an event with sweets and Meadowland apples for the children who came to see what was ado. The booksellers children always appeared, hand in hand and solemn as little owls, even in their nightshirts when it was late.

In part because of the time the apartment was unoccupied, we decided to replace the all-glass front door, which led directly on to the staircase, with a stout wooden one. We bought the door in Bath; Liz gave it six good coats of varnish and carried it to Newcastle on the roof rack. I set-too next morning, removed the old door, adjusted the new door to give a good fit in the door frame and fitted the hinges and locks to it. This took most of the day. At about 4.00pm I had the door propped up in position on books and things and had just entered the first screw in the top hinge, when I was pushed to one side and a broad Geordie voice said "Ma wife tells me that tha' has been all day putting up a bloody door. I have built half a house in that time" whereupon he picked up my hammer and smartly hammered the screws best part of the way in. With the judicious use of the plane and hammer and occasionally the screwdriver Alan finished the job. Liz loyally volunteered that she thought that the gap around the door was a little bigger (and hence would let in more draught) than it had been at 4. 00pm but really this was all down to me.

Alan, his wife and small son, lived in a detached house next door. To keep in work he had been on a government aid scheme to teach the natives in Africa carpentry and how to build simple houses. He had had a terrible time in Kenya and Uganda including being imprisoned by Idi Amin. The moment that he hit the first screw I recalled the plaintive report by the RN Captain in Kenya on the subject of the difference between a nail and a screw. I could not help wondering whether Alan could be in part responsible for this!

Julie, who occupied the flat under ours, made some comment to her husband Laurence about new doors with the result that he slammed their door in a temper and broke the glass. Lawrence was a skilled shipyard worker who had lost his job and was now seeking work in Scotland in the oil industry. "Why can't we have a door like that" was rubbing salt on an already battered ego. The result of their reconciliation was a daughter, born nine months later.

One morning we were awakened by people from the Gas Board who insisted on sealing our gas fired central heating boiler. We learned that in an apartment nearby, a family of four had been found dead, it was thought as the result of fumes from a defective system. Examination of our system showed that the trunk to take the exhaust fumes from our boiler to the open air had not been fitted and that the boiler was exhausting directly into the roof space. There was also considered to be insufficient area for the supply of fresh air;(the Gas Board would not accept the gap around the front door). Days passed and no-one seemed to be initiating remedial action or to care that we were freezing and so we got somebody in to do the work. The cost was less than a hundred pounds and it took firm action by our solicitor (now judge) Mark Rutherford to recover the cost from the builder, who meanwhile continued to advertise with his helicopter on the TV.

Despite the fall in the housing market we sold the apartment unfurnished for what we gave for it furnished and moved the contents south. We left with our admiration

244

for the people of the North East and Newcastle undimmed; putting in a Japanese motor plant or two is scant compensation for the wholesale closure of the shipbuilding, heavy engineering and coalmining industries. They deserve better.

In the last 30 years I had been a modest rail and air traveller on duty to destinations in the UK and overseas and in so doing I would occasionally encounter one or other professors of my acquaintance. Now that I was flying to Newcastle once or twice each week I became conscious of the number of times that this occurred. In many cases they were arriving for, or leaving after, attending a meeting of a learned society or symposium in London. Quite often they were going or had just been overseas to attend similar events. Examination of the office holders and members of council of the many British Institutions and Learned Societies today shows the same preponderance of university academics who are able to allow their names to go forward for election in the knowledge that their university will pay the costs for travel and accommodation for attendance at council meetings and the like. Representatives of small firms and private members find it hard to afford the time and expense for such attendance. This is a sad reflection of Britain's industrial decline, as the old Yorkshire saying goes " Them as can, do – them as can't, teach".

When there were just a handful of universities and postal mail, the learned societies played a vital part in spreading knowledge through interactive debate and the circulation of papers but in the last quarter century this has changed dramatically. Today, with electronic mail and the internet, such knowledge is at their fingertips and at their students fingertips and the nation can no longer afford to have them swanning around like old–time Oxford Dons. Ministers and Vice Chancellors should grasp this nettle.

In politico-economic terms there is good reason for finding the means to increase the number of computer-literate young people and the use of existing colleges and staff and student loans allows this to be done at minimum cost to the taxpayer. In this the UK is mirroring what US Presidents Kennedy and Johnson did in the 1960's and 1970's. In 1940 about 13% of US college-age young people actually went to college. By 1970 this figure had risen to 43% largely by grant of university status to colleges – some said that they had simply changed the name board.

In the early 1990's E.D. Fiske, an education staffer on the New York Times, made a survey of over 2,000 US institutions that awarded Bachelors degrees (NY Times Selective Guide to American Colleges). He found that out of the 2,000 only 256 had any merit. Only 13% of the young people actually went to colleges of repute and the other 87% went to places whose standards just did not measure up. This was reflected in their earnings, the 13% enjoyed an average income 52% higher than the 87% who, in fact, enjoyed little advantage over non-graduates in their localities. In Britain as well as in the USA, where one obtained one's degree will become increasingly important.

Although much reduced today, another academic con was the awarding of honorary degrees by iron curtain universities. A professor in Gdansk or Prague decides that he would like to visit the West. He picks someone working in a UK university who has written a recent paper in his field and invites him to Gdansk or Prague to receive an honorary degree. The UK University is honoured to accept and naturally invites the foreign professor to visit the UK. Perhaps he takes home the latest electronic gismo, unobtainable in his own country.

An interesting twist to this in the mid 1980's, at Hamburg airport one evening I noticed that in a separate glass walled section of the departure lounge there were about fifty poorly dressed men waiting for a flight to Warsaw. The floor was covered with cardboard boxes, each man had several videos, boxes of calculators, stereo systems and a computer. I wondered how they had managed to afford such things and how they would be welcomed aboard the aircraft before I realized that they had probably been sent by their government to buy things with chips in them because chips and similar electronic devices were on the banned list for communist states at that time.

Sometime in late 1979 /early 1980 Mr Geoffrey Pattie, the minister responsible for procurement under Secretary of State John Nott in the Ministry of Defence asked me how soon British Shipbuilders could take over the work of the Navy's departments in Bath, that is, the total design and technological support of the navy. I replied that if he was serious and provided the money, we might be ready in 5 years. He expressed surprise and said that he had something like 6 months in mind. I said that the only way to do that was for British Shipbuilders to take over the existing establishments and staffs, to 'change the name boards' outside Foxhill, Ensleigh and the other establishments and for the MoD to provide BS with the necessary funds to employ the same people as were there now and then we would start to rationalize the work within British Shipbuilders. I endeavoured to point out the unique nature of the MoD's technology support; in many cases the original makers of much of the navy's electronics and machinery in warships were no longer capable of supporting those equipments and certainly not the systems in which they featured. The only people who had the knowledge were in Bath and in the outposts. In many cases the safety of the lives of the officers and men at sea depended on that knowledge and on a few expert's judgement.

This was clearly not what Mr Pattie wanted to hear nor to his liking. For some reason Mr Pattie was not sympathetic to the navy's design experts, an attitude that he seems to have shared with Alan Clark according to the latter's 'Diaries'. I remarked earlier about my quip to Secretary of State Fred Mulley about giving more credibility to what someone told him in the House of Commons latrines than to the views of his own ministry's experts. Mulley readily accepted the reality and the humour of this. Not so Mr Pattie and to a lesser extent Lord Strathcona. According to Professor Kenneth Rawson who was the navy's Chief Naval Architect at the time, he was summoned to Mr Pattie's office on more than one occasion to be questioned in a fairly brusque manner by Mr Pattie on why the navy's experts clung to traditional design concepts. On at least one occasion other Conservative MP's were present.

It was very much like the woman in the James Thurber cartoon, *"mere proof won't convince me"*. Perhaps it was part of the pressure that Ministers were exerting on the navy. I was the Deputy Chairman of the NATO Frigate design company, ISSGmbH at the time and my colleagues from the other seven nations found it difficult to believe that UK Ministers had questioned the advice given by their experts and that such a situation appeared to have existed for nearly two years. As Kay Meyerhoff, a director of the German surface warship design agency said, "Surely not in the UK where Froude pioneered the science of applied ship hydrodynamics".

Much later Mr Nott asked the Chairman Robert Atkinson and I to see him. It was a Friday afternoon and was at the time when BS had decided that, because of the change in the patterns of trade, the use of supertankers and container vessels, and the limited size of British graving docks, there was little prospect of making its ship repair yards a commercial success. Mr Nott said that it was the government's decision to reduce its civilian industrial labour force in HM Dockyards. Portsmouth Dockyard was to be closed and the MoD would be pleased to give the yard, lock, stock and barrel to British Shipbuilders. He assured us that the MoD would see that the yard continued to receive a fair share of the navy's refitting work for a few years after which it would be out on its own to compete for work. The Chairman looked at me and I said that we were most grateful for the Secretary of State's thoughtfulness but regretted that there was no way in which BS could take on additional ship repair facilities when Frank Noah, the Managing

Director, Ship-Repair, was in process of shutting ship yards in the north and sacking their workmen. John Nott did not seem overly surprised but asked that we should think about it over the weekend. I recall saying "Very well Secretary of State, but the answer will still be the same on Monday morning". It was. Some time afterwards the MoD made Portsmouth a maintenance base for the fleet.

Keith Speed, when a junior minister in the MoD seemed to have the best grasp of what made the navy tick and he was always helpful. He spoke out against the proposed cuts in the Royal Navy and lost his ministerial post! The fact that the Falklands War proved the correctness of his position reinforced his non-acceptability with the Iron Lady; 'How dare he be right'.

We had many discussions with the naval staff and with naval attaches serving in London concerning the sort of ships they required. In collaboration with Ship Department Bath we produced the design of a well-balanced general-purpose frigate, the Type 24 in which we endeavoured to interest the Greek Navy. Regrettably there were changes in personnel in the RN naval staff and their interest and support for the design waned, almost overnight.

It seemed to me that the RN and most other navies were slow to come to terms with the consequences of modern weapons development. For example, when enemy weapons can be accurately guided at a ship at over 600 knots, does it matter whether the ship can do 24 or 32 knots? Perhaps a good close-in anti-missile gun system and high manoeuvrability, radar stealth and endurance might be more useful. One of the factors quoted by Denis Healey for cancelling the CVA 01 aircraft carrier design was that some 70% of its available ship and aircraft weaponry would always be required to defend the ship itself and here we were in the early 1980's agonising over the air defence capability to be given to new frigate designs. Lack of follow-on funding for the Seadart missile system meant that the idea that the escorts would be able to provide anti-aircraft and anti-missile defence of convoys was a non-starter; they would scarcely be able to defend themselves against anything other than a very low scale attack.

Since the major threat to allied shipping would be enemy nuclear submarines and our best means of deterring and attacking these and enemy surface forces were our own nuclear submarines, I argued that what we required was a large number of cheap ships to provide a surface presence and collect radar and sonar intelligence for the Fleet Headquarters to re-transmit to our SSNs. Ships like the Leeds Castle Class, diesel driven and capable of something over 20 knots with a huge endurance, could be equipped with a hull sonar, an ASW helicopter, and a close in anti-missile gun system, like the US Phalanx. They might even be given one or two anti-surface ship missiles. The requirement would be to have sufficient ships at sea. Such ships would each cost about a third of the cost of a modern frigate, would require less than a third of the crew and would be excellent for the protection of the UK's EEZ, disaster relief and fishery protection. In times of low-order threat all that is required is to provide a presence.

The Leeds Castle Class was a private venture design that I initiated in Ship Department just before I left. We had sponsored the Island Class of Fishery Protection vessels, which was designed and built by Messers Hall Russell in Aberdeen, and I wanted to build on this experience to produce a cheap, faster ship with the best sea keeping shape possible — a characteristic that the Island Class manifestly did not have. I told my design team not to be constrained by previous practice, which perhaps explains a remark made subsequently by David Brown that I told them to make it look different. The design was all that I could have wished. Unfortunately the naval staff could not be persuaded that they, too, wanted it. There was no glamour in fishery protection; it evoked memories of the Cod War and the navy hadn't exactly won that because playing bumps-a-daisy with the enemy is not in the manual of seamanship.

Hall Russell was completing ships six and seven of the five ships Island Class when I joined British Shipbuilders and was looking for more orders. Ships six and seven? It was like this. The MoD had provided money for a class of five ships. Towards the end of ship number five, Hall Russell's MD John Wright came to us and said that building five ships at a time had proved cheaper than they had expected and under the Ministry's contract rules Hall Russell would have to pay back a lot of money to the Crown. "Not at all" said Admiral Clayton, Controller of the Navy, "that would be penalising efficiency, build us two more". That's how the navy got seven for the price of five.

Hall Russell was looking for more orders and the naval staff could not be persuaded to budge. So I instructed Hall Russell to build two ships to the new design using British Ship-builders money. You can build a lot of steel hull for not much money and soon we had a lot to show. I continued to lobby the MoD and finally when I had spent 6.25 million pounds (that was a lot of money in 1979) the MoD took over the order. Lord Strathcona, then Minister of State in Defence said to me with a smile, that he had been backed up against the wall.

When war came in the Falklands the only British warships that could make the entire passage from the UK to the war zone without refuelling were the two Leeds Castle Class ships. In the rough waters of the South Atlantic they behaved beautifully and reports show that their sea keeping was as good as a frigate three or four times their size. I would not be surprised to find that they are still down there, providing our naval presence in the South Atlantic.

Why hasn't the navy built any more? Well fishery protection isn't very glamorous and is not seen as the way to high command.

I can recall saying all of this (well, not the last bit) to Admiral Sir Henry Leach, when he was First Sea Lord. The Chairman, Robert Atkinson, was there and as the holder of three Distinguished Service Crosses won when commanding a frigate in anti-submarine operations in the Atlantic war, he fully supported the argument that numbers of ships is vital for success. Henry listened and agreed that the Castle Class had been a success and that more would be useful. He then added with a smile "The trouble is, Jack, that I don't have enough frigates".

We left the room convinced that he had not really understood that what was being suggested was that the time had come, now, to really think about ordering a different mix of ships and to get off the 4,000 tonne frigate treadmill because they are too vulnerable to air flight weapons, but, of course, we were not then aware of the extreme pressure to which Henry was being subjected by John Knott to save costs by reducing the overall size of the navy while Ministers approved about five new aircraft projects for the RAF.

It was the practice to invite people to join us for lunch in the Boardroom. It was on such an occasion that Ron Ellis the Head of Defence Sales in the MoD, told us about the MoD marketing mission to Oman which was hi-jacked by Prime Minister Thatcher and where, no sooner had the plane landed than her son Mark had appeared and with whose business she proceeded to devote herself for the rest of the stay. Some years later, in 1984, this was the subject of a question in the House and enquiry in the press concerning the account with Barclay's Bank of her son's company, Monteagle Marketing, into which the proceeds of whatever he was doing in the Arabian Peninsular were paid. The Sunday Times discovered (and published) that Mrs Thatcher's husband was a co-signatory on this account although he was not a director of Monteagle.

Other luncheon guests included the PM's husband Denis, in 1980 and James Callaghan in 1983. We had all read and enjoyed the "Dear Bill" letters in the satirical magazine, "Private Eye" and I suppose that I expected a bit of a Colonel Blimp in manner if not in appearance. Not so, Mr Thatcher was a modest, reflective man who listened (I suppose he'd have to, wouldn't he) as well as joined in the general conversation. On arrival we had a gin and tonic or two. Late in the meal he spoke of his wife's great concern about Britain's social and industrial problems and her conviction that there was much that needed to be done to reverse the decline that had taken place in the years of socialist government. She was desperate to gather round her ministers who had the same sense of urgency and vision about what had to be done. If only she could have six Sir Keith Josephs! He said that she allowed herself only a few hours sleep each night and shed tears of frustration that so few of her colleagues realised how desperate the task was. He left at about 3 o'clock having pleasantly depleted our stock of beverages and I was left with the impression of a rather nice man.

James Callaghan was different and obviously much changed from when I had known him quite well in the war and subsequently as a minister in the Admiralty. During lunch he spoke of politics and politicians and one became slowly aware that he was, perhaps unconsciously, rewriting recent events to present his part in them in the best light. We all do this, of course, it's what Harold Wilson styled "practicing the politicians art of retrospective rationalisation" but James was bending known facts. In regard to what is now seen as the disastrous change of leadership of the Labour Party when he eventually stood down and was replaced not by the able Denis Healey but by the left-wing Michael Foot, James said "I left the date of my resignation to Denis and he left it too long". There was no mention of the disastrous shift to the left of the Labour Party during the 1970's, with power moving from parliament to the factory floor, and of his inability to reverse this trend.

Throughout the lunchtime talk there was an undercurrent that all businessmen are Tory; towards the end he said, "How many of you have ever voted Labour?" Frank Noah and I put up our hands. No one else moved., not even the deputy chairman, Ken Griffin, who had been put on the Coal Board and then the British Shipbuilders Board as the 'trade union man' by Tony Benn in 1977. The irrepressible Noah tackled him about his non-show afterwards and he explained that "Jim knows that I am a Labour man" but we were sure that it had more to do with the fact that BS Chairman Robert Atkinson was glaring directly at him from across the table.

Curious tales had attended Mr Atkinson's arrival at British Shipbuilders. The one that went round like wildfire was that the secretary of Mr Atkinson's company in Sheffield, an ex-Paymaster Commander in the navy, had been in and had brought a list of the new Chairman's likes and dislikes. It appeared that trousers on women and beards (on men) were out and that it was as well to be a WASP. These were the same as J. Edgar Hoover had imposed on the personnel of the FBI. There were many more. As far as I am concerned this is heresay. What I know to be fact is that Clive Benton was asked why he had that hair on his face, one young woman was sent home to appear properly dressed and Reg Arnell explained to his colleagues that for a long time he had been meaning to shave off his beard. Sources within the Department of Trade and Industry let slip that Mr Atkinson had put his name forward originally in regard to the chairmanship of British Steel but 'she who must be obeyed' had a man from America in line for that, so, what about British Shipbuilders?

Whilst it would appear that the man from America was expected to do a hatchet job on the steel and later the coal industries, the man from Sheffield fought to preserve all that was good in British shipbuilding and engineering and did not earn any Ministerial thanks for so doing. In his autobiography 'Upwardly Mobile', Norman Tebbit, who was the Secretary of State for Trade and Industry, says "Robert Atkinson had proved a great disappointment at British Shipbuilders and I was relieved to find Graham Day, a tough Canadian, in charge". Note again the Thatcher government getting someone from overseas to dismantle a British industry.

I quickly learned that when my colleagues at BSHQ had what they thought was a tricky organisational problem; they engaged consultants to prepare a report. Since I had been brought up with the US definition that a consultant is a son of a bitch from out of town I was not overly surprised at this manifestation of DTI culture or to find that the people who came from the widely known and more widely advertised firms of consultants were pretty mediocre brains. Their technique appeared to be to visit the works or yards, talk to the people there and then present an impressively printed report in shiny blue covers, expressing the yard opinions, with a final paragraph inviting BS to spend a further £ 50,000 on a more in-depth study. I was persuaded to use them once. Since the views summarised were those I had already heard ad−nauseam directly from the managements concerned and the consultants contributed no views or recommendations based on their experience elsewhere, the whole thing was a waste of time and money and soon I was saving BSHQ a lot of money by talking my colleagues out of employing consultants.

The warship building yards had been kept up to date by the need to build the most cost−effective and technically advanced warships. The money for these improvements had come from the MoD votes in nearly every case. The merchant shipbuilding yards were not thus blessed except those that built both types and even here the MoD overseers kept a watchful eye that things supplied by the taxpayer were not being over-used on merchant work. It was evident that many of the yards would require drastic overhaul and modernisation. In some cases this would just not be worthwhile and they would be closed. In others the workforce would be reduced. The challenge was to achieve this contraction without massive strike action by the workers.

The position in our European competitors was better than in the UK. In most cases their shipyards had needed rebuilding and re-equipping after 1945 and their workpeople had known what it was like to be unemployed and desperately hungry. These continental yards were still unable to match the low prices of the Far Eastern shipbuilders but were substantially cheaper than the UK yards. The EEC agreed that member nations could subsidise their shipbuilders by a set percentage, I think 30% initially, and this would be reduced annually assuming that the EEC yards would improve their cost-effectiveness and the Far Eastern yards costs would rise, to produce some sort of parity in the not too distant future.

Without question most of the continental countries had some form of constructive accounting to keep their prices competitive. The most obvious savings would be freedom from national taxation and insurance and access to cheaper money. Then there would be enlightened local authorities who waived local rates, water and sewerage charges and also in some cases charges for electric power on the grounds that it is better to have prosperous citizens working in industry and contributing to local taxes and trade than unemployed citizens on public assistance. In Eastern European yards the state owned everything in any case so why should it charge itself for rent and power?

These sorts of yards set the EEC subsidy levels and BS still found it hard to compete. It was suggested to the Department of Trade and Industry that government should take full account of the true social cost of people becoming unemployed; in our case the state would have to meet the one-off redundancy payment and the continuing cost of unemployment pay, housing benefit and so on. It was suggested to ministers and officials that with some imagination, these costs could be offset against the cost of ships, thus making us more competitive, maintaining the workpeople's self-respect and keeping the yards in-being for better times ahead. Our pleas were rejected out of hand ostensibly because it would not do for the UK to be caught cheating but actually, I suspect, because officials shrank from the problem of inter-departmental transfer of paper funds and the tradition of no trespassing in another department of state's area of responsibility. With ministers seemingly hell bent on shutting down Britain's basic industries they could not be persuaded to budge.

Some years later, Norman Lamont was to earn a certain notoriety when he was the Chancellor of the Exchequer. He concluded a speech in Parliament with words to the effect that if his policy caused a loss of jobs this was a price well worth paying. This was no surprise to those of us who knew him from his days as a minister in the DTI. British Shipbuilders fought hard to keep the yards open but they went one by one. A curiosity was that the old and poorly equipped yards could still win modest local orders because they had no overheads worth talking about whereas the modernised yards had to carry the cost of their re-equipping. But it was always a losing fight. When finally after a long struggle to find more work, we had to shut Smiths Dock and sack the labour force of near a thousand people, the Chairman told Mr Lamont. "Oh good" said Mr Lamont "I must tell the Prime Minister, she'll be pleased".

At this time one felt exactly as Joan Smiley put it in her classic novel "Moo" ; — "Those who saw the world as inherently cruel and didn't mind it, who saw people as inherently materialistic and didn't object, who saw capitalism as natural and shrugged off the inherent inhumanity of it, had won. And they were thrilled to have won, as if cruelty, materialism and inhumanity were benefits".

I would add that, to a man, they seem to be people who are everlastingly watching themselves in an invisible mirror.

British ministers and officials refused to budge even when the Dutch government allowed its social security ministry to pay the cost of the hulls of some submarines for Taiwan, in order to cheapen the price to win the order and hence keep the work people in employment.

Another thing that was happening was that huge oil tankers and bulk carriers were being ordered and these ships were too big to be built in existing British yards and harbours, save perhaps for the Lower Clyde. No one was prepared to recommend that the UK made the required investment to enable BS to produce such ships in view of the Far Eastern yards' dominance in this market. So we talked learnedly of going up-market and winning orders for the more advanced technically and specialist ship types while the only products emerging from our merchant yards at costs meeting the EEC guidelines were the most basic SD 14 merchant ships and tugs for local owners.

To become competitive we had to reduce costs in our traditionally low wage, low productivity, over-manned, industry. We knew it and so did the trade unions at national level. That there was scope for increase in productivity no-one could deny; this applied as much in the engineering and other companies making marine equipment and widgets to go in ships, as it did in the shipyards themselves.

Research showed that across the industry the average worker worked effectively for only 5 hours and 20 minutes in each 8-hour shift. Overtime was the order of the day to meet the men's earnings expectations and after the first few weeks the output was no more than if they had been given no overtime at all. The lost 2 hours and 40 minutes per day was accounted for by; —

- getting to and from the work position;
- fetching materials;

- waiting time;
- tea and coffee breaks.

Each of these reasons is valid. It is the responsibility of management to eliminate them. Most employed men are not self- starters and it is the duty of management to create conditions in which it is difficult for a man not to work.

The first necessity was to tighten up supervision. Modern planning and quality procedures generate paperwork and it is all too easy to decide to 'deal with the mail' in the first half-hour on arrival. And have a cup of tea and perhaps just a glance at the newspaper instead of walking the job and seeing that the men have got their work instructions and materials and have actually started work. In the warship-building yards we instructed the MoD overseers to be seen early on the ships for this reason. They were not popular.

Materials should be delivered as close to the workplace as possible and ahead of the work, by a provider to avoid the need (and excuse) for skilled people to queue up at storehouses and walk around the yard carrying a hammer or a piece of paper. It is remarkable how many more people have to go to the store or to the Drawing office on a sunny day than on a cold winters one.

Waiting time is a great problem. It will be appreciated that building and fitting out a ship is a vast and sometimes dangerous jigsaw puzzle. Trades are inter-dependent and must perform their tasks in the right order, usually in cramped conditions in congested spaces where access is difficult and other people also wish to work or to pass by. It is no good putting electric cables in a position in which a welder still has to do work and so on.

No-one objects to workers having a cup of tea but it must not be allowed to become a social event that lasts twice as long as the permitted time.

The answer to all of these problems is to change the method of building ships. Working inside the hulls of ships is costly as well as being uncomfortable. We had long ago started to build our submarine hulls in ring sections and advance the fitting out of the sections before joining them up into a continuous hull for launching these most congested of ships. The same principles were being adopted in the surface warship builders yards in large covered halls and we now sought to extend these methods to all the yards as space and facilities allowed.

Experience showed that working on a module about 2 metres high, in a shop, with all material to hand and the whole job accessible from floor level, a given job might take say, 1 hour. When the modules were assembled into a hull section with open ends in a big assembly hall, the same job would take 5 hours. When the hull was complete and launched, the same job would take 8 hours. The advantage of planning and performing the work in accessible modules, under cover, with materials to hand and the whole, workers and work easily visible for supervision and oversight, is profound.

The problem was that the cost of introducing the new technology into our better yards dramatically increased their overheads and all but swallowed up the material and labour savings otherwise achieved. A more benevolently inclined ministry might have allowed us to find an actuarial way out. For simple tasks these modern yards could be underbid by our primitive yards which had nothing more than a graving dock, an old crane and open workshops with corrugated iron roofs arranged around the inside of the yard's perimeter wall. No mollycoddling here and no wonder that they died young. What these old yards could not do was to meet the delivery time-scale and modern quality standards. Nor could they perform complex tasks.

The historic trades employed in the yards and the resulting trade union structures no longer properly reflected the work requirements of modern ships. For example, many important systems and equipments embody electrical and mechanical or hydraulic elements and there was a need for people who would be equally skilled in working at 'both ends' of such systems. There was the need to update and re-qualify employees. We agreed with the trade unions that we would establish a number of BS Training Companies for this purpose. They had trade union representatives on their Boards and were given charitable status. (This proved to be a double-edged sword because when the dying BS sought to recover the considerable cash sums of "BS Money" that these companies held, the Charity Commissioners refused.) The training companies set up a number of training modules to suit modern shipyard requirements and trainees could pick which group of modules their trade ambitions required. Gone, alas, was the four-year apprenticeship.

I was particularly pleased with Vickers Shipbuilders and Engineers behaviour during the lean years of the early 1980's. With the shipbuilding industry in trouble and manpower reductions the order of the day, most companies ceased recruitment and the entry of apprentices. The warship builders were the exception. At the bottom end of the scale Vosper-Thornycroft took about 20 each year, falling to zero in the mid 80's, but Vickers Shipbuilders and Engineers continued to enter about 450 apprentices annually, providing splendid job opportunities for local boys and girls. Since Barrow in Furness was essentially a one-company town, this provision of job opportunities was of crucial importance. It was not all pure altruism, however, because the turnover in some of the skilled trades, notably electricians, was about 20% a year.

National discussions with the trade unions represented in the industry were with the Confederation of Shipbuilding Trade Unions. The Chairman was the leader of the Boilermakers Union When I joined, this was John Chalmers and the Secretary was the most able Alec Ferry. Following John Chalmers early death, John Hepplewhite replaced him.

The most important meeting with the Confederation was the annual wage negotiation. They would submit their annual claim for changes in wages and conditions. This would be studied by the Member for Personnel and his staff and then by the BS Board and a response agreed. This would take some weeks and BS would then call a meeting to respond. We would meet in the Board Room in the Newcastle Headquarters, the BS Board on one side of the table and the Confederation, comprising national representatives of the various unions, on the other.

The warship building yards made a profit of about £35 million each year, principally on orders from the Ministry of Defence but the merchant yards could not avoid making a loss of more than a £100 millions each year in the face of Far Eastern competition. This would all be brought together in the Personnel Member's response to the Confederations claim. As a loss-making corporation that could only continue to exist with a government subsidy we had nothing to hide, our books were open and we had no secrets from our workpeople. A feature of our response was presentations by John Parker and myself on the present state of the yards and future prospects for orders and employment for the merchant yards and warship yards, respectively. As the story unfolded one felt idly, that, were independent observers present, they would conclude that the workers should accept a cut in pay to keep their jobs. Which of course was really, in a way, the name of the game. The Confederation representatives would listen to the BS response in silence; at the end of which they might seek clarification of a point and then adjourn. For convenience we would usually leave the room since we had offices to which we could go.

We would then reassemble to hear the Confederations interim response by the secretary, Alec Ferry. Tradition was that we listened in silence. The first such meeting that

Robert Atkinson attended as BS Chairman, he interrupted Ferry almost as soon as he started his response. Ferry was most affronted " Be quiet, Mr. Atkinson" he hissed across the table " Ye've had your turrn, noo its oor turn". Following the Confederations response it was usual to adjourn to a future date when we would meet again, hopefully to endorse agreements reached by the experts in separate negotiations.

As a Board our aim was to keep open the more efficient yards and preserve the industry against the time when world conditions improved. There was need for slimming down the numbers employed and a demonstrated scope for substantial improvement in productivity to capture which we were quietly introducing, changes at the workplace. Thus the Personnel director was usually able to put together a package in which the Confederation would be able to agree a net reduction in the workforce in return for a small percentage increase in the hourly wage rate. The age structure of the industry was such that the reductions could be realised by normal wastage or voluntary redundancy. Thus we strove to keep Britain as a shipbuilding and marine engineering nation.

Although we strove always 'not to send the unions away empty handed', after a few years of this, the union activists in the yards decided that the Confederation leaders had become 'bosses men' and demanded that they should be allowed to attend and participate in future meetings. To get the leadership off the hook BS agreed that some conveners and shop stewards could attend. For the next meeting 44 turned up. BS said that there was room for only 20 in the actual Board Room; the others must wait in a room downstairs.

We gave our presentations showing that without a government subsidy, all of the non-warship building yards would have to close and that BS could not give an increase in pay. There were two interjections by the shop stewards. The first came directly after we had given our presentation showing that we would lose over £ 100 millions and could not afford to increase wages. Up stood Sammy Gilmour of Upper Clyde fame. He stood sideways on to the table, silhouetted against the window, looking fixedly at the end wall of the room and said gravely "The lads will no' be satisfied wi' less than 14%". The second questioner remarked that the government had no problem about subsidising the Farmers or the British Motor Corporation where workers enjoyed high wages so why shouldn't BS demand a higher subsidy to pay its workers more, Why couldn't it be their turn'? I could not help remembering Henry Ford's reply when faced with a wages strike in the early days at Detroit that if he shared all of his wealth with his workforce they would each have $11 and no job.

Some years later I happened to be at a meeting held in the room in which the overflow shop stewards had been accommodated. I found that they had passed the time in carving their names on and around the table. On reflection, they probably left a more enduring mark on British Shipbuilders than I did.

The Confederation Chairman, John Chalmers had hopes of political preferment of some sort. His predecessor had received a knighthood (but had died before being dubbed) and John hoped for a Life Peerage but saw his prospects receding with Thatcher's ascendancy. Casual discussion with our Deputy Chairman resident 'union adviser' about the succession always drew back from the possibility that John Hepplewhite might succeed. Chalmers sudden death precipitated events and Hepplewhite became the leader of the Boilermakers and of the Confederation. Since Alec Ferry always ran the meetings that I attended efficiently on the trade union side I saw little change except that perhaps John was sometimes more difficult to persuade than the cheerful Chalmers had been, but we got there in the end.

As far as I was concerned the fact that Hepplewhite had been an air- gunner in the RAF in the war and had flown many missions over Germany was enough to earn him my respect. I rather liked his Thatcher story. It had been the practice of Labour Prime Ministers to have discussions with union leaders over sandwiches and beer at No 10 Downing Street. Margaret Thatcher was persuaded to do the same, perhaps only once, and John Hepplewhite was one of those who attended. He told me that it was a traumatic experience because she talked non-stop for two hours and nobody else could get a word in. Furthermore, he confessed in RAF style, "he hadn't even fancied her".

The representative of the Technical and Supervisory Staffs union, which represented mainly white-collar workpeople usually caught the same early evening flight back to London as I did and we would share common experiences over a drink. I was most surprised to learn one day that he had been sacked. It was explained that the union had been prepared to overlook his conviction for shop-lifting but when it was found that he had claimed expenses following a fraternal all-expenses-paid trip to East Germany, a line had to be drawn and he was sacked. It might be thought that the union's policy was that its OK to steal from the public but not to steal from the union.

One of the biggest problems for trade union representatives is drink. It's an occupational hazard that the good ones must learn to handle. I first noticed this when Liz and I were Cammel Laird's guests at a pre-launch dinner. We were at a table for ten and when the meal was over I found myself at the table with five wives. The men, two directors and two union men were deep in discussion at the bar. The wives accepted this as normal. The logic is simple; people are more reasonable with a glass in their hand. The firm would not offer the man a bribe but they can offer him a drink, or two. The man would not dream of accepting a bribe but he can accept a drink, or two. Conversely when the union man has to 'sell' something to his shop-stewards or vice- versa, its sometimes better done over a drink in a small group in the working men's club than in a formal meeting.

Both the management and the unions in the Warship yards could not help conveying the impression that their profitability relative to the merchant yards was the result of their personal cleverness. This was far from the truth. Their solvency was because their yards had been kept up to date by grants from the MoD and their contracts were not intended to drive them into bankruptcy. They built designs prepared by the MoD and had resident in their yards teams of experienced MoD overseers to interpret, correct and advise. The convener of the shop stewards in Vosper Thornycroft at Southampton put it this way. "Its not that we, as trade unionists, don't think that nationalisation is a good thing, we do. Its just that we don't see why the profits that we make should be taken away to subsidise those inefficient yards in the North".

The world market for submarines was seen to be more in the 1,000 tonne zone than the large ocean going 2,000 tonne boats favoured by the RN. On behalf of the BS Board I drew Vickers attention to this and directed them to prepare specimen designs to meet the military requirements that I set out for 1,400 tonne submarines. Nothing happened. After some time it emerged that many years earlier Vickers had entered into an agreement with the German submarine design organisation., ILK in Lubeck, that the latter would not enter the big submarine field and Vickers would not produce smaller boats. Viewed objectively this was a no-lose situation for IKL and the builder, HDL, since the Germans were, at the time, precluded from building big submarines under rules established by the Western European Union. When I instructed that smaller designs be prepared, the Germans had already been released from these limits and had built 1,700 tonne submarines. Walter Brown, who had been my Operations Director in BS at the time the 'get with it' instruction was issued and was now the go-ahead Armaments Director at Barrow, recalled this saga with some wry mirth in 1991. The fact was that, at that time, Vickers had no in-house capability for conceptual submarine design.

Throughout my time with British Shipbuilders there were many meetings, conferences and symposia on warships and naval affairs that were usually organised and run by Institutes and Societies active in this field. These usually attracted an international attendance from overseas navies, governments and industries as well as the home team. There was a tendency for me to be asked to write and present the Theme paper on many of these occasions and it was predictable that during the meetings I would be asked sometimes sarcastically whether British Shipbuilders had won any export orders lately. Invariably this would be asked by one or other of the retired Captains' RN employed by a weapons electronics company such as Plessey, Racal , Smiths, GEC, British Aerospace and so on. For a year or so I would make some deflecting remark because of the presence of prospective overseas customers for British equipments. Privately, I pointed out to these idiots that because the British weapons electronics industry had failed to produce the sort of systems required by the navies that buy warships from other nations, such nations receiving from a British Shipbuilder's yard a proposal that featured a French gun, a French missile and a French radar might well conclude that it would be more sensible to buy the whole ship from France and that was what was happening.

To a man they blamed the MoD for not providing development money for these low-level weapons systems notwithstanding the fact that as recent retirees they knew full well what the MoD's priorities were. The development of weapons electronics systems for the British forces had for decades been concerned with the Soviet threat and had become more specialised, more complex and more costly. It was the responsibility of industry to survey the world and evaluate the sort of weapons the small and middle ranking navies might require and decide whether they should use their company's money to produce them. This, with a very few exceptions, industry had patently failed to do. Those within the firms who made proposals for private venture projects for export were denied development funds ; one major company that could have funded many such projects was reported to deny funding of such work unless it could be guaranteed to make a profit within two years. In British industry, as in government, the accountant was supreme; short-termism and industrial decadence were the order of the day.

My concern with this state of affairs was such that I had raised the matter with Cliff Cornford when he was Chief of Defence Procurement. I suggested that he really should have a word with Sir Arnold. Sir Clifford stopped chain smoking for a moment, smiled and said that he was sorry that there was not much that he could do about it. And of course he was right, officially. What was wanted was the sort of thing Michael Carey would have done.

For many years it had been evident that we had to change the methods of construction assembly and fitting out of our war ships. It was no longer efficient or acceptable to build the hull, launch it and then fit it out in the manner that had been traditional for the past century. Building the hull was important but nearly 90%. of the cost would be in the armament, electronics, machinery, equipment and fitting-out and reduction in the timescale and cost of this, and the risk of damage, was paramount. Constructor Stunden had been building T Class submarines at Chatham in 1942 as a series of circular hoops to be partly fitted-out prior to joining together as a completed hull in Chatham's 16th century covered building berth. Cammel Laird's modernisation in the late 1970's featured a hall from which ships would be extruded down the berth as construction and fitting out progressed and other companies had ideas for improved facilities when money was available. On the merchant side Jim Venus had led the way at Appledore and later at Sunderland, with methods way ahead of his contemporaries. Such procedures require space; covered space. Following nationalisation, all of the warship builders dusted off their plans for bigger and better module halls, covered berths and covered docks.

Vickers Shipbuilders at Barrow required more drastic treatment because of the undesirability of continuing to launch ships in a light condition into the shallow, tidal Walney Channel. The firms officers had plans for modernisation, the most sweeping and costly being to fill a major part of one of the three basins of the Barrow commercial dock system - built in the mid-1800's to rival Liverpool as a departure port for emigrants to the USA - and build on it a vast assembly hall and lifting dock. The government's decision to deploy the large Trident missile from a new generation of missile submarines meant that this scheme and all that went with it must go ahead. To obtain approval we had to convince officials in the DTI who in turn had to put the case to the Treasury and Ministers and agree how much of the cost should come from MoD funds. This was done on the BS side through a working party, which I chaired. Although the case was good we had to sell it hard to the officials. The extraordinary thing was that the people who attended from Barrow were not always helpful; one man in particular bridled at every question asked by officials; his body language (and sometimes his actual language) screamed "Who are you to question what we, Vickers Barrow, are saying". It did not help.

The scheme was approved at something over £230 millions at 1982 prices and the first contract placed for the landfill and foundations and civil engineering work for the lifting dock. When tenders were called for the next phase, the construction of the vast hall (big enough to build four destroyers simultaneously) we were worried because the first part was running a little behind programme. Mercifully McAlpines who had the first contract came in with the lowest price and were awarded the big contract; both jobs could now be managed together.   Philip Hares, the BS Finance member said that he had had a call from Trafalgar House and asked me if I would see Mr so and so to see what it was all about. This man, who was to rise even higher in the firm in due course, had the effrontery to suggest that I should take the steel fabrication sub-contract away from the McAlpine associate and give it to Trafalgar House's people in Darlington. He quoted the exact tender price and said that he would undercut it. I asked him where he had obtained this confidential information and he grinned and said something about friends in high places. I told him in nautical language that his proposal was outrageous.

Rightly, we were under intense ministerial pressure to limit the cost. One outstanding item for review was the design and management cost for our agents, represented by John Elliot. They were down to 14. 25% and I was trying to get a little more off. Graham Day was now the BS Chairman and he nominated someone he knew to sit on my committee. This man was busy with a major construction project in Hong Kong and was stated to be an expert in such matters. He came to the first meeting and almost before I had explained the project and how I wished to reduce the 14.25% management fee, Day's nominee said that such things were always difficult and he had difficulty ever getting it below 22%. He then drivelled on without apparently realising that he had just risked costing the British taxpayer an additional 15 million pounds. John Steele who was a BS committee member could scarcely contain his indignation.

We did all that we could to entertain prospective customers and friends. Mostly it was small dinner parties or lunches but there were more public events. Frank Noah had obtained Centre Court seats at Wimbledon and on our day we took the New Zealand Naval attaché and his wife. The journey there was slow as six lanes of traffic converged into two as Wimbledon drew near. We were stopped in the Kings Road in Chelsea when a Chelsea pensioner walked by ; I suddenly realised that he probably looked younger than I did ; he was certainly younger. We had the usual slap-up strawberry lunch and repaired to our seats for tennis. To and fro went our heads and after two hours our guests confessed to being tired and so we all left. Liz gave our passes to four young people in the waiting queue and made their day. Another big event was the opera at Covent Garden. Here our guests stuck it out but clearly were not Placedo fans.

Generally I found the business people whom I met in the City and people being pushed forward by the DTI as experts, a big disappointment. I suppose that they felt the same about me, but I would not have employed any of them. I found them to be inferior in intelligence and integrity to the military and civil servants of my acquaintance and I missed the depth and professionalism and the honesty of the RCNC and the MoD generally. The City always took the short-term view for no better reason than it was simpler. As a learned professor once remarked "thinking is a painful business". Although we were embarked on the lonely task of trying to raise the productivity of our workpeople by actually having them work for more than five and a bit hours in each eight hour shift and success was slow in coming, I nevertheless found it offensive to be told repeatedly by a City gent consuming his third lunchtime brandy that the British working man was bone idle. I was happy to find that Robert Morley shared my views. In his piece "City Bluff" included in 'Morley Marvels' published by Robson Books in 1976 he comments —

'When people start telling me what exactly is the trouble with this land of ours I find myself looking round desperately for my hat... those who are so anxious to condemn their fellow citizens are nearly always holding a glass or scraping their plates after a hearty meal. I have never met a stockbroker who didn't assure me over their second martini that he worked a good deal harder than a miner... Bluff is the stock-in-trade of the square mile that encloses the Mansion House. They bluff their way, these city gents. They dress themselves up in jabots and furbelows and pretend to be Worshipful Fishmongers or Worshipful Bowyers when they have never cast a line or shot an arrow and don't intend to. They have a compulsion to cast judgement".

What he would have said of a city business community where abject failure as a company chairman or chief executive or the negotiation of a merger that puts thousands out of work, is rewarded with a million pound going-away payment, I do not know.

Another illusion that I had long outgrown was a belief that industrial management is efficient because it is able to hire and fire and thus shed its duds. We had some duds among our naval and civil service staffs in the MoD and Royal Dockyards and I arranged the early retirement of a dozen members of the Royal Corps where time (and smoking) had taken its toll but for the less senior staff perforce we must keep them because in my time it was just too difficult to discharge them or pension them early. Industry had even more duds. Industry was full of duds from Managing Directors downwards. favourite sons, sectional interests and sectional numbers were jealously guarded and the overall standard was poor, there were no exceptions. While it was still within their gift, the later BS Chairmen made efforts to introduce new blood at Board level into the firms. At Vickers Barrow, a Non-Barovian Chairman, Personnel Director, Commercial Director and Finance Director were appointed. The last three played a key role in organising the management buy-out of the company, yet none of them survived into the 1990's.

At the time that I had been recruited to join the British Shipbuilders board the ' two year rule' obtained. This meant that no government servant could join any company that he had or might have had occasion to deal with earlier in an official capacity. Exceptions to this rule required special permission at Cabinet level. In my case James Callaghan had approved my appointment to British Shipbuilders Board with the condition that I should not receive my civil service pension while holding the position. In the light of the changed circumstances brought about by the election of a Conservative government and the dismissive attitude of Tory ministers to the preservation of a worthwhile merchant and offshore shipbuilding industry, I had no great wish to continue as a Board member and forego my pension and I did not ask to continue for a second term when it was suggested that I could continue as Managing Director Warship Technology under the same conditions, with all the other subsidiary directorships. The warship yards were put up for sale.

The MoD was increasing the amount of work put out to contract with specialist agencies and I suggested that BS should set up a technology company on the MoD's doorstep in Bath. In so doing I was breaking an unwritten rule that we had established when I was serving in MoD Bath, namely that design agencies should not locate themselves there and poach our staff. In our case the emphasis was to be on weapons systems work and our employees would be retired officers. No poaching. This was agreed and I became the Managing Director of Warship Design Services Limited. With the fragmentation of BS it was thought sensible to place WDSL under a large warship company and with the tremendous assistance of Geoff Fuller, Tony Peake and Frank Noah, the company was soon up and running as part of VSEL.

WDSL could have been a minor success story for Vickers as the government ran down the MoD's in-house resources and put more design work out to contract. Instead, the Barrow staff set out to undermine it. Part of WDSL's attractiveness to the MoD was its access to Vickers data and systems. The Barrow technical departments never refused WDSL's requests for data. They were simply ignored. Where there had to be co-operation, Barrow insisted that they must always be the leader and so we had weapons specialist ex-commanders RN with Cambridge degrees and 25 years experience in the design and operation of advanced systems in HM Ships, working under the day to day direction of blatantly less able people in Barrow. The General Manager in WDSL was John Wade the ex-deputy head of the Barrow Weapons Department and he strove manfully to reverse this situation but he was clearly no longer one of the elect. No matter what was done at Board level, at working level the Barrow offices just went on in the belief that the navy would always need them.

The MoD's experts were becoming more and more unhappy with the complacency of the British companies engaged in defence work and their universal assumption that they could sit back and wait for defence contracts to maintain their leisured tempo of work. Some years earlier, at the first Whale Island Naval Equipment Exhibition, a senior executive of VSEL had said to me that he didn't understand why they bothered with exports ' why not simply sit back and take the MoD's 5%'. In Ship Department we always saw a ship or submarine, its weapons and their control systems as one overall system. Lack of systems design innovation in submarines by our contractors was a matter of serious concern. By the late 1980's I was being told privately that DPT considered the position to be irreversible. One day in February 1988 I went to a meeting in a rather upmarket German army college in Hamburg at which the results of the NFR 90 Feasibility Study were presented to senior NATO naval and industry representatives. It was dark and snowing when we finished and I stood outside talking quietly with Bill Sanders, the MoD's Director General Submarines (DPT's new title) while we waited for transport to arrive. He told me that unless there was a quantum improvement in performance, the main contractor for the next submarine design could well be a weapons electronics company, not a shipbuilder. Late in 1995 it was announced that the prime contractual responsibility for the next nuclear submarine design would be GEC. Later, GEC acquired VSEL. My advice to the MoD would be to watch that the tail doesn't wag the dog.

Chapter Thirteen

I am sure that today the Great British Public has only a hazy notion of the vital role that the North Atlantic Treaty Organisation played in deterring Soviet aggression and what recollection it has is fading with the passage of time. The Soviet leadership was more evil and more bent on world domination by subversion and military conquest than Adolf Hitler ever was. NATO stood between them and the realisation of their aims. Like Marshal Aid, NATO was a supreme example of US enlightened self interest and without the massive US moral and material support, the efforts of the other participating nations of whom the UK was one of the leaders, would have come to nought.

One of the most intractable logistic problems that faced (and probably still faces) NATO commanders was lack of standardisation between the national forces. All nations agreed that standardisation of armaments was vital but clung on to its own weapons because 'it had just started development' etc. The USA was robust in its view that the standards to be used should be theirs, a not unreasonable view since they would contribute about half the total forces in an emergency, but other nations had different agendas with, one suspected, the prospect of sales to third parties in the back of their minds. Someone had the bright idea that since all of the major NATO navies had frigates in their long-term plans, there should be a 'NATO Frigate'. The frigate would be primarily an anti-submarine ship.

The NATO military staffs drew up an outline staff requirement in the most general terms and invited the industries of the nations to prepare a design, which would fill the requirement. Eleven nations took part in the Pre-Feasibility discussions, meeting usually in Brussels. The UK representatives were myself and Vice Admiral Sir Philip Watson from GEC. Philip had been Director General Weapons when I had been Director General Ships and we had long been used to working together. It was good to be visiting Brussels and NATO headquarters at Evere, again.

In NATO HQ some people seemed to have become fixtures by successfully moving from their national delegations to the permanent staff. Thus Canadian ex-Commander Bill Kinsman suddenly appeared in this new guise, conducting a visiting party of senior officers from the Canadian Defence College around Evere. This had a particular interest for me since the Commandant of the College, Major General Sam Davis, led the party. Sam had been a British naval constructor and had been in my term at the Royal Naval College, Greenwich. He had transferred to the Canadian Navy and had eventually become its Naval Constructor in Chief. When the Trudeau government had unified the Canadian forces, giving them all army ranks and the same uniform, the navy had resisted strongly. Rear Admiral Sam Davis had earned a certain opprobrium among his peers by being among the first naval officers to embrace the new order. This unification of identities was reversed in the mid 1980's and it was no longer so difficult to differentiate between a Captain(A), a Captain(AF) and a Captain(N).

Two additional pleasures about visiting Brussels were that I could now afford to stay at the Royal Windsor Hotel and I could occasionally take Liz with me and help her renew her childhood acquaintance with the Grand Place, the Manekin Pis and other delights of the city as well as Bruges and Antwerp. It was at the time when some idiot had invented nouveau cuisine and we found that the microscopic dinner at the Royal Windsor was so unsatisfying that we went to a nearby cafe for a second meal and ate out thereafter. One evening I proudly took Liz to the small seafood cafe that Commander Mel Hocken and I used to patronise in the 1960's. In those days the wooden tables and benches along the walls, the fish paintings that adorned those walls, the different smells and the cheap wine had a romance all of their own. It was still the same, same benches, same paintings, same smells but alas now 20 years older and seemingly untouched by human hand in the intervening period. Close to the door to the kitchen sat a man talking to a younger woman over a bottle of wine. Madame was in the kitchen dropping saucepans and tight lipped. When our burnt fish came we could have soled our shoes with it. By the time we gave up and left, Liz whose French is much better than mine, had worked out that the man was Madame's husband and that she had said openly as she passed them, that she was not best pleased at his dalliance while she did all the work.. Next morning we walked through the same narrow streets to see them in daylight and discovered that the younger woman owned the wine shop a few doors from Madame's cafe.

The Pre-feasibility Study concluded that the nations' requirements could be met in a common vessel of something over 4,000 tonnes and that there would be substantial cost savings by centralising the design work, procurement and administration for the multi-ship order. Rationalising the nations' timescales was a problem since the USN stated at the outset that it would not require a new ASW Frigate until something like the year 2,005 while most other nations wished to have their ships in service more than a decade earlier. Planning was for a 50-ship order of which the US would take about one-third with the other nations sharing the remainder according to what they could afford. The UK wanted 8.

Following the submission of our report on the Pre-feasibility Study, NATO agreed to fund a Feasibility Study. Eight nations who had requirements for ASW frigates would participate, Canada, France, Germany, Italy, Netherlands, Spain, UK and the USA.

The national industry members agreed to establish a company to undertake the study and a team from NATO discussed the potential sites to judge their suitability and commitment. The British companies whom I had urged forward, walked backwards from what could have been a nice little money-spinner and it was decided to locate the joint venture company, to be called the Internationale Schiffs Studien GmbH, in Hamburg.

The ISS GmbH would have a supervisory Board with one member per nation. The resident staff would be made up from people with the necessary skills drawn from the nations.

In the UK we had already set up an informal group of representatives of the major British electrical, engineering and equipment manufacturers and shipbuilders. It was agreed that British Shipbuilders would represent the UK formally and that as British Shipbuilder's Warship building Board member, I would join the ISS Board. There followed an intense period of negotiation by the new eight-man Board to agree the company structure, senior resident appointments, more junior staff positions and the general plan for the study.

Notwithstanding the high sounding rhetoric that could be advanced for building the hulls at one or two sites, the Board recognised that there was a wish by all nations to build their own ships. The more complex machinery, equipment and weapons might have to come from other nations but as long as most of the assembly and installation work would be done in a nation's shipyards, national pride would be satisfied - they had built the ship. Let us be honest, they had preserved their ability to build such ships for export customers should this one-day be allowed. Thus we took it for granted that each nation would build its own hulls.

Propulsion machinery manufacture was somewhat more limited. The USA and the UK had the major gas turbine developments, with other nations building variants under licence. There was a more varied number of suppliers of diesel engines, gearing, propeller shafts and propellers.

The major challenge would be in the field of electronics and weapons.

With eight participating nations it was essential that we should have a structure with eight senior management positions. There were four functional roles, Management, Ship, Weapons and Logistics and we agreed that there should be a leader and a deputy for each of these roles. Nations would have staff in each of the ship, weapons and logistics groups. It was my view that the best long-term benefit to British industry might come from taking the lead in the weapons and electronics field. The same idea had obviously occurred to the French.

Westinghouse had provided the US representation in Pre-feasibility. For the next phase, since US government funds would be involved, the privilege of representing the USA must be the subject of competition. One month passed, two months and finally we felt that we should go ahead with what we, the other seven nations, had agreed.

With great assistance from MTG and Blohm and Voss, the ISS was established in Hamburg and the following appointments made; Managing Director and Deputy - Canada and Italy; Ship - Germany and Spain; Weapons and electronics - France and UK; Logistics - Netherlands and USA.

A good month or so later, Westinghouse were appointed to represent the USA and their Board member Bernie Harris arrived and said he would like us to meet Bob Johnson "the new ISS Managing Director". We told him that he should have read his mail, we already had a Managing Director, Earl Barondes from Canada, and so on and his man would be the deputy Logistics manager. This was clearly news to Bob Johnson, whom I had known and much respected when he was associated with the preliminary design group of the old Bureau of Ships in the US Navy Department. In the end the position was accepted and actually turned out quite well because people were pleased to consult and accept advice from Bob's wide experience of ship design and in logistics.

The British senior resident as deputy weapons manager was Joe Morris from British Aerospace, Bristol. He did an excellent job supported by a dozen or so chaps spread among the three groups. It was the responsibility of firms in the UK to ensure that the people in Hamburg had information on the expertise and products that they had to offer. We all provided a channel into the ISS for such material.

The ISS Board were an impressive group who worked freely for the common task. The Chairman was Dr Rocham from Blohm and Voss and I was the Deputy Chairman. In those days there was tremendous good will towards Britain. I doubt whether it would be so today.

Although they never gave a reason, the USN brought forward the required in-service date for their next anti-submarine frigate. I suspected that it might have something to do with the severe cracking being experienced in their FFG 7 Class ships. The Germans were keen because they must order some ships soon.

The plan upon which we settled was to design a basic common ship and outfit for which a centralised design and procurement organisation would purchase 50 ship sets of all common items on behalf of the eight nations building the ships and lesser numbers for those parts where individual nations had introduced variants. In theory cost sharing would be on the basis that no currency should change hands. Thus the nation building 5 ships out of 50 would receive equipment orders to the value of 10% of the total common equipment value, adjusted as necessary for any departures by that nation from the common base ship equipment fit. Where nations wished to depart from commonality the basic design would be configured to allow this. Most nations opted for a 5-inch calibre gun modelled on the USN version. The UK wished to stick with its 4.5-inch gun, which at that time fired a heavier projectile, further, than did the USN 5-inch gun. The UK would also fit Rolls Royce gas turbines as we hoped would some of the other nations whereas the US would fit the LM 2,500 engine.

In preparing the design we had to agree the standards to be used for such things as stability, strength, accommodation, protection, powering and so on. Thanks to the frequent exchanges of information between the nations through such bodies as the Hydrodynamics Symposia, the Ship Structures Committees, the ASME publications and other Societies there was already much commonality and no conflict in agreeing what to use. The USN standards always tended towards producing a bigger ship than at first required by the European navies, a not unexpected situation. The USN also required a slightly larger crew; I felt that they had the more realistic approach and had no problem with a marginally larger ship because initial hull costs are so small and I had not yet met a ship design that we had not wished it had been bigger when we came to updating it at mid-life to meet the updated enemy threat.

An interesting difference concerned the ships structure. USN practice for the hull required thicker hull plating supported by more widely spaced transverse frames than adopted in European designs. This would lead to a slightly heavier hull but with some secondary benefits. The logic was that welding the thicker hull plating to wider spaced frames would take less man-hours than welding thinner plating to more closely arranged frames with an additional bonus of clearer space inboard. Furthermore, the argument went, since the plating keeps the water out, why not put the available weight in plating and resisting damage and corrosion.

I was most impressed with Hamburg and the careful restoration of its buildings. It stretches out along both banks of the Elbe and is perhaps the most cosmopolitan city in Germany, beautifully restored after devastating bombing in the war. Lakes and parks are lovingly maintained and used by the citizens. They are not without superstition; they believed that it was lucky to touch the bronze statue of a young Adonis situated beside the Binnen Alster and so he stood, a testimony to superstition, green with verdigris with a bright shiny penis. My one objection to the citizens of Hamburg was that everyone spoke English. I would walk into a hotel or shop or restaurant and say something (in flawless German?) and they would invariably reply in English.

A small incident that bolstered my spirits arose from a visit one day to Dr Rocham at the Blohm and Voss shipyard where there was, and I hope still is, a truly splendid model of the battleship Tirpitz in the foyer. I bent and gazed along the hull and my thoughts went back to 1942 and the Royal Naval College. Part of the final qualifying examination for naval constructors was the preparation of a design of a major warship. We worked in pairs. Constructor Lieutenant Raymond Hawkes and I designed a 40,000-ton battleship.

Put crudely, a battleship consists of some big guns forward and aft with magazines beneath them and machinery spaces amidships. An upside down armoured box covers the magazines and machinery spaces for protection against shells and bombs and air/fuel/water tanks are arranged below the waterline along the extent of the armoured hull to provide protection against torpedoes and mines. Around this, of course is the streamlined hull. A most difficult thing is to arrange sufficient width of ship abreast the forward magazine for the 'sandwich' underwater protection in a ship of the required size (and cost) without the forward bottom corners abreast the forward magazine wanting to stick out through the sides of the ship's streamlined hull shape. Ours did by something less than a metre on each side of the ship.

The classical solution would be to make the ship longer forward and beamier, thus substantially increasing its size. Our solution was to cover this corner on both sides of the ship with a streamlined bulge moulded into the ships hull form. Our Professor whom earlier generations had nicknamed "Pinhead" did not disappoint us; he recoiled in horror and vetoed the whole idea. "What would the Admiralty's Battleship Section say.? "

40 years later I bent and looked along the underwater form of *Tirpitz* and saw that exactly abreast the forward lower corners of "A" magazine, her hull had a small streamlined bulge port and starboard, just as Hawkes and I had proposed. Clever chaps these Germans.

There was a well rehearsed story that had obviously improved with the telling that some years before the 1939 war, Constructor Lieutenants Vincent and Penfold had fallen-out over some technical matter early-on in this design exercise and had thereafter each designed separate ends of their ship, agreeing only on the shape and arrangement of the midships section where the two bits came together. When I was Lillicrap's aide after the war, I had assisted him in the difficult task of facilitating the resignation of Penfold from the Royal Corps, and, as a result, I had a deal of understanding for what John Vincent might have had to put up with in the legendary Vincent / Penfold battleship design.

Occasionally the ISS Board would meet in one or other of the nation's cities such as London, Paris, Madrid, Brussels and Genoa. The Brussels visit finished up in Paris. It was at a time of mounting industrial unrest in Belgium and Liz drove me there via the hovercraft from Ramsgate in Kent. We arrived at the Royal Windsor Hotel and found that the other members had arrived from Canada, the USA, Spain, Italy and the Netherlands, everyone except the German and French members. Late that evening Rockham phoned to say that he had spoken with the French member Michelle de Thomason by phone and suggested switching the meeting to Paris, the day after next. Michelle phoned me and said that due to the Paris Motor Show and the Hairdressing Show there was absolutely no room to be had in Paris. He gave me the address of the hotel that he had found some 20 km south of Paris and advised "stop at the first garage on the outskirts of Paris, buy a copy of Michelin Route Map Number so and so and take the R 20 South."

We drove south the next day. It was a lovely sunny day without too much traffic. In my childhood the battles and the hardship endured by the troops in Flanders in the 1914/1918 war were of recent memory and names like Cambrai, St Quentin, Somme were as familiar to me as the names of the towns of my native Kent. Memories came flooding back as we passed these places.

We bought our map and Liz joined the five or six lanes of vehicles driving clockwise round the peripherique. Flushed with success and relief we exited at the Porte de Italie and continued our way south. We missed the turning for Narcusis because we were up over the fly-over before we realised that we should have taken the slip road but we got there eventually by taking the next exit and driving north and then east. Our accommodation seemed to be in an old peoples home. Although we were grouped together in the dining room all the other diners were very old, dressed in black and many were being spoon fed by their attendants. All attempts at polite greeting were pointedly ignored. This insularity even extended to the room maids.

Michelle de Thomason had assured me that he would see that we arrived safely at the meeting to be held at Thomson CSF in the Bvd. Haussman. He arrived clad in black leathers and white helmet astride a huge motorcycle, looking every inch a cop. I hitched a lift with Joachim Coello, the Spanish member and off we went, three cars following our leader. Joachim's small hire car had difficulty keeping up as we sped past the science city and entered Paris. I began to notice policemen's friendly salutes as we passed. Miraculously we arrived at the Etoile ; there were three lanes of traffic; we swept past them and formed a fourth lane. Midst a lot of police whistling we moved off first and to our destination in Bvd Haussman. I already knew that Michelle's hobby was collecting old military motorcycles, which he said that he kept in a barn somewhere in the country. I now learned that Michelle was an adviser to the Paris Prefecture on motorcycle operations and had performed the same service for the Los Angeles PD. He clearly had influence where it mattered.

Joachim parked the car beneath the boulevard. The meeting finished at about 5.3Opm and the ever-willing Joachim went off to fetch the car while Canadian Captain Tom Maxwell and I settled down with a glass of beer in a pavement cafe. Half an hour later a worried Joachim returned to say that he couldn't find the car; it must have been stolen. Tom and I joined the search. I saw for the first time the remarkable engineering feat that had inserted six levels of underground car parking between the tall buildings of this famous street. We went along all six levels; no car. Then we decided to try the adjoining section some distance from our starting point and there, sure enough was the car.

Liz had had a terrible time. Although feeling ill she had been required to keep out of the room for most of the day and the only places to visit were the church and the village shop. Gone was our wish for a quiet weekend in Brussels—now Paris—and the next morning I took over the driving and drove my sick wife to Calais passing those same battlefields. The hovercraft people were splendid and were able to get us on the next flight.   To my horror as I drove confidently through the green channel on arrival at Dover, the customs officer waved me into a bay for inspection. I hadn't until that moment realised that the car smelt of cauliflower and I suspected that I had a bottle of gin too much; the one intended for the weekend. I said that Liz was not well. He put his head in the passenger window, took one look at her and waved us on our way.

We were both not surprised at our lost weekend. Before we were married we had been to a hotel in London for a sort of trial run and the place caught fire at 2 o'clock in the morning.

We held a Board meeting in Genoa. The approach path to landing was parallel to the coastal hills and passed over the shipyard in which I could see four frigates and a small aircraft carrier. The four frigates were the order for Iraq that we in British Shipbuilders had been prevented from tendering for by the government. Anyway, there they were, completed and unable to be delivered because of the Iran - Iraq war. But I was sure that Fincantieri had been paid most of the cost already as we had been for the other sides, *Kharg*.

The visit to Genoa was noteworthy for two things, the hospitality of our hosts from Fincantiari and the visit to their shipyard at Riva Trigoso. In Genoa we were entertained to lunch and dinner in the same restaurant on both days. All of the meals were pasta, pasta in the soup, pasta main course, pasta dessert and pasta savoury. The only concession to vegetables was that some of the pasta was green. The food was excellent but I wondered how my good looking and healthy Italian friends got their vitamins. That's all by the by because the really unique thing was that all the walls of the restaurant were totally covered by black on white posters and pictures of Frank Sinatra. Frank Sinatra laughing, Frank Sinatra singing, Frank Sinatra sitting, Frank Sinatra standing and things that he had said. It seemed that he had visited the place several times and had praised the food. These quotes were big on the posters in English. Whether Sinatra could speak Italian, I don't know, but the quotes were in English.   A restaurant must be sure that people understand the nice things that are said about it, thus confounding the oft-quoted notion that there is no such thing as bad publicity and I wondered if they had an Italian set. I found the overall effect of wall-to-wall Sinatra somewhat claustrophobic.

I do not remember much about the Riva Trigoso shipyard except that to launch a ship the launching ways had to be brought out of the yard and laid across the sandy, public beach. With a modest average rise and fall of the tide I rather wondered how they managed it, but obviously they did. The thing that I remember was the car journey there and back. We were driven at breakneck speed along a road cut half way up the side of the coastal mountains; one minute we were in bright sunshine traversing a bridge spanning a cleft in the rocks next we were in the darkness of a tunnel only to hurl out across another ravine at about ninety miles an hour with the driver (who had been to America) turning round to make some friendly comment in fractured English. I am sure that road is a civil engineering marvel but those who use it take the expression 'the quick and the dead' a bit too literally.

On the return journey I detected a change in the engine tempo and opened my eyes to find that we had left the autostrada and were driving into a small town. We went to the cobbled waterfront. The water was calm, old houses piled high with windows came down to the quay and motor boats put-putted out into the bigger bay beyond. The scene that we observed I have seen many times since in tourist brochures, for this was Portofino. On that late afternoon it was somewhat lost on all the non-Italian visitors as we tottered, shaken, from cars which seemed to be driven by descendants of Fangio. How calm an earlier visit to Rome had seemed in comparison. Mind you, the traffic outside our hotel was so congested that it scarcely moved at all, but each vehicle sounded its horn. Rome is a city one cannot forget; the truly eternal city.

Our Spanish hosts for the Board meeting in Madrid did us the slight disservice of putting us in an hotel close to the Empressa National Bazan building in which the meeting was held. Thus it was possible to do the normal businessman's visit routine of not seeing anything of the city other than the airport and the hotel. I cannot visit or fly over Spain without being impressed once again at how vast the country is and how civilised Spanish-cum-Moorish society and architecture was much more than a thousand years ago and still endures today. I was reminded of a different sort of antiquity in a small way when I was presented with a Bazan necktie, which features small golden galleons on a navy blue background. I remarked on the galleons and was told "Oh yes, we are an old firm. We built the galleons of the Spanish Armada that fought Sir Francis Drake". Before the Thatcher regime, the British Royal Dockyards provided the same sort of longevity and tradition through the centuries.

Work progressed on the design of the NFR 90. The equipment to be fitted for the ship's principal role, anti-submarine warfare was relatively easily defined as the best possible hull mounted sonar, two dual role helicopters and tube-launched target seeking torpedoes. Variable depth sonar would be fitted as required. The big problem was the selection of the air defensive capability; what scale of air or surface launched missile attack should the ship be capable of combating without serious damage and to what extent should we rely on the successful development of advanced radar and missile systems still in the research phase'?

This led to our confrontation with the NATO scientists. We said that in our ranks and in the companies represented on the NFR 90 frigate project we had the capability to manage the development of the advanced anti-air system required and still meet the NFR 90 timescale. Our weapons group naturally had much knowledge of what was already going ahead in this field in the eight nations and were a long way down the road in specifying the system.

The Chairman, the Managing Director and the weapons managers went to Brussels several times to present our findings and seek authority and finance to develop an autonomous defensive system. NATO HQ agreed that such a system was required but that it must be developed by that part of NATO responsible for such things and they would start from the very beginning of the procedural chain with discussions by the military staffs followed by discussions with industry then perhaps a pre-feasibility study followed by a feasibility study... We pointed out that by the time that collection of experts had finished, the NFR 90 ships could well have completed their life and been scrapped - but other threats to the NFR 90 were developing.

The ISS Gmbh design was thoroughly researched and presented: a frigate well able to meet the NATO Staff Requirement and capable of meeting future developments in AS warfare. Centralised detailed design and procurement for the proposed batch of 50 ships would show substantial cost savings. There were, of course, problems ahead in realising these cost savings. Take, for example a nation that had 10% of the material supply and manufactured a diesel engine, gear box and some electronics that would meet the NFR 90 requirements and cost close to the 10% Sounds fine but what if another of the nations decides for politico-industrial reasons that it must use its own manufactured diesel engine or, in the case of the USA, that under the law, there must be set up a second production source in the USA in which the engine would be built under licence for the US Navy's ships. And what about the nation whose industrial share value could only be made up by supplying a piece of equipment that is adequate but known to be inferior to similar equipments available from the other seven nations?. There is a limit to the extent to which things like paint and floor coverings and non-engineering items could be substituted to make up the required value. The other members of the ISS Board could see the same difficult choices and deals having to be made in the near future but agreed that this should not be allowed to deflect nations from the eventual benefits that commonality would bring to the NATO naval forces.

I advanced the view that wherever possible each nation's product share value should be divided equally between ship and weapons / electronics items, to preserve the nations industrial capability. Thus a nation taking 8 ships and hence a 16% value share should be allowed to provide 8%. Ships mechanical, electrical and equipment items and 8% Weapons / electronics items. For good reason I was concerned about the UK's ability to win an appropriate share of weapons / electronics items in a free-for-all.

Proposals were made for the next phase. The same nations would participate. Proposals were invited for a suitable location for the joint venture company to undertake this more extensive phase. Such location would be in or near to a sizeable city with modern housing and schools, able to be made secure and served by an international airport. Three suitable sites in southern England were nominated in association with companies and brochures prepared. Other nations did the same and a NATO team visited all of them ; but the game had really been lost years earlier when Hamburg had been chosen as the home for the pre-feasibility study. Hamburg offered two sites, one of which was an unused secondary school with a big fence around it and Hamburg was selected. When it was all decided this school was withdrawn for some reason but Hamburg remained the choice.

UK companies felt that the emphasis in the new ISS should move towards the weapons / electronics companies and that representation on the Board should be by British Aerospace. I was no longer British Shipbuilders and now with VSEL. I was asked if I would like to join British Aerospace for this purpose and declined. They took the lead in setting up the British end with great gusto and I formed a considerable respect for the work of their commercial people in setting up the British joint venture company. For planning purposes we named it "Fred"; eventually it became "Supermarine."

Dr Rocham and I resigned from the ISS Board on the same day and Michelle de Thomason took over.

The approach to the NFR 90 studies in which we had participated had demonstrated remarkable collaboration between the industries of the eight nations.

Problems would doubtless emerge in the next phase but the ground rules that we had attempted to establish should allow these to be resolved without bloodshed. One could not be unaware, however, that officials within the nations' Ministries of Defence were already chipping away at the concept and had already made parallel studies to demonstrate their concepts and orders of cost. Officials were sensible enough to realise that going it alone was no longer politically correct and so groups were being formed. One could but not suspect, however, that there was a certain element of 'not invented here'.

In due course we were shown typical cross sections of some UK / French / Dutch proposals which were claimed to be considerably cheaper than the NFR 90. I was surprised that such could have been agreed by officers of an organisation of which I was once the Head. Wafer thin hulls designed by computer with seemingly no awareness of what actually happens to ships in service, the unavoidable bumps alongside a jetty in a gale, the water barge driven by a madman in Port Said or the progressive effects of corrosion. The steel hull is the one part of the design that must last the full 25 years life of the ship and is, ton for ton, the cheapest part of the design; it costs about 10% of the total ship cost. My instruction would always be go for a big robust hull. The Germans, Spanish and the US understood the reasons why the NFR 90 design was bigger in size and more robust than earlier European standards would produce, and stood firm.

I wondered at the time whether the UK MoD was aware that one of the collaborators was already playing footsy with the Italians.

Subsequent to the NFR 90 studies the US Navsea Command and the UK Sea Systems Controllerate made joint studies of a frigate to meet a given set of military requirements using US design criteria and then UK design criteria to investigate and explain the reason why the US design was bigger. The results were reported in a paper to the SNAME in 1991 and included a comparison of the US study, the multinational baseline NFR 90, the USN variant and an 'all American equipment' variant of the NFR 90. Again, I find the US Navy's arguments compelling. All the designs featured a steel superstructure.

The successor company to the original ISS Gmbh never got off the ground. Nations expressed their misgivings about the cost and withdrew from the project. The NFR 90 was shelved

It should be a matter of concern that the UK is gradually losing its collective experience in real ship design, that is, designing ships of all sizes and types for the long haul with the minimum of maintenance. When I joined the Royal Corps we were designing and ordering four cruisers and eight destroyers each year plus submarines, aircraft carriers and some battleships building and these ships were being designed and built by officers who had actually been responsible for the construction and in-service maintenance of similar earlier classes in the Dockyards and in Industry. And had served in such ships in the Fleet. With today's much smaller navy it surely should be the aim to maintain this overall balance instead of sweeping it all away in pursuit of imaginary economies. I wonder for how long the loyal band of constructors and naval engineering and weapons engineering specialists in the MoD will be able to keep the flag flying? On past performance, to rely on British industry for innovation and significant investment in future systems could prove disastrous to the forces and to British exports.

Chapter Fourteen

If corruption is a custom, it is no longer corruption since everyone starts equal. It becomes merely a national trait, which you must learn about, like learning the local language. - Derek Jewell

In 1996 the result of a survey to determine which were the most corrupt nations was published. Nigeria headed the list followed by Pakistan, Uganda and Kenya. Is it significant that all four of the worst offenders are members of the Commonwealth or was it simply that those conducting the survey only spoke and wrote in English?

The success of British companies in obtaining export orders for warships was always a mixed blessing to us in the Ministry of Defence design and production business. Where the overseas customer was buying ships that we had designed, there was quiet satisfaction at their good sense. Where they were buying ships to a non-ministry design we hoped that they would not bring us their problems. Nationally, as a manufacturing nation, it had to be good to export high value things like submarines and surface warships to friendly navies but it did present problems with security and priorities.

The security problem was most severe at Messers Vickers, Barrow where we were building nuclear submarines and where any breech of security could be of concern to Admiral Rickover's organisation as well as our own. During the construction of our first nuclear submarine, HMS *Dreadnought*, there were two security breeches, one of which was a joke and the other more serious. The part of the sub-dock where she was being fitted out was fenced off and access was only possible by passing through a check point where one's special identity card was checked and exchanged for a separate badge that had to be worn and checked by a separate guard before access on board was allowed. At night there were watchmen on the submarines deck.

One grey morning it was found that someone had rowed or swum across the dock and painted RAG in huge red letters on the side of the submarine. This coincided with Rag Week at Manchester University and the son of one of the Vickers directors who was a student at the time was given some attention. We pointed out to the firm that employing octogenarian ex-employees as watchmen must cease, they should not be more than 70.

The second breech was more serious. Although passage through the 'tunnel' above the nuclear reactor that connected the fore end of the submarine to the after end was permitted, access to the actual reactor compartment was prohibited to all except those with very special security clearance and passes to match. Lingering in the tunnel was also banned. One night one of the nightshift challenged a stranger he found in the tunnel and it turned out to be a sailor from one of the three small submarines of German design that Vickers was building for Israel, and which were afloat nearby. The sailor acted a little tipsy and appeared to have little or no English language. He was marched off the boat by the Vickers security people who then too promptly sent for his commanding officer. The C.O. undertook "to see that Able Seaman Zin Zin was severely punished and thus avoid the unwelcome publicity that action by the UK Authorities would bring". He was placed in the custody of his C.O. By the time that we in Bath were alerted to the situation the sailor had already left Barrow 'in disgrace'. He was probably spirited back to Israel (in a crate?) that day.

Reviewing the evidence, he had clearly got on board from the seaward side and had help in so doing. We found that the firm's watchman who was there to keep an eye on the floodlit topsides always went ashore for a cup of tea with the gate security men at the same time each night and careful observation from the Israeli submarine could have established this pattern. However since the alert workman who had challenged the intruder had passed the watchman as he came ashore we were confident that the Israeli sailor could not have been on board for more than a few minutes and had not entered the reactor compartment.

Of course, at the time, we had no idea that Israel was hell-bent on becoming a nuclear power, that France was providing the know-how and that under a contract signed in 1957,French contractors had been for some years, building a heavy water moderated reactor and giant underground chemical reprocessing plant at Dimona in the Negev, a few miles north of Beersheba to provide weapons grade plutonium for bombs. The whole installation was a copy of the French plant at Marcoule in the construction of which Israeli scientists and engineers had assisted their French colleagues. The most elaborate stratagems were used to conceal what was going on and to obtain secret data from the US and Britain. The first French bomb detonated in February 1960 at the test site at Reggane in Algeria with a yield of 60 kilotons was a copy of a US weapon. So one cannot be certain whether Able seaman Zin Zin was an acute embarrassment to the Israeli authorities or was Professor Zin Zin doing his bit for the Mossad.

These small German designed submarines were to us an example of the un-maintainable submarine. Their equipment was built-in so tightly that even normal operation was difficult and upkeep to our standards nearly impossible. We were already familiar with some of the short- comings of the early post-war German designs because overseas navies would consult us about their problems. I recall a main motor ventilation problem from Argentina, noise from Peru and much ado from much nearer home. The Germans were at that time prohibited from building large submarines and navies wanting large, ocean-going boats bought the British Oberon Class. As members of the NATO alliance, the German IKL organisation, led by the dour Professor Gabler, lobbied assiduously to have the displacement restriction raised and to obtain access to British experimental work on the shock resistance of submarine structures and equipment. Since IKL were located in Lubeck on the border with communist East Germany, we were concerned at the security implications.

Of the Oberon Class, Canada purchased three, built in the naval dockyard at Chatham, Chile two, built by Scot Lithgows, Brazil three, built by Vickers Shipbuilders and Australia six built by Scot Lithgows.

There were two disasters during the construction of these vessels, both the result of quality or procedure failures by British companies. Both of the countries affected have gone elsewhere for their subsequent submarine acquisitions.

The Australian navy had insisted that the contracts for their submarines should be placed by the British Ministry of Defence and covered by back-to-back contracts between the British and Australian governments. The British were most reluctant to enter into such an arrangement but the Australians were insistent and the contracts were arranged on this basis. In the last of the submarines, Scot Lithgow found evidence of cable deterioration while building and told the overseers. They alerted their MoD colleagues at the cable works who quickly examined the firm's records of materials used in the manufacture and found that they were not in accordance with the specification. We were then alerted to the problem in Bath. There was no alternative to replacing the cable and hundreds of metres of defective cable had to be stripped out of the submarines and replaced, causing great delay in the vessels completion and at a cost of several millions of pounds. We did all that we could to reduce the consequences of this colossal lapse in quality control on the part of one of the UK's major cable companies but the UK Treasury was adamant that this was a matter for the Australians to resolve with the companies. Their subsequent experience with the Patrol Craft Fremantle being built by Brooke Marine would have reinforced the Australian view that British industry had lost its way.

Some years later the Australian government received several million pounds in settlement from the cable manufacturer but the damage was done, my Australian friends told me that Australia would never again buy a British submarine and so it has been. In 1979 they decided to buy German submarines and tripped themselves up through the perceived closeness of some of their officers to the German contractor, resulting in the purchase of a Swedish design. This is recounted in another chapter.

The Brazilian navy's second submarine *Tonelero* was within a few weeks of final completion at Vickers, Barrow when the Control Room centre section of the vessel was destroyed in a disastrous fire during a night shift. The enquiry established that this was the result of two failures on the part of employees to follow the company's set procedures. In commissioning these extensive and complex systems it is essential to keep a rigorous control over their status at all times and to monitor this control from a central location on board. The most obvious situation would be to avoid pressure being applied to a piece of system from which a big or small fitting had been removed. If a component is removed it is tagged and the tag placed in the central location where the tag would remain until the fitting was made good. The first failure in procedure concerned a small fitting removed from or otherwise compromised in a hydraulic system in the submarine's control room. The second failure to follow procedure concerned a fireman. A welder was to weld some small brackets at the crown of the pressure hull and in accordance with procedure a fireman was present with an extinguisher and other safety equipment. The welder asked the fireman to hold a screen to prevent spatter from his welding hitting valuable equipment and the fireman put down his fire-fighting gear to 'do something useful'. At about this time someone elsewhere did something that put pressure on the hydraulic system in the control room and an atomised spray of hydraulic oil was ignited by the welder's arc. This instant blow torch was between the fireman and his equipment and all was lost; by the time the supply of hydraulic fluid was stopped the control room was well alight and flames emerging from the conning tower were soon illuminating the Barrow night sky.

Although the contract was between Vickers and the Brazilians, the latter paid for oversight by the M.o.D. and, of course we were the design authority upon whom the Brazilian navy relied. The hulls of this class are made of heat treated steel and I told Vickers that I considered that the high temperature could have affected the qualities of the pressure hull steel and also distorted its shape from the true circle; most obviously from the fact that the bottom part was in water and the top part in the air during the fire. I told the firms Managing Director, that in these circumstances it was my view that the entire centre section of the hull - about 20 metres -would have to be renewed and that I had so informed the Brazilian Naval Representative in Europe.

I had much else to do and was surprised many weeks later to find the firm trying to make the hull circular by means of a forest of chains with turnbuckles stretched between welded cleats. The situation would have been farcical if it wasn't so serious. I pointed out that the forces necessary were hundreds of tons and then could not be relied upon not to produce lobes elsewhere and in any case, as the Brazilian Navy's advisers we would not allow them to accept the submarine with the present centre section.

After many months, during which, I suppose, they were busy with their insurers, the firm contracted with Chatham Dockyard for them to build a new centre section, which was then substituted for the fire-damaged section in a dock at Chatham. *Tonelero* was then towed back to Barrow for completion. She was expected to be commissioned into the

Brazilian navy in the summer of 1974; she was actually commissioned in December 1977 having been passed by the third ship of the batch.

Although all was sweetness and light on the surface, the Head of the Brazilian Naval Commission in Europe expressed to me his amazement at the lack of urgency in the way in which Vickers had dealt with his submarine. He felt that they didn't care because they were covered by insurance, but the Brazilian navy did care, it had to bear the cost of keeping people in Britain and the costs of late delivery. Subsequent orders for submarines for Brazil went to Germany.

The most successful British firm in obtaining orders for warships for overseas navies was Vosper-Thornycroft. From a small beginning with motor torpedo boats and the like the firm moved upmarket culminating in the construction of their Mark 5 frigates for Iran (shared with Vickers) and the larger Niteroi Class frigates for Brazil, backed by a fairly constant stream of orders for fast patrol ships of about 50 metres length for Egypt, Oman and other navies.

Throughout my career I was a fairly frequent visitor to the many navy related establishments in the Portsmouth area. The journey was usually made by road and prior to the construction of the M27 Motorway involved passing through delightful Wiltshire and Hampshire villages and usually, the outskirts of Southampton. Part of the Southampton route was past some rather nice secluded houses with landscaped gardens, which I came to learn were owned by retired sea captains, pursers and marine superintendents. Since the latter were ex-chief engineers and surveyors whose life-time salaries would have been much the same as the navy, I thought it a bit odd but did not accept the commonly held navy view that much of this affluence must have come from people like bunkering agents, ship-repairers, and chandlers keen to obtain orders. Some were thought to be less than honest. Years later, as a member of British Shipbuilders Board I found that this was a not unreasonable supposition. But these were merchant ship people; Warship business was different. Or was it?

I was not really aware of what went on in the murky world of armament export sales until I became the Director General Ships responsible for all British warship procurement and started to take a greater interest in the global scene and had more contact with the Defence Sales Organisation. We were concerned with the loading of shipyards ; orders for the RN would not keep six warship building yards going and we welcomed orders for export. However we did not want to find the RN pushed to the back of the queue because of export penalty clauses. We favoured overseas navies buying equipment developed for the RN since this spread the cost of development over a greater number of units.

There was much interest in sales for Iran. The Shah was embarked on the creation of a deep-water navy to operate in the Indian Ocean as a counter to the Indian navy, which was becoming more and more Soviet equipped and orientated. The bulk of his fleet was being built in the UK and in the USA and parallel programmes for the Iranian army and air force were also in being. The naval programme included the creation of a modern naval base, dockyard and support complex at Bandar Abbas in which work British and German companies were associated, among others. According to the people in Defence Sales, it was accepted that senior Iranian officers should be rewarded by the successful bidder (and often by the unsuccessful bidders). The Shah knew that this went on and accepted the situation provided that something like 10% of the kickback was paid into a fund organised by his wife to be used for charitable purposes with the poor. The Shah and his Empress were genuinely concerned to spread the ownership of land and other benefits more widely. Woe betides him who was suspected of cheating on payments to the Farah Fund. One day, a member of the MoD Defence Sales organisation was sitting in the navy C in C's outer office when in marched the army Chief of the General Staff and a squad of soldiers. Half an hour later they emerged escorting an ashen-faced C in C who had been stripped of his badges of rank. Our social contacts in Teheran provided two stories.

The Shah had recently celebrated 2,000 years of his dynasty with a brilliant display of wealth typified by the number of pavilions in the palace grounds. Some time later the captain responsible for the construction of the naval base and dockyard at Bandar Abbas had been promoted to Rear Admiral and had thrown the-party-to-end-all-parties. Silly fellow had more and bigger pavilions than the Shah had had. The Shah had decided that the Navy should be taught a lesson.

The second story, the straw that broke the camels back was much more personal. It was said that the Empress had been in Paris and had fallen in love with a diamond necklace in Cartiers. Its cost was more than her daily jewellery purchase allowance and so she had gone back to the embassy and telephoned the Shah who had said the equivalent of "If you still want it tomorrow, buy it". When she went back to the shop she found that someone else had bought it. She was furious and refused absolutely the idea that they should get her a copy. Some months later at a glittering reception in the palace the Shah and his Empress received the members of the court formally. As the C in C of the navy bowed low and his wife curtsied Farah saw "her" necklace around Admiral Attei's wife's neck. The rest is history.

In the late 1970's UK firms were building some large landing ships and a large replenishment ship for Iran. A particularly stringent contractual requirement for the landing ships at Yarrows was their ability to maintain their course for considerable distances when going astern, a difficult design and seamanship requirement in these rather square ships with only one propeller. This requirement was to enable them to operate safely in the narrow Shat el Arab that separates Iran from Iraq. Extensive model tests were made but when the first ship went on trials the ship handlers couldn't maintain a steady course astern. Changes were made but still they couldn't meet the astern requirement. British forces landing craft are operated by the Army's Royal Corps of Transport and this regiment had provided army advice on the design. Yarrows asked the army for advice and the major who commanded the unit with which Yarrows dealt came up to the Clyde and drove the Iranian ship astern straight and round corners with seemingly no trouble at all.

The MoD Defence Sales people had been very active in securing the order for the replenishment ship *Kharg*. It would be the largest ship in the Iranian navy and was ordered from Swan Hunters at Wallsend. As the date for the launch approached we learned that the wife of the Shah's brother would name her. The Iranians asked informally how the Queen intended to travel to Newcastle to accompany their Royal Highnesses. They were diplomatically told that all the members of the British Royal family had previous engagements. I understand that the wish list then went down through Admiral Mountbatten, the Prime Minister and the S of S for Defence. Even Dr John Gilbert would not be available, nor would the Controller of the Navy. I was told not to argue and to go to Swan Hunters and be Queen for the Day.

It was an experience that was at the same time impressive and entertaining. The launch was preceded by lunch at the Gosforth Park Hotel. I was ushered in and presented to Her Imperial Highness, a strikingly beautiful girl with blonde hair and blue eyes in a matching blue frock and to His Imperial Highness, a hulking brute of a man with the family features and a five o'clock shadow at 12 noon. All the Iranian ladies were uniformly beautiful and elegant. They all had mink coats; it was winter. A necessary item of jewellery seemed to be a gold ingot nestling near their cleavage on a gold chain. Careful covert observation (at the risk of being thought to be a dirty old man) showed that the ingot had a picture of the Shah on one side and a representation of Allah on the other. The significance of this emerged during the ceremonies.

We took lunch at a table arranged in an open square with flowers in the middle. I was opposite their royal highnesses and next to an elegant, charming Iranian lady in blue (I should have known, shouldn't I?) who told me that her husband had been the Iranian ambassador in Paris and in Washington DC. She asked me whether I had spoken with the princess and I said not really, other than the brief presentation on arrival. We spoke of other things. When we rose from the table my luncheon companion suddenly appeared leading the princess by the hand and said "You said that you would like to speak some more to my daughter". We spoke and in a few moments she was whisked away to her car. The motorcade formed up and we were away speeding eastwards and then south escorted by police outriders, across intersections where the police halted all traffic. The timing and traffic control by the police was superb.

We assembled on the launching platform. Like a jack-in-the-box the mufti appeared, clad in black with a black beard and black turban. Before the launch of the *Kharg* he was to bless the battle honours of the first landing ship built at Yarrows and present the ship's badge to its captain. Unfortunately the mufti had the badge for the first ship but called it the name of the second, and not yet completed, ship and despite the captains obviously acute embarrassment no one seemed able to stop him. When it was explained the mufti insisted on going through it again, with Swan Hunters looking anxiously at the tide and the depth of water at the head of the slip to check that it would still be safe to launch the *Kharg*. Then he proceeded with the *Kharg* launch.

According to Iranian law and custom the Shah was only a little bit less holy than Allah and each time the mufti said Allah during the dedication services, and this obviously was fairly frequent, he would add something like "and Shah il Shah" at which every uniformed Iranian officer present stood up and saluted. They were doing this more than twice a minute for about ten minutes. The British officers present didn't know what to do. Most of them stood up and saluted the first few times and then seeing that not everyone was doing it, desisted but one or two saw the whole course through. I suppose that really we should all have bobbed up and down. What the assembled workforce standing down below to witness the launch, thought of all the leaping up and down, I don't know. To the British it was hilarious and one was hard put to keep a straight face. Of course since I was representing Queen Victoria's descendants I had no trouble at all; I was not amused.

Actually, I remembered a pageant at Greenwich and wondered a bit about the stability of the launching platform. In brief, just before the war there had been a pageant in the grounds of the naval college at Greenwich. The College staff and families were invited to the dress rehearsal during which one of the stands swayed alarmingly when the audience stood for the national anthem. What should be done - there was no time to rebuild the thing. Professor Haigh was consulted. "Don't worry", he said. It seems that most people put their weight on their right foot when standing up and this gave a push to the right. His solution was not to strengthen the stand but to have the band introduce the national anthem with a long roll of increasing loudness on the drums to cause the audience to rise raggedly rather than all at once.

The final event of the *Kharg* launch day came at Newcastle airport. Somehow I was the first to board the BA flight followed in due course by many Iranian officers and their ladies, each of whom I discovered seemed to be carrying a spare mink coat in a plastic bag. Whether this was a precaution so that they could wear their old one in order not to upstage the princess, I don't know. Anyway the stewardesses could see the funny side of it as I helped them stow the No.2 mink coats on the racks and put the No.1 mink coats in the hanging locker. No one gave me their gold ingot to carry.

Within a year or two the Iranian scene had changed entirely; the Shah and his officers had been swept away and to a large extent killed and the new rulers were at pains to demonstrate their hatred for the western powers and in particular for the United States. In a further year or so they were at war with Iraq. Throughout this time the Iranian naval personnel in the UK behaved with dignity although they must have been appalled at some of the things that were happening and fearful for themselves and their families. There were two MoD advisers at Bandar Abbas ; they and their families and belongings were safely delivered to Bahrain one night by the Iranian navy.

Work proceeded on the *Kharg* and the Iranian government paid the instalments as they fell due. The ship was complete in 1981 when the UK government, in the person of my friend Mike Power (son of the Admiral on whose staff I had served in the Eastern Fleet in the war), informed British Shipbuilders that we would not be permitted to deliver the ship to Iran and that we should mothball her on the River Tyne. John Steele of Swans pointed out that moving *Kharg* to a secure deep-water berth and providing security and preservation would cost several hundreds of thousands of pounds and that we would expect the British government to meet these costs. The MoD then said that since the ship had not been accepted and the Iranians still owed about 10 or 11 million pounds, the question of costs was between British Shipbuilders and Iran. Mike had the grace to look embarrassed at this one. We spoke with the Iranian agent in London, we had no quarrel with his navy, the British government was trying to hide behind the outstanding instalment; the Iranians promptly paid up. The UK government finally agreed to meet Swans costs and *Kharg*, which already had its Iranian crew and was now flying the Iranian flag, was moved to a berth that had been prepared for her. The Iranian navy hauled down their colours in a simple ceremony and the crew marched off the ship with a dignity that impressed all present; to return to Iran and who knows what.

There was a final moment of high drama. The ship had been connected to shore power at the berth and the last thing that the Iranian engineer officer did was to switch off this shore supply. There were muffled explosions within the ship and momentarily it seemed that the crew had scuttled her as a final gesture of frustration but it was simply the ships emergency diesel generators starting up as they were programmed to do in the event of a loss of the ships main electrical supply.

I am reminded of a nice story about Admiral Power in retirement, which my informants swear is true. He had a high hedge, which he took a personal delight in keeping properly trimmed. He was slowly aware that the same old lady in her chauffeur driven car passed him each day that he was trimming the hedge. One day she stopped and addressed this aged bearded figure wearing old corduroy trousers up the ladder. "My man" she said " I have been admiring your work and I would like you to come and work for me. I will pay you £5 a week more than you are getting here". Sir A.J. entered into the spirit of the situation and replied in broad accents "Ah, yes Mum, but you sees I also gets me perks" "That's alright" said the old lady "I will give you those as well, what are they?" "Well, to start with, I gets to sleep with the lady of the house." The old lady got slowly back into her car and was driven away.

Vosper-Thornycroft and Yarrows had been given the responsibility for the design of the Royal Navy's Type 21 frigate and had received orders for three and five ships respectively. VT would prepare the detailed working drawings and build the class name-ship, HMS *Amazon*, while supplying drawings and other lead yard information to Yarrows on the basis of the arrangements proven in Amazon. Some time into the programme John Rix, the Managing Director of VT went into Whitehall and told the

Controller of the Navy, Admiral Griffin, that although VT were duty bound to complete HMS Amazon, the lead ship of the class, work on the other two ships would not proceed until after completion of the firm's order for four Niteroi Class frigates for Brazil. According to Admiral Griffin John Rix had said that VT saw their future very much in the export market and would not actively seek future orders for warships for the Royal Navy, in part because the ministry's experts interfered too much.

It will be noted that John Rix was playing the 'Controller of the Navy' ploy; if you want to get away with something tell the Controller, don't go near to the professional directors. Go to the Controller and say your piece, if you can get out of the door without the Controller saying "NO" very loudly, you've got away with it. Go ahead. When sometime later the people in Bath see that the programme is not on track, say that the Controller agreed.

In the case of the VT Type 21's Admiral Griffin passed on John Rix's intentions to me as if they were cut and dried and agreed. VT had told the navy that if they didn't like it they could lump it. This cost the British taxpayer tens of millions of pounds in due course.

Within two years VT were again in Whitehall soliciting orders for RN ships and in due course the order for HMS Southampton was placed with them.

Some years later when I joined the Board of British Shipbuilders the corridors were still buzzing with the events that had led to the decision to ask the Managing Director of Vickers Shipbuilders, Bill Richardson, to become, additionally, the MD of Vosper-Thornycroft following the retirement of John Rix. Rix had designated a marketing man as his successor and this man had promptly asked the British Shipbuilders Board for a 'slush fund' of several tens of millions pounds claiming that without it he would not be able to win further warship export orders for his company. The funds not being provided, he had gone. At about this time I saw a copy of a memo to Admiral Griffin telling him the commission paid to an agent in the near east in regard to a quite small order. It was over 20%. The agent was a cousin of the emir or sultan or sheik or whatever. I am absolutely sure that this was news to the BS Chairman. I also recalled that at an intimate dinner party for the Brazilian navy minister in 1977 in a country hotel near Southampton, I had been told laughingly by a Brazilian who had had a somewhat liquid evening that the reason the Minister had come personally was to make sure they had the right bank account numbers.

It is extremely sad that the excellence of the product is not of itself a sufficient reason for choosing it. In the spirit of the opening quote from David Jewell it is usually argued that the end justifies the means and when in Rome do as the Romans do. On the face of it, if an absolute ruler wishes to pay more than he really needs for a product in order that up to 20% might be kicked back to his relatives as fees, that's his business. Where that ruler is in receipt of overseas aid or has an impoverished population, the practice might be viewed differently. There is another factor; sometimes gifts are offered to the agent who is selling the goods, very substantial cash gifts where the order is large, provided that the contract is suitably arranged and so on.

Remember the theme; the purchaser pays more than he should in order that money might be returned to someone or something that he, the purchaser, desires. British governments court popularity by 'cutting the civil service'. The media is inspired to paint a picture of fat cat officials with guaranteed employment for life and inflation-proof pensions. Ministers talk of putting the work out to industry on the assumption that industry already has the specialized knowledge and capability to undertake the work. And the great British public swallows it.

Defence projects are obvious candidates for the treatment and the argument goes that of course industry must be expected to make a profit but they are so clever that this will still lead to financial economies, furthermore with no long term commitment to life employment for their staff. The reality is quite different. It should be remembered that doing things in house does not release the sort of funds that Ministers want; Ministers want to release funds to company boards and/or chief executives who will be aware of the desirability of making contributions to political party funds. Having announced the successful contractor, Ministers then come under pressure to guarantee the prospect of long employment to the sort of experts the companies must employ or poach from the civil service or armed forces. It is announced that Messers Bloggs will provide 20 years through life support for whatever system they are to produce. So nothing has really changed except that funds have been placed where political donations might be forthcoming. Why do you think that ex-ministers are given seats on company boards or, more usually, the institutions that will provide financial backing to those boards? It's not because they are clever!

There were at least three important export prospects occupying British Shipbuilders in 1979; the Canadian Patrol Frigate, the Australian Submarine and the Greek Frigate.

British Shipbuilders was a late entrant into the Canadian PF contest and never really got its act together in a way acceptable to the Canadian procurement system. There were many consortia seeking the order, BS had not entered the fray and was asked to do so by the Canadians, hence the late entry. Yarrows would be the design lead yard and we offered the Type 22 frigate, which would be modified to meet the Canadian armament and other requirements. For this BS simply offered the package of information similar to that which was usually offered to other nations, a statement of characteristics, a discussion of the operational requirements, general arrangement drawings, specifications, production schedules and procurement costs for UK and Canadian build. This would have been a splendid ship.

This offer had been forwarded prior to my joining BS. Discussion with Canadian friends indicated that we were ignorant of the Canadian procurement processes. Unbelievably to me, getting the process right was more important than the technology. We were expected to have a Canadian associate or partner, preferably one already in the defence field. We entered into a joint venture with the Canadian conglomerate Genstar Inc. headquartered in Montreal. This was at a time when the Quebec partitionists were very active and many companies were re-locating into upper Canada. Genstar moved their HQ to Vancouver but most of their staff to San Francisco. The joint venture would be styled GenShip; Nick Liberatore and James Byrne represented Genstar and I and Bob Easton, of Yarrows, represented British Shipbuilders.

There is no doubt that our ship would have been superior to that finally produced. Since our type ship was already in the water, the displacement and performance would have been fixed. We did our best to structure our bid in the manner required by the Canadian government agencies but we were singing off the wrong song-sheet, the Canadians were determined to do their own thing and lift their technology levels even if it eventually caused greater overall cost. We were eliminated. As provided for in the Canadian procurement system, Genship asked for a meeting at which officials would give reasons for our non-selection. It was evident that the Canadian team was simply going through the motions of having the meeting and the sooner that it was over the better. One of the reasons given for our non-selection was that we had not demonstrated that we had the financial resources to undertake the programme. I said that obviously they must know that we were a British government agency and Captain Ed Healey replied "Yes, we knew it but you didn't put it in writing in your submission".

The Canadian navy has got its patrol frigate; built in Saint Johns, New Brunswick. In purist naval architectural terms it's not the ship that they selected in preference to ours; you see it grew by about 1,000 tons (an almost unbelievable 20%) between the order and completion, which means that it's slower, has less freeboard and hence is wetter in rough seas, has less stability and survivability, the hull is more highly stressed and has much less scope for future updating. And it cost a whole lot more.

We were very active in our attempts to sell frigates to the Greek navy in 1979-80. As betokens a port in which every second person seemed to have a part share in a cargo ship of some sort, we had a resident agent, Nick Petmezas, who worked assiduously on our behalf. Yarrows was our lead yard for warship sales and already had an agent, a retired octogenarian Vice Admiral. The memory of the regime of the four colonels was still fresh in Greek minds and to have worked with them was a great disgrace as far as government preferment was concerned. The Yarrows admiral had worked closely with them and we were advised to distance ourselves from him. This Yarrows flatly refused to do. Bob Easton of Yarrows always became a dour and evasive Scotsman whenever the subject was mentioned and as far as I was concerned, knew the Greek scene better than I did at that time. I never met the man.

I was puzzled why the Greeks wanted frigates. They were building some fast and well-armed La Combatante Class craft of French design that seemed to me to be well fitted for operations in the Aegean Sea around the Greek islands. Frigates would simply be an expensive status symbol. To me NATO was the sure shield that enabled the free nations of Europe and North America (and the rest of civilised mankind) to sleep easily in their beds at night. From the North Cape of Norway to the eastern borders of Turkey, the NATO allies stood shoulder to shoulder, confronting some of the most hostile and oppressive regimes of the century in Russia and her satellites, or so I thought until I reached Athens, expecting them to be concerned, as we were, with the threat from the north. Not a bit of it; Greek defence policy in a nutshell was "don't bother us with silly things like the Bulgarians to the north, our eyes are firmly fixed on those bloody Turks to the east and that's why we need a navy; to stop them stealing our islands. Look what they did in Cyprus".

I was amused at the number of Greek ex-officers who offered their services as paid agents for British Shipbuilders. Each of them claimed to be a term-mate of the Chief of Naval Staff or to have a sister, cousin or niece who was the admiral's mistress. In the end I decided that they must all be in the chalet in Germany that, rumour had it, a previous occupant of the post had acquired as the result of the submarine contract. Some of these would-be agents were remarkably well informed, however. There were also the wealthy business men who held court at worn desks, dropping names of government ministers and officials to impress naive foreigners who would soon engage them as agents because of their supposed influence with ministers they had never met.

Not much has changed in the last 2,000 years. Although most of the Roman aristocracy admired the Greeks' achievements they mistrusted those whom they termed 'Greeklings'. Cicero expressed a fairly widely held view when he wrote "This I can say of the whole race of Greeks. I grant them literature; I grant them knowledge of many arts; I do not deny the charm of their speech, but 'truth' that nation has never cherished".

In the 1970's the Greeks had realised that there was money to be made in Defence Exhibitions. Posidonia was held in a large concrete building on the waterfront at Piraeus. The building was probably a shipping warehouse or a multi-story car park for the rest of the year. Rumour that Greece was about to order some new aircraft or guns or helicopters or ships would ensure a good attendance by exhibitors, agents, hangers-on and delegations from the near-east, Europe and further afield.

At the first Posidonia that I attended I met the Jollife's from Malta. They were full of criticism of the BS chief executive's behaviour at the previous exhibition. Mr Jollife was a shipbroker and had dealings with the BS Ship Repair Division. There had been considerable debate in official circles and in parliament as to whether ship-repair should be included in the shipbuilding nationalisation package; the outcome was an arrangement that only the British Department of Trade and Industry and its senior personnel could have dreamed up and / or allowed to exist. All of the ship repair yards above a given size were nationalised and a Mr. Butler appointed Managing Director. He was, however, allowed to keep his own yard on the River Tyne. Human nature being what it is, it doesn't take a genius to work out where the plum repair jobs went. Mr. Jollife was not enthusiastic about the BS Ship Repair Division because none of its managers except Mr Butler seemed to understand the way the shipping marine superintendents and chief engineers did business. "If I ring up one of your yards and say that a condition of getting such and such ship diverted to a British yard for docking and refit is that £ 10,000 should be paid into a numbered account in a Swiss bank, your people argue. The only man who says OK and pays the money is Mr Butler".

Remember those big houses outside Southampton in days long ago ?.

It was at Posidonia that I became conscious that I was always encountering one particular Tory Member of Parliament at exhibitions and conferences that had a maritime theme. I found that he was a member of the Conservative MP's Defence Committee and seemed to attend nearly every 'free-be' defence-related event in the world. He had developed to a science the art of silently hovering nearby, particularly when one was just going for a meal or getting a car back to the hotel, when naturally, he was pleased to join us. His behaviour was the same in the UK. John Parker, then the member for Merchant Shipbuilding and doubtless others received their share of cadging requests. Perhaps he had a slight twinge of conscience; one day he remarked to me that "He felt that he was justified in accepting hospitality from British Shipbuilders because we members of parliament sort of own you, don't we?" My wife did, however, decline to carry his bookcase across the length of Britain on the roof of her car and John Parker and I (and possibly others) feigned not to hear his more-than-vague hints that BS should provide him with help with his constituency typing. It might be of interest to know that the average MP makes four all-expenses paid fact finding trips abroad totalling 8,000 miles, each year.

It is perhaps worthy of note that when the question of MP's 'cash for questions' and other outside interests for which they received payment became a matter of public concern in 1995 and led to an enquiry by Lord Nolan, this member was very, very, high in the list of the number of paid consultancies held by MP's. What a contrast with people like Dr Jack Cunningham MP with whom I used to chat, usually on the train to Newcastle, open, frank and with no hidden agenda.

In 1980, a Labour MP would turn up for a function, have a drink or a meal as appropriate, chat with people and depart. Most of the Tory MP's that one had to entertain extracted all that they could from the situation. You were left in no doubt that they considered themselves to be Very Important People. Most would "only be able to spare the time" if they could be collected by car and taken somewhere afterwards. One occasion was Mr Wall MP who having flown to Barrow in Furness with his colleagues in our aircraft, asked to be taken by car to Brough. A reasonable enough request, we thought, since the small town is barely 30 miles away. But no, it wasn't Brough, Cumbria, it was Brough, Humberside, all of 200 miles away, and involved the overnight absence of the driver. It should be a matter of public concern that 20 years later, instead of the self discipline of their forebears, even Labour ministers and MP's now seem to see no shame in using the public purse for personal and family transport, accommodation and elaborate refurbishment of official suites and offices.

One Friday afternoon my secretary buzzed me to say that a member of parliament, a Mr Spicer, was demanding to speak with me. He wished to complain that he had just spoken with my Director of Marketing (Captain Ian Wright) and had not been treated with the respect to which he felt that he was entitled as a Member of Parliament. I am not aware of any Act or Statute that requires an MP outside the Palace of Westminster to be treated any differently than an ordinary citizen or to ignore the proper channels when seeking or giving information. Ministers and members of Select Committees, (on Committee business) yes, but not simple MP's. I forget the subject and Ian had given the answer anyway. I dealt with the man and during the exchange was reminded of Chapman Pincher's comment that "MP's suffer from an excess of vanity which leads most of them to assume that they have some special capability to govern". They quickly forget the definition of a democratic election 'where one chooses between one nondescript candidate and another in secret'

The Greek Navy wanted a new frigate. A Greek domiciled in London who claimed to be able to secure the order for Britain if we gave him £20 millions, presumably for distribution in Athens, plus 20% for himself visited British Shipbuilders. We explained on several occasions that we did not have access to such funds.

We endeavoured to interest the Greek navy in the new Type 24 frigate being designed by Ship Department and British Shipbuilders particularly for overseas navies which might prefer a more general-purpose ship than the RN's specialised anti-submarine designs. The Type 24 would have a gun, anti-surface and anti-aircraft missiles, torpedoes and helicopters but the Greeks wanted something cheaper.

The Greek Minister for Coordination, Mr. Mitsotakis, visited London early in the frigate selection process. His message for the British was that we 'were not offering enough money'. I had started to say "But I thought that you paid us" when the import of these words registered and I knew that no matter how good our ship might be, we would not obtain the Greek order. We weren't in the bribery business.

The contest was essentially between a modified British Type 21 and the Dutch Kortenaer. We were offering delivery in three years and the Greek navy; having got the promise of money in their hot little hands wanted it tomorrow. We asked the Royal Navy to surrender one of its ships and after a great deal of discussion this was agreed, provided that BS replaced the ship at no cost to the MoD. At the going rate of inflation this would have cost about twice the sum we would get from Greece and arguments that there should be some cross-ministries deal (for after all we were creating jobs weren't we?) fell on deaf governmental ears.

The Dutch had deliberately built a frigate surplus to their navy's requirements and could deliver it almost at once and so they got the order. I am sure that the Greek navy got a good warship from the Dutch, but pace Mitsotakis, I wonder how much they 'offered'. They have since sold three more ships of the class to Greece and I suppose that they got their money back that way.

In my term in the RNC Greenwich there had been two Greek naval constructor officers and one in the term ahead. I had also had some Greek students when I lectured there some years later on the resistance and propulsion of ships. One of my term-mates, Caldis was still active as the General Manager of the shipyard at Scaramanger, and one of the younger officers whom I had taught hydrodynamics was now a Rear Admiral at navy HQ. He never spoke or hinted at what might be going on in high places with the Dutch but he was distressed and it showed. These officers had great goodwill towards Britain but they could not carry the day in a basically corrupt system.

In our effort in Athens we were well supported by Ambassador Sutherland and his team, but traditional links and the right diplomatic climate were plainly not the dominant factors in the Greek decision making process.

A visit in May 1980 coincided with a British business mission to Greece, led by Lord Jellicoe. They kindly included Liz and I in most of their social events. On the first evening there was a big reception in the Embassy. Midst all the noise it seemed to me that there was a sudden hush and I turned round to see Liz gently collapsing to the floor, pouring gin and tonic down the front of her pale blue knitted suit in the process. Lady Parker, the wife of the chairman of British Rail and a doctor, was most attentive and we managed to convince her that it was simply too much sunshine and too little food that day that had caused Liz to faint and that she wasn't pregnant. At the time Liz had been speaking with the president of the bank of Egypt. He confessed that his descriptions of the wonders of ancient Egypt did not usually have that effect on young women.

The Greeks are charming people and made Liz welcome. One day she was in the Alafouzis' yacht off Athens in company with several members of Athens society including Marina, the Prime Minister's mistress. Liz and her hostess were dressed fairly informally but to Liz's surprise the other women came dripping with jewels and gold as if to a ball at the palace. If they had fallen overboard they would assuredly have sunk! Such occasions were good fun but we doubted whether the President wanted his mistress's opinions on frigates. We met the wives of lots of shipping magnates and the business community but we never met the admiral's wives.

I noticed that on visits to the embassy, Liz always seemed to carry a larger bag than usual and discovered that she was bringing out from the UK, pounds and pounds of mature cheddar cheese for the embassy wives and Branston pickle for the defence attaché.

Unfortunately the visit coincided with the election of a new President, Mr Karamanlis, the election of a new Prime Minister and substantial changes in ministerial positions, but Mr Averoff and Mr Avrimedes stayed at Defence. Mr Mitsotakis was made Foreign Minister. When I asked Greek friends the reasoning behind this appointment they said that this was the one job where he couldn't get his fingers in the till. He subsequently made Prime Minister.

The British - Greek Parliamentary group of MP's visited Greece at the very end of May. During a meeting with Mr Averoff he stated that our credit proposals were the best but our price was 20% above the other competitors. Could BS get its price down? Our problem, of course, was the high labour cost - not only in the shipyards but also in our equipment suppliers - because British industry employs too many semi-skilled and unskilled workpeople. But we tried, oh how we tried.

There are small recollections that we cherish, like sitting outside Athens airport in a taxi and saying "Hilton Hotel please" to an uncomprehending taxi driver. Being British we said it repeatedly and with increasing loudness, still with no effect until Liz had the wit to say "eelton otel" at which the driver beamed and off we went. We liked the 'eelton 'otel. Some of the early parties of Japanese tourists stayed there and were to be seen being marshalled about by their guides carrying little flags. We were there when the officers of a visiting British Leander Class frigate had a competition to see who could attract the most Japanese around him by the simple expedient of standing in a corner of the hotel foyer and holding a small coloured flag above his head. The winner got seven.

We are all only too aware of the 'towels on the poolside loungers before dawn' technique of German visitors but few are aware of a British habit that puzzled the Mediterranean hotel managers in the 1970's. Holidays for the 'over 60's' were popular at the time and the hotels found that these elderly visitors would quietly form a queue outside the restaurant half an hour before the appointed time for breakfast. If the time was 07.30am, the queue would form at 07.00. The managers reasoned that these elderly British guests wanted an early start and announced that breakfast would start at 07.00am ; the queues then formed at 06.30 so the managers gave up.

Athens was always a delight with the narrow shopping streets of the old city nestling beneath the Acropolis. Like the underpass on the main road to Piraeus there were no drains and when it rained hard the water would sweep around ones feet to the lowest level where presumably it quickly evaporated. The streets were arranged with all the shops selling one sort of goods grouped together, thus there was a street in which all the shops sold men's shirts, another with underwear, another with curtains and so on. On one occasion Liz asked me to bring back 35 metres of a certain patterned curtain material, 3 metres deep, from such and such shop from which she had obtained a sample on a previous visit. I found the shop, they had the material and I negotiated a small price reduction. Greek friends told me afterwards that I should not have done this - I who would never have done it except that I had been told that such negotiation was expected in Greece. But this was the least of my troubles. I emerged into the narrow street with a giant parcel that I could scarcely carry. No vehicles frequent the narrow streets so I staggered along to Syntagma - Constitution Square - where none of the taxis outside the Hotel Grande Bretagne had drivers. I moved out into the road a few times to attract attention of passing taxis but they simply ignored my parcel and me. I carried it all the way to the hotel. En route I was overtaken by a platoon of Evzone marching to change the guard at the palace. These are the soldiers in white ballet skirts, white tights and black, pompommed clogs who stand guard outside the presidential palace and at the tomb of the unknown soldier beneath the pink-washed old royal palace; now the seat of the Greek parliament. They have the physique of young giants and the loyalty, pride and fighting ability of the Brigade of Guards. Smile friend if you dare as they march past with the slow clump, clump, clump of their clogs.

This was not the end of the parcel saga because I had to attend a board meeting of the ISS GmbH in Hamburg before returning to London. It only just went into a large suitcase and accompanied me through the customs of Zurich and Hamburg airports en route.

One day when I called on the Chief of Naval Staff, Vice Admiral Konofaos, his flag lieutenant told me with some amusement that a delegation from the Chinese navy was due to call on the CNS the following day. The cause of amusement was his recollection that when the British cannot understand something they say that "its all Greek to them" and when the Greeks cannot understand something they say that "its all Chinese to them". He wondered whether the Chinese say "its all English to them". Charmingly put in faultless English.

A disquieting occurrence in the Greek saga came right at the end. In the first days in July 1980 I received an urgent and over-dramatic message from Hildrew in Lloyds about arranging secret meetings and from Sharpe in the Department of Trade & Industry more reasonably, suggesting that I should speak with a Greek, Mr Bekatoros at the Tower Hotel. I said that I knew ex-commander Bekatoros and had met with him at the Yacht Club in Piraeus as recently as the 2nd June. He had not approached British Shipbuilders but I would see him at his hotel. Mr Bekatoros mentioned his closeness to Admiral Konofaos and to Mr Averoff "because of his refusal to serve under the Colonels" and covered the earlier ground about agents. He mentioned the man who had visited BSHQ several times and volunteered to ensure that the frigate contract came to BS provided he was paid 20 million pounds in advance plus 20% for himself. Bekatoros criticised British

Shipbuilders for its failure to discharge the Yarrows agent "who had worked with the Colonels". I could not resist remarking that I supposed that every officer and man in the Greek armed forces who was over the age of 30 could be said to have "worked with the Colonels" because it was the authority of the forces and the police that had kept them in power. That would include Bekatoros. It was not clear what Mr Bekatoros was up to. He seemed to be urging me to contact the £20 millions in advance man.

Mr Bekatoros produced a folded paper and showed me one paragraph and quoted other important facts. I recognized the document and was sure of its authenticity because I had written it! Everyone engaged in marketing must accept that in most nations there is a high probability that what one says or writes to the potential customer nation will find its way to the other competitors. What one does not expect, however, is that information written and typed within the inner secure area of a British Embassy, classified Confidential, and sent by secure means to the MoD's Defence Sales organization, should surface in this way.

Since the document of which he was carefully showing me one paragraph was signed by me, Bekatoros behaviour was curious. I said "yes" and "no" where it was safe to do so and left. My major concern was how at least two people in Athens had got copies of a UK classified document. I reported the matter to the MoD Defence Sales people and heard not another word.

My experience with the Chinese navy had started in 1977−78 when a 20 plus team had visited Ship Department in Bath. That is not exactly true. In the late 1940's two charming Chinese officers had come to the Naval Construction Department in Bath after graduating in Naval Architecture at RNC Greenwich. They were given some design experience before returning to China in a Dido Class cruiser that was transferred to China and which had been promptly sunk in collision at the mouth of the Yangtze. The time of their return was the upheaval when the communists finally assumed total control over mainland China. One went to Taiwan and the other joined the Red Navy. I recall him assuring me that China would be great again.

Thirty years later I met the Taiwan man, now a rear admiral, in Washington, DC.

In 1980 a Chinese navy mission came to British Shipbuilders seeking assistance in the modernisation of their Luda Class frigates and design ideas for a new large destroyer. In preparation, my Director of Marketing, Captain Ian Wright, had visited Beijing in mid-winter for preliminary discussions and had almost died of the cold in unheated hotels and offices. Chinese teams now came to the UK in droves; there were never less than twenty in each team. Because of the value of the orders about which they were speaking they were taken to the shipyards where they crawled all over things like ants with notebooks. We had mastered the Mao suit code of ranks; starting at the bottom with two jacket pockets with no flaps, then a top pocket, then flaps on the side pockets with a top pocket and so on. The interpreter was the only one to speak English but I couldn't help thinking that some of the inscrutable ones with only two side pockets were probably PhD's from UCAL, who were inwardly rocking with mirth or seething with indignation.

On the basis of the drawings, the Russian designed/Chinese built Luda Class certainly needed modernisation. By about the third meeting we had sketched out what might be done to modernise them and what a new large destroyer might be like and said that British Shipbuilders had done a great deal of work and that the Chinese would have to consider paying for any future studies and other work. Twenty-four pairs of Chinese eyes were instantly hooded and one understood the meaning of the inscrutable orient. I noticed that these non-English speakers seemed to have understood the reference to money without the interpreters help.

The other really silly thing that I recall concerned manpower. In the western navies every effort is being made to reduce the number of officers and men required to man and fight warships because manpower costs are such a significant part of the cost of ownership. We proudly demonstrated to the Chinese how we could reduce the size of the Luda's crew. They reacted as it we were out of our silly minds; manpower is a commodity of which China has no shortage; couldn't we get a lot more in? Who said that ships accommodation should be comfortable'?

Sometime shortly afterwards Liz and I were invited to a cocktail party in the Chinese embassy at Blackheath. We entered a room, which had a central table loaded with small eats, a milling throng of people and a small bar. A white-coated man asked if we would like Chinese beer or coke. We said gin and tonic. We said gin and tonic several more times and eventually a man in a grey suit brought them. The crowd slowly circulated and after a while we were on the other side of the table. Here there was another drinks table serving gin and tonic, and as I watched the attendant pouring drinks I suddenly realised why Liz's eyes were shining so brightly, the man was pouring gin in the glass, glug, glug, glug, glug and then the tonic, glug. Which, I reasoned, translated into English means that gin was duty free and tonic wasn't. One Chinese G and T was enough and the ever-faithful George Rogers was there to drive us home.

A lesson that all who frequent the diplomatic circuit should learn is don't eat any of the small eats that are offered at receptions. The canapés and sausages that you are being offered tonight in Embassy or High Commission A are probably the survivors of those offered last night in Embassy or High Commission B, usually by the same equally tired looking waitresses.

I cannot comment about the Chinese small eats, they probably did their own thing. The serving staffs were from the embassy. It was at the time when they were at odds with Britain and three or four of them, while waving Chairman Mao's little red book, had recently assaulted a policeman patrolling outside their boundary wall. The general impression from press reports was that they were very poor and downtrodden. "Don't you believe it, old boy" said my friend the Pakistan naval attaché "I dine there quite often and they serve twenty eight courses with wine to suit? They live like Lords in their closed world". At the time the China-Pakistan axis was a counter to the developing USSR-India axis.

Vosper-Thornycroft continued to do work and to seek a contract. After a difficult and protracted negotiation Peter Usher finally got the Chinese to initial a contract for 50 million dollars. This was the breakthrough that we had worked so hard to achieve. After three months had elapsed with no further word from Beijing in response to VT's prodding, we were told that in accordance with the Peoples Republic's procedures, if the minister had failed to endorse the contract within such and such a period, then the agreement was null and void. The minister had not endorsed the contract with VT and the whole thing had been a gigantic fishing exercise to extract the maximum of design information and know-how from the British at no cost.

Participation in defence equipment exhibitions such as the Royal Navy Equipment Exhibition, the French and Italian equivalents and Posidonia were in my opinion, a waste of money. Like advertising in general, the advocates are the practitioners whose livelihood depends on it, not only those who organize the events but also those within companies and defence forces who like to attend. Anyone contemplating buying a large and expensive piece of equipment should already know much more about what is on offer, world-wide, than they will learn from the brochures and the salesmen on the exhibition stands. OK, you say but what about the suppliers of smaller equipments and components? Well, these are usually of interest to the less senior service personnel who don't get the chance of a trip to Athens or Genoa. Better really to spend the company's money on advertising in the technical press that the target nation's personnel should read and in that nation's language.

The transfer of the British RN Equipment Exhibition from the RN College Greenwich to Whale Island at Portsmouth was a severe cultural shock to some overseas delegations. The bigger space, the bracing air and the visits to Britain's latest warships in Portsmouth Naval Base were scant compensation for the distance from the delights of London. The Algerian Navy delegation sponsored by VSEL would only consent to visit Whale Island on the strict under-standing that they would be returned to London immediately and supplied with the wine and women that they had come to England for. What is more VSEL had to send one of their senior people with them with a fist full of money to see that their wishes were satisfied.

I hosted a luncheon for the C in C of this navy at the Lancaster Gate Hotel and then sat with him for the afternoon's presentations. To my shame my attention wandered and I suddenly switched on again just as the long serving (ex-navy) commercial director of one of our biggest companies was saying "You have to realise that building submarines is a lot more difficult than climbing up palm trees and picking dates".

The next popular misconception is that naval attaches, visits by senior naval officers overseas, visits of overseas officers to HM Ships and overseas exchange officers serving with the Royal Navy, help in the sale of British defence equipment in cases other than where an overseas customer has already made up its mind to buy British. They do not; in the main because of the good old British habit of telling everybody what is bad about things and not what is good about things. Coming right up to today one only had to see the ghastly BBC series about HMS *Brilliant* to understand what I mean.

In a well run Embassy or High Commission overseas, the commercial attaché is better informed and is just as able to get one entree' to visit the people who influence procurement decisions as is a service attaché. Thereafter if a UK firm is serious it should get a good local agent and follow his advice. The naval attaché is usually outside the game. In Canada we actually had the Canadian Chief of Naval Staff asking us to get Whitehall to remove the British naval attaché because he was judged to be damaging the Canadian navy's interests while in Australia the defence attaché played no part in the submarine sales effort.

Visits by senior naval officers are usually counterproductive. They seem to come-over as rank conscious and will instinctively talk down to someone who has less rings on his sleeve, even if it does happen to be the C in C of the overseas navy. In Canada I found the CNS, Vice Admiral Chuck Thomas in an icy rage following such a visit, while the officer responsible for defence procurement, former Rear Admiral Ed Healey said to me that if another British admiral or lord visited him to tell him to buy British submarines or helicopters he would simply refuse to see them ; his complaint in brief was that "they don't do their homework about the thing that they are presumably trying to sell, let alone about Canada and the way the Canadian government does its business". There was one retired admiral who started talking when he got off the flight from the UK and was still talking non-stop when he got back on the flight home, having apparently not heard a word that any Canadian had said during the visit. Since his company was associated with a Canadian company in a costly joint venture and the Canadians had already discerned that the parallel UK helicopter programme had all the signs of not exactly being the management success of the century, he was a source of some embarrassment. Perhaps the next generation, coming from a slimmed down navy, will do better.

Exchange officers are a disaster. The intention is that they become familiar with the British materiel and procedures and provide a fairly low level of information exchange at the coal face.. What happens, of course, is that they live in the mess and hear all the gossip, which is usually about the things that have gone wrong. No one sits at the lunch table and goes on and on about how well his ship's widgets are performing; it would be rather like boasting; but everyone will tell his messmates ad-nauseam about his problem with the motor regulator or torpedo transponder or that the thingamajig will now be six months late. The exchange officers listen to all of this. They are required to make regular reports to their own navy and naturally, amid whatever else they report, they report back all the adverse tittle-tattle.   In both Australia and Canada I found the submarine people in possession of inaccurate and adverse information that had been fed back by their officers on exchange duty with the RN. I am horrified to find that in the year 2,000 the Australian navy that refused to give honest consideration to our submarines and frigates has got a submarine-liaison officer in the MoD design department. Since the RAN is in big trouble with the Swedish designed Collins Class, this is tantamount to giving the Swedish shipyards free access-once removed- to the RN's nuclear submarine operating experience.

The same goes for visits by HM Ships. The officers and men will tell visitors that theirs is a splendid ship and then recite all the things that they think might be improved and the problems that have occurred. This British failing has become noticeably worse in the past 20 years.

An example of this was the visit by Vice Admiral George, the Commander of the Canadian fleet, and other Canadian officers to HMS *Turbulent* at Barrow. The submarine was just completed. As befits the importance of the visitors to the newly commissioned ship the Commanding Officer and his First Lieutenant showed them round. We started in the Control Room with the usual comment about what an excellent submarine it was. The CO then remarked that he would not have arranged it the way it was, he would have put that there and all of those over there. The next compartment received the same treatment. In about the fourth compartment that the ship's officers would have arranged differently I gently pointed out that I had been responsible for the design of the submarine and that there were very good reasons why it was the way it was; one of which was that this was what his boss, Flag Officer Submarines, had asked for.   This was the sort of thing that led the Canadian Chief of Submarine Acquisition to comment on the generally low morale of the RN's nuclear submarine officers in his report to Minister McNight in March 1989.

One of the reasons for this sort of behaviour is that the Commonwealth officers wear the same sort of uniform, speak the same language, have usually attended the British naval colleges, and simply are treated as 'Brits'. And of course we Brits have learned not to take this routine carping seriously. Everyone associated with marketing should have engraved in their hearts, Australians are Australian, Canadians are Canadian and New Zealanders are New Zealanders, they are splendid people but they are not, repeat not, British.

Vosper-Thornycroft had been successful in supplying fast, well-armed, small warships to Egypt and Oman. A further high level Defence Sales mission to Oman was planned in 1981, which it was hoped might result in further orders. Some months after his retirement from the post of Head of Defence Sales, Sir Ronald Ellis lunched at BS HQ and told of this visit.   He had expected to lead the mission and learned with some surprise that Prime Minister Thatcher would be present and lead. No sooner had the official team arrived in Oman than Mrs Thatcher's son, Mark, appeared 'from out of the woodwork' representing a civil engineering contractor. According to Ron Ellis, Mrs Thatcher devoted herself solely to forwarding the civil engineering matter, so much so that he, Ellis, protested to the Prime Minister that he might as well return to the UK "because she was spending all her time with her son, who wasn't even a member of the official mission". This had somewhat compromised the entire military purpose of the mission. Some years later the story of Mrs Thatcher's assistance in the matter of the Oman civil engineering contract was featured in the UK press as part of the on-going interest in how the young Mr. Thatcher had amassed his considerable wealth.   Lest it should seem that Ron Ellis was making a big thing of this, I should add that his principal topic of lunchtime conversation was the cabin cruiser that he had just bought, that had three big Mercury outboard engines, and his wish to explore the French waterways in her.

In 1980 we learned that Iraq had a requirement for four small frigates and we expressed an interest. We were immediately warned off by the Defence Sales organisation, which stated that the pursuit of all defence sales prospects in the area was to be the concern of a body called International Military Sales. We were told that if we attempted to go there the British Embassy would not pursue our visa applications. INS seems to have been most active because whenever I went through Heathrow I would meet Captain David Hepworth of INS en route to Baghdad or Bahrain or some equally exotic destination. The Italians won the order, which eventually proved to be a mixed blessing.

In addition to my frequent visits to Australia, Canada and the USA I also visited Brazil, Argentina, Morocco, Saudi Arabia, Singapore, Israel, Turkey and New Zealand in efforts to advance British armament prospects. I had been in Argentina with the Imperial Defence College in 1966 and had been captivated by Buenos Aires. This second time was no different; London and Paris around every second corner. Argentina had been 'opened up' by the railways; her prosperity had been built on an ability to bring produce to harbours for export to Europe and North America and bring back the materials to push the frontiers ever further to the south and west. The railway was still king and vast sums were still being spent on rail subsidies. I was not altogether surprised to learn that the huge building in BA that housed the navy headquarters had been built originally as a convalescent home for railway employees.

I am always angry with people who ask stupid questions of their overseas hosts; I was therefore doubly embarrassed when descending a wide staircase I heard myself say "Is this Italian marble?" The young Argentinean commander who was my escort gave me a slightly incredulous look and said "No, Argentinean'. Here we were with the mighty Andes Mountains a few hundred miles away to the west and other mountains to the south, probably solid marble from base to peak and this stupid Englishman asks if it comes from Italy. The generals were still in power and a strong military presence was everywhere, including on the roof of navy HQ.

We had been introduced to an agent called Mauricio Suarez who employed ex-navy captains and treated them like dirt. This put me off for a start and I did not warm to this overweight bully. If someone ever made a Spanish language version of 'Animal Farm' here was the man to play Napoleon.

The naval attaché was Captain Jack Thomas, an ex-Ship Department engineer officer. I went to his home for dinner before flying home and met his wife and 17-year-old daughter. The daughter was going out to a party with one of the young men from the Netherlands embassy. She appeared in a blue one-piece suit called, I think, a jump suit and explained to her Mama that she had put it on "because he's a groper".

On the return flight the aircraft landed at Freetown in West Africa at dawn and the passengers were herded into the waiting room. The room was barely large enough for this number and as the temperature rose the air became stuffy and people became visibly distressed. Soldiers inside and outside the room would not allow the doors to be opened. Poster portraits of the national leader, Sergeant Stevens, covered the walls. When the time came to re-board the aircraft the passengers were made to visit the airport gift shop en route. As the aircraft lifted off over the green jungle and then golden beaches and blue ocean I think that all on board were relieved.

In Brazil I met several of the officers and wives that I had known in Britain when the Niteroi Class frigates and Oberon Class submarines were being built. On the first visit I was with Roger Harding from Defence Sales. The Naval attaché, Captain Tony Stephenson, was another ex-Ship Department engineer. Tony met us at the airport; as we drove into Rio before 6.00am on a packed four-lane highway he remarked that this was the morning rush hour. I said that I thought it sensible in that climate to start early and finish in mid-afternoon and was told that the homeward rush hour is after 6.00pm and that people have to work hard and long in this developing nation.

We did the usual rounds of Rio, Sao Paulo and Brazilia. The Brazilian navy made no secret of their intention of becoming the most powerful navy in the southern hemisphere and that their Oberon Class submarines were regularly patrolling off the coast of Africa. I was approached again and asked if I would consider joining the University of Sao Paulo to help them with the design of a nuclear submarine and its reactor. They already had some Germans teaching them submarine design.

A Vice Admiral Schacht - an engineer, commanded the naval arsenal in Rio. We discussed the warship designs and equipment that were available from the UK and the possible ways in which we might assist him in the construction of small frigates and submarines. I also learned that his wife organised and ran weekly cookery and sewing gatherings at which the wives of the petty officers were encouraged to make things to be given to the poor in the shantytowns around Rio. She was a very shrewd woman, for most of these young wives came from very poor backgrounds themselves and had little idea of cooking and sewing when they married sailors. Now they were in married quarters, had babies and a man who expected to be fed and this is really why Mrs Schacht ran her classes. To me, the amazing thing about the shanty towns was that although there was said to be no sanitation or running water, the children emerged each morning to go to school with spotless white shirts or blouses over blue shorts (with shoulder straps) or skirts.

The final night in Brazilia I drank some mineral water from the bottle in my room mini-bar. I thought at the time that the cap of the bottle came off easily; clearly a previous occupant had drunk the water and refilled it with tap water. By next morning I was most dreadfully ill and will always be grateful to Roger for getting me back to Rio and then home.

Roger Harding was also associated with the Colombian lunch. The story is a bit convoluted. The President of Colombia paid an official visit to the UK in 1979. His Minister of Defence, a General, accompanied him. There was a long standing tradition that a certain British warship builder always provided the sword of honour presented to the best cadet passing out of the Colombian Naval Academy and it was arranged that British Shipbuilders, in the person of Admiral Griffin, would present the sword to the minister; where better than at the Ministry of Defence, in Whitehall? It really was unforgivable but the Colombian general arrived in uniform at the main entrance to be met by a young man in a grey suit who conducted him along dusty corridors to a room in which were a group of rather scruffy chaps in plain clothes, one of whom gave him the sword; and then they all went away and he was led by the return route to his car. He had arrived expecting a guard of honour drawn up in Horse Guards Avenue and some generals and admirals, too. The Defence Sales people should have been alerted to see that those responsible for MoD protocol were aware of the distinguished visitor or alternatively British Shipbuilders should have invited the general to BSHQ.

But that was not the end of it, oh no. The President had been invited to lunch with the Queen but not the general. The general was not pleased. A luncheon for the general and the other VIP's from Colombia was hastily arranged at Edinburgh Castle. Roger and I with our wives were invited. We four flew up in the British Shipbuilders HS 125 jet, which burst a tyre on landing, and we arrived in the airport terminal riding on the airport fire engine. The castle reeks with history, the president of the Colombian national airline sitting opposite to Liz confessed that they are not too keen on genealogy in Colombia because every time they trace their ancestry, they get back to a catholic priest.

On another visit to Brazil I was accompanied by ex-Commander Tony Price and David Montgomery, the son of Field Marshal Montgomery. His proper address is Lord Montgomery of El Alamein. When he laughs or is indignant, he snorts.. The practice in Portuguese and Spanish society is to add the mothers surname to the husbands either before or after., depending on the country and is confusing. This is made the more so by the Brazilian navy officially giving their senior officers 'war names' which are distinctive first names followed by the fathers surname. Perhaps they had too many of the Portuguese equivalent of John Smith.. Anyway I always became confused by lengthy names and then being told that my war name is so and so.

An amusing little incident (for me) occurred when we called on a Brazilian navy captain. David gave the man his visiting card, which said quite clearly Lord Montgomery of El Alamein. The captain studied it for some moments and then looked David in the eye and said, "What do I call you, Mister El? " David's snort could have been heard in Europe.

In addition to touching base with Brazilian navy friends the visit was to develop further a relationship that Frank Noah had established with a prominent agent in Rio and to explore a possible joint venture with a Brazilian engineering concern. These tasks were accomplished.

I had to leave a day early to fly to Hamburg for a NATO frigate Board meeting. When I went to pay my bill at the hotel desk I learned that the account had been prepaid by the UK travel agent in US dollars for one night longer than I would require. I was entitled to a refund. Nothing in the world would make the cashier part with US dollars; I must accept the Brazilian equivalent, at the black market rate, of course, so I was presented with one million, seven hundred and eighty thousand cruzeiro's. Momentarily I was a millionaire with it all in my one hand.. I gave the rather grubby pile to Tony who was to stay a further few days.

The Kingdom of Morocco was engaged in defending its southern frontier against the Polisarios. The terrain is desert followed by more desert. The best way to move forces south would be by sea in landing ships or craft. We were asked for proposals. I flew to Casablanca and thence by road through well cultivated fields to Rabat with a French husband and wife team who undertook marketing tasks for the BS warship companies in francophone countries. The thing I best remember about the outward flight was looking down on the southernmost tip of Spain and suddenly realising that I was looking at a miniscule Gibraltar and the narrow strip of the athwartships runway of the airport.

We were politely received by the Moroccan navy and described what we might have to offer, followed by questions. I can recall little of Rabat except for the walls and entrances to the vast palace grounds. Before leaving I called on the British ambassador to tell him about my visit and to exchange gossip. On the return flight to Paris I found my French companions to be extremely upset that I had not taken them with me to call on the ambassador. The wife managed tears at this insult to their honour. We had a subsequent meeting with the Moroccan navy. I took along a colleague who had spent many years in Paris and Brussels. He spoke only English when anyone else was present and sat listening throughout the meeting. Afterwards he reported that what our francophone agents were saying to the Moroccans as translations bore only a passing resemblance to what I had actually said.

People complain that the problem with the major international hotels is that they are all the same. Personally I have always found this assurance of an acceptable standard to be a joy ; never more so than in Riyadh, the capital of Saudi Arabia. I was accompanied by Francis Ponsonby, a charming ex-naval officer whose standard reply to the rather rude question "why do you pronounce your name Punsonby" was to say "why do you pronounce L o n d o n , Lundon". We arrived in Riyadh airport at about 10.30 pm. We were taken to a VIP lounge and served bitter coffee in small cups. No one had instructed us in the etiquette and as fast as we drank the coffee (and thought of a cold shower and bed) the cups were refilled. In the end I noticed that one of our hosts had inverted his cup in its saucer, I did the same and shortly afterwards we were taken to the Sheraton Hotel.

Riyadh airport had four large terminals; one for domestic flights, one for international flights, one for the Royal family and one spare. At the time of the visit in the mid-1980's all Saudi Arabians received a cash allowance from the state and few worked apart from those in government posts and even these were under-pinned by a non-native. Most of the teachers were Egyptian or Jordanian and the administration and the armed forces were strongly dependant upon Pakistan. Vast dual carriageways radiated from the centre of the city and disappeared over the desert horizon going I know not where. At the centre of the city is the old walled fortress with its massive wooden door. In this door is a low picket door through which people have to stoop to enter; an ideal posture in which to chop off the head of an unwelcome intruder. The market square is immediately adjacent to the old fortress as is the gold market. Public executions and maimings still took place in the market square every Friday.

There were two sorts of police, what I would call regular police and religious police. The latter have special powers to ensure that the laws of Islam are observed. One such law bans females from riding in the front seats of cars driven by men. The British naval attaché, a young electrical commander had just had his fiancé to stay and had insisted on driving around with her beside him, receiving dirty looks from the police in the process.. He lived in an apartment block reserved for diplomats and therein had access to alcoholic drink. Since he had a Pakistani servant this must be known to the authorities and in my view was a potential hazard should the religious police wish to stir things up

My meetings with Rear Admiral Prince Mahmoud were in the navy department. The building was in the shape of a hollow square with the central quadrangle covered to form a vast ceremonial room, carpeted for prayer. At the appointed times each day the call to prayer sounds throughout the building, I noticed that if a discussion was going well for the Saudis they ignored the call to prayer (for clearly Allah is guiding their tongues), whereas if it wasn't going so well they adjourned for prayers (for clearly Allah had provided this welcome chance for reflection).

One morning while I was seated in the Admiral's outer office a Pakistani captain came out and in passing looked at my IDC tie and gave me a broad wink. Protocol was that he could not speak with me without a Saudi present. His white tropical uniform was reminiscent of the Royal Navy in its heyday.

We took the overnight Saudi Airlines flight. It flies southwest to Jedda and then northwest non-stop to London. Leaving Riyadh had been interesting. We went to the exit channel. The uniformed staff who should have been there were on the landside chatting and smoking. After about five minutes I indicated to them that I intended to walk straight through and they grudgingly came to their desks and sullenly passed us through; at which other passengers appeared as if by magic. I noticed how relieved people seemed to be once they were on the airside of the security people. I swear that the women's skirts rose a few inches or perhaps they trod more jauntily. We were now in quasi-international territory and the airport signs were those used the world over. I wondered about the toilet signs; in a country where the women wear pantaloons and men wear long smocks how would they distinguish between the male and female toilets? They managed, but it took a keen eye to tell the difference.

At Jedda a Saudi family embarked and occupied the two rows of two seats behind us. They were the parents and teenage son and daughter with both females dressed as the religious police require with only their eyes uncovered.. When we landed at Heathrow I noticed that a minor miracle had happened overnight for seated behind us were a mother and daughter in fashionable dress, high-heeled shoes and the latest cosmetics. When in Rome.

I accompanied Minister Norman Lamont on a trade mission to Turkey. We flew to Ankara for meetings with ministers and officials and then to Istanbul for meetings with industrialists. When I made my nightly telephone call to Liz at 22.00 British time, she said that it had just been announced that Lamont had been moved from the Department of Trade to the Treasury. We agreed that the announcement might have been better timed. No 10 Downing Street is reputed to have the best switchboard in the country, capable of finding anybody, anywhere, anytime; we speculated that Margaret Thatcher had probably said to her staff "get me Norman Lamont on the phone". They had telephoned around and finally got him in the embassy in Ankara and had probably put him through without saying where he was. In her usual manner the PM wouldn't have given him the chance to get a word in, other than "Yes" and she probably thought that he was just along the road in Victoria Street.

When I sat down beside him the following morning I asked him how he liked the shift to the Treasury. When I explained that it had been announced in London he said, "Oh lord, I'm not going to say anything here". Everywhere we went a young girl reporter kept appearing and asking me whether what their London agent was saying was true to which I would dutifully say "No". It was not until the final session at the end of the week that Norman Lamont told our Turkish hosts that he was moving to become Chief Secretary to the Treasury. Since Minister sounds much more important than Secretary, even Chief Secretary, the Turks probably thought that he had been demoted.

Have you ever paused to reflect on how odd many of the titles used in British public life must seem to foreigners, even to those who share our language. Bernard Thimont was an assistant secretary when he visited India with the Imperial Defence College. He said somewhat whimsically afterwards that the Indians hadn't taken much notice of him because he wasn't even a secretary. In fact, the civil service rank of assistant secretary is the one with which the salary of British members of parliament is loosely aligned. Then there are people like Black Rod and Ladies of the Bedchamber, Keepers of the Privy Purse and so on.

When Kemal Attaturk decided to move the capital of secular Turkey away from Constantinople and back to Alexander the Great's capital, he envisaged that it might grow to have a population of 150,000. Alas, it has spread up and over the surrounding hills and now numbers several millions. Even in the centre of the city the streets were pockmarked and uneven and retained huge puddles when it rained. There appeared to be two policemen to each block of buildings but perhaps some were there because of official visitors like us.

One of the stupidities of the nationalisation process in 1977 was that the shipbuilding parts of Vickers and Vosper-Thornycroft still kept the names Vickers and Vosper-Thornycroft while those parts of these companies that were not nationalised also kept the same names, Vickers and Vospers. This led to much confusion overseas, typically, when I was in the Brazilian Navy Minister's office in Brazilia his aide produced the Vospers file in which correspondence with VT and Vospers was all mixed up. We sometimes got their correspondence. This is why on privatisation, Vickers Shipbuilding and Engineering became VSEL.

For the government mission to Turkey some genius in the Department of Trade had me down as Vickers and when I reached Ankara the Turkish army were there in strength to learn the latest on Vickers main battle tanks from a man who had come to tell the Turkish navy about surface ships and submarines. Luckily VSEL manufacture a splendid 155mm howitzer and I had the literature with me so it wasn't all a waste of time. But I could see them wondering if they would be allowed to spend US military aid dollars on British guns when US companies make a similar weapon.

The embassy residence in Ankara was the last to be built on the old generous scale before post war Chancellors began to question why Britain's representatives overseas should live in the style of minor royalty. I thought that it was rather nice and fitting but I could see the Chief Secretary taking it all in for possible future reference.

If Ankara was a little sleepy, Istanbul was dynamic; a seething mass of different cultures restlessly on the move. On the road along the waterfront were men leading heavily laden donkeys, unchanged since biblical times, while in the city above were smart shops, modern hotels and the like and all the trappings of modern urban civilisation. My hotel room overlooked the Bosphorus and the mighty bridge that joins Europe to Asia Minor.. I noted that at no time day or night were there ever less than two soviet merchant ships visible and frequently three, entering or leaving the Black Sea.

We were entertained one evening by an industrialist in his villa on the eastern shore of the Bosphorus. The villa was surrounded on the landside with a high wall patrolled by security guards. His yacht was moored nearby.. The family business included the manufacture of white goods and Sony television sets, the latter for the German and Swedish markets. They had had a big contract to supply refrigerators to Iran during the war with Iraq. They went to front line units for medical purposes. The firm had so many complaints that the refrigerators supplied were defective that in the end they sent in their own quality inspectors. They found that the usual method of delivery by the Iranian army transport people was to push the refrigerators off the back of a moving lorry. Teheran agreed that this was the probable cause of the defective units and took steps to stop it. On the next visit the firm's inspectors found that each lorry had been supplied with an old rubber tyre and told to stop and push the refrigerators off on to that.

I visited the television factory. The electronic components came from elsewhere but the printed circuit boards, carcases, facia panels and all else were made and assembled in the factory, as far as I could see by about ten men and twenty women. The latter sat at a long bench and put colour coded transistors and other miniature components in the PCB's which were secured in place by passing over a vat of liquid solder at the end of the line. They then went to other women who were assembling the whole sets, testing them (on power for several hours) and then packing them for shipment. It really did look to be a smooth operation, performed not in an air conditioned semi-hygienic laboratory but in the sort of shed and environment that might house a small electrical jobbing company in England. So much for my vision that all .Sony products are produced by keen young people who do a half-hours exercises while singing the company song before starting work at 6.00am.each day.

My visit was really a waste of time. No matter how we tried, the Turkish navy wouldn't play. They had contracts with their traditional allies, the Germans and they would not rock that boat by entertaining a visit to their shipyards by the British at that time.

With the finance member of the BS Board, Maurice Elderfield, I visited Israel for discussions about warships that they might purchase for their navy and for others. We flew in the BS HS 125 and took Liz. Having one's own company aircraft sounds sexy but was really a mixed blessing because of the limited range of this particular type.   We would embark on the private side of Heathrow to fly to Athens, say, at about the same time as commercial passengers were climbing into a big jet over in Terminal 1. Off we went and when we arrived in Athens the ordinary people would already have arrived and left the airport simply because we had had to land in Munich or somewhere to refuel. What's more they had a hot meal and we might have had a roll and butter.

On the flight to Tel Aviv we had to land in Crete to refuel and nearly flew into a mountain in the process. There was some confusion between the signals being received from the military airfield on one side of the mountain and the civil airport on the other and in the bad visibility at the time we nearly flew down the line between them. Our pilot confessed that one of his nine lives had gone.. Maurice, a qualified pilot, was a bit white while Liz and I had merely assumed that all the zooming up and steep banking manoeuvres were how one always landed in Iraklion.. Fifteen years later the Greek air traffic control system is still so bad that Lufthansa and some other airline pilots have refused to fly into their airspace.

On arrival late at night our hosts insisted on taking us out to dinner and next morning there was Mr Danreuter all bright and ready for discussions and ministerial introductions. We discussed various ship design projects and ways in which BS might be able to help the Israeli armed forces. The managing director of the Haifa Shipyard described the proposed extension to the SAAR series of small fast patrol ships, inevitably bigger than the SAAR 5. We discussed the possibility of usefully operating a helicopter from such a small platform where the limiting feature might be not (only) the small space but the liveliness of the ships motion. We also discussed submarines and their not-too-happy experience with the small ones.. We met Mr Perez at lunch.. . Liz had been put in charge of a soldier - a really beautiful girl officer who was shortly to complete her period of service. They got back a bit shaken by a bomb that went off just where they had been in old Jaffa.

The hotels along the sea front each had their quota of guards.   That evening we rode upwards in a crowded lift. At one floor no-one got out and the elderly man standing there holding a small girl by the hand said, "Oh, its full up, we'll wait for the next one"." No" said a man behind us, "there is always a place for the President of Israel and his granddaughter" and the speaker and another man stepped out and the President and the little girl got in. Among other things I was interested that they all naturally spoke in English.

I am eternally grateful that our hosts insisted that we should visit Jerusalem, driving up through the lush countryside that the settlers had created out of veritably nothing and past the reminders of their recent wars to this ancient and modern city that has a unique place in the Jewish, Muslim and Christian faiths. I had not before been aware of the remarkable feat of engineering in the preparation and placing together of the huge blocks of stone to create the old city. When we were there they were still excavating down below the wailing wall level and finding that the masonry went on and on to what was presumably ground level or moat level in ancient times. These perfectly fitting blocks of rock, measuring some 36ft by 8ft square were put in position some thousands of years ago and to me are one of the wonders of the ancient world. To my generation there is a magic in sign-posts to Bethlehem and Nazareth just up the road.

Chapter Fifteen

In the mid 1970's the Australian naval authorities approached Ship Department concerning the design of a replacement for their British built Oberon Class submarines. They had some broad outline requirements; a preliminary study indicated that a submarine to meet these requirements would be substantially bigger than the Oberon. At the time I was concerned that because of their initial cost and crippling support costs, membership of the SSN club would mean that the Royal Navy would finish up with too few submarines. I was strongly of the view that the UK should seriously consider the construction of a new class of non-nuclear submarines, exploiting the latest technology in detection, silencing, weapons and air independent propulsion to capitalise on the expense already incurred in the development of such systems for the nuclear subs. We had built and operated two submarines driven by turbines using High Test Peroxide and had made successful trials with submarine diesel engines running underwater using stored oxygen. We had also done some work on fuel cells. Although an enthusiast for nuclear submarines, I was sure that a system using fuel cells could be perfected to provide submarines which could cruise under water for several weeks without coming near the surface, thus giving worthwhile performance and survivability at modest cost. I reasoned that such vessels should appeal to navies already operating deep ocean submarines, such as Australia, Canada, Brazil and Chile.

I was, of course, mindful of the unhappy history of delay and increase in cost of the last two Oberon Class submarines of six built for Australia by Messers Scott Lithgow at Greenock. When these vessels were approaching completion it was found that some of the electric cables supplied were defective necessitating extensive rip-out and replacement with much extra cost and delay. It was several years before a financial settlement was reached and by then relations were not good. Captain David Stevenson RAN remarked to me when we were both students at the Imperial Defence College in 1966 that "the Australian navy will never buy another British Submarine". As usual David was smiling when he said it; he was destined to become Australia's Chief of Naval Staff in 1973.

Vickers Shipbuilders had made a whole series of aircraft carrier design studies at the request of the RAN and with the 1976 approach I thought that perhaps the Australian navy had put aside their resentment and were considering buying British if we had a suitable design. Vickers had received a copy of the outline requirement for a submarine through their part ownership of Cockatoo Island Dockyard in Sydney and they increased their pressure on Ship Department to prepare an RN / RAN design. Vickers had no worthwhile in-house submarine design capability at this time.

For several years successive Flag Officers, Submarine, had asked me not to rock the boat by advancing the case for non-nuclear boats, ("They will take away our nukes") and there was some lack of enthusiasm for providing money to develop non-nuclear underwater propulsion systems, but now that it seemed that the RAN was serious I had my people start concept design work in cooperation with Vickers. To emphasise the intent to embrace the RAN's wishes, I invited Canberra to send people to join the design team in Bath or Barrow, but this was declined.

There was some talk of Vickers setting up a team at Cockatoo to handle liaison, design development and eventually, submarine construction in Australia, but we were all mindful of the earlier RN / RAN frigate exercise for which Glasgow based YARD had set up a design office in Australia and to which project Admiralty staff were seconded, only to have the whole thing founder at some financial loss to the UK when the RAN decided to buy US ships.

A formal staff requirement for the RN submarine was produced in the late 1970's and Vickers argued that its scope be enhanced to more obviously meet the RAN's requirements. The design proceeded on these lines with the British naval staff insisting that it was marginally bigger than they required. Eventually they came up with the remarkable idea that because the vessel was a little bigger than they had intended, British Shipbuilders (of which Vickers Shipbuilders was now a part) should pay a levy to the Crown for each submarine ordered for the RN. I resigned from the Ministry of Defence at about this time to become the Board Member for Warshipbuilding in British Shipbuilders and, from the other side of the fence, became responsible for accepting this levy (which of course would simply be added to the cost of the submarine in some way).

I actually joined British Shipbuilders while en route from Singapore to Melbourne on a marketing mission. During discussions in Canberra we learned of the RAN's unease concerning the prototype of their new class of patrol craft, HMAS *Fremantle* building by Messers Brooke Marine at Lowestoft. This was the first we had heard of any problem with this valuable contract under which Brooke Marine would provide the design, build the first of class ship and provide lead yard services for the construction of a further nine ships in Australia.

It appeared that when the partly complete lead ship was lifted into the water for the first time at or shortly after Christmas 1978, the Australian Naval Construction Liaison Officer had suggested that the ship was floating more deeply in the water than he had expected. In all the circumstances with an incomplete ship, half the equipment still to be installed and draughts fore and aft quite different from what they would eventually be, the RANCLO was very bright to pick this up. The company had shrugged this off pointing out how difficult it was to predict the final draughts in an incomplete ship. The Australian officer had persisted; he estimated that this nominally 212 tonne full load craft would be close to 10% overweight and in consequence would have difficulty meeting its performance criteria. Although the contract contained the usual financial penalty clauses against non-compliance, Australia did not want the new class to start off 'in the red'. Obtaining no satisfaction from the company he had expressed his concern to his superiors in Canberra and Canberra closed the loop back to British Shipbuilders. I asked Clive Benton, my Director of Operations in BSHQ Newcastle, to investigate and report.

His report fully supported the RANCLO and revealed a notable lack of coordination and communication within Brooke Marine. The design was good but tight; the production drawing office had tended to use marginally thicker plating than the designers had specified and in construction, whenever the correct material was not immediately available, slightly thicker was substituted. Add to this inadequate monitoring of the machinery and equipment makers and the one or two places where the RAN had made small changes and it all added up to a potential increase of over 20 tonnes in displacement.

Sweeping changes in organisation and senior management were made in Brooke Marine and the design reviewed to restore the original displacement. Where possible these changes were made in HMAS *Fremantle* and in the first ships already building by Don Fry at NQEA Cairns. In consequence of this overweight problem in the lead ship I negotiated a cost penalty with the RAN authorities.

The problem with small warships when in service is that the operators will keep putting things on board and thus adding weight. This is entirely sensible from their point of view when they are operating at very long distances from their bases such as in northern Australia but it gives problems with diesel engines and propellers. These relatively high speed propellers cannot be designed to give high efficiency at ship displacements 15% below and 15% above the designed loaded displacement; under overload conditions they cavitate with resulting noise and blade wear. Furthermore, and perhaps more importantly, under overload conditions the engines become torque limited and just will not deliver extra power.

The Brooke Marine investigation also disclosed a request from the New Zealand navy for assistance in resolving propulsion problems that had seemingly developed in their smaller Lake Class patrol craft supplied by the same company. Their diesel engines were stated not to be developing the power necessary to propel the craft at the designed speed. Investigation showed that the craft were being operated at more than 10% above their designed full load displacement and that the diesel engines were torque limited. But that was not the whole story; analysis by University College London showed that there was a mismatch between the diesel engines, the German ZF gearboxes and the propellers supplied by the Dutch firm, Lipps. Both ZF and Lipps provided replacement items appropriate to the greater displacement at which the RNZN wished to operate the Class, at little or no cost to New Zealand and the RNZN fitted them when the ships came in for refit.

HMAS *Fremantle* was completed and passed her sea trials with success before making the passage to Australia without problem. The speed trials were interesting; large ships usually go more slowly in shallow water than in deep water. The effect is more pronounced on slow merchant ship forms than on fine warship shapes but it also depends in a complex way on the speed and size regime applicable to the ship type. The measured mile off Brooke Marine's yard at Lowestoft is not in deep water. Received wisdom in the firm was that at high speeds the shallow water effect would be reversed provided the wind and tide were in the right way. In *Fremantle's* case she went faster in deep water than on the Lowestoft mile but there wasn't much in it.

The contract to build the follow-on ships of the Fremantle Class in Australia had been awarded to North Queensland Engineering Associates (NQEA) of Cairns. The company had been built on the manufacture and repair of machinery to service the sugar industry. With the decline in this type of work and Don Fry taking over from his father, they had diversified into building craft for operation in local waters to meet the growing tourist trade to Green Island and the Great Barrier Reef and then bigger and further afield. The Fremantle contract had been won quite early in this diversification process and demonstrated a considerable faith on the part of the government procurement officials. This faith was being completely justified by NQEA's performance. The ships were being built in a shed like a hangar, open at both ends, situated in the middle of a field, and moved to the dock for launching and completion. In my view by the time they reached their fourth ship their product was quite as good as Brooke Marines, and for considerably less man-hours, for which the climate should be given some credit.

Don Fry's energy and enthusiasm was boundless. He was keen to qualify as the builder of submarines and with the support of the then Premier of Queensland he proposed to excavate the adjacent mangrove swamp (and the crocodiles) to build a dock in which he would build Australia's submarines. And I believe that, eventually, he would have mustered up the resources and manpower to do it.

Talking of crocodiles; to protect the species and provide opportunities for native people, only aborigines were allowed to manufacture crocodile skin products. In consequence the number of crocodiles had increased and instead of being found only in the extreme northern coastal regions, crocodiles were being seen much further south. One had been seen off NQEA's dock in 1980. Being British and a strict adherent to the code of "women and Daniel first" I kept a wary eye out for crocodiles particularly after Liz and I had visited the Crocodile Zoo on Green Island and seen the awesome power of the biggest crocodile in captivity and his relations. Ugh. Driving one day past Century Lakes in Cairns I saw a small crocodile basking on a rock. "In no way" said Don Fry," that's not possible" or words to that effect. Some three weeks later, back in London, I read with some satisfaction (being some thousands of miles away) that while walking home one evening in Cairns a man had been bitten on the leg by a small crocodile that popped up out of a street drain.

We went to Green Island aboard an aluminium catamaran built by NQEA. It had seats for 200 people and made about 28 knots. Beside the pier at the island was a submerged chamber with big portholes from which hundreds of fish of all colours of the rainbow could be seen, treading water while opening and closing their mouths and gazing steadfastly with big eyes at we poor creatures trapped inside that big iron thing.

In many visits to Australia one of the nicest days was the day we visited Mrs. Fry's parents up on the Atherton Plateau and went down their modest gold mine. One began to sense again the rugged life of the pioneers whose persistence and hope that one day they would strike it rich, features so much in Australia's history. They lived in a small bungalow made of corrugated iron in a clearing in the forest. The stream that ran beside the house and in which they bathed was dammed upstream to create a lake from which the water for the mining operations was taken. There were snakes in the lake and our hosts said that they had to look out for snakes when they bathed. The toilet was outside and we were warned to look under the seat for red spiders. The mine had first been worked in the 1890's and abandoned but our host was certain that extending it along fault lines that he had mapped out would yield more gold than the few ounces that he had found so far. Thanks to his son-in-law's ownership of an engineering firm everything was now power driven. We were due to fly to New Zealand via Sydney that evening and Liz was in an 'arriving in an hotel in NZ' sort of frock but down the mine she went and chipped away at some rocks. When we were walked around the claim to see its potential we kept a wary eye out for snakes; our host was barefoot.

At the end of the visit he wanted to give Liz a piece of gold. He produced a sack and delved in it to produce some pieces of quartz. He agonised, oh how he agonised, over those pieces and finally gave Liz his choice, pointing to a minute speck of gold about the size of a grain of salt. I am sure that all of his samples were equally small.

Someone in Australia should erect a statue to the man who invented corrugated iron.

In New Zealand we stayed at the James Cook Hotel in Wellington. Although spacious the exterior and interior decor was either grey or mud colour. The only illumination was by low wattage table lamps and it was difficult to see to write reports and things. At the time this was 'the' hotel in the nations capital. It was this and other equally dull hotels that convinced Liz that there was a potential market outside London for self-service apartments for short-term business and holiday visitors and helped her towards her first million.

The first time that Liz came to Australia with me was in the days when British Airways and Singapore Airlines operated a joint Concorde service between London and Singapore. We took the service. For the first leg to the Gulf we were served by British Airways 'jolly hockey sticks' sort of girls and for the second leg by the elfin-like lotus blossoms of Singapore Airlines; the contrast could not have been more marked especially in the ease with which one could pass them in the aisles. Concorde is a marvel of engineering and gets you there quickly but it is not a comfortable aircraft in which to travel. Liz thought that it was wonderful to see the curvature of the earth and the deepening blue of the sky at high altitude and to know that she was travelling at the speed of a bullet. The fact that the heat due to the friction of our flight meant that she was now some 4 inches further away from the pilot than when we had taken off from Heathrow and those in the rear were a further 6 inches away gave her cause for thought and when I told her that the pilot couldn't see where he was going because (in those days) a steel shield had come down over the windscreen, there was a definite frown. Soon we were there, but alas my suitcase was on its way to Sydney.

Having settled into our hotel, our first thought was the cool of the swimming pool. I was in the pool when Liz jumped in and bobbed up minus the top of her bikini. Norman Sloan QC was directly in front of her at the time and confessed that he hadn't enjoyed a swim so much in years. In those days much of old Singapore was still there and Exchange Alley was given a thorough going over in the search for bargains.

We took the overnight Qantas flight to Melbourne. As we climbed away from Singapore the captain of the aircraft gave a talk of about 10 minutes, about the history of Singapore and the region over which we were flying. When he came down and spoke with us, Liz told him how much she had appreciated his talk. We learned later that the cabin crew could have killed her on the spot ; it seemed that he required them all to study the history of the places along the route and tested them on this knowledge. They had had rather too much of it. I told Liz that she must settle down and sleep after dinner and on no account should she watch the movie. I woke up in the night and there was my lovely Liz, sitting upright with tears streaming down her cheeks, living every sad moment of a film called "Kim". The other thing that I recall was the smoothness of the landing in Melbourne and the bumpiness of the following flight to Canberra as the small aircraft met turbulence over the mountains.

I was due to visit Hong Kong in connection with the proposed Hong Kong Patrol Craft and return via a Genship meeting in Vancouver for which we would fly directly from Hong Kong. Something happened and we found that we were routed through Tokyo and Seattle. No sweat, you may say except that Liz had no US visa. The ever helpful people in the US Embassy in Canberra said come on over and we will give you one while you wait (those were the days!) Canberra is well spread out around the lake and designed for travel by car and not for walking. It is also windy. Jogging and cycling around the lake is OK but walking beside the roads is seldom practiced. Liz took a car to the embassy and said that she would walk back across the lake bridge. Her wardrobe consisted of lightweight non-crush summer dresses and suits and as she walked across the bridge her skirt was blown up over her head. She received a round of applause and some whistles from a pleasure boat that just happened to go under the bridge and arrived back at the hotel with her skirt tucked up like one of those Japanese wrestlers, reasoning that once is permissible but when it happened for the second time the joke had gone far enough - she felt that while she hadn't yet seen enough of Canberra, Canberra had seen enough of her.

In Hong Kong I had discussions with government officials about the patrol craft that was under consideration and to assess the potential of the local firms for building them. Jack Cater who had been a fellow student with me at the IDC in 1966 was the Secretary to the government and it's chief civil servant and was able to steer me in the right directions. As I left the hotel for the first meeting in the morning I had realised that Liz had not much local currency and thrust a book of travellers cheques in her hand. When I came back in the evening we met outside the shirt shop in the Mandarin and she proudly presented me with a great pile of Hong Kong dollars, about 2 inches thick: she had changed the lot.

The Hong Kong government was to provide 75% of the money to build six patrol craft for service in Hong Kong waters. The craft would displace 700 tons, be just over 200ft long, and have a speed of 25 knots and a high performance 3inch gun. If possible, some of the craft would be built in Hong Kong. There were six companies who expressed an interest. The Star Ferry Co which built and maintained the ferries that ply around the harbour was the only yard that built any sizeable craft and they did not push their claims once they learned how sophisticated these small warships were. A shipping tycoon owned the most persistent and awkward candidate yard. The yard had built some 37ft launches for the police. The day that I inspected them, the manager and his deputy appeared at the Mandarin Hotel at about 7pm and literally besieged Liz and I in our room demanding an instant "Yes" decision that they should receive the order.

The Hong Kong government accepted that it would not be economic to equip a HK yard with the equipment and skills necessary to build these small warships and the order was placed with Hall Russell in Aberdeen. Five Peacock Class ships were built. One or two years later Prime Minister Thatcher demanded of the UK MoD why the HKPC had not been ordered from the shipping tycoon's yard. I was asked to give the reasons. I recall that at the time the tycoon was seeking tenders for four bulk carriers and we wanted the order; was Mrs Thatcher actually trying to get work for British Shipbuilders? But no, the orders went to Japan, the tycoon received a knighthood and there was much speculation in the press about contributions to Tory party funds by overseas people.

We were the only passengers in the front end of the North West Orient flight to Tokyo and we had to politely ask them to put the heating on as we flew up the western coast of mountainous Taiwan. It was freezing!. No one in Tokyo wanted Hong Kong dollars: they were quite brusque about it.

There was no provision for transit passengers in Seattle and we took our turn in the immigration queue with several hundred young male orientals who each had their documents in clear plastic bags and whose future, I judged, would depend critically on their acceptability or otherwise to the men at the immigration desks. We waited for an hour and a half for the man to eventually say that he was sorry that we had been kept for so long and we wanted Terminal 2. Actually what we wanted was the toilets, but lesson one for all travellers in US airports is never but never make jokes with a US immigration or customs man. What did they have in those vast books, the pages of which they turned over so quickly after picking up ones passport?. Nowadays they have computer terminals and I suppose that it is just credible that some giant computer somewhere is programmed to confirm, when asked by any one of several hundred thousand terminals around the good old US of A, that a certain DANIEL, R.J. has a valid visa to enter. It must be subtler than that, but it's a problem.

We went down in an elevator to a deserted underground station. We were being followed by two Chinese looking women who had clearly concluded that we knew where we were going or at the very least that we understood the language. Shortly afterwards an unmanned train slipped into the station. A disembodied voice recited which airlines were served by the next terminal and when it reached No 2 we got out. Not because we had understood a word of what disembodied Fred had said: he had clearly taken the equivalent of the British Railways station announcers' course on unintelligibility. The Chinese looking ladies also got out and I had to dissuade the ever helpful Liz from trying out her few words of Cantonese for, after all, they might be Japanese (unlikely, no cameras) , Vietnamese, Korean or even Chinese. My observation in 1945 that Chinese women had nice legs and no bust and Japanese women had busts but short legs hidden in black trousers was of no practical use at this point. In any case they probably both had degrees from UCLA. But it is interesting to see how the physique of females of both nations has visibly altered for the better in the past half century.

On another occasion it was my wish that Liz should see some of the places that I had visited during the war. The great mistake was stopping in Fiji. When we left Wellington Liz had been presented with an enormous floral decoration, which she was pleased to give to friends in Auckland with whom we spent the day. The aircraft for Fiji left Auckland at near midnight and landed at 5.30 in the morning. The airport is 70 miles from the capital, Suva and we stayed at an hotel nearby which we found had been more than half demolished in a typhoon. There were many frogs. We dined beside the swimming pool and became conscious of a small splashing noise in the pool. Liz knelt down and fished out an unfortunate frog; no one else moved a finger. The aircraft for Hawaii left at midnight and in the early dawn we were arriving at the Royal Hawaiian Hotel that had been the Pacific Fleet Submarine Officers Club when I had stayed there in 1946. It was now part of the Sheraton chain and much dwarfed by its more recent sisters. We spent two days there but there was no Hawaiian magic, just another place seething with tourists. Our flight for San Francisco departed at 10.00 pm and we could not extend our room beyond 6.00 pm so we went and sat in the airport with our baggage and ate oranges because a large notice said that we could not import vegetable matter into continental USA. We didn't know that an exception was made for pineapples. It was Saturday when we reached San Francisco. We stayed at Fisherman's Wharf and after sightseeing and visiting all of the usual places like Chinatown, Nob Hill and the Top of the Mark and Golden Gate Park, we spent most of our time there because, being the week-end, downtown San Francisco was dead. The whole trip was a miracle of mistiming.

Liz's last trip to Australia was not happy like previous ones. In addition to my work I gave two lectures at meetings in the Universities in Sydney. One evening we walked to the Circular Quay to catch a cab. There was no one there and Liz went to look at something nearby by which time a few other people were also waiting in line. When Liz came back to stand with me she was roundly abused by an Australian man and told to get back in the ****line. This upset her more than I would have thought. Next day she was window shopping and became aware that she was being followed by a man stalker; everywhere she went he was a few paces behind and she was conscious that she was being herded away from the hotel. After an hour she managed to escape by asking to leave by the back door of a shop and hurried back to the Wentworth. I asked her why she hadn't walked right past him to go back to the hotel and she said that she was too frightened.

We were due to return to the UK but something came up and I would have to go to Newcastle and then back to Sydney. Liz said I love you but I am going home. I took her to the airport. When she boarded the aircraft the purser said, "Your husband is already on board" and took her to a seat beside the one in which a large black man wearing a skirt was already seated. He was a senior Fijian police officer called Daniel, en-route to an Interpol meeting in Europe.

I was booked into an hotel up the Hunter Valley and some miles south of Newcastle I took a branch road to cut the corner off. It was now dark and the road was not wide. People had told me that lights attracted kangaroos and I didn't want to hurt some poor animal. I was mindful of John Cameron's wife, Jane, who had had a large deer or moose collide with her car and die when John was our liaison officer in New England. I arrived without incident. The country hotel or wine lodge in which I stayed was surrounded with vineyards. Periodically a brightly painted red, yellow and green tractor would pass up and down between the vines like a Noddy Toy putting on a show for the visitors. In the daytime I visited the shipyards and works at Carrington on the Hunter River and in Newcastle where I had several friends and in the late afternoons I visited some of the beautifully kept Hunter Valley vineyards.

It was at a private dinner during this visit that I was told about the decision of the RAN Navy Board in 1979 to confirm that under no circumstances would they ever have a British submarine and the decision that Rear Admiral Rourke RAN should go to Germany to seek a German design.

HMAS *Fremantle's* sea trials had been run with the third propeller design in which bubbles were seen at the blade roots. To cure this cavitation we adopted the well-proven remedy in high performance propellers of drilling holes through the roots. The Australians argued that this was an interim measure and asked that a fourth propeller design be made. This was done and the Mark 4 was supplied to Australia in 1980. The ships went slightly slower and the decision was made to revert to the drilled Mark 3 as suitable for the modified range of displacements agreed with the Australian navy. Remember that the basic design had been for a full load displacement of 212 tonnes. Due to the shipbuilders errors in building this had increased to some 230 tonnes of which some of the increase was clawed back by design changes in the follow-on ships. The displacements now agreed with the RAN for the drilled Mark 3 propeller were Standard 211, Full load 231 and Overload 246 tonnes.

Nothing further was heard until Rear Admiral Rourke visited BSHQ in March 1982 when he said that principally as the result of some propeller viewing trials on the third ship of the class the propellers were still considered to be less than satisfactory. He agreed to forward a copy of the trials report and Brooke Marine received this in early October. In the interim, Brooke Marine had received requests from the Dutch propeller company, Lipps, for hydrodynamic data on the Fremantle Class design and apologetic comments about an Australian trials report that Brooke Marine hadn't seen.

The report was of trials with the ship at 258.8 tonnes and 25.8 knots and had been approved by the RAN's Director of Ship Design. The kindest thing one can say is that he obviously hadn't read his junior officers report for it revealed an almost total lack of knowledge of the subject, was mutually contradictory and was critical of the shipbuilder and the propeller manufacturer in terms that would have justified substantial damages if taken to the courts.

On 18th November I attended a meeting in Canberra, chaired by Commodore (later Rear Admiral) Calder. The author of the report was not present - privately, we knew that at the time he was visiting the Netherlands Hydrodynamic Research people - nor was the Director of Ship Design - it was hinted that he was diplomatically sick. I said that the report was inaccurate and that wrong conclusions had been drawn; in any case at 258.8 tonnes and 25.8 knots the RAN should not be surprised to have propeller cavitation, this is a gross overloaded state. More seriously, the report contained statements that accused Brooke Marine and Bamfords the propeller designers of gross incompetence, such that we had considered taking legal action. The Department of Defence was of course free to prepare and circulate internally any material that it chose but British Shipbuilders took the gravest exception should the report or its contents be given to any person outside the DoD. I didn't say that I was aware that the substance of the report if not the report itself had already been passed to Lipps. Admiral Calder assured me that the report would not be given to third parties and I am sure that he personally believed this to be true at the time. We subsequently sent a copy of the offending report back to the DoD with our comments on pink pages opposite each of the report's white pages. We offered to produce new propellers for a 258 tonne, 25-knot condition at a price but this was not taken up.

I thought about using the RAN report as the basis for a learned paper for debate at the Royal Institution of Naval Architects, a sort of 'a little learning can be a dangerous thing' piece, but decided that this might not be welcomed in Canberra when we still hoped that they would chose a British submarine.

Ottawa was a small hamlet when Queen Victoria selected it to be Canada's capital city. Canberra, like Brazilia was a barren site when chosen to be a national capital. Faced with the real difficulty of choosing between Melbourne and Sydney a site somewhere between was selected. Early photographs show an open valley with a small stream, one or two trees and one small cabin. Today, Canberra has a large man-made lake and claims to have more trees than any other capital city, thanks to an enlightened policy that gave every incoming builder 20 trees and /or shrubs to plant in their garden. Whereas Ottawa has developed along the lines of a European city with government buildings, commerce and domestic buildings existing cheek-by-jowl, Canberra is purely and simply a place where bureaucrats and those who provide services to bureaucrats work, a place of government and government buildings. People do not live there, they live in satellite towns nearby, served by excellent roads and public transport ; at night Canberra was a dead city ; all the action was somewhere else.

Bush fires occasionally threaten Canberra. On one occasion when I was there, there were a number of fires on the surrounding hills, some of which, the police thought, were started by an arsonist. One of the fires on the hill behind the university, trapped people all night in the restaurant part way up the broadcasting tower until the scrub burned itself out. In the 1980's work was well advanced in building a new parliament building on one of the hills to replace the small and rather unimpressive building on the lakeside, which had long ago become inadequate for modern government. The new building seemed to me to be built of more millions of tonnes of concrete than any other building that I had seen but I was sure that when landscaped this would be a magnificent setting.

Back to the submarine story. During the visit to Canberra in March 1980 we were told at a meeting with Captain Tom Brinkley, RAN, Director Submarine Maintenance and Repair, that serious lobbying had begun. Italy, Germany, France, and Sweden were very actively promoting submarine designs for the RAN. The Germans represented both IKL/HDW and Thyssens and the design offered sounded much like the latter's Type 1700.

We were told that the Germans had detailed performance data on the Type 2400 which they showed not to equal their own design. They told the Australians that Vickers had given them the data. I had become aware on joining British Shipbuilders that there was some sort of marketing agreement between Vickers and IKL/HDW and was a little surprised to find them so active in this country; I was even more surprised to learn that Vickers had given them UK defence classified data. I was to learn a year or so later that the Germans were not there on a coat-trailing mission but because they had been invited by the RAN at the highest level and given every assurance of success.

The submarine desk officer summarised the thinking on the ship characteristics; compared with the British Type 2400 design the RAN wanted increased speed, increased diving depth, increased range, increased submerged endurance, more weapons, and a much smaller crew with super accommodation. The armament would be torpedoes and air flight weapons. An ability to fit a propulsion plant to give prolonged submerged endurance of more than two weeks would be a powerful advantage. Further the RAN wanted three diesel engines rather than two and preferred MTU engines to Paxmans.

The invitation to register interest in supplying a design and build submarines in Australia was issued in 1982 and Vickers responded on behalf of the UK. The process required the preparation of substantial volumes of plans and data covering all aspects of the design process, performance, construction methods, spares and support requirements and equipment, manpower and environmental issues and initial and through life costs and of course, 'offsets' meaning undertakings to buy items manufactured in Australia to more than the value of Australia's expenditure overseas. The insistence on 'industrial participation' is intended to use contracts with overseas suppliers to provide not only local employment and to reduce foreign expenditure but also to raise the national industrial level by extending product ranges and introducing entirely new manufacturing capabilities. The invitation went to Germany, France, Italy, Netherlands, Sweden and the UK

The responsibility for establishing these enhanced industrial capabilities would rest with the successful bidder for the submarine contract who would have the onerous task of persuading the manufacturers of the equipment and machinery fitted in his submarine to establish a capability in Australia to manufacture their products, either through an Australian subsidiary or by a licensing deal with an established Australian firm, all of which costs money. Where items would not be sourced in Australia the offshore supplier would be required to establish a capability to make something else or to buy manufactured Australian products to something like 120% of the value of those items. All of this had to be set out in some detail in the response to the Australian request for proposals; vague generalizations would not earn many marks. The bigger UK equipment companies such as GEC were no strangers to this sort of situation and made encouraging noises about making things in Australia, but the dozens of smaller suppliers were much more resistant to the idea that they should pay good money to equip the Australians to make their product and eventually to compete with them in the world markets; to them it was more sensible to put their money in the local savings and loan bank.

One could write a book about 'offsets'. All trade is really barter, exchanging so many baskets of product x for so many baskets of product y. For convenience the amounts are given money value (which lets in the middleman) and people and companies and nations endeavour to balance their books. It was once easy; I will sell you manufactured widgets and take from you bananas or tea or coffee or something in exchange. No problem because I know that there is an existing trade in bananas or tea or coffee or something, so they got the widgets and my nation continued to buy bananas etc from them. After a while they start to make things and point out that the banana trade exists anyway, so you must take my manufactured widgets in exchange for your manufactured widgets. This is much more difficult because someone in your country is already making the widget that he is offering.

Companies in the United States are experts in the offsets-promises-business. The usual scenario is that the UK wishes to obtain say 50 super new aircraft of such and such capability. The US is manufacturing 1,000 aircraft that meet this specification and Europe is about to start negotiations on the process of producing a similar product but nations cannot decide whether the total production run will be 400 or 250 over the next ten years and at any time which nations are in or out. Persuasive US voices suggest that buying American would position UK industry to supply components for 1000 plus aircraft and provide many more jobs in the UK than would, say, a 20% share of 250 European aircraft. When discussions are somewhat advanced and the UK has substantially compromised it's position vis-à-vis it's European allies, they mention in passing that under the Bogart-Garbo amendment to the Raft-Rathbone Fair Practices Act of 1972 or some such thing, they cannot actually guarantee this offset work to UK companies, it will have to be competed for, but, nudge, nudge, wink, wink, it will be alright on the day. Meanwhile there is favourable noises-off by air marshals who have been given a ride in a US aircraft.

A commitment is made to purchase the US system. There is much to-ing and fro-ing by British firms who are told by Ministers to get on their bikes and seek the promised sub-contract work. "Ah yes, can you manufacture to US MILSPEC so and so?" is the first hurdle. Enquiry shows that each relevant MILSPEC calls up about 20 others which each call up about 10 others in turn, many of which have been out of print for some years.

Visits to the Government Printing Office and the Library of Congress in Washington DC yield sympathy but no MILSPECS. By now the UK companies have acquired an expensive array of agents and lawyers whose last wish is to solve the problem and put them out of work. The prospective UK supplier is then hit with the requirement under another Act or directive of the Congress that if successful the UK company must establish a second source of supply in continental USA for important equipment. Eventually the UK companies put together and submit their proposal only to learn in due course that the contract for the advanced avionics suite for which they were bidding has been awarded to a company that assembles hay wagons in the Ozarks whose congressman is up for re-election next Fall.

So much for offsets. We were told by the Australian DoD in March 1980 that the Germans had still not honoured their offsets undertaking associated with the notorious purchase of the 100 Leopard tanks and that the US had spent only 10 million dollars of the 90 millions promised on the frigate programme. On the basis of the tough way the DoD talked with us about contracts, one would have expected that they would have banned the German and American defaulters from future supply contests; not a bit of it, there seemed to be other considerations.

While the submarine procurement selection process was going on, Australia was reviewing its defence strategy. To some extent this was being driven by the decision not to replace the RAN' s aircraft carrier, the post war symbol of a deep-water navy. Australia's strategy had hitherto been based on contributing to an allied (US) force in the Pacific and Indian Ocean theatres with a naval task group centred on the carrier operating in the forward area together with long-range aircraft.

The new strategy would be the defence of Australia. Submarines to operate 1000 miles from the homeland would be necessary together with patrol craft and their support to provide surveillance and deterrence along the northern sea frontier backed up with air transportable army units and artillery. Some frigates would be justified for the rapid deployment of a more powerful deterrence force against limited threats until more powerful allied naval and air forces could come to Australia's assistance.

This new strategy was the subject of a study in the Australian National University in Canberra. In discussion with the author I suggested that someone should make a computer simulation of the logistic problems that an invader would encounter after landing a moderate force on Australia's northern coast. It would show that such an invader must secure somewhere like Darwin on Day One to obtain access to the domestic infrastructure and airstrip. To establish a beachhead elsewhere would become an increasing drain on an invading nations resources where, apart from bombing to prevent them establishing a forward airstrip, the best policy for Australia might be to leave them alone. The exercise would show the value of helicopter troop carriers and helicopter deployable guns, such as VSEL's lightweight 155mm gun, in containing such a threat. The slightly sick joke in this context would be to ask the army where they are locating their one hundred Leopard tanks? Alice Springs'?

In response to the request for proposals, Vickers shipbuilders submitted two proposed designs, one was for the basic RN Type 2400 submarine and the second for a slightly bigger variant of the RN type 2400 to fully meet the RAN's staff requirements; in this way we hoped to meet the stated requirement upon which the DoD placed great emphasis, that the design for Australia should be fully proven; either in service or fully committed to entering service with a major navy. Of the other competing navies only France came near to this with a diesel version of the SSN Rubis. They tried to interest the RAN in going nuclear and when this was rejected they rather drifted away. The RAN set up a Submarine project team under Captain Graham White RAN with the responsibility of assessing the merits of the various proposals submitted by the overseas companies, using the expertise of the DoD specialists.

As was later to be the case in Canada, the UK was seriously disadvantaged by the closeness of the two navies. Australian submariners had served in British subs, they had served on British staffs and they had many British navy friends. Many had British wives. Those enjoying British hospitality faithfully reported all of the minor breakdowns of, and moans about, British submarines and their equipment back to Australia. No one reported how intensively the RN worked its ships and men compared with other navies - just the negative things. An example; one of the Australian requirements was that the new submarine should take no more than half a million man-hours to refit. With its modular design, big hull hatch and demonstrated access and upkeep profile for all equipments Vickers had no hesitation in stating that this requirement would be met in the RAN type 2400. Imagine our surprise one day when Frank Noah and I called on the Director General Design, Harry Dalrymple, and casually noted on his blackboard a table of figures which we realised from their pattern and value must be the various nations estimated man-hours to refit. Against the UK was 1.8 million. We asked why and Harry explained that the submarine project had asked one of the RAN' s exchange officers at the RN's submarine base at Gosport. He had wandered into the submarine maintenance office and asked the Chief Petty Officer what he thought. Although the RN type 2400 submarines were barely ordered and the maintenance authority had no information about them, the chief had lived up to the highest traditions of the naval service −"never admit that you don't know", − looked up at the ceiling and said about 1.8 million. This had been reported back to Canberra and the submarine project had ruled that it be used instead of the figure given by Vickers in the formal response to tender. And so it went on.

In 1980 British Shipbuilders had set up an Australian company. With the privatisation of Vickers Shipbuilders, in future to be known as VSEL, the BS Company lapsed and I became a director of VSEL Australia Pty Ltd. We had Rear Admiral Max Read RAN (rtd) as a navy consultant and Captain Tom Brinkley RAN(rtd) as our resident man. Tom had been a nuclear qualified officer in the RN and the first engineer officer of the first British Polaris missile submarine, *HMS Resolution*. He had transferred to the RAN and held a captain's post in submarine maintenance before retiring. In Canberra, Hawker Pacific provided us with office space and support.

It is remarkable how little interest and influence Australian ministers appeared to have in the submarine project and similarly the members of the Navy Board save for Rear Admiral Rourke. Despite our best efforts we saw ministers very infrequently. Without question Prime Minister Bob Hawke was the best of the bunch and was always relaxed, whereas the other members of his cabinet whom we met seemed to be unbriefed and uneasy; detached would perhaps be a better description. Most times I wondered whether Foreign minister Bob Hayden gave a damn whether Australia had submarines or not. The minister for Industry was Senator Button; he too seemed to have been pleasantly brainwashed beyond uttering generalities but I do give him credit for remarking in a TV interview that he didn't know how the submarine selection process was going but what with all the overseas visitors " it was sure good for the Canberra hotel trade." Kim Beasley, the minister for defence, was reputedly destined for greater things but as far as we and our advisers could judge he had little influence on the day-to-day work and thinking of his officials. There was a young lady reporter in London working for the Australian press; she claimed to have a direct line to Mr Sinclair the leader of the opposition in the Australian parliament, by whom she could advance the British case by having him ask questions in the House. This proved to be another damp squib.

Looking back on our efforts to have the RAN adopt the British submarine it is remarkable how, despite the best efforts of the High Commissioner, the British High Commission in Canberra was only able to play a minor role in the affair. It was all rather low-key stuff. This was a consequence of the Australian position where Ministers seemed to play no part in the submarine country of origin debate and left it all to the navy.

The airport in Canberra was extremely primitive in the 1980's with a small terminal building and manual luggage handling- it came off the aircraft and was put on the ground outside the terminal. Hard luck if it rained. Somehow it was out of scale with all the money that had been spent on the other buildings in Canberra. But then although the people arriving might be ambassadors and other VIP's there were not too many of those in a week.

One day we took our seats on a flight from Sydney to Canberra and found that the front row seats were occupied by the Archbishop of Canterbury and his secretary, the row behind that by Terry Waite, alone in the aisle seat, with Noah and I in the two seats behind him in the third row. When we were on the final approach, the Archbishop stood up and his secretary helped him put on his robe and vestments. Terry Waite had risen at the same time and his massive bulk blocked the aisle. For the first time in all the years I realised that Terry was the archbishops 'minder'. His role was to ensure that His Grace would appear first and with dignity when the aircraft door was opened and the steps in position. And thus it was, but when the arrival and stately progress across the apron was shown on the TV that night, two little figures could be discerned to emerge and scuttle away to outflank the official party. That was Noah and Daniel.

In Canberra we usually stayed at the Lakeside Hotel. Frank always got excellent service after someone called him Lord Noah, you see the hotel was properly styled the Noah Lakeside Hotel, part of a chain originated in New Zealand by a Mr Noah. The staff weren't taking any chances, after all, he might be a relative, he acted like one and he was seen on TV with the Archbishop of Canterbury, wasn't he?

I only made one trip off the beaten track and that was along some side roads to try to see some of the birds and animals. There was one small kangaroo sitting behind a wire fence about 30 cm high. He gave the impression of having come down to the road to watch the humans go by and being disappointed with what he had seen. The other sighting was a group of kangaroos beneath a tree in a meadow, big one, three smaller ones and several little ones. The really exciting thing was to round a corner and find a store and a few houses buried in the gum tree forest with hundreds of the most beautifully coloured parakeets everywhere, on the ground, in the trees and in the air. Unforgettable.

The submission of further submarine papers and the evaluation process dragged on through 1983 and 1984. There was little or no formal or informal structured discussion with officials, one called on them and chatted or took them to lunch. We were never accorded an opportunity to properly discuss our proposals and alternatives with the project team officers. There was no chance to sit around the table with DoD's experts to describe and discuss the pro's and con's of our designs and how they might be made to meet the latest Australian thinking, It always had to be on the basis of written submissions. Perhaps our submissions were not good enough but we did happen to have designed and built and supported in service bigger, faster, deeper diving and more powerfully armed submarines than any of the other competing nations. Surely that should have some attraction?. But no; we were kept at arms length throughout.

The submarine programme manager, Captain Graham White, treated us with extreme discourtesy. His attitude was always distant and rude. We were only permitted to call on him five or six times and on each occasion he avoided shaking hands and sat impassively behind his desk while we said our piece. He never commented or took a note, simply heard us out in silence (Frank Noah called it his Buddha pose) then said that he had another meeting. Another pointer to our poor prospects was the one occasion that any official invited us to his home. Most of the Australian Admirals and Commodores had spent some time in London and in my various posts in the Ministry of Defence they had become friends and more than occasional lunch or dinner guests. This had continued in London after I joined British Shipbuilders. We were invited to an al-fresco lunch of beer and sandwiches at Admiral Rourke's home. Our reception by Mrs Rourke was unsmiling and, whether she realised it or not, her body language made it clear that no-one in that household was singing the praises of the British.

I was also surprised to be told by an Australian admiral that they had been let down by the British who had not come to their aid in January 1942. All I could say was that we had had our own troubles at that time but I do see how maddening it must have been to have the best part of the Australian army in the Middle East and unable to be got back in time. The fact that it was raised some forty years later I took to be an indication of how desperately they were seeking to justify their anti-British submarine attitude.

Throughout the entire period I was busy meeting industrialists, politicians (both state and federal) and the media and getting to know what makes Australia tick. During my visit to the Hunter Valley a member of the Board of Newcastle State Shipyard told me what a friend of mine, Geoff Woolrich, a recently retired Rear Admiral, had told his fellow members of that Board. The substance of what he said is as follows. In 1979, the Australian Navy Board had confirmed that it did not want any more British warships or submarines and that they should buy German. In 1980 Admiral Rourke had gone to Germany to ask IKL to prepare a design to meet the RAN's specification for construction in Australia. IKL had replied that they were tied to the German shipbuilder, HDW and unable to help. Rourke had then approached German government officials who had said it was a commercial matter. HDW had said that if certain post-war constraints could be cleared away they would be prepared to do a part Germany / part Australia build. Someone in authority, perhaps External Affairs, had then decided that for political reasons there should be a competition. In due course the invitations to register an interest were issued to a number of nations but the navy's firm intention was to have a German submarine.

The procedure was that two of the submarines offered should be selected for a final more detailed competition; rumours in the media were that this would be the Germans and the Swedes. The oft-repeated attraction of the Swedes was in part that the country had a comparable population and political philosophy to Australia. It is interesting that after more than a decade of business with overseas visitors, Liz would fully endorse this comparison as regards social behaviour.

Towards the end we were much helped by a labour member of the Australian parliament, one of the two members representing the whole of Western Australia. His constituency was everything outside Perth; a small area about the size of Western Europe, while the other member, who happened to be the Minister of Defence, represented Perth. Graham felt that we were getting a raw deal and started to ask questions in the House. He felt that the ruling party should do more than simply rubber stamp what the admirals said and he got it agreed that the competing nations should each give evidence to, and be questioned by, the Foreign Affairs and Defence Committee and the Industry Committee of the Caucus; consisting of back bench members of the Labour party. Nations would be expected to submit a written paper in advance.

It is important to understand on such occasions that the other competing nations will get hold of a copy of your paper just as you intend to spare no effort to get to see what they have written. Your paper should not blatantly rubbish the opposition; if its possible to let published data do this, then include the substance of that data and be sure to draw attention to it, in passing, when giving evidence. In the days leading up to the meetings I began to receive from various sources, copies of the papers submitted by the competition. The Germans seemed to have written two papers; there was the "Sir, We are honoured to present our submarine design. Yours faithfully" bit and attached was another two sheet document.

Wednesday 20th March 1985 came and we were ushered in for our half an hour or so of questioning by the caucus. The first question put to us by the Chairman was "Why does the British navy have such a low opinion of the Australian navy's submarine service and doubt its ability to operate more modern submarines"?. There were five other questions of a slightly less poisonous nature. We answered the questions.

I learned that a list of suggested questions for each nation had been prepared by the submarine project team and given to the Chairman just before the meeting. Some days later I received a copy of these questions. There, bold as brass, were the six questions that we had been asked. There was a separate sheet for each competing nation, none were hostile in the way that ours were and all were asked just four or five questions, in fact those for the Germans were quite helpful and constructive. Suddenly I realised that I had not only seen the German questions before, I had also seen the answers! The sheets attached to the back of the German briefing paper submitted to the caucus about a week before the 20th March meeting had actually answered the questions, one by one in the order given, that the caucus hadn't asked yet.

I pointed this out to the MP for Western Australia. The caucus was due to take evidence from the navy's project team and its leader. The navy was told to be prepared to justify the questions that they had suggested. In fact what the caucus got was the Chief of Naval Staff, other Board members and lesser fly. According to my informant the project team leader was not present. The first question that the Chairman asked the CNS was "Why do your officers dislike the British navy?"

The CNS protested that the RAN did not dislike the British Royal Navy; they were its friends, many had served together and he did not know what had put that idea into the Caucus's mind. So they told him, again, and reminded him of the questions prepared by his officers.

At about this time Rear Admiral Rourke's retirement from the navy was deferred by a month; he told me that this was to ensure that the navy actually got a submarine. Think about it.

As the result of their deliberations and the German briefing paper, members of the caucus drew the attention of the Parliamentary Ombudsman to what seemed to be peculiarities in the relationship between the navy and at least one of the nations competing for the submarine contract. The acting Ombudsman, a retired Air Commodore, at first declined, saying that his small staff was no match against the resources that the large Department of Defence could deploy. I am told that it was pointed out to him by friendly MP's that this is the usual position of his office and unless he wanted to be an exacting ombudsman he had better get on with it. After some time the ombudsman issued a report to parliament indicating that there was evidence of some irregularity. A very high level source told me that the Chief of Naval Staff had made a much deeper investigation into the matter, the results of which were in his safe and no-one would be allowed to see it. Shortly afterwards the senior members of the submarine project team were appointed to other posts and Rear Admiral Oscar Hughes was made Submarine Project Director.

Notwithstanding the fact that they were paper designs, bigger than either company had previously built and thus did not meet the 'type already in service or nearly so' criterion the Australian navy had made so much of earlier, the Swedish and German designs were selected for the run off.

Quite soon thereafter the Australian DoD people approached my old Ministry department, Ship Department, saying that they did not have people capable of properly assessing the merits of the competing German and Swedish designs when received and would the British lend them some experienced submarine designers to help with the selection. I was consulted on the old-boy network and they were told politely to bugger-off.

We withdrew. Tony Peake, Frank Noah and I seriously discussed whether we should seek to sue the Australians for gross misrepresentation and I was fairly sure that we could have achieved a cash settlement. Frank was asked by the UK MoD Defence Marketing people not to do this because they hoped the UK might obtain the RAN frigate order. I said that the UK had no chance whatsoever of winning the frigate order and gave the UK MoD people chapter and verse about the debt someone in Australia now owed to the Germans but they persisted that Yarrows had a chance and we backed off.

This was not the end of it. When the more thoroughly worked up German and Swedish designs were received in Canberra, surprise, surprise, both were larger and more expensive than the UK boat.

Now the RAN had to decide between them and something very, very, odd took place. It was as if the word had gone forth that the Germans must NOT be allowed to win. According to someone who had access to what was going on, the results of any comparison of capability were biased upwards for the Swedes and downwards for the Germans. The informant felt so strongly about what was going on that he sent the highly classified Australian-eyes-only papers showing this 'the Germans always overstate their performance so cut them down a bit' and 'the Swedes always understate their performance so mark them up a bit' philosophy to the national news papers who published it, Secret classification stamp as well. The leaked documents also revealed some serious disagreement within the navy concerning the evaluation process. The Swedish submarine was chosen.

In July 1987, in an article in Jane's Defence Weekly, Dr. Jurgen Ritterhoff, the project manager (Australia) of the German submarine design firm, IKL, made an unprecedented attack on the Australian navy accusing them of, "grossly distorting normal tender evaluation procedures by deliberately removing the HDW/IKL Type 2000 submarine from the competition by upgrading the offered performance of the Swedish Kockums Type 471 boat and downgrading the German Type 2000 offered figures". He then went on to give chapter and verse.

Some time later the Australians invited proposals for frigates. I again advised the UK not to bother since I regarded it as certain that the contract would go to Germany. It did and if you study the financial structure that linked the elements of German industry at that time you will appreciate that the chickens were bound to come home to roost in the end. Having said that, they are nice frigates.

At the request of Transfields, Frank Noah asked me to visit the Dockyard at Williamstown and advise them on its possible use for the construction of frigates. The sun shone, gentle waves slapped at the dock gates and I walked around the workshops and offices of this delightful and well-equipped small yard on which the Commonwealth had spent so much money in recent years. Of course they should buy it was my recommendation; managed by good people and with the high tech. area of Melbourne close by it should be able to compete for price and certainly for quality with other locations in Australia. Their problem, as always, would be the labour unions and this would be so for most locations in Australia. I heard later that they had been beaten in the bidding by another company and had then remedied the situation by buying up that company. I like people who think big.

It was December 22nd and flights to the UK were fully booked. I got a flight with Thai Airways via Bangkok. The flight from Bangkok was supposed to depart at 23.30 but finally left an hour late. An hour into the flight, the captain said "Sorry, we have a problem and we have to go back". There were not many first class passengers and the stewardesses chattered and started looking everywhere and I gathered that it was thought that there was a bomb on board. I went to sleep; there was little that I could do about it. At Bangkok we were accompanied down the runway by fire engines and police trucks and parked on the other side of the airfield. We were taken off as quickly as possible and after a short but chaotic delay I was taken to the Sheraton Hotel. Next morning we were all rounded up and required to identify our baggage and allowed to board the aircraft as our baggage was loaded. No problem for me because since the first time my luggage went astray I had never checked any baggage when travelling alone. I took three suits, six shirts and all the other necessities in a Hartmann valise over my shoulder and kept it in the cabin with me.

In the night I had managed to telephone home and say, "Do not go to Heathrow. There has been a delay. I will be on the Siamese Airways flight". Why I said Siamese I will never know.

In due course all the passengers were on board and sixteen items of baggage were still on the tarmac plus a large TV box. The police who I thought had found some sort of potential incendiary device, behaved with considerable skill and discipline throughout the entire emergency. We took off. There was one stop, New Delhi, where we were parked about 400 metres from any building and a small army of dhoti-clad cleaners came aboard. Through the open doors of the aircraft came that unmistakable dry Indian climate smell that I had first experienced in 1944, out of the sight of land when HMS *Ameer* turned left at the marker buoy and made for Cochin. Four separate men emptied and cleaned my unused ashtray. The only joining passenger in my cabin was a man with both legs in bandages who was carried on board.

We took off. For some reason I had assumed that our route would be towards the head of the Persian Gulf and Syria and I was surprised that after some time we were passing over successive ranges of snow capped mountains. Only then did I think about great circles from Bangkok to London and what this might mean. The aircraft captain was from Scandinavian Airways with whom Thai had a sharing arrangement and he confirmed that we would pass about 50 kilometres south of Moscow. He would have preferred to be 100 km to the south but he had to keep to the Soviet commercial air corridors. He said that the Soviet air-traffic controllers who dealt with international traffic were good. Our route would then be overhead Riga, Copenhagen and Amsterdam and into London.

When I had been with the UK MoD my security status was such that I was not permitted to visit any of the communist or associated states and this prohibition was still in place when I was with British Shipbuilders although obviously common sense would suggest of rapidly diminishing importance. The blank spot in the system was that flights to the middle and Far East refuelled in the Gulf States and flew over Bulgaria in getting there. In the early days Frank Noah used to joke that if we crash-landed he had orders to eliminate me. Since at my heyday my personal estimate of the financial value to the Soviets of all that I knew was about £5, this seemed a rotten bargain. With the introduction of the 747-400 series and non-stop flights to Hong Kong, Bangkok and Singapore the whole thing was now farcical, one flew for hours and hours over territory that one was not allowed to set foot on at pain of death.

The flight to Heathrow was delightful. It was December 23rd and the aircraft's internal announcement system played Christmas music and carols the whole time. Since I like everything to do with Christmas this was OK with me but I did wonder a little about this being an aircraft from a Buddhist nation. I couldn't imagine that Chinese lot (whose planes we avoided like the plague just as we avoided Pakistan International, but for another reason) playing Christmas music.

We landed at 6.OOpm and there was Liz, smiling as ever, and the two little dogs wagging their backsides off. Liz had her story to tell. My call had come just when she had been about to drive to Heathrow. She had tried by phone to discover when the rescheduled Siamese flight would arrive. Of course at 6.OOam UK time she might as well have been speaking Swahili and it was only after a couple of strong cups of tea that she suddenly realised that for Siamese read Thai and by then the people in Bangkok had started to put the new flight plan on the line. Liz maintains that I wasn't the life and soul of that Christmas. It was a little difficult to explain that I had had ten hours of Good King Wenceslas about 50 km south of Moscow a day or so earlier.

As for the Australian submarine programme; well, with all the delays and troubles and the wholesale replacement of bits they must be costing several times what a German or British submarine fleet would have cost. And those nice SAAB cars must now be looking quite old.

It would not be an overstatement to say that the Australian submarine programme has been one of the great non-successes of recent times. None of the submarines has proved capable of properly performing in the intended anti-submarine role and successive get-well measures have simply added to their woes. The seriousness of the failure to perform was set out in the McIntosh Prescott Report and we are told, one year later, that the work to fix the problems is now on track. Three of the Collins Class are operational to some degree and it is hoped that the two "fast track" submarines, when upgraded by December 2,000, will be able to operate successfully in their intended role. An Australian Navy spokesman said the deficiencies to be overcome are the submarines operational deficiencies and their poor reliability, adding "the problems are being fixed and we have significant improvements to the noise signature on the upgraded submarines". He added, "In the longer term I believe that it will be necessary to replace the combat system on all six submarines which will be the biggest additional expense for the project". This would cost an additional A $1 billion. " To achieve the necessary reduction in noise will include reshaping the hull and fitting new propellers". Almost unbelievable!.

Hardly a testimonial for the Swedish designers of the Collins Class and their weapons systems associates. And, of course, any discussion of the cost that I have seen does not take into account the cost of tying-up all these defence funds for the past 15 years for little operational use.

Chapter Sixteen

My lifelong love affair with Canada began when I was eight years old. I wrote to Canada House in Trafalgar Square in London and they sent me a big dark blue book, the size of a road atlas, on the front of which was inset a picture of a train steaming through Kicking Horse Pass. The Hudson Bay Company and the RCMP featured in the adventure stories that I read. The Hudson Bay came up years later when I was consulted by another government department about the possibility and economics of operating a nuclear powered bulk carrier between Churchill and the Atlantic ports. I produced an outline proposal and also a proposal for a very large nuclear powered submarine version that might be capable of yearlong operation under the ice. Economically, both would have been disastrous.

My move to the Board of British Shipbuilders brought many visits in our attempt to win the frigate design order in association with the Canadian company GenStar and some years later, as VSEL's Canadian Project Director, we sought to win the submarine design order.

Vice Admiral (rtd) Bob Stevens was our usual GenStar escort in Ottawa and Jim Byrne in Vancouver. One Sunday morning in Ottawa we witnessed the drill ceremony of the Canadian Guards Regiment on the lawn in front of the Parliament Building. A substantial military band dressed in the then common olive brown uniform led the parade followed by the guard in their scarlet tunics and bearskin hats similar to those worn by their British counterparts. To the musical accompaniment of the band the guard went through their drill display for about 20 minutes and then marched off to their buses and away. I was surprised that some of the uniforms appeared not to fit very well and that some of the soldiers had longish hair. I knew Bob well enough to be able to remark on this and he explained that the young people of the display team were not soldiers at all ; they were students who were paid to put on the Sunday show. Someone in the Department of National Defence had calculated that it was less costly to do it this way than to keep a troop of regular guardsmen in Ottawa for the purpose and the non-discrimination laws meant that girls could not be excluded from this employment. I cannot speak for the Canadian public but I would have thought that the band playing and marching would have been a sufficient attraction and it would have been even cheaper. Around the corner from the guards display some young people in costume were re-enacting a minor historical skirmish with the aid of an ancient cannon, muskets and pikes and much shouting.

In the very early days I was keen that Liz should visit Quebec City, a place of history and great charm. We took the afternoon flight from Montreal, emerged from the small airport into stygian darkness and engaged a cab. We were driven at speed with walls of snow high on each side and confessed to one another afterwards that we both had remembered the story of a couple who, some weeks earlier had arrived on this same flight and taken a cab in which they had given a lift to a Chinese girl. They had been driven out into the country, stripped and robbed. And here we were being driven who knows where by a seeming deaf mute. Eventually lights appeared and we were safely delivered at the Quebec Hilton. The next day I marched Liz over the icy pavements to see old Quebec, the Chateau and the icebreakers busy on the frozen St Lawrence. She seemed not to share my delight; she had just flown in from Hong Kong and was not really dressed for arctic exploration. We repaired to the excellent shops beneath the hotel to make good some of the deficiencies and then it started to snow again. We were isolated for three days in the hotel — I thought that it was lovely.

Jim Byrne's family fortune was based on the tugboat and barge trade, hauling vast quantities of timber and wood pulp along the coast and rivers of the western seaboard of Canada and the USA. To people like myself, familiar in childhood with Thames barges, a 100-ton load was a lot but the Canadians were regularly towing strings of three barges from Vancouver to San Diego with each barge containing 6,000 tons of wood pulp. Like all really great maritime cities, Vancouver embraced its magnificent harbour, much of which, at that time was unspoilt by man. There was a fleet of bulkers off English Beach waiting their turn for loading with wheat for China. Jim was into prefabricated apartment buildings, he had recently acquired a twenty-odd story building in North Vancouver and occupied the penthouse from which the views of the harbour and city were breathtaking.

In most of the countries that we visited in the early 1980's people would talk about Margaret Thatcher and how they envied the British people because we had a strong leader. They were surprised that, notwithstanding the courageous way that she had fought the trade unions and the Argentineans, we had reservations, largely we explained, with the way the income from the North Sea was being used to keep taxes low rather than to rebuild the essential infrastructure of the nation and the fact that the lady was surrounding herself with 'yes men', ministers and officials who would not argue with her; a sure way to weaken her own party in the fullness of time. Even some of my own colleagues thought that it was a little odd that I was not a 100% Thatcher man.

Canadian government contract regulations are framed to ensure cost competitiveness and require the contracting authority to solicit bids wherever possible and to evaluate those bids against stated criteria. The problem in Canada is that having stated these ideals and placed full contractual and financial responsibility with one contractor, ministers then seek to dictate where major parts of the work are placed. This is invariably to ensure that Quebec gets work.

The Canadian Patrol Frigate (CPF) is an example of this. We offered the RN Type 22 frigate design, modified to take Canada's preferred weapons and machinery outfit. The RN's first of class had just entered service and we knew all about performance, man-hours to build and cost. Instead, the Canadians had selected a paper design. The actual contract as framed by the Assistant Deputy Ministers in DND and DSS was very good. St. John Shipbuilders were appointed prime contractors to detail the design and build the first six ships. They were, however, required to place sub-contracts for one and a half frigates each with two shipbuilders in Quebec and to sub-contract the entire weapons and control system to a new software company called Paramax in Quebec; a company with strong links to US companies. Mercifully one of the Quebec shipbuilders went out of business and the vision of towing half-ships up the St Lawrence no longer haunted the programme manager. Paper designs always grow. The contracted displacement was 3,900 tons. Towards completion in 1989 the displacement was already 4,750 tons with consequent loss of freeboard, stability, speed, sea keeping and lifetime development potential. Cost-wise the situation was even more depressing for the prime contractor. The Quebec shipyards, which were owned by the Quebec government through a holding company, were hopelessly over budget and were being sued by the prime contractor, St John's, for non-performance. The prime was also suing Paramax for contributing to the delay in completion of the first ships. The Quebec government was saying "Don't look to us for money, the federal government arranged this contract (sic) so its their responsibility to bail out the Quebec yards" and so on.

Although the 1987 Defence White Paper was to make much of the need to re-equip the Canadian armed forces, the process had begun tardily with the CPF orders under the previous, Liberal, administration. That this was much overdue was illustrated by a visit to a ship in Halifax. It was at the 1987 meeting of the Canadian Avionics Industries Association.

A side event was to be a cruise in Bedford Basin in a frigate of the Canadian Navy. We assembled on the ship only to be told after some delay, that the trip could not take place because it was so long since the main turbines had been run, they were now suspect. The Commanding Officer who came to the stern to make this curt announcement, perhaps mindful that we represented an avionics association added, "We have a good helicopter" turned on his heel, mounted a ladder and disappeared. We also walked through one of the Oberon Class submarines, during which our guide, the ship's supply officer, complained about how old the ship's equipment was. The Canadians asked him what did he expect from a government that wouldn't spend money on the forces. Some time later I got a copy of their operational schedule and noted that they did a quarter as much time at sea each year as did one of our boats.

Canada's three Oberon Class diesel electric submarines had become due for replacement in the early 1980's. The Canadian Department of National Defence (DND) issued an invitation to seven overseas nations to provide proposals for their replacement, such proposals to be made through a number of Canadian shipbuilding companies. The overseas designer / builder would have to provide information about the design, construction methods, man-hours to build and refit, cost to build and total lifetime ownership costs over the predicted life of the fleet, among other things, in the hope of winning the contract!

To ensure that the proposals were realistic, it was mandatory that only designs that were already in service or about to enter service would be considered. The Canadian companies would then select which overseas partner they considered best met their government's requirements when measured against such criteria as whole life cost, Canadian industrial involvement, offset and operational characteristics. These selected designs and sponsors would then compete in a final selection process. The assessment would be made by a Canadian Submarine Project Team (CASAP) headed by a DND project manager and comprising representatives of the Department of National Defence, the Department of Supplies and Services, the Department of Industry and the Department of External Affairs. DSS would place the contract and monitor the construction.

Since the Canadian Navy had a continuing dialogue with the British Ministry of Defence (MoD) and had used the Type 2400 Upholder Class staff requirement in formulating their own, we assumed that the Type 2400, of which the first of class boat was nearing completion, would be a useful contender, provided the UK MoD did not object to information on their latest diesel submarine and its equipment being given to four or five Canadian companies. We obtained the MoD's permission and the consent of the major equipment suppliers, modified the design to meet the Canadian navy's requirements and entered into a dialogue with the Canadian companies.

In the course of our visits we learned that, notwithstanding the insistence on a proven design already in or near service, most other nations had submitted 'paper' submarines. Paper submarines are always smaller and cheaper than real submarines. We had seen the same thing in Australia. The German and Swedish designs chosen for the final run-off were both smaller and cheaper than the British proposal based on the Type 2400. At the end of the run-off both were bigger and more expensive. We then had the pleasure of watching the Australian navy bend the results in favour of the Swedish design because the parliamentary ombudsman had found that there was evidence of some sort of collusion between the navy project team and the Germans. Lest you should think that was the end of the story, note that the Germans were awarded the ensuing Australian frigate contract and the Swedish submarines have been plagued with problems.

In the middle of the previous year the US vessel Manhattan had sailed from the Atlantic to the Pacific through the North West Passage and had been roundly attacked in parliament by the Canadian Minister for External Affairs, Joe Clarke, for transiting Canadian waters without notification or permission. The US claimed that the North West Passage was an international seaway. Loud voices were raised in Canada about sovereignty while wiser voices pointed out the truism, "If you can't defend it, you can't claim sovereignty over it". The one vehicle that could maintain watch in all seasons and demonstrate sovereignty over these hostile regions would be a nuclear submarine.

As had been the case in Australia, we learned that the French were offering a diesel-engined version of their *Rubis* nuclear submarine with the possibility of changing it to nuclear should Canada wish to acquire SSN's. Following some rather vague discussion in Whitehall about the possibility that the UK might be prepared to release the Trafalgar Class design to Canada, subject to all sorts of safeguards, Frank Noah and I had a meeting with Assistant Deputy Minister (Material) Ed Healey, Assistant Deputy Minister (Policy) Bob Fowler and Chief of Naval Staff Chuck Thomas in DND on 14th February 1987 at which we said that "should Canada ask for a British nuclear submarine, the light might be amber, if not green". Fowler immediately asked "What about the 1958 Agreement." and displayed a considerable knowledge that could only have come from a British or US source. Admiral Thomas commented, "The sure way to ensure that Canada gets nuclear subs is for an American admiral to tell her that she shouldn't have them".

We had no idea that Canada had been having discussions with the US, British and French navies on the subject of nuclear submarines. Our rather naive assumption at that time was that the US government and navy would welcome Canada making a bigger contribution to the seaward defence of North America in a sort of maritime Norad; that Canada would wish to have submarines comparable with those operated by the USN and the RN, 'the best', and that the US would recognise Canada's unique position vis-à-vis themselves and the UK in their approach to amending the 1958 Anglo-US Agreement. On each count we were to be proven wrong.

A month or so later we were informed by the UK MoD that they had received a protest from US Admiral McKee that VSEL in Ottawa was supplying nuclear information to the Canadians and must be stopped. I replied that this was not so; all that we had done had been to repeat Admiral Sir John Fieldhouse's comment. Furthermore the US Navy might be reminded that Canada had a mature nuclear industry in which were many people who had once worked for Westinghouse, GE, the US Navy, General Dynamics, Rolls Royce, the US Atomic Energy Authority, the US atomic weapons plants and so on and each had probably contributed his bit to Canadian know-how.

In June 1987, a Canadian government White Paper announced that Canada would acquire nuclear submarines and thus give her navy a three oceans capability ~ in the Atlantic, the Arctic and the Pacific. The competition to provide diesel-electric submarines ceased. We were aware that the UK submarine had not been the front runner even though it existed and we had full cost and man-hours data; a classic case of do not confuse us with the facts and the Canadian DND's habit of moving the goalposts in defence procurement exercises. The announcement also included changes in the way large capital projects would be funded in future. Although not remarked on widely at the time, a cynic would recognise this as Finance Minister Wilson's joker in the pack.

Very soon after the publication of the White Paper, Defence Minister Perrin Beatty visited the Pentagon in Washington DC to explain Canada's intentions to the US

Secretary for Defence, Cap Weinberger. Beatty was accompanied by his Chief Staff Officer Bruce McLennan, Chief of Naval Staff Vice Admiral Thomas, Chief of Submarine Acquisition Rear Admiral Anderson, Assistant Deputy Minister (Policy) Fowler, Commodore Bowkett, Captain Harrison and Ambassador Gotlieb and staff members of the Washington embassy. The Canadian team gave two presentations based on a 1,500 page report by Commodore Bowkett, prepared following his teams visits to the US, UK and France.

Following the presentations, Cap Weinberger excused himself saying that his officers would comment and he would rejoin Beatty for lunch. US Admiral McKee then commented on the presentation pointing out the pitfalls, expense and complexity of the engineering. He was followed by US Vice Admiral Bruce De Mars who was more critical and asked whether any operational studies had been made. Learning that there had been none De Mars said, "I thought so, otherwise you would not be considering that noisy little French pick-up truck". This and similar pointed but fair criticisms of the shallowness of both the study and the Canadian officers understanding of that upon which they planned to embark, had Anderson red with embarrassment and Bowkett so obviously distressed that, according to my informant who was present throughout, he was practically in tears after the meeting.

Beatty considered that the US admirals and Frank Gafney, who was present and had criticised the study, had insulted Canada and himself and only refrained from walking out for "fear of provoking an international incident" (his words). He went to lunch with Weinburger and protested at his treatment to which a relaxed Weinberger remarked that "He often had to remind the Admirals who was in charge here, he was". This did nothing to assuage Beatty's pride and he returned to Ottawa determined to justify the nuclear submarine study, which was the kernel of his 1987, White Paper and the inclusion of the French submarine.

According to my informant, Beatty was so angry that he would have ordered the French submarine there and then to avoid any further entanglement with the Americans. This dislike of the US Navy remained with him for the remainder of his tenure of office For its part the US Navy remained incredulous that decisions of such defence, financial and industrial importance could be based on such fragile research and understanding.

As befits a company endeavouring to foster trade links with Canada, VSEL became a member of the UK - Canada Chamber of Commerce. We met alternately in each other's country; in the UK it was always London and in Canada we visited Quebec City, Montreal, Toronto and Ottawa. At each occasion we were addressed by a minister, in Canada usually by two, one federal and one provincial and given a resume of current concerns, legislation, trade and industrial hopes.. The larger corporations would sponsor hospitality events and provide free-bee's like folders and plastic pens. The Premier of Ontario gave us Alfred Sung umbrellas — this was before he badly misjudged the mood of his province and went, unnecessarily, for a snap election when he judged the tidings were good, only to be soundly beaten. He had made the cardinal error of expressing support for Quebec on some issue in which the French-Canadians were in dispute with the federal government.

During the Quebec City meetings something about the submarine came up nationally and I was asked to take part in a televised debate on CBC. I sat alone in a small room and spoke to a TV camera. I was not permitted to watch on a TV monitor the other members of the panel who were in Montreal or Toronto, but must respond just to their voices. I noticed that thereafter my UK -Canada colleagues treated me with new respect; it's a rum world.

At the Toronto meetings someone with influence enabled us to jump the queue and ride to the top of the Toronto tower. We also went to the Niagara Falls. The US falls are clearly a big disappointment to all red-blooded Americans; they were always smaller but now their lip had fallen to the base to make them look more like steep rapids than falls. Beside them is the mighty arc of the Canadian falls with millions of gallons falling the 170 feet every second. It's enough to make a guy emigrate. For a small charge the public can go behind the falls. I was kitted out with a yellow sou'wester and oilskin and rode the elevator down to a tunnel from which three branch tunnels went to the actual back of the falls. From two of them all that could be seen through the spray was a grey wall of falling water but the third led to a platform to the side of the falls and one could look along the wall of water. The noise was indescribable. Back on the surface and divested of my yellow protective clothing I realised that I now had a lightish grey suit with about 10 inches of darkish grey, damp trouser bottoms and shoes. Looking around I could identify other people who had had the underground spray treatment. Down in the millpond below the falls there were pleasure steamers, which approached and disappeared into the spray at the bottom of the falls. The visitors who took this trip were kitted out with blue souwesters and oilskins and they got even wetter than I did before the steamer reappeared. I reflected on why people went to Niagara for their honeymoon? Going to the delightful small town of Niagara-on-the-Lake I could well understand. The other interesting thing was that they were making a costume movie about the man who walked across the falls on a tightrope. At some distance from the falls a crane jib was stuck out horizontally and from this a taut wire about 30 metres long was stretched at an angle back to the cliff edge.   Filmed with the correct lenses and angles, a walker on the wire would seem to be crossing the span of the falls.

Most visits were a gastronomic challenge; typically lunch with the Montreal City Authority, dinner with the government of Quebec. Next day, lunch with the Toronto Metropolitan Authority, dinner with the government of Ontario. Next day lunch with the Ottawa Civic Authority, and dinner with the federal government. This was 'eating for England' with a vengeance.

Transatlantic flights did not land at Ottawa and one had the choice of Toronto or Duval, a new international airport some kilometres north of Montreal.   The British Airways flights to Duval went on to Detroit. Walker Morrow came from the Detroit area. We first met him when he stayed in one of Liz's holiday flats. He was then in his 90's and accompanied by his nurse whom he subsequently married. He had been a close associate of Henry Ford in the opening years of the twentieth century, not making automobiles but in Ford's aviation company set up to develop an all metal airship [a blimp] intended for the US forces. Henry Ford had no place for fabric; the skin of his airship was of riveted light alloy. Aware of our perennial problem of containing fluids without leakage I questioned him closely on this. It seemed that they achieved acceptable gas tightness and the craft flew and was evaluated by the US Navy. Alas, no production orders were forthcoming. He gave me a copy of the book that he has written on the subject.

The Air France and Alitalia return flights to Europe left Duval a short while before the British Airways flight. It seemed that each Alitalia passenger had at least four people to see them off and so the landside was a teeming mass of Italians from about 8pm onwards. When the flight was called they moved out on to the viewing balconies and waved. They waved at the mobile lounges, they waved at the plane on take-off and were still waving when the aircraft was a mere speck in the sky. Canada might be prosperous, welcoming and the land of opportunity but at that moment it was not Italia.

The competition was now between the UK and France since no US company wished to court Admiral McKees displeasure and seek a contract which most of them felt would not be proceeded with, once Canada fully understood the magnitude of the task. VSEL had formed a subsidiary VSEL Defence Systems Canada and the French government formed a company SNA. The Board of VSEL's Canadian company comprised VSEL's Commercial Director, Frank Noah, Vice Admiral (rtd) Jock Allen, Rear Admiral (rtd) Bill Christie, former ADM (Mat) John Killick, Sam Hughes, Peter Cathcart and myself, VSEL's Canadian Project Director.

Rolls Royce and Associates as the design agents and suppliers of the RN's nuclear plant would also be closely associated in the British effort. VSEL had already engaged Sam Hughes as consultant in Ottawa and, when it became clear that the US Navy would be difficult, engaged consultants in Washington DC. Rolls Royce was, of course, already well established in Canada and in the USA. Treaty-wise it was a minefield. If the UK were to be permitted to supply nuclear propulsion information and materiel to Canada, the 1958 Anglo-US Agreement would require amendment. If Canada were to be permitted to read these data and receive these materials, the 1959 Canada-US Agreement would require amendment.

It was good that the RR&A effort in Canada was led by Rear Admiral (rtd) John Burgess supported by many old friends of mine from Derby. John and I had been colleagues for years, most recently when he was the Naval Assistant to the Controller of the Navy and then Admiral in the Rosyth Naval base. We could trust each other implicitly to maintain the other company's interests. There were many other major UK companies who supplied equipment for the Trafalgar Class submarines and these expressed a preparedness to seek partners in Canadian industry. With Frank Noah's initiative we formed the Trafalgar Consortium.

The Canadian Staff Requirement outlining the performance characteristics required of the submarine had been deliberately 'written down' to embrace the French *Rubis* Class submarine, a vessel not explicitly designed for an anti-submarine role. The navy's attitude was that as long as these values were achieved the competing submarine would receive 100% score in this part of the assessment procedure. The much higher speed, deeper diving depth, greater silence, bigger weapons capacity and so on of the British boat would not attract one additional merit mark. A new, negative, approach for a nation that, according to the former Canadian Chief of Defence Staff, General Ramsey Withers, prided itself that while their armed forces accepted that their equipment might be inferior in numbers to an opponents, they knew that it was never inferior in quality.

The Canadian Requirement had three mandatory items:
- It must be a fully proven design in service with an allied navy;
- It must be able to fire and control the US Navy's Mark 48 torpedo;
- It must be able to surface through one metre of arctic ice

The British Trafalgar Class met all three criteria. The French *Rubis* Class could not meet the last two. Furthermore the changes necessary to enable it to do so would require, among other things, a substantial lengthening of the boat, such as to be virtually a different design and hence by definition would not fulfil the first mandatory requirement. In these circumstances we felt that honesty and natural justice would result in the selection of the British vessel provided that the problem of the US agreements could be overcome.

There began the pilgrimage of French ministers and officials to Ottawa and, of course, Quebec. In one month alone ten visited. Within a short while President Mitterand was there on a seven-day visit. In our innocence, we pleaded for a British minister to come to Canada. They were keen enough to visit the USA; could they not be persuaded to drop-in on Canada. Finally George Younger, the UK Secretary of State for Defence came to Ottawa in September. His visit lasted just over a day and we were told by Beatty's

Chief of Staff, Bruce Mc Lennan, that, to their surprise, he had not made a powerful sales 'pitch' for the British submarine, rather that he had just mentioned the submarine in passing.

The Defence attaché and the Commercial counsellor in the High Commission had been supportive during the diesel saga and the move to nuclear submarines, with the political overtones of amending agreements with the USA, brought in more members of that staff. The High Commissioner Sir Derek Day, promised every support but was vague and clearly disinterested. At about the fourth desultory meeting at which we exchanged banalities, I made the true but unfortunate comment "Since the question of amending the 1958 Agreement was urgent and would finally have to be determined by President Reagan and Mrs. Thatcher, it should be referred to them at once and not left to bumbling bureaucrats". Frank Noah dined out on the story for some weeks.

What we didn't know, and of which Day made no mention, was that he was about to retire. He would be seen being driven around in his ancient ambassadorial Rolls Royce and then he was gone, Rolls Royce and all. The post was left empty for some months but the Deputy High Commissioner and his wife (the Commercial Counsellor) were very active. The new High Commissioner, Sir Alan Urwick, was a breath of fresh air that galvanised the entire staff. One day when he got to know me better he said that he had been surprised to find that his predecessor had not made a single file note on the subject of the submarine. The Defence attaché, Captain James Laybourne was a submariner, ex-commander of a Valiant Class SSN and a friend of thirty years standing. Captain Keith Potter, an electrical engineering specialist from my old department in Bath, relieved him.

The early reaction from both the US and British navies had been that the Canadians did not have the engineering depth and resources to build and support a fleet of nuclear submarines. This was not a reflection on their ability which was second to none in the fields to which they had devoted their resources but a conviction that they had not comprehended how much of their defence budget and skilled manpower the submarine fleet would absorb in future years. As the American Senators were quick to point out, only Luxemburg of the NATO nations spent a smaller proportion of their GNP on defence than Canada and a fleet of SSN's would eat up a sizeable chunk of that modest sum.

It was no part of my brief to warn them off. Our submarine was built and in service; we supplied the most accurate cost and manpower information that we had and it was up to the Canadian government to decide if they could afford SSN's, in the most global way.

Visitors from the UK MoD did not help us. Sir David Perry who seemed to be between appointments at the time led the first visit from Whitehall. He and his colleagues warned the Canadians of the technology and cost burden that ownership of SSN's would bring and rehearsed the problem of the 1958 Anglo-US Agreement and the 1959 Canada-US Agreement. Urgent action was required to advance the former. To the Canadian's surprise, Perry departed not to Washington to deal with the 1958 Agreement, but to a routine NATO meeting in Spain. The immediate comment from Vice Admiral 'Chuck' Thomas was that the British had better get their priorities right; is Canada less important than a routine NATO meeting; surely there were plenty of people who could have gone to that? This impression was added to by the fact that after the first meeting Perry just disappeared from the scene. Being excluded from these discussions did not help VSEL's position in Canada.

The few follow-up visitors from the UK all had the same message, they went on and on about the cost, complexity and special safety requirements that nuclear systems entailed. Not one man seemed to be aware that Canada had had an operational nuclear reactor before Britain did and that more than 50% of the electric power generated in Ontario came from nuclear power stations. Vice Admiral Hugh Thompson the Director General Ships came over with people from his nuclear propulsion group and they had the same uninspiring off-putting messages.

Notwithstanding the strong support that we were getting from the High Commissioner, his new Naval Attaché never hesitated to remark that the Canadian government's decision to go for a fleet of nuclear submarines was wrong and that what Canada should have was diesel-electric boats.   I assumed that this was his private opinion expressed to people like myself within the High Commission until one day Vice Admiral Thomas buttonholed me and said "Look, your Naval Attaché is going around Ottawa telling everyone that we are stupid to want nuclear submarines and that we should stick to diesel-electric. We don't care if he destroys the UK' s chances with the Trafalgar Class, that's your business, but his remarks have reached some pretty influential people and he is now endangering the Canadian navy's chance of getting nuclear submarines at all and that definitely is our business. We want him moved; you send that message back to the MoD." The message was duly reported back along the old-boy network to the navy in Whitehall. Admiral Thomas noted that no action resulted.

Senior Canadian officers visited the RN's submarine bases and VSEL's building yard where they were shown round Trafalgar Class ships under construction. They also went to similar activities in France. Wherever they went they were quietly checking up on what we had told them about performance, man-hours and cost. Since everything they visited in France was government owned and manned, they presumably all sang from the same song sheet. By contrast the British must have seemed like a disorganised rabble giving what each individual felt to be honest answers and in the good old tradition of never admitting that they didn't know. Typical of this; in consultation with the nuclear power people in Bath and with Rolls Royce and Associates we had given the Canadians an order of cost figure of about £40 millions to equip a modern submarine refitting yard to handle SSN's. Canadian visitors to the French dockyards had been given a comparable but smaller order of cost of £ 30 millions by DCN. They had visited the British dockyard at Devonport and had been told £450 millions.

We suggested that there would be great benefit from a visit by an SSN to a Canadian Atlantic port and we also stressed that publicity should be given to one of the RN SSN's excursions under the arctic ice, both events intended to drive home the message that we alone already had in service a submarine that met, and exceeded, the Canadian requirements. It was finally arranged, navy-to-navy, that the latest Trafalgar Class submarine, HMS *Torbay* would visit Halifax, Nova Scotia, in October 1987. The French submarine *Saphir* would visit one month later.

Now was our chance. But no, the Naval Attaché insisted that the visit was to be treated as a normal ships visit to an overseas port and VSEL was to have no part in the programme other than to pay for the cost of entertainment associated with the visit. The submarine was berthed at a remote jetty across the harbour from Halifax and we were told that we could use a small hut some 70 metres from the submarine from which Frank Noah and I would emerge like Jacks in-the-box to speak with, but not accompany, passing Canadian VIP's. The final event was to be a day at sea for six VIP's and everyone assumed that I would accompany them; after all, I had been responsible for the design of the submarine and every other class of British nuclear submarine, so who better?. The night before the trip the Naval Attaché announced that he had received a signal from Flag Officer Submarines that I was not to be allowed to accompany the Canadians.   He declined to show us the signal.

It was not all negative, however, we went to the cocktail party and we gave a dinner party for about sixty people in our hotel. At the cocktail party I was speaking with Bryan Boyd, an Assistant Deputy Minister and pointing out how difficult it was for us to give whole life support costs for a nuclear submarine force whose navy could not tell us where or how they would be based; it might be a greenfield site. He replied, "At least you know something, the navy appear to know nothing about anything".

In any case the UK had scored another marketing own-goal that we didn't know about until the second day of the visit when some large, heavy wooden boxes arrived at the local Canadian air-force base and were delivered to the jetty and some VSEL workmen were flown in. This new submarine had arrived with a defective pump. It probably hadn't met the rigorous noise standards when the submarine had done her post-completion noise trials. Instead of taking a chance that World War III would not start before she got back to the UK, it had been decided to make the repair during the Halifax visit. No one anywhere appeared to have given any thought to the image this would present. All of the personnel at the air force base and the naval base and soon their wives and children and the local press knew that the new British nuclear submarine had something wrong with it.

The French performance a month later was flawless. They took two floors of the local hotel, they brought in a fleet of white limousines and one or two white helicopters, all with French markings, to ferry people between the airport, hotel and submarine. They built a full-scale replica of an automated control room of the future and they allowed everyone sponsored by the Canadian authorities and the press to go on board their submarine and a great number to go to sea in her on successive days. They were lavish in their hospitality.

Up to that time, outside Perrin Beatty's charmed circle, the French had not had much credibility with the Canadian navy and media. The show that they put on for the *Saphir* visit and the lacklustre, take-it-or-leave-it nature of the *Torbay* visit changed all that.

We were much exercised by what we considered to be tardiness on the part of the British government in facing up the question of amending the 1958 Agreement and the Canadian government in regard to the 1959 Agreement. The initial approaches were made through the Zuckerman - Wagner channel and were not very productive although by October 1987 the US Navy / Dept of Energy had agreed that the British might talk nuclear propulsion with the Canadians in general terms..

The US Navy's Office of Naval Reactors and the Department of Energy's Naval Reactors Branch — same people, different hats — were opposed to Canada acquiring nuclear information. The early Canadian enquiries had not been taken seriously. The first public manifestation of the US Navy's opposition was at a conference organised by the Financial Post on 18th November 1987 at which I was asked to present a paper on 'Nuclear Submarine Procurement'. This was to be followed by a piece by a US Assistant Secretary for Defence entitled 'The US and Defence Procurement; will the partnership grow?' Unfortunately the scheduled speaker could not leave Washington and the US naval attaché chose to be out of town and so the assistant NA, Captain Bob Hofford USN inherited the role at four hours notice.

His formal speech was fine but he rather let his hair down in answering questions and the press were quick to seize on this. Points that he made included; "It is common knowledge that Mr Beatty's first trip down to meet Admiral McKee did not end in a very successful or satisfactory meeting." "When Canada approached us for information two years ago, the answers were very brief". "When Canada said we will have SSN's there was complete disbelief in the Pentagon and the Department of Energy." "Admiral McKee did not know what a White Paper was". "If you are having these submarines for the sake of sovereignty then I am afraid that you are going to have a tough time with the US Congress. We have long memories when someone steps on our tail." "DOD and DOE did a years work in three weeks to get agreement that the British could talk nuclear with you". "We still have to convince Congress who are usually six months behind and there is the 90 day rule for tacit acceptance".

In the light of developments this looks fairly tame but it cost him his job in Ottawa. He did say, interestingly enough "The decision that the (Canadian) Department of National Defence took last November (1986) to opt for nuclear propulsion was again something that never registered (in Washington DC)". Could it be that seven nations had been spending good money advancing their diesel electric submarines for six or seven months after the DND had told the US Navy that it was going nuclear? But of course Beatty might not have had the agreement of his cabinet colleagues at that time. Did they tell the British at the same time and was this why Admiral Fieldhouse said that " the light might be amber" in response to our questions in February 1987?

In Washington, Admiral Bruce de Mars was in process of relieving Admiral Mckee. The British admirals who had confidently spoken of changing Kenny McKee's opposition "over a glass of gin" had retired hurt. The Office of Naval Reactors was marshalling opposition to the British proposal that the 1958 Agreement might be amended to allow nuclear propulsion data to be supplied to Canada, by briefing key members of the House and Senate Armed Forces Committees. This took the form of classified written and oral briefings. It is of course proper that members of the Congress should be informed on matters concerning their nation's armed forces and security but members generally must also be conscious of the subtle flattery implicit in this process when members of the House and Senate Armed Forces Committees are given classified information by important people like admirals, information to which their fellow congressmen are not privy and which puts the recipients on the side of the admirals.

Should the US Administration agree to Canada having access to the British data they would have to place the proposed amended 1959 Agreement before Congress. There were usually several hundred such measures which were agreed by being placed 'on the table' of Congress for 90 working days. If a member raised a question in the House or Senate, the matter must be debated and the timescale became unpredictable. There was some question whether this process would be required for the 1958 Anglo - US Agreement but we were told that it would certainly apply in the case of the 1959 Canada - US Agreement.

We employed lobbyists in Washington and visited the Capitol many times to speak with Senators and Representatives and members of their staffs. We were received courteously and told of the high regard they had for the UK and Canada. They were sure that the Canadians did not understand the cost and difficulty of the operation of nuclear submarines and were concerned lest a Canadian effort might draw labour away from the US Navy's programme and an accident might reflect on the US Navy's reputation. It was clear that they were quoting from briefing papers supplied by the Navy and we were soon so familiar with the words that we could give the paragraph numbers. Senator's staffs were usually more direct and as the months went by there was no doubt in my mind that the US Navy had no intention of allowing Canada to acquire Trafalgar Class submarines. We had several discussions with senators Warren and Exon but this did not dissuade both Senators from eventually addressing the Senate on the subject in March 1988, warning Canada of the cost and difficulties of ownership of nuclear submarines and how difficult it would be for the US to modify its position to allow sensitive nuclear information to be supplied. The most significant part of the Senators address was a reference to the US Atomic Energy Act of 1954 and an indication that whatever we and our friends in the administration and congress succeeded in doing, the members of the Senate Armed Forces Committee would see that it was discussed by the Senate and probably talked out. So much for our hope that the amendment to the 1958 Agreement would be 'nodded through' the House and Senate under the 90-day rule.

It was not all trouble and strife. We spoke of many other things. One that sticks in my mind was a remark that Senator Warren made when we were riding up in a lift. Apropos of something that was said he remarked, "When you've had three wives and two mistresses like I have, nothing should surprise you". (It might have been two wives and three mistresses). One of those wives was Elizabeth Taylor.

Frank Noah and I arrived in the Mayflower Hotel one evening and found that it seemed to be busier than usual. At dinner the ever-observant Noah remarked that the other diners were preponderantly pairs of men and when we learned that on the morrow there was to be a mass march of gay men on the Capitol, understanding dawned. We had no nightcap but scuttled off to our rooms. By the following evening all was back to normal in the hotel. I have since learned that whenever he was in Washington, and this was most of the time, J. Edgar Hoover, the now largely disgraced long-time head of the FBI, would lunch at the Mayflower with his male lover, Clyde Tolson. One day I entered the lift and turned to face the doors as one normally does. The voice of the man standing behind me was familiar, much more familiar than that of the man with whom he was talking. Both were in evening dress. When we reached the lobby there was a lady waiting for them whom I recognised as Dorothy Lamour; the men were James Stewart and Burt Lancaster and all three were on the way to a charity reception at the White House. On another occasion on arriving from the airport, I was stopped by a young man on the wide pavement outside the hotel and politely asked to wait a minute. I noted the small earphone. A few seconds later a limo drew up and Mr and Mrs Lee Kuan Yew entered the hotel, closely followed by a second car bringing Vice President and Mrs Bush. The timing was faultless.

In the submarine base mess in New London there used to be, and perhaps still is, a large notice that proclaimed that there are only two types of vessels at sea, 'Submarines and Targets'. The US Navy's submarine service's approach to the oceans of the world and in particular those washing north American shores, is that there is only room for themselves i.e. US submarines and potential targets. Friendly submarines are a nuisance but acceptable as long as they are diesel—electric or noisy nuclears. The British Trafalgars were a nuisance because they were as silent or even more silent than the US boats and handled themselves rather well.

There were initially three different opinions in US official circles. The President, his Secretary of State, Schultz, Secretary for Defence, Weinberger and National Security Adviser, Powell, were in favour of acceding to the British request. They probably wished that we hadn't asked but recognised the particular status of Canada and that the US public at large would welcome a Canada able to contribute more to the defence of North America. The Pentagon and the Chairman of the Joint Chiefs of Staff, Admiral Crowe were ambivalent at first but gradually hardened against release. The third opinion was the Navy's submarine service (the Jesuits) and nuclear reactor people and the Department of Energy headed by Admirals McKee/De Mars and Watkins respectively, who never weakened in their opposition.

Why Jesuits? It comes from the fact that at that time, so many of the commanding officers of US nuclear submarines and particularly ballistic missile submarines were Roman Catholics. It will be recalled that Admiral Rickover personally interviewed every officer candidate for service in nuclear submarines and again for fitness for command. He was aware that in the war in Korea, the Chinese and North Koreans, under Soviet guidance, had made great efforts to 'turn' US prisoners of war and enlist them as their agents. They had categorised the prisoners into four groups from 'easy to convert' and hence worthless, to 'very difficult to convert', and potentially people who would maintain their new loyalty once persuaded. It was the latter category on which they concentrated, using malnutrition, solitary confinement and beatings in attempts to break their will. Percentage-wise there were more Roman Catholics than Protestants in this very-difficult-to-convert category, not unreasonably in view of the strong anti-communist stance of the Church of Rome. Admiral Rickover and the personnel Admirals were aware of this and tended to reflect this bias in their search for commanders who could be relied upon absolutely to launch their missiles when commanded to do so.

There came the day when the Pope was selected from Poland. No chance of him changing the churches stands against communism but he might be persuaded to condemn all those who would launch death and destruction on their fellow men. What then would be the reaction of the Roman Catholic CO's of submarines armed with Polaris and Trident missiles? And so in recent years the Jesuits have become less so.

One of the more important channels for exchanging information was the Canadian High Commission in London. The Defence and Naval attaché and assistants were acquaintances from way back and more recently from assisting the Canadian navy in drawing up its Statement of Requirements for the diesel-electric submarine. The shift to nuclear and the need for secure means of transmission of information and documents between the nations gave the role of the High Commission a new importance. In Ottawa we heard stories of the strong support that the Canadian ambassador in Paris, M. Bouchard was giving to the French contender, including a message to Prime Minister Mulroney that "President Mitterand would regard it as a reflection on French honour if the French submarine is not chosen".

The Canadian High Commissioner in London, Mr McMurtry was a much less assertive man. It was difficult to discern whether he felt strongly about anything. He spoke of painting and fishing and the weather in the UK and Canada. The closest he came to endorsing our product was one day when he said "I hope that your submarine is chosen" and then immediately looked at his Commercial Counsellor and asked "I am allowed to say that, aren't I?"

The greatest condemnation of Mr McMurtry and the Canadian External Affairs Department was the failure to deal with their resident spy. We had our Canadian company; VSEL Defence Systems Canada and the French had their Canadian Company, SNA. The chairman of SNA was M. Lawrence Herman. His brother Barry Herman was the representative in London of the Canadian Intelligence Service – the resident 'spook' with the responsibility, among other things, of protecting every facet of the High Commissions activities. To paraphrase Peter Wright he need not have 'bugged and burgled his way across London' but he certainly had the authority to penetrate all the offices in Grosvenor Square. He was described to us by a senior Canadian official as a man very close to his brother.

I was made more aware of this potential problem by a chance meeting in Washington, late in 1987, with one of the three US civilian officers from the State Department who had been with me at the Imperial Defence College. I had long since discovered that he had an office in a large building in Langley Va. I brought up the subject of the submarine and he said that he judged that US Navy opinion was hardening against helping the British and they would see that the thing got bogged down in Congress. The Administration's power and influence was waning as the presidential election approached and the best we could hope for from them was best wishes. On parting he said, cryptically "I hope that you are sending anything confidential through your High Commission in Ottawa and not the Canadian one in London".

There is no evidence that anyone did anything improper but we felt that the Canadian High Commission should be like Caesar's wife and be seen to be above suspicion and that it was the boss man's duty to make it so.

The Canadian Submarine Project Team (CASAP) , set up to conduct the diesel-electric submarine procurement process was led by Captain Dent Harrison, a submarine officer with engineering qualifications. His DSS opposite number was Mike Fisher and Bill Jamer represented the Industrial Benefits side. The same team took over the same role for the SSN evaluation.

At the beginning, the UK MoD instructed the Canadian DND that all questions concerning the performance and equipment of the Trafalgar Class must be directed to themselves and not to VSEL or RR & A. But within the UK MoD's administrative and costing structure there was no sub-head against which officers to answer questions from Canada, might be charged. After some discussion and because of the sales nature of the work, Frank Noah agreed that VSEL would pay towards the cost of retaining an officer to act as the point of contact. Commodore Dick Husk took up the duty. Late in 1987 it was agreed among officials that a nuclear experienced naval engineering officer, would be seconded to Ottawa for a period of six months initially, to assist the Canadian submarine project and more particularly, the nuclear propulsion group under Bowkett to interpret the information being supplied from the UK. We had drawn attention to the fact that the French had 24 officers of DCN, Technatome and Thomson-CSF on the spot in Ottawa.

In May 1988 a junior Canadian officer in the nuclear propulsion group asked for help. He complained to me that he couldn't get answers to his queries of the British. When he asked the French, an officer would come round immediately and either provide the answer or get it from Paris by the next day. When he telephoned London, Commodore Husk was never there and furthermore did not seem to have a secretary to answer the phone. This was true; the MoD would not provide one. So the Canadians had given up trying. "But", I said "what about Commander McFadden, why don't you ask him?" The Canadian was astonished to learn that VSEL had not been told that at desk level MoD Bath had cancelled the nuclear commanders secondment some weeks before he was due to arrive. Questioned, Bath said that Canadian Commodore Bowkett had said that he did not need any more information from the British.

Negotiations started on the Memorandum of Understanding, which would govern the conduct of the British and Canadian governments in the matter of the supply of information and the construction of the submarines. The Defence Export Marketing organisation of the MoD led for the UK and Captain Harrison, the head of the CASAP, led for Canada. I was allowed to sit in on these negotiations. Although Husk had been named as the single point of contact with the MoD, he did not attend the meetings, which were loosely chaired by the Regional Marketing Director, a fact that rather perplexed the Canadians.

Captain Dent Harrison knew commodore Husk. By one at those quirks of fate, Commodore Husk, when Commander Husk, had been the 'trainer' who several years earlier, had failed Dent Harrison on the RN's Submarine Commanding Officers Qualifying Course (aptly known as the Perisher), I think, on the grounds that Dent was a little too dashing. This had not soured the levelheaded Dent.

At these meetings it became embarrassingly plain that there had been little or no policy briefing of the MoD team who behaved as if it was an internal meeting in which the uninformed picked things up as they went along and made fairly outrageous comments (in Canadian eyes). Typically, the Canadians had prepared an outline of their proposal for the memorandum. In discussion the Canadians indicated which clauses were important to them. Overnight the UK prepared an updated revision; all of the clauses that the Canadians had said were important to them were omitted. When challenged the UK chairman laughingly explained that 'we were trying it on'. The MoD Director of Nuclear Propulsion could not be dissuaded from his homily on how difficult it all was; this led to Mike Fisher, the representative of the Canadian Department of Supplies and Services, semi-jokingly asking me afterwards whether DNP's salary was being paid by the Americans. It was a misguided compliment to the Canadians that they were treated as 'one of us'. The British officials never appreciated that when the Canadians ceased to argue about a clause and moved to the next one, this did not mean that they had conceded the point. Usually it meant that the Canadians had given them 0 out of 10 and passed on and of course the Canadians were the customer.

This then was the climate generated by the well-meaning British in these Anglo-Canadian meetings.

After a short while we became aware that much of the information requested by the Canadians was commercial data such as the breakdown of cost and man-hours and that at desk level the MoD was asking VSEL Barrow for information without revealing the purpose and sending these data to Canada, thus possibly pre-empting VSEL's commercial position. This culminated in the preparation and supply of comprehensive MoD/VSEL volumes of information in January 1988.

Ever since the June 1987 White Paper the Canadian anti-nuclear protest lobby had maintained its opposition to Canada having nuclear submarines. Central to this was Charles Lamb and the Centre for Arms Control and Disarmament, a well-respected body. They were particularly caustic about France's record on nuclear proliferation in supplying nuclear know--how, equipment and fissile materiel to Iraq, Iran, Pakistan, Israel and so on. We were asked by Beatty's office to rubbish Lamb and his Centre in the media whenever possible. This we declined to do; but we did point out the several thousands of incident free submarine-years of operation in US and British submarines of the type of reactor we were proposing for Canadian submarines.

The handling of nuclear information presents unique problems in government and in industry. Canada's DND had set up an office separate from the CASAP to handle this; the question now was what to do in industry?. There was also a resolve in DND to configure future contracts so that responsibility was clear and unambiguous from the outset. There had been problems with the definition of machinery systems and their interface with the rest of the ship in earlier contracts and the Assistant Deputy Minister (Material), Ed Healey (the Canadian Chief of Defence Procurement) was determined that this should not happen in the submarine.

For RN nuclear submarines, Rolls Royce & Associates are the MoD's design agent and supplier for the nuclear steam raising plant. VSEL are the main contractor for submarines and place a sub-contract with RR&A for the supply of the nuclear steam raising plant which VSEL then fit in the submarine with help from RR&A. RR&A are fully integrated into the Test Groups which test all the equipment and systems and eventually the submarine itself in accordance with test documentation approved by the appropriate national safety authorities. Responsibility is clear in the UK.

The solution outlined to us by ADM (Mat) was to create an entity, which would be responsible for the entire machinery installation 'from atoms to propeller nut'. Atomic Energy Canada would be the leader in the entity together with the offshore designer / supplier and one or two other Canadian companies, such as Canatom. As in all things Canadian, a space must be made for a company from Quebec.

Both John Burgess and I said that we would not have chosen such a broad 'atoms to propeller nut' approach which might create as many problems as it solved, but we recognised that there were powerful reasons why he might wish it. We recommended strongly that, as in the UK when RR&A was created, the main contractor (usually the ship-builder) when selected, should be a member of the entity. This would avoid a 'them and us' mentality developing. Over the ensuing year we had a series of meetings with AECL regarding the formation and working of the entity and prepared outline Memoranda of Understanding. I was much impressed by the speed at which AECL worked. Classified information was not discussed - only how it should be handled.

After a while we learned that we had been much more cooperative with the AECL team than had been the French who had steadfastly declined to enter into meaningful discussions because apparently, they did not accept that an 'entity' was required. There were several signs that the French intended that the bulk of the nuclear work would be done in France.

The submarine project team was strongly opposed to the entity concept and recommended that something on the lines of the British arrangement be adopted. The opposition of the project manager Captain Dent Harrison was one of the factors that led to his being summarily relieved from this post in 1988 and replaced by Captain Bruce Baxter.

As a research tool and as a possible source of power and heat at remote locations such as in the Northern Territories and along the arctic fringe, the AECL had produced a low energy nuclear reactor with good safety characteristics, called Slowpoke. DND was interested because in 1988 it was taking 18 tons of aircraft fuel to deliver 1 ton of useable fuel at the most remote Canadian forces base. A similar but smaller development was proceeding commercially by an outfit called AMPS, to produce a small nuclear plant capable of topping up the battery of a diesel-electric submarine without recourse to atmospheric air or dangerous chemicals. During the initial Canadian diesel-electric exercise we had liased with this company in Ottawa and provided them with information on typical submarine structures and power requirements for 2,000-ton submarines like the Type 2400. The office in Ottawa was run by a retired Canadian naval constructor who, when on exchange duty with the RN, had been a member of the crew of one of the first, if not the first, RN diesel-electric submarines to venture for a day or so beneath the arctic ice.

The company was associated and shared offices with, a well known ship design and engineering company, several members of whose staff were from the UK. One evening I was present in their office when there were present five ex-members of the UK Royal Corps of Naval Constructors, plus the current exchange Constructor Lieutenant Commander in DND. One was retired Constructor Captain Keith Farrell who had graduated with me in 1942 and another was Andrew Kendrick whose father, Bill Kendrick, a member of the Royal Naval Scientific Service, had done more than any other person in the 1950's to 70's to advance our theoretical knowledge of submarine strength.

The prototype hardware for the AMPS proposed submarine mini-reactor was being developed near Toronto, and had reached tilting tests to measure the effect of submarine manoeuvres on heat transfer and control. I was enormously impressed with the preparedness of the Canadian business community to back this proposal financially, including negotiations with the US General Atomics regarding the supply of low-grade fissile material. I could not help but compare it with the unwillingness to risk / financial safety first, approach of UK companies over the past 30 years which, in many cases, has lead eventually to take over by an overseas competitor.

1988 was a presidential election year in the USA. We were conscious of the passage of time and that under the 90-day rule, in the most favourable circumstances, it was essential that the proposed amendments to the 1958 and 1959 Agreements should be placed before Congress by the end of May to give sufficient congressional working days before they rose in August preparatory to the November elections. Since there were only three senators and three representatives who were known to be concerned with the issue, it was hoped that in the event the US Navy would finally advise them not to oppose the amendments. We had no idea at that time of the lengths to which the US Navy would go to oppose their retiring president's instructions. We were receiving private reports of the efforts being made by various US subordinate commanders to persuade Canadian officers of the problems and lack of wisdom of Canada building and operating nuclear submarines. In many cases the tone and manner of their intervention gave offence. "But nothing traumatic" said one of my informants. In March 1988 I was told by a very senior Canadian friend "It's too late, Jack".

In late March, doubtless alerted by the navy that discussions were taking place at presidential level concerning the transfer of nuclear know-how from the UK to Canada, US Senators Warren and Exon read their warnings into the congressional record. President Reagan was advised by officials not to agree to the transfer of nuclear information from the UK to Canada but in April the President and his closest advisers decided to go counter to this advice and favour the US's two closest allies, while acceeding to the request of his admirals that such action should be conditional upon Canada first choosing the British submarine, a doubly sensible caveat since US intelligence sources suspected that the Beatty charmed circle had already struck a deal with the French or were about to. The White House was being much cleverer than the Navy. They could see that an outright rejection might leave the way clear for Beatty to place an order with the French 'as the only possible supplier' whereas time might show the Canadian government that they really could not afford nuclear submarines at all.

From the time of the June 7th 1987 White Paper, there had been speculation in the Canadian press concerning the eventual whole life cost of the nuclear submarine programme. The original figure given by Perrin Beatty was C$ 5 billion. This was hastily amended to C$ 8 billions when it was realised that the lower figure was the cost of the ships and did not include the cost of running and maintaining them for the next 20 years. It quickly became known that there were differences between the Treasury Board and Defence regarding cost and Perrin Beatty was rather rude to one of his Treasury Board critics, Madam Vezina, in public with a reference to riding bicycles or some such thing. Beatty, who perhaps saw himself as a future Prime Minister, behaved like one and brushed criticism aside. We know that quite early in the event he was stoutly maintaining the C$ 8 billions figure in an interview for the Globe and Mail when he already had his own official's estimate of C$ 9 billions in his office and Madam Vezina in the Treasury had a figure of over C$ 10 billions. In the Canadian system these figures were "class D" estimates — rough orders of magnitude. Recent government projects at final contract stage had typically exceeded their class D estimates by anything from 30% to 100% and no project had ever come in below its class D estimate.

Towards the end of 1987 the submarine project office and the Department of Supply and Services had jointly worked out a figure of C$ 10.7 billions. The DND charmed circle rejected this but Captain Dent Harrison refused to withdraw the estimate. For this refusal and his expressed doubts concerning the nuclear propulsion entity he was relieved of his post, it was said, at one days notice.

On 14th April 1988 the French and we were summoned to the submarine project office and told that the formal evaluation of our proposals would now take place for completion by the end of June. The evaluation would be made by an augmented team under five subject headings, Operational requirements, Cost, International Relations, Industrial Benefits and Nuclear Safety and the results - the five envelopes - would then be reviewed by an interdepartmental review board at 2 star (Rear Admiral) level and the result placed before Ministers. It was stated that there would be no decision before mid-July at the earliest.

Canada was to host the Group of Seven Finance Meetings in Toronto in mid-June and Prime Minister Mulroney was anxious that the meetings should be a personal success in the eyes of the Canadian public, not least because there would be a general election within the following 12 months. He instructed his cabinet and senior officials to avoid contentious issues; above all he wanted the submarine thing put on the back burner to avoid being ignored by President Mitterand or handbagged by Mrs. Thatcher.

It is interesting that even I noticed that there seemed to be many extra lights burning on the executive floors of the DND building on the first Saturday in May. Several other people, including John Killick, commented on it and that it wasn't only in DND that midnight oil was being burnt and guessed that this unusual activity was to do with the approaching summit and Mulroney's wish to advance the Canada / US Free Trade Agreement. I hoped that the DND activity was submarine related and that the Canadians might at long last be doing something about amending their 1959 Agreement in the light of the mid-May congressional deadline.

We were therefore very surprised in mid-May to receive advice from a source that we could not ignore, that we should, as a matter of urgency, engage consultants with much closer links to the Cabinet than we had at the time. Who better than Government Consultants Inc, headed by General Ramsey Withers? GCI had an interesting record of success in representing clients, initially under its founder Frank Moores, who was now a rather remote figure.

Articles started appearing in the press that the French were furious about something and saying that the British were intent on wrecking the submarine project.

The Group 7 meetings were a success with President Reagan and Mrs Thatcher giving effective support to Mr Mulroney's chairmanship. Following the meetings in Toronto, Mrs Thatcher visited Ottawa where she addressed both houses of parliament on the 22nd of June. Her speech was considered to be so supportive of Mr Mulroney that members of the opposition Liberal Party said afterwards that they had actually considered walking out in protest.

Afterwards, at a reception in the High Commissioner's Residence, I was assured by Derek Burney, Mulroney's Chief of Staff, that she had strongly recommended the British submarine over lunch. As usual it was the Canadian ministerial aides who told me things. On this occasion Mrs Thatcher's press man, Bernard Ingham, stood on the fringes and glowered at one and all from beneath his beetle brows. I spoke with her. That is not exactly true; the moment she knew who I was she launched into a mini lecture on submarines much to the surprise and then amusement of Admiral Jock Allen and others nearby. One had the feeling that if I had been a brain surgeon I would have received a mini lecture on neurology. When we were relatively alone the High Commissioner asked her if she thought that they would buy our submarine. She replied very slowly and deliberately, "I don't know".

We had assumed that the goodwill engendered by the Thatcher visit would create a better climate with the Chief of Submarine Acquisition, but there was no evidence of this. In this CSA job John Anderson seemed a changed man; he was no longer the relaxed John one had known of old; he spoke in monosyllables, he would not sit down but wandered round his office while offering jerky sentences; he seemed acutely nervous. His deputy Captain Lund was at ease and was plainly of the view that the French submarine should be or had been selected. Several leaks to the media and others, that the French had been selected, were traced back to him.

There was no rushing to and fro' between Ottawa and London and the British embassy in Washington could detect no action and little interest on the part of the Canadians there. Further, if the Canadians had any real interest in our vessel they should be talking with us about ordering long-lead items, the bits that have to be ordered and manufacture started so that they are ready to be put in the hull before completion. Optimistic as always, I rationalised that this inactivity could be explained by the fact that under the rules for funding major capital projects, introduced in mid-1987, officials could not enter into any commitment until the whole programme received Cabinet approval. This would be a considerable problem and delaying factor.

In conversation with Jock Allen, John Anderson said that he would be prepared to reopen discussions with the UK on the Memorandum of Understanding provided the UK would modify the clauses prohibiting design changes on the propulsion plant of the first submarine. He must have known that this was a ridiculous statement and he could not be persuaded to repeat it through official channels. I found myself having some sympathy with some of the more outrageous things the Americans had said about the Canadian DND.

We had asked the Royal Navy for some publicity that would demonstrate the ability of its submarines to operate in the Arctic. One day in the summer two British and one US sub-marine rendezvoused at the North Pole. This was a public relations coup and the Canadian press gave it good coverage. But what of the Chief of Submarine Acquisition? His only comment to me was to question whether the British submarines had passed under 'Canadian ice' in getting there. And his deputy Captain Lund? He was quoted in the press as remarking that the submarines had simply surfaced 'through holes in the ice'.

But was the Trafalgar Class design really available?' The Canadians had approached Admiral Fieldhouse once again and had been told that the UK MoD could go no further "For reasons that he could not discuss with them". Margaret Thatcher had said that in the final analysis the UK's highest priority must be the preservation of its defence relationship with the USA, and furthermore John Anderson and his team had seen no softening of the US Navy's attitude since Reagan's announcement in April 1988. Rather, their position had hardened,

This did not prevent a rush of press reports that the Trafalgar had been chosen because the British had offered access to future nuclear technology. The source was stated to be a senior UK MoD official and this was calculated to set all the alarm bells ringing in the Pentagon.

We had continued to lobby on Capital Hill in Washington and on 1st June 1988 no less than 83 members of congress signed a letter to the president recommending that the UK be permitted to provide technology to Canada. Privately, we were told that there was growing evidence that US government money, Navy or Energy, was being spent to oppose the proposal and that some of this was being spent in Ottawa. An item appeared in the 'Wednesday Report' alleging that US money was being spent by our consultants GCI, and more particularly by Frank Moores, its founder, in an attempt to sabotage the entire Canadian nuclear submarine programme. This was formally denied by GCI in a letter to the government. However, some of the actions or comments that were ascribed to the British could possibly have had a US origin.

John Lehman, former US Secretary of the Navy, and a friend, felt that Canada should be allowed to acquire Trafalgar Class submarines and thus be better equipped to play a bigger role in the maritime defence of North America. He had had his troubles with the admirals when in office. He learned that the US Navy was providing funds for a study of the Canadian 'problem' by an outfit called Systems Planners Inc. Former Chief of Naval

Operations, Admiral Zumwalt and Norman Palomar were mentioned as intermediaries in this matter. Subsequently, John Lehman was somewhat ambivalent about the existence of this study and its results; there was certainly a preliminary study. Next we were told that there had been no deep study because the estimated cost of US$ 250,000 was considered to be too high. On the next occasion, John said that he was certain that Zumwalt had sent something to members of the Armed Forces Committees with the conclusion that Canadian nuclear submarines would be a nuisance to US underwater operations; that Canada still did not really appreciate the cost and complexity of ownership; and that if she persisted in having nuclear boats, it was better from the US Navy's standpoint that she should have the noisier French one because they would be easier to detect at sea and in the event of an accident the US Navy could distance itself from any reflection on US technology.

It is interesting that the nuclear admirals felt it necessary, or were persuaded that it was helpful, to engage SPI to make a study because the Congress is well served by the Congressional Research Service and was receiving an excellent Issue Brief entitled 'Canadian nuclear-powered attack submarine programme; Issues for Congress' prepared by Ronald O'Rourke, which was updated monthly.

An article published in the Chronicle Herald of 5th August 1988 suggested that American fears that Canada might build nuclear boats equal to the US subs of the current Los Angeles Class at a lower cost, might also be a contributing factor in the USN's ongoing opposition to the plan. What the author of the article did not know was that a Committee of the US Congress had approached VSEL in the UK and asked to visit the yard at Barrow to discuss the cost of construction of nuclear submarines. At the urgent request of the US Navy, the UK MoD had refused to allow this visit and any discussion to take place.

Since the French had been stated to be furious, I expected that they might make some gesture to influence Canadian public opinion. Most of the world is not aware that France has two tiny islands in the Gulf of St Lawrence. There was an ongoing fishing dispute between these islands and the Maritime provinces. France could have made a gesture in 1988 to take some of the heat out of this dispute and thus present themselves as good guys; evidently they did not think this necessary.

In the summer of 1988 when we hoped that the US Congress might be persuaded to look favourably on the transfer of nuclear know-how from Britain to Canada and were working hard in this respect, the US Department of Defence asked Canada for permission to flight-test their latest air launched cruise missile over the desolate regions of northern Canada as had been allowed on previous occasions. The Canadians refused, thus making it less likely that Congress would agree any release of nuclear propulsion information, which might benefit the Canadian forces. ("We have long memories when someone steps on our tail")

The tempo of events in Washington slowed down in 1988. The President's first rank advisers went back to their business interests and their stop-gap replacements saw no point in getting into an argument with the Pentagon. The attitude of the US Navy to this near political vacuum was to spread its wings; they did all sorts of things like trailing their coat off the Libyan coast and shooting down two aircraft that came to investigate, shooting down an Iranian civil airliner and other less publicised actions. George Lindsay then the Director of a Canadian government research establishment visited the northern capitals of the NATO nations during the second half of 1988 and told friends afterwards that several officials had expressed their concern that the US Navy seemed to be capable of starting World War III all on its own if it carried on the way it was behaving.

The US Congress really should address this problem of the political vacuum that occurs every four years. I said as much to John Lehman and he replied without much visible concern that "There had not been any political control over the Navy for several months and this would be the case until the new administration is in place in January 1989". He said again that he had had the same problems with the admirals.

The attitude of the US naval nuclear propulsion people became harder as the year progressed towards the election. They insisted that they should see and approve the memorandum of understanding between the UK and Canada and that the more onerous clauses going into the amendment to the 1958 Anglo-US Agreement should also be incorporated in the amendment to the 1959 Canada - US Agreement. A not unreasonable position observing the US concerns already expressed but Beatty's office took considerable exception to the fact that these clauses might be debated and published by Congress and make Canadian ministers look small. A decision in favour of France would require no such disclosure.

Throughout the whole exercise we had been puzzled by the lack of activity by the Canadian Embassy in Washington DC on the submarine question and in particular, on the amendment to their 1959 Agreement. Cynical observers suggested that the lack of activity was due to Ambassador Gotlieb's preoccupation with his wife's tendency to making scenes in public, such as slapping her personal assistant. It was also suggested that from the occasion of the initial wounding visit, Perrin Beatty had told him that he, Beatty, had no intention of asking the Americans for anything and that the French were the choice. The British Embassy was always better informed than the Canadian. It was known that the US State Department was, if pressed, in favour of a Canada / UK deal and the DND clique probably did not wish to open up a diplomatic dialogue through the ambassadors bosses in the Department of External Affairs, that might advance that line.

In the end I worked out that the real dialogue between the US and Canadian navies was not taking place in Washington at all but in Norfolk Va between the US Fleet Commander's staff and the Canadian Rear Admiral resident in that staff. It was this officer who was reporting back to Ottawa and Halifax that 'the strain on the US Navy's resources such as underwater ranges and exercise areas that the Canadian navy was allowed to use at rock bottom per-diem rates, was now being felt. Indeed it was only by bending the rules that they might be able to help with trials of the new Patrol Frigate and it was to be hoped that Ottawa would not do anything to upset any tentative understanding that might have been entered into. There was no possibility of their use by, say, a new nuclear submarine'.

That the French must also have heard about this explains the stories that I heard again and again that the French had assured the CSA that their navy's trials facilities for surface ships and submarines would all be placed at Canada's disposal.

We had excellent support from the diplomats in our Washington embassy. However, Frank Noah and I were aware that although polite and friendly, the scientific people within the embassy were not necessarily on our side. They were concerned with far bigger issues than ours and these might run counter to our effort to sell Trafalgar Class to Canada. So be it.

The extraordinary thing about marketing in Canada was that we were expected to place advertisements recommending our submarine in the national press ; usually associated with some occasion of an armed forces or national flavour. There were many such days each year. We were expected to help mobilise public opinion in favour of having nuclear submarines and the Trafalgar Class in particular. In addition to advertisements in the press I wrote articles for technical and political journals. The emphasis was on the Toronto, Montreal and Ottawa dailies read by the movers and shakers of Canadian public opinion. Other than the big shipbuilders on the east coast, there was little interest elsewhere.

It wasn't only little old ladies in Moose Jaw, Saskatchewan who were indifferent. I was invited to speak to the caucus of the ruling Conservative Party at breakfast in the Parliament Building. Now was my chance. They listened politely and a few asked questions. Of those who spoke, all would prefer to have the British submarine but half of those present saw no reason to have submarines at all, they said quite openly that "They had always relied on the Americans to defend them and why not continue to do so."

There seemed to be little awareness outside Ontario and Quebec of the large amount of sub-contract work that the submarine programme would bring in making components and systems and this could be shared by the other provinces. One sage had remarked that "The navy might pick the French submarine but the Anglo's in the cabinet won't buy it". We felt that the people who elect those Anglos should be given the chance to learn about what it could mean to them and perhaps it might stiffen the resolve of their provincial and federal ministers. In the late summer of 1988 Frank Noah suggested that the Trafalgar Consortium should visit all the provinces to spread the message. Sam Hughes handled the arrangements in his usual quiet, efficient way. A minor hitch at the last moment led to a change of aircraft and we were off with representatives of twelve of the consortium firms.

The first week we flew east to Montreal Qu, Saint John NB, Halifax NS and St. Johns NF and in the second week we flew to Vancouver BC, Calgary Al, Winnipeg Man, and London Ont. Frank was with us in Montreal. The schedule was tight; at each place there was usually a breakfast meeting with speeches, a morning presentation, a lunch time meeting with speeches, afternoon sessions with potential equipment suppliers and off to the airport for the flight to the next destination, possibly to meet some people for dinner. Then bed and next day it started all over again.

Everywhere we went we were surprised at how little the companies knew about the large amount of the cost of a nuclear submarine that goes into components and equipment which they might manufacture and their resigned acceptance that the politicians would see that Quebec and Ontario got all the work. We strove to convince them otherwise.

Some things that one remembers have little to do with the submarine. In New Brunswick the Premier McKenna came to the televised breakfast and made a political speech. Since his party occupied every seat in the provincial parliament I wondered why he bothered. My concern was much more with Mr Irvine who owned Saint John Shipbuilders and, with his brothers, most of the loyalist province of New Brunswick as well.

I was told that in deciding where to site the new International airport for Nova Scotia, extensive surveys were made to select the most fog free location. It was agreed that the middle of a vast forest some 20 kilometres from Halifax was the best place and so they removed several square miles of trees and built a fine modern airport. There are no prizes for guessing what changing the environment did to the incidence of fogs at that place.

Our 20 minute flight across the Bay of Fundy from Saint John to Halifax took over an hour, in a snowstorm at dusk with little red lights telling our pilot that he had an undercarriage problem. The air hostesses went and sat at the back, the flight engineer - a small ape like man - hurried to the rear. I was relieved to see that he was not wearing a parachute and assumed that he had some sort of device or periscope with which he could check on the undercarriage. No such thing, he selected the rearmost seat and strapped himself in. We dumped fuel and flew low past the control tower while they peered through the snowstorm to see if the wheels were down. They couldn't see. Finally the pilot said that there was no sense in staying up any longer in the deepening gloom (outside and in) and lined up to land. We all crouched down and said prayers to an oft forgotten God and to the sound of sobbing from the back, made a perfect landing accompanied by fire engines, rescue trucks and snow ploughs. Robin Wood from VSEL, a long time teetotaller, had several large whiskies that night.

In St Johns, Newfoundland we were made honorary Newfies by kneeling blindfold, kissing a salt cod and downing a tot of rum. I was interested to find that, just as Bristol, England, has a tower on a hill to commemorate John Cabot's departure, St Johns has a tower on Signal Hill to commemorate his arrival. Signal hill was where Marconi received the first radio transmission from his assistant in Cornwall in 1901.Newfoundlanders are hardy, hard working folk who deserve everyone's support.

I was to visit St. Johns NF several more times, well, actually just the airport because some flights to Halifax landed there. One such flight was that which I took with Tony Peake en-route to the other Saint John, New Brunswick. We arrived at Heathrow to be told that there had been a change of aircraft to a 747 instead of the scheduled Boeing 757. This turned out to be an all-economy 747. One could stand in the front and look along the vast open cabin in which the 100 or so passengers were completely lost amid the 550 or so seats. It was a glorious afternoon in Newfoundland and I was surprised when the pilot flew along the coast over St Johns, then back again and then did it once more before turning out to sea and making a long slow approach. It reminded me of the landing that a Qantas 747 SP had made at Wellington NZ with Liz and I on board, where the runway was rather short and we had needed every inch of it. It was the same story here; we stopped just short of the end of the runway. At Wellington we would have gone into the harbour but here as far as I could see we would have rolled down a steep embankment. As the aircraft taxied towards the terminal, the captain informed us that we were only the second 747 ever to have landed at St Johns.

This was not the end of the fun. We stopped abreast the terminal and they wheeled out the mobile stairway to off-load the passengers. They were not equipped for 747's however and the tops of the stairways were several feet below the aircraft doors. We then enjoyed the spectacle of little old ladies being lowered down to the platform by the cabin crew. Meanwhile other aircraft arrived and taxied to their allotted spots or as near to them as they could get with this vast 747 sitting in the way and when we were at last ready to depart, our path was blocked and we could not move until these other aircraft had gone. So we were on the ground for well over two hours.

Calgary is on the River Bow where it is joined by its tributary, the River Elbow. In the distance can be seen the snow capped peaks of the Rockies I could see why the early settlers stopped right there. It was in Calgary that a government man volunteered that he had worked for DSS in Ottawa. "Everyone from Quebec who wanted government contracts brought gifts" he said, "it was so common that I found that I was looking for gifts. It was then that I decided to move west". An alternative construction to this story might be that he left just before the RCMP arrived. The RCMP were very active in this sort of thing at high levels, Mr Mulroney had lost some six members of his government in little more than two years because of some alleged misuse of funds or influence.

In Calgary I gave our presentation and asked for questions. A man in a check shirt stood up and said that he was from the government of the North West Territories and had been instructed to formally protest at the proposal of the British government to clearly label, on import into the UK, animal fur and garments made from animal fur that had been got by trapping. Trapping wild animals for their pelts gave a living to over 150,000 people, many more than would ever be employed in building submarines. An attractive lady with Indian features stood beside him and pointed out that trapping was a way of life, perhaps the only way of self-sufficiency, for many of her people. I learned later that she was a member of several Federal committees concerned with the welfare of the Inuit.

No sooner had they sat down than a huge man stood up. He had long black hair swept back into a pigtail, leather trousers and a leather jerkin with a zigzag bottom, big leather boots and round his waist a belt from which hung a fearsome array of knives and choppers. He wanted action, or else!. I promised action.

We escaped to our aircraft and flew over the endless plains and lakes of the middle west to Winnipeg, more than ever convinced that Canada could feed the World. The next day, after the usual breakfast meeting and speeches, I did my stuff at the presentation and asked for questions. To my horror the huge trapper from Calgary stood up, plus five others, similarly attired and equally as big and well armed. They stood in a row and demanded to know what I had done about it since yesterday?. I was able to say with truth that I had spoken with the British High Commission in Ottawa. Furthermore we had a senior member of the High Commission there today and he, Tony Boardman, would be happy to talk with them and draw up the sort of message that they would wish us to send to Whitehall. Whereupon they trooped out and so did Tony; I felt a bit of a cad for dropping him into it, but not for long. Some weeks later Margaret Thatcher made Alan Clark, the minister who had sponsored the measure, withdraws the proposed anti-fur legislation; the wearing of real fur remains a matter of conscience, not of law. My personal sympathies remain with the animals and Alan Clark.

The visit to London, Ontario was overshadowed by our departure. Our aircraft had seemed to age visibly as the days went by and at London as we sat, ready for the last leg of our trip, the aircraft's engines refused to start. They brought up another starter trolley ; soon that was exhausted. There was a long wait and then a similar aircraft to our own appeared and taxied to a nose-on position. Obviously we were about to be asked to change aircraft, but no, out came some long wires which were connected to both aircraft ; the second aircraft started its engines and, lo, jump-started ours. I think that we were all relieved when we landed at Ottawa without further incident. John Burgess and the other members of the Trafalgar Consortium had worked hard to make the mission a success and companies had established links upon which they might be able to build in the future.

The exchange of information was, of course, two-way and we learnt much of the capability of the people and industry of this vast country. A common yardstick with which our hosts sought to impress us was the number of potential customers within a 24 hour trucking distance. Each of the places that we visited claimed to have more than a million people within a 24 hour trucking distance and without exception these people were to the south in the USA. It is in the USA that everyone west of Niagara sees their market.

There was a Financial Post Conference on defence topics in October 1988. The major topic was the nuclear submarine and centred on the Trafalgar Class. Every speaker felt that this should be the choice but all of the insiders were sure that the choice would have to be the French because of American opposition. Richard Sharpe, the then new editor of Janes Fighting Ships, Norman Friedman and Richard Barnard presented papers and answered questions. The latter, who represented Defence News, USA, had clearly been given the briefing that De Mars and Co were known to have given to the CNO and the Armed Forces Committees.

They gave the following well-rehearsed reasons:
- the Pentagon's belief that Canadian Ministers did not yet understand the complexity and cost of building and supporting SSN's;

- a wish not to have other submarines occupying waters into which USN submarines might have to operate;
- a wish to restrict the number of people who have awareness of USN/RN reactor technology;
- a wish not to create a precedent;
- the possibility that Canadian industry will attract resources away from the USN programme;
- a belief that Canada should reinstate its commitment to send forces to northern Norway.

The question period was more instructive and the two US speakers said, inter alia:

- US officials are totally opposed to Canada acquiring SSNs - no reflection on Canada s armed forces is intended;
- Canadian public is ill-informed;
- People who control SSN technology do not want to give it to anyone;
- If this policy is breached God knows what would follow.
- We are seeing Rickover culture. USN submarine service will stop at nothing to prevent Canada acquiring SSNs. It's the way they go about things, create rumours and innuendo to undermine other peoples opinions; its standard operating procedure among the Jesuites. Its the way they treat the rest of the USN, the US Congress and the US President. Keep off the grass.
- The US Army and US Air Force are much more concerned with squashing the marines and aircraft carriers respectively.

French ministers and admirals were frequent visitors in Ottawa. Friends in DND did wonder whether the absence of British ministers indicated reluctance at high level to offend the Americans but every time a British minister did appear his visit was described graphically to us as a non-event or a disaster submarine-wise. There was the first visit by Secretary of State for Defence, George Younger. We knew that he had been fully briefed and his staff confirmed that the submarine had been discussed. Our Canadian friends reported, however, that the reference to the Trafalgar Class had been made in passing, as it were, without any evidence of strong conviction. The same thing happened at the November 1988 NATO meeting in Brussels. Beatty's Chief of Staff pointedly referred to this as a meeting that the British had requested, "Beatty had nothing that he wished to talk to the British about". The discussion had lasted barely 20 minutes and had been pleasant and cordial but Younger had made no reference to any new developments within his area; in fact "Younger's reference to the SSN programme was perfunctory". This was reportedly also the style of the next encounter. Clearly if biased towards the French, the Minister would wish to play down the British effort but my source for disenchantment was not only Beatty's office.

Our admirals did their bit by talking down to their Canadian opposite numbers. According to Sir Alan Urwick, one British hero achieved the remarkable distinction of getting up the nose (I quote) of the Canadian Navy, the BHC Ottawa, the US Navy and the ambassador in Washington in the space of a four day visit. Mercifully he had other more important duties to attend to.

It was about this time that I received a copy of a Canadian government paper, dated 9th May 1988 and classified Secret. The paper swept aside any illusion that the UK had been engaged in an open and fair competition to supply nuclear submarines to Canada. I supplied copies of this Secret paper to the BHC Ottawa for onward transmission to the UK Government.

It appears that, perhaps afraid that President Reagan's approval in April for the limited UK – Canada exchange of nuclear information would be followed by positive action in Congress, and ignoring his own Prime Ministers reported advice that no action be taken which might prejudice the success of the June Toronto Group Seven meetings, Beatty had elected on the weekend of 7th May 1988 to go for broke and select the French submarine. Whether the Canadian / French company SNA was jogging his elbow, I do not know.

Anyway, without any reference to the CASAP submarine project team's half completed appraisal, he had initiated proposals and forwarded them to Deputy PM Mazankowski, Finance Minister Wilson and one or two other key ministers for endorsement, ready for a cabinet meeting on 11th May. The Finance Minister's copy went to a naval constructor officer, Lieutenant Commander Gary Wiseman, who was on secondment to the Treasury Board and was on duty at the time. This officer wrote a remarkable ten page paper, which summarised all the important issues on policy (no consultation or open discussion), technology (real versus paper submarines) and cost (the fact that the Class D estimate of C$ 8 billion was already false). The paper concluded with a half page summary cast in more moderate tones than the trenchant comments in the body of the paper; as follows:

"In summary., there is a very disturbing sense in the submarine project of it 'being above critical examination', internal challenges are stifled and external challenges are avoided or swept aside. Information essential for officials to properly advise their Ministers is withheld or, when supplied, is of suspect quality.

There appears to be a flexibility in requirements beyond technical reason; the goal – posts appear to have wheels.

Known design changes required to allow the French submarine to meet even the minimum requirements will introduce a level of technical risk commensurate with an entirely new design.

There is evidence that some fundamental performance requirements were reduced to accommodate the limitations of the French design.

The financial risk is high and undefined.

To proceed with a commitment to the project at this level of uncertainty does not make sense.

The decision on country-of-origin will be the last effective chance for Ministers to exercise their options. There are no off-ramps.

An independent assessment of all aspects of the project is both prudent in the circumstances and the responsible approach, given the international and national implications of the decision being requested by the DND."

Because of the urgency with which Beatty was demanding the paper be treated, the Lieutenant Commander had personally delivered copies of his Treasury Board paper to the other Ministerial addressees, including Deputy PM Mazankowski who chaired most of Mr Mulroney's interdepartmental committees. The danger of 'blowing' the G 7 meetings had been Dan Mazankowski's first thought, closely followed by why was Beatty so determined to commit Canada to the French?. Thereupon the whole process had been stopped dead in its tracks.

This was presumably why the French had been so furious in May/June, blaming the British for sabotaging the Canadian SSN programme and I suppose why John Anderson was so boot faced all the summer. The fact is that we knew nothing about Beatty's dash for the French at the time but clearly someone in the French camp did — for why else should they have been so angry?

A friendly Canadian MP told me that he had asked Mazankowski what they intended to do about Beatty. The reply was "move the ******".

It was about this time that Bryan Boyd told me privately that during the summer the French had made great efforts to restart the dialogue. The French government had guaranteed their costs by some means and had undertaken to associate Canada with the development of the Canadian Amethyst technology and updated technology for later submarines of the programme. An offer stated to be 'unbelievably good' and 'impossible to reject'. One remembered the French government bonds for the Saudi Arabian frigates. The French were spending French taxpayers money. We were trying not to spend VSEL's shareholders money.

By the midsummer of 1988 I had already become sure that Beatty would not change his view that the French submarine should be chosen and thus avoid any possibility of a US Navy veto and that officials were dancing to this tune. Ed Healey told me sometime in October that he had warned the UK Head of Defence Procurement that the game was all but up for the UK because of the UK's inability or unwillingness to move on certain issues raised.

The May 8th paper convinced me that there was no point in continuing to spend VSEL's money in an endeavour to sell the Trafalgar Class to the Canadian DND. What we should do was to withdraw with maximum publicity about Perrin Beatty's bias towards a submarine that did not meet his navy's stated mandatory requirements, his divisive actions of early May and how he had nearly sabotaged his Prime Minister's summit. I suspected that the US navy was now using the British contender as a stalking horse to frustrate the choice of any SSN. I made a recommendation to the Board of VSEL Defence Systems Canada Inc. on 30th October that we should withdraw from the competition.

Perrin Beatty's Chief of Staff was told of this by Sam Hughes and he asked to see us; Frank Noah had arrived and said that we were conscious of the minister's bias, we felt that he must be aware that the French submarine did not meet his own Department's published requirements and only the Trafalgar did and we would like to know how he reconciled these facts?. We received no answer to this sort of question but decided not to pull out.

One does not know what pressure they were under, but Canadian behaviour reached some pretty silly heights in early November. One could imagine that the minister's office had said, "Do something to pretend that you are still considering the British thing". They wrote to the UK MoD to ask that the UK should accept visits by Canadian personnel on subjects and at times to be decided by the Canadians. Initially two visits were arranged. I told the UK MoD that I was aware that the Canadians had had discussions on the same subjects in France some months earlier and that they had also had discussions with the four Canadian potential prime contractors during which the latter had been told, in as many words, that the French submarine was the choice.

One of the claimed advantages of the French reactor was its ability to produce power by natural circulation without the need to run potentially noise-making pumps to circulate the cooling water through the reactor core. Only at higher powers would the pumps be required. We had examined a similar reactor design in the early days, in which the heat exchanger was integral with the reactor vessel and had not adopted it because we couldn't get the power we wanted within the height likely to be available in our submarine. We were also concerned with possible problems when the submarine heeled or dived at large angles - remember that these vessels heel over at more than 30 degrees in a high-speed turn. It was instructive therefore, to see an admission, very late in the day, that the French vessel must run its pumps if the submarine turns or dives steeply. In real anti-submarine warfare - which is what the Canadians wanted their submarines for - it is changes in the background noise level that an enemy is most likely to detect, not the absolute level of overall ocean noise and this means that an intelligent commanding officer would not wish to be starting and stopping pumps when an enemy might be listening and so he would have his pumps running most of the time. So much for natural circulation in war.

The Chief of Submarine Acquisition should have known all of this. I made certain that the CASAP project team knew and was doubtless noted somewhere in the five envelopes, unless for some reason Baxter and his team were precluded from remarking on such things even remotely nuclear. Some rather odd things were going on in this area. Ask the AECL.

There was much that went on in the final months of 1988 and early 1989. The CSA wanted a guarantee that Canada would have automatic access to all future development of submarine nuclear reactors and the UK MoD said that this was not possible. I suggested to John Anderson that Canada should to be prepared to take their assimilation into the nuclear submarine club in easy stages — to adopt a pragmatic approach. He stated flatly that he could not accept such an approach; he must have it firmly in black and white, now.

Contrast this with his approach to the under-ice problem. We knew that the Canadian government's own research establishment had concluded that the French so-called 'ice-pick' would not work. I asked Anderson what he intended to do about this inability to meet one of his government's three mandatory requirements, an ability to surface through a metre of ice. He replied that he intended to 'take a pragmatic approach', presumably in the hope that the French would come up with another solution. He could not be made to see that this would have to confound the natural laws of physics. Penetrating the ice must be approached carefully, otherwise the submarine could finish up on her side, the ultimate determinant is the submarines main ballast tank capacity. In boxing parlance "a good big-'un will always beat a good little 'un'.

Throughout the whole saga we could not understand how the CSA managed to avoid public discussion of this under-ice question. Was the French ice pick meant to chip away at the underside of the ice like some underwater woodpecker and if so had no Canadian ever listened to how sound carries under the arctic ice. Who was fooling whom?

At government level there was pressure on the AECL Board to become more commercially active by selling assets, shutting down research projects and entering into joint ventures. AECL management was demanding some financial recompense from the DND for its assessment work and also that the role to be undertaken by the 'entity' in the submarine project be agreed. This was done on 28th November 1988.

President Bush had been elected on November 9th 1988 and despite the winter snows, Mr Mulroney had called a snap election for November 21st and was returned to power with a substantial majority. Mulroney had been running well behind the Liberals in the polls and on this evidence it was expected to be a much closer run thing. It was Sam Hughes who pointed out to me that the poll-percentages do not necessarily mean seat-percentages and thus it proved.

The Liberal Party had been somewhat ambivalent on the subject, although we had reason to believe that had they won the election, they would not have cancelled the submarine project without a very deep examination of the pros and cons.. That I speak with some authority on this matter is perhaps illustrated by the following. During the November election campaign the leader of the Liberals, John Turner, was about to arrive at the Westin Hotel to address a rally in the Conference Centre. I was about to leave the hotel with Peter Cathcart, a Member and Secretary of the VSEL Defence Systems Canada Board, when he asked that we should delay for a moment. A cavalcade of cars stopped outside, the doors opened and amidst a blast of icy air, John Turner and his wife came in. With cries of genuine pleasure they spied Peter and hurried to embrace him. I was introduced. Peter was from McMillan Binch, our legal associates in Canada and so was the leader of the Liberal Party.

Mr Mulroney announced his new cabinet. Beatty was moved to Social Security, where he would have to compete with Defence for scarce funds, and William McNight took over at Defence. Parliament met briefly to ratify the Free-Trade legislation and adjourned. Its new sittings started in February 1989.

The negotiations to combine the US and Canada in a Free Trade Area had been a major preoccupation of both governments in 1988. In those product areas in which it had a capability, Canada had hitherto been able to compete on price and quality with US manufacture but in recent years had suffered due to the increasing tendency for US companies to manufacture in Mexico or at the very least to employ cheap Mexican labour and to the restrictions that Congress was able to introduce at crucial times to virtually exclude every supplier other than some congressman's 'favourite son'. At any given time there might be as many as five hundred such orders in existence. The Free Trade Act would avoid this.

A feature of the new parliament was an increased use of Cabinet committees, of which the three most important were those dealing with Priority and Planning, Operations and Expenditure Review.. Every major decision reached by the other committees had to be ratified by one of these three bodies, all of which were chaired by the Deputy PM Dan Mazankowski. For the first month of the new parliament these cabinet committees met each day, with no officials present, to discuss the deteriorating financial situation and consequential policy changes and economies that might be made. The recommendations and decisions of these cabinet committees went to Departments from 23rd March onwards in preparation for the mid-April budget.

There had been much speculation at the end of 1988, that the selection of the submarine would be announced now that Mr Mulroney had been returned to power. The CASAP said that they could turn round their papers within 36 hours ready for the Senior Review Board and the Minister's approval. I thought that although this might be possible, this particular incoming minister might have some difficulty in carrying his Cabinet colleagues with him, in the light of the Deputy Prime Ministers reaction to what his predecessor had done the previous May.

Parliament reconvened. The speech from the throne made no significant comment about defence. Budget day was expected to be on the 17th April but it was rumoured that it might be postponed until after the Newfoundland provincial elections on 22nd and this proved to be the case, April 27th was the chosen date. There was speculation in informed circles whether the nuclear submarine programme would be cancelled in what was expected to be an austerity budget. Opinion was that if it were mentioned at all by Michael Wilson, it would be to cancel it. Otherwise the opposition could be relied on to raise it in the debate and the country of origin would be announced a few weeks later.

The other preoccupation of the Mulroney government and of Mr Mulroney personally following his re-election, was the amendment of the law to bring Quebec totally into line with all the other provinces by repatriating the outstanding relationship with the British Crown — a feature that Quebec had declined to lose when all the other provinces severed this link many years earlier. This would only be possible provided that the provincial governments ratified the measure and Mr Mulroney expended great effort throughout 1989 and early 1990 to bring this about, culminating in a conference and provisional agreement at Meech Lake. Three provinces refused to agree, Mckenna's Tory party in New Brunswick agreed and then there were two. Premier Wells in Newfoundland sat on his hands and said that "There was no point in taking it to his legislature while that Indian was still holding out in Manitoba" and the said Indian in the mid-west refused to allow it to be placed before the provincial parliament. Mulroney's aides made all sorts of promises but to no avail. These two provinces stuck out until the deadline of June 23rd 1990 had passed. The Manitobans then demanded as a right all the things that had been dangled before them.

Christmas in Canada was a schoolboys dream, the Rideau Canal was frozen and the country blanketed in snow; with all the blessings of modern civilisation as well. I could sit in my hotel and watch people skating beneath trees adorned with Christmas lights. There were many Father Christmases who, I was told, must take a course to qualify for the job.   Late one evening one came into the downstairs bar of the Westin Hotel. He weaved a somewhat unsteady path towards the bar and tripped over, whereupon a deep voice uttered the traditional "Ho,Ho,Ho". But it did not come from the old man; it came from a tape recorder in his pocket. He was from County Donegal.

In mid-December 1988 Jock Allen heard a hint that someone had suggested that Canada should carry out a detailed appraisal to ensure that the reactors would satisfy the Canadian civil safety regulations. He told the British High Commission.   Directing attention to this subject was in part a French effort to stress the advantage of their low-enrichment core. They had raised it as early as September 1987 and we had put out a rather robust reply at that time. This time, after much to-ing and fro-ing by MoD officers, the UK MoD, RR&A and VSEL did a considerable amount of work to reassure the Canadians that we had indeed thought deeply on this subject.   The results of this further work were parcelled up, sealed and hand-carried to Canada by UK security personnel.

Meanwhile the UK MoD had thrust another iron in the fire. Should the British submarine be selected, all information sent to Canada concerning the construction of the submarine would be through official channels manned by UK MoD personnel. Fair enough, but in marked contrast to the French who, to judge from what they appeared to be saying, were prepared to hand over their documents to any old Tom, Dick or Harry. When the UK MoD revealed the number of MoD personnel and their ranks and the fact that Canada would have to pay for all these people and their expenses, the balloon went up inside DND and DSS since it appeared that the British MoD personnel costs would be as big, if not bigger, than the budget for all the Canadian government personnel on the entire project. The Canadians pointed out to me that the information would have to pass into Canadian hands for the work to be done so why would there be what appeared to be, the equivalent of naval captains and supporting staff, charged to Canada in each of Barrow, Derby, Bath, London, Ottawa and at the 'entity' and the shipyard. Obviously this was intended to reassure the US nuclear admirals that no unauthorised release of data would take place but it did seem to be extravagant; simple instructions to the issuing authorities should suffice. However I could not be very helpful because no-one in the UK MoD had bothered to consult or tell me about this, even though for three years I had been trying to sell their submarine and British engineering to Canada and by now I knew more about the way Canadian officials thought and behaved than anyone in the UK MoD did. Perhaps they thought that I had gone native.

Sometime about now I was summoned to Whitehall and mildly reprimanded by a man who used to work for me in the RCNC because, in a letter to Minister McNight I had used the words 'the UK view' in making some contrast with the 'French view.' Frank Noah was with me and before I could tell Peter not to be so silly, Frank said how sorry we were and we would issue a correction and pushed me out of the room. He could scarcely contain his mirth. We knew that no correction would ever get to the ministers desk and mar the good impression that the first letter might have made.

The submarine was not the only important export prospect that Britain was endeavouring to sell to Canada. There was the Westland helicopter that was also occupying a deal of the various Assistant Deputy Ministers' time. I used to get a run down on progress on this project from John Killick who, having retired from the position now occupied by Ed Healey, was now with Marconi Canada and very much involved with the Canadian avionics package.

Now its OK for me to complain mildly about what I regarded as a lack of realism in the Canadian DND's approach to nuclear submarines, but avionics and aircraft are a quite different matter; these boys have tangled with the US giants, won contracts for their industry and survived. So when I started to get messages that in the Canadian's view, the British prime didn't have a firm grip on their own costs or programme - which meant by implication that the UK MoD was on very thin ice - I started to take notice and passed warning messages back to the High Commission for discrete forwarding to the UK MoD. Time has passed and the Canadian doubts have proved only too true..

There was a problem with personalities, or rather with one retired Admiral from the UK because he would be talking as he got out of the plane from Britain and still talking when he boarded the return flight and as far as his Canadian associates and the DND people that he had met with could judge, he hadn't heard a word that anyone else had uttered during the entire visit. They took to arranging meetings when they were sure he couldn't come - a trifle difficult when he was the Chairman.

In early March, Ed Healey told Jock Allen and I all about the Levine discussions and said that despite the protestations of instant action, he had had no word from him since. The DND therefore intended to go ahead as if the UK had made its final points.

Once more it was rumoured that the French submarine was about to be selected notwithstanding the warning that Admiral Thomas had been given by Mulroney's Chief of Staff to the effect that "It would be pointless recommending the French submarine because the cabinet wouldn't wear it". Former Chief of Defence Staff, General Ramsey Withers commented again on the departure that this would represent in Canada's defence procurement policy of always purchasing the best available equipment.

In my heart I knew that there was no chance that the British submarine could be selected. President Bush did not have the same commitment to defy his naval and energy advisers and there was no chance that Congress would agree without a messy debate. I had for some months felt that the question now was not whether Canada would have the British or the French submarine, but whether Canada would have new submarines at all.

Our Canadian advisers set out to make sure that the issues were being fully explored. We wondered whether we should approach other cabinet ministers. We found minister McNight strangely relaxed on the 28th of February and not greatly exercised on the subject of the submarine. We asked whether the minister would have any objection to our proposed action. We saw the minister again on the 14th and on the 29th March, and gave him a condensed version of a paper that I had prepared originally for the Canadian Institute of Electrical and Electronic Engineers presenting the strategic case for nuclear submarines. Our advisers were insistent that copies of this, also, should be sent to other members of the cabinet. I consulted the minister's Chief of Staff, Greg Fyffe, on the 14th April who replied "The minister does not care one way or the other; in the ministers view the article would not move a great deal of opinion and would not cause any upset in DND".

On 17th April 1989 I learned that there had recently been a serious argument between the CASAP programme manager Captain Bruce Baxter and the Chief of

Submarine Acquisition, because in the previous month, the latter had given technical commitment briefings to the minister without consulting Baxter's assessment team and that Baxter and Mike Fisher were intending to resign. Another source confirmed this heated exchange and said that the five envelopes prepared by Baxter's assessment teams remained in Baxter's safe, unseen by the Senior Review Board, yet Anderson had given the technical commitment to the minister. It was stated that Anderson had advised the minister that the French submarine was the only viable choice.

The reasons given for selecting the French submarine were:
- reduced manpower and training requirement and personnel cost;
- low enrichment core avoids non-proliferation problems;
- early delivery from French production lines;
- no long-lead expenditure problem;
- no liability problems;
- ease of contracting with the French government;
- freedom from external constraints;
- no encumbrance by third power.

I have no problem with any of this; they are all valid reasons. But they relate to procuring a submarine that would not meet the three mandatory requirements specified by the Canadian navy, namely that the submarine should already be in service with an allied navy, be proven in under-ice operations and able to fire and control the US Navy's Mark 48 torpedo.

The Prime Minister's office was aware of Anderson's briefing and asked how the navy had got itself into the position of favouring the submarine that represented an unacceptable technical and political risk when it had set out to purchase a fully proven design.

Perhaps as a result of this, Constructor Lieutenant Commander Gary Wiseman who had shown such remarkable knowledge of the submarine situation, and courage, in May 1988, was instructed by his superiors in the Treasury Board, to prepare another paper setting out the possible alternative paths that Canada might follow. His paper commended the British submarine and damned the French vessel as not meeting the Canadian requirements, but concluded that neither should be acquired by Canada. He suggested that US interests be co-opted to produce an alternative US/UK/ Canadian design as a possible way to get round the problem of the 1958 and 1959 Agreements.

Mr Mulroney was aware of the contents of this paper before he met Margaret Thatcher during his two-day visit to London in mid-March 1989. Both British and Canadian staffs said that the talks had been useful. Prior to this London visit, Mulroney had hosted newly elected President Bush on a visit to Ottawa during which Secretary of State Baker had privately volunteered that the new administration would honour President Reagan's undertaking regarding the British submarine.

Thursday 27th April was budget day in name only. The contents of the budget, which included the cancellation of the nuclear submarine, were leaked to the media and broadcast on the evening of the 26th. Vice Admiral Thomas was dining with the visiting British First Sea Lord at the High Commissioner's residence and in order to keep things even (that's how daft the submarine acquisition office had become) Rear Admiral Anderson was dining with the French. Neither had been told that the budget would announce the cancellation of the nuclear submarine programme and both dinner parties broke up in disarray with the Canadians hastening downtown in half belief that the broadcast was some sort of Orson Wells's alien invader's hoax.

The announcement proved to be true. The government had correctly discerned that there was little public support for nuclear submarines or defence in general and that a decision in favour of the French (which was really the only possible one in view of the US Navy's implacable and active opposition,) would have been very unpopular across Canada. Furthermore and perhaps more tellingly, Canada could not afford such a programme.

The RCMP enquired into the leak. It transpired that an insurance office in Toronto had had the 'Budget in Brief' booklet on the 25th April, obtained apparently from a young man who worked in the printing plant and who had thought that the booklet looked interesting and so had brought home a number of copies. He had thought that it was OK to take some since the booklet did not have a security classification: he had been warned that he must not take things marked Secret.

Examination of the budget showed that Defence and Overseas aid, which together comprised 14% of expenditure had taken 60% of the cuts. As the Globe and Mail said on May 3rd, 'they couldn't cut child care, family allowances, old age security and unemployment benefit while building nuclear submarines'.

If one is absolutely objective it would appear that from the outset there was never any intention on the part of Finance Minister Wilson that Canada should acquire nuclear submarines unless the economy was improving at a far greater rate than it had ever done before. The equipment promises set out in the 1987 Defence White Paper were largely illusory.

Prior to the election of the Tory government in 1984 the Defence budget grew at an annual rate of 3% plus a very generous allowance for inflation, higher than the Finance Department's National Model. 1984 changed this, followed by the 1987 White Paper which made a commitment of 2% real growth plus the national inflation model for a 15 year period, to include all procurement except for major crown projects valued at over C$ 100 millions. For these major projects special additional funds would be provided following submission to the Finance Department and Cabinet. They would thus always be in competition with all the other demands on the national exchequer at that time. Meanwhile the shadow allocation of funds earmarked in the DND forward capital equipment plans were quietly absorbed into the general defence running costs on the assurance that these new items would be the subject of major crown allocations at the appropriate time.

At the time of the 1987 White Paper, only John Killick of my Canadian colleagues expressed the view that under this new system it might be nearly impossible to get finance for defence crown projects at some future date, when faced with the more urgent and publicly evident demands of civil social programmes.

The Canadian economy grew by 4.5% in 1988 / 89 but the deficit grew faster. Taxation was increased and the defence budget fixed at C$11.2 billion with a 1.2% planned annual increase and no major crown projects above that line. But there was now no possibility of re-instating the Oberon Class replacements or the 3.rd batch of frigates since the shadow funds earmarked for these had been allocated elsewhere, possibly to the army or air force. So Canada embarked on a further substantial defence review.

The fact remains that no nation can have a first line navy, army and air force, even for home defence, while spending only just over 2% of its GNP on the armed forces and this situation is getting worse. The rate of increase in cost of modern military systems far exceeds nations' domestic inflation and hence substantial constructive disarmament is taking place as the percentage of GNP that once would have bought, say 250 main battle tanks will now buy only 50 of today's new all-singing-all-dancing variety. And so on through the entire inventory of armaments.

Two ministerial performances at this time were noteworthy - if that's the right word. Minister McNight was the principal speaker at the ARMX 89 dinner held in Ottawa in the week of 23rd May. We all sat down and the minister entered. Before any food or drink was served he stood up and made his speech in which the reduction in the defence budget and the cancellation of the SSN programme was presented as a marked strengthening of Canada's defences and ability to contribute to world peace and so on. The Chief of Defence Staff, General Manson, seated beside him smiled fixedly throughout. It was done so well that I found myself half believing him.. The one thing that the business men present fastened on to was his statement that, henceforth, Canada would spend her defence dollars in Canada buying Canadian-made equipment. Having made his speech, McNight departed and we could then proceed with the serious business of drinking and eating.

The second minister was a member of the House of Lords who was a junior minister in either defence or trade (he moved between them at about this time). I was permitted to be present in the High Commission to be briefed. He showed the usual vagueness of the up-to-date Canadian scene and told us that the cancellation of the SSN gave us the ideal opportunity to sell things. There was more in this vein until even the Commercial Counsellor could stand it no longer and she interrupted the minister to tell him in diplomatic language that he did not know his arse from his elbow about Canada. It was a great tragedy when Charlotte, this most gifted diplomat, was killed in a road accident a year or so later.

The British navy should take the comment about crew size and cost in CSAs technical commitment briefing to Minister Bill McNight, very seriously.

We had claimed a cost and manpower saving because our SSN's had only one crew of about 100 officers and men while the French had two, each of over 60. This came about as follows. In approaching the manning of our SSN's the USN and we had followed previous diesel submarine practice and provided a single crew who always took their submarine to sea. When the ballistic missile submarines came along with their extended patrol times, the USN provided two crews to undertake alternate patrols and the RN followed suit. The first nuclear submarines in the French navy were missile boats and they did what the American and British navies had done and had double crews. When their SSN's came along they, too, were given two crews. Ergo British SSN's have one crew and French SSN's have two. I was stupid enough to assume that the Canadians would follow the USN and British practice.

The following is a verbatim repeat of the confidential briefing that I was given on 17th April, at the same time that I was told of the technical commitment brief to the minister: "The British have emphasised the single crewing of their SSN's as a manpower saving compared with the French double crewing. Canadian visitors to the French submarine organisation have been impressed with the thorough training that the officers and men receive on simulators and with the generally high morale. A factor in this morale is the double crewing arrangement with time for recuperation and family. This double crewing is a natural extension of the ballistic missile submarine arrangement that was already in being when the French commissioned their first SSN. The reactor and machinery in the French submarine is effectively managed and operated by ratings; a confidence engendered by certain automatic safety provisions in the system. In contrast, the British SSN's with their single crews are considered to have low morale and officers have a generally negative attitude towards their submarines and to be burnt out by overwork. This applies particularly to the engineering officers but commanding officers and executive officers that do every patrol are also included. The readiness of officers to criticise their submarines had surprised Canadian visitors. In consequence, the Canadian Navy had decided to double crew her submarines".

To explain this away by arguing that whingeing has become an art form in the UK in the past quarter century would be a dangerous delusion. This same source, who had been present, gave a complete blow by blow account of Perrin Beatty's meeting with Secretary of Defence Cap Weinberger and the US nuclear admirals in the Pentagon in the summer of 1987 and Beatty's consequential attitude thereafter.

It was now necessary to retrieve the classified documentation concerning the Trafalgar Class and its nuclear propulsion plant that had been supplied to DND. Security officers from the UK MoD and RR&A worked together on this. It was found that the batch of classified material forwarded in January 1989 that had been prepared as the result of the Chief of Submarine Acquisition's representations, had never been opened and was brought back to Britain still in its original wrappings.

There can be no doubt that the minister Beatty had chosen the French submarine long, long before and that the hapless John Anderson had to go along with this. The British were only kept in the competition as suppliers of information, to make the French more competitive and because our early withdrawal would have brought political questions from outside the Defence Department.

This was confirmed at a private dinner party in June/July 1989 at which John Anderson admitted to Dave Dawson, the Managing Director of RR&A and John Burgess, that the detailed analysis of the competing submarines made by the CASAP team (the five envelopes) had played no part in the decision making and that there had been no contest from the outset, the French had always been the choice because of the US problem. VSEL's running interference on the political level had certainly stopped Beatty announcing the selection of the French boat in 1987 and 1988 but in reality there had been no prospect that the US Navy would allow the UK's Trafalgar technology to be transferred to Canada.

It is perhaps noteworthy that despite all of the evidence to the contrary that we and doubtless others had provided to the UK MoD, someone seems to have advised the UK Chief of Defence Procurement that the UK submarine would have been selected had the Canadians not cancelled the project and the CDP wrote in these terms to the Chairman of VSEL plc in mid-1989 - a dangerous example of self-delusion or misrepresentation.

Canadian ministers had been concerned that some senior service officers might resign. No admirals or generals went. It was rumoured that the minister had assured Vice Admiral Thomas that he would move to the post of CDS or VCDS when General Manson retired. Anderson moved to Chief of Maritime Doctrine and Bowkett became the CASAP project manager following Bruce Baxter's resignation in protest. The CASAP would be responsible for selecting the new submarine but as evidenced by Bowketts appointment, there were still nuclear undertones being fiercely fanned by the French.

Vice Admiral Chuck Thomas breakfasted with Jock Allen and me on 23rd May. He knew what he wanted; he wanted simple submarines with no complications like air independent propulsion systems in the first instance. He wanted an existing design, which he could have quickly. They would make a parallel study, a paper study, of air independent systems for the second batch. He then departed to make the opening address at the ARMX 89 Symposium on the theme of training all sailors ashore on simulators and only sending fully trained men to join operational ships. Where a fair number would presumably discover that they were prone to seasickness.

John Anderson visited London "to say thank you" by hosting a small luncheon party. I was not told of any discussions that he might have had in the UK MoD, but I know that the mood would have been to sigh with relief and say "Thank God that's over and we no longer have to try to persuade the Americans etc etc".

John Anderson and Bowkett also visited Paris. This was no social visit but a period of intense discussion on future cooperation between the navies. In the following months various snippets leaked out. It was learned that Canadian officers would be trained in French nuclear submarines and that one such officer had already completed a training period begun while the choice of nation was officially still to be decided. Two French nuclear trained exchange officers would be permanently stationed in DND. French Admiral Castellan visited Ottawa in June to discuss the arrangements, followed by a deeper visit by Admirals Barnauld and Guilham-Ducleon in September during which they sought some Canadian funding for work by Technatome on low energy nuclear power plants.

The nature and extent of the continuing co-operation envisaged at these discussions is perhaps best illustrated in a letter sent by Ed Healey to M. Yves Sillard in the French Ministry of Defence in August 1989 in which, in addition to 'welcoming the reflections, suggestions and offers of co-operation and assistance in a new Canadian submarine programme made to Admiral Anderson during his visit to Paris', DND addressed four co-related items highlighted by the French, namely:

- improved co-operation between the two navies especially the training of officers and men in France in the field of nuclear engineering and nuclear propulsion;
- means of supplying power, both for heating and the generation of electricity in our remote northern bases, for which a small pressurised water reactor represents one of the most attractive options;
- the establishment of safety codes for undertakings in the nuclear field to continue on a bilateral basis;
- the need for large submarines (over 2,000) tonnes) with an AIP capability to operate with autonomy in the Arctic areas.

It was noted that a modified diesel--powered version of the "Canadian Amethyst" proposed by DCN during the nuclear phase of the submarine programme could fulfil those pre-requisites and offer a suitable base for an iterative programme.

Healey added that, "We had all hoped, up to the very last minute, that these sterling efforts (by the competent and dedicated French team in Ottawa and France) would bear substantial fruit. Unfortunately they didn't and now the programme is reduced somewhat, both in scope and ambition, but I would be most pleased if we were able to continue our co-operative efforts through the revamped CASAP office now under the direction of Commodore Bowkett".

MacLeans magazine obtained a copy of this letter and published extracts in its issue of 2nd January 1990 after interviewing Healey regarding the import of its contents.

Various reasons were advanced as to why officials in DND were prepared to give C$100,000 to the French navy's atomic arm Technatome after the submarine was cancelled. The French were stated to be angry that the much, much larger figure promised had failed to materialise. Be that as it may but coming at the time when Canada's excellent AECL was being reduced and its work on the low power Slowpoke reactor curtailed, there were many who felt that the navy was just hell bent on buying French technology to sustain a future dream of acquiring SSN's.

My reading of the Healey-Sillard letters and the MacLeans article is that Ed Healey was perhaps carefully using weasel words to extract his Department from a pit that more junior, and perhaps French biased officers, were about to let it fall into.

It is timely to review the behaviour of the four nations concerned with this choice, France the USA, the UK and Canada. Internationally France is always at some pains to assert its independence and has shown a willingness to ignore the 'western club' rules in its pursuit. The most dangerous examples have been a willingness to sell nuclear know-how and materiel to other nations, without much concern for their stability and eventual end use. The 1995/96 atomic bomb tests and the supply of nuclear reactors to revolutionary regimes are examples of this perverseness.

France has sponsored the Francophone, an association of nations that use the French language. Most are poor and see the association as a source of aid. Canada has three seats at the Francophone table, Canada is a country member and Quebec and New Brunswick are government members under a deal struck by Mr Mulroney in 1985. Canada stands out as a sophisticated and prosperous western nation and hence a prize target on which it is worth spending French government money and effort to bind her more closely and extend French influence and language in North America. Thus the French navy and national companies like Thomson-CSF could afford to locate a staff of 24 people in Ottawa to promote their submarine. The financial ingenuity displayed by the French in the matter of contracts and commissions is also well known.

The French have the great advantage of having a government and higher civil service that know what they want, are willing to take a long view and to deploy the resources necessary to ensure success. Because most are the product of the grande ecoles they have an identity that embraces both industry and government. This resolve was well summarised in the message that Ambassador Lucien Bouchard sent to Mr Mulroney in 1987, that failure to select the French submarine would be considered by M. Mitterand to be a reflection on French honour.

Personally I have the greatest liking and admiration for the French people, for their achievements and for their magnificent country. The officers from DCN behaved impeccably throughout the Canadian submarine affair. The same cannot be said, alas, for some of their Canadian supporters.

The US Navy sees itself as the dominant force for the preservation of world peace and the American way at life. It has seen the contribution of the other NATO nations to western collective defence decline in numerical terms with more of the burden falling on the United States and has in consequence come to discount such contributions, certainly outside European coastal seas. In most cases the number of friendly warships that the other nations deploy is not worth the sea management problem they present. This is particularly the case with submarines where control is so much simpler if "everyone who is not one of ours must be one of theirs".

The US Navy does not want anyone to deploy submarines in northern waters and particularly silent submarines such as the Trafalgar Class. They have to put up with the British Navy because they have always been there and handle their submarine operations rather well, but the US Navy doesn't want anyone else and is gradually freezing even the British out. Despite the support of President Reagan and his cabinet, including Colin Powell, the submariners were opposed to the proposition that Canada should acquire SSN's and used their influence at all levels within the Congress, the Pentagon and the media to frustrate that aim.

When it seemed that Canada was determined to acquire SSN's they concluded that it should be the French submarine 'because they are so noisy we will always know where they are' while quietly warning the Canadian navy that a closer Canadian - French relationship could affect the intimacy of future US - Canadian co-operation and the use of the US Navy's areas and facilities for trials and exercises. Whether non-DND Canadian ministers were ever told of the US threat to make things difficult I do not know. Somehow I doubt it; McNights comment to me in March that "the US matter would not bear much upon our decision, the attitude is local" is seen in retrospect as an indication that ministers had concluded that Canada could not afford the SSN per se.

The US Navy was fortunate that it was an election year with an outgoing president who could not stand for re-election. The other NATO powers were rightly concerned at the lack of political control over the admirals during that year. There were stories that the US Navy was spending money in Ottawa to scupper the nuclear submarine proposal. Without question they spent money with Systems Planners Inc. in justifying their concern about Canada's industrial capability, the possibility of an accident, the recruitment of US labour and so on and some of this money might have finished up across the border.

Seen in retrospect, our chance of providing the Trafalgar Class to Canada disappeared on the 25th March 1988 when Senators Warren and Exon addressed the Senate on the subject of the proposal that Canada should acquire SSN's. What was significant was that John Warren read into the Congressional Record, sections of the 1954 Atomic Energy Act, a warning of rugged opposition ahead should proposals to amend the 1958 and 1959 Agreements be put before the Congress.

Although I was engaged in the task of seeking to sell the British submarine to Canada, I had considerable sympathy for the US Navy's position. In 1958 they had 'bent' their own 1954 Act to provide nuclear propulsion technology to their great wartime ally, the Royal Navy. They had been at considerable pains to word the Agreement(s) so that the UK alone should have the benefit of this generosity (which I now know also included nuclear weapons know-how) and the Royal Navy's nuclear arm had kept faith and based its training and operating procedures on the US Navy's systems for over thirty years. Now a wretched British company was trying to break this solemn agreement and pass this know-how to Canada with the help of people in government on both sides of the Atlantic who did not begin to understand the nature of the commitment that had been entered into in 1958.

To an outside observer (and to many insiders), the British performance was farcical. UK government departments collectively wished that Canada had never thought of acquiring nuclear submarines and that the whole thing would quietly go away   There were three separate teams, who seemed not to talk much to each other, the UK Ministry of Defence, the Foreign and Commonwealth Office and British Industry.   In each of these teams there were sub-teams, which expressed variants of their particular team line. To the MoD, British industry people were 'outsiders' not to be taken fully into one's confidence. On the other hand the FCO people recognized that not all patriots wear sailors suits.

Within the MoD, two teams were in play; the submarine designers and operators who were appalled that anyone should suggest that they should pass about 30 years of hard won technology and experience to anyone. This included the nuclear people to whom special security conditions applied and whose engineering disciplines and operating methods were firmly rooted in the US Navy's systems pioneered by Admiral Rickover. Although the RN had been doing its own thing for 30 years the Rickover ethos was still discernable.   Then there were the Defence Marketing people who strongly supported the idea of selling anything to anyone provided that this had some, no matter how vague, ministerial authorisation.

The designers and nuclear people were judged by the Canadians to be seemingly ignorant of the extent of Canada's nuclear power industry and its impressive track record. They were also judged to be 'too stripe conscious' and treated Canadian officers according to their rank and not the high position they held in the Canadian defence hierarchy. The RN submarine Commanders always found something about their submarine to criticise. They doubtless thought subconsciously that they were presenting themselves as honest brokers upon whose word the Canadians could rely but it seems that all that they conveyed was an impression of low morale and disenchantment with their service.   The officers concerned would be deeply hurt at these comments but I am afraid that they are only too true. The Defence Equipment Marketing people were initially the designated single point of contact between the UK and Canada. From the outset they were constrained by lack of resources, there was no budget for the work on the Canadian project and not even a person to answer the telephone. The attitude from above was 'if industry needs support, industry must pay'. There was no effective central co-ordination. Above all, no one wanted to rock the Anglo – US boat. This, at least, I fully understand.

With the exception of the first High Commissioner in Ottawa the diplomats did all that we could have expected them to do. Of course I do not know what they knew but didn't tell me but on the evidence, I was always better informed in regard to the submarine project than they were because I knew a large number of friendly US and Canadian officers, civil servants and industrialists. The Ottawa High Commission or the Washington Embassy knew of none of the important Canadian and US documents that revealed so much of those nations intentions; I got them through my contacts.

On reflection there was the woman from the Cabinet Office. I was invited to a small dinner party that the British Overseas Trade Board gave in Covent Garden on the 16th September 1987 in honour of Tom d'Aquino the President and Chief Executive Officer of the Canadian Business Council on National Issues (perhaps the closest equivalent would be the Chief Executive of the Confederation of British Industries). He had asked to talk with me about the Canadian submarine project. We had no sooner sat down at the circular table and were unfolding our napkins and surreptitiously sizing up our fellow guests when the woman called Kathleen from the Cabinet Office leant forward across the table and opened up the dinner conversation by saying to me in a loud and scornful voice "What do the Canadians think they want nuclear submarines for?" She did not need to say, "stupid Canadians", her tone said it all.

UK industry did rather well. Following the lead of VSEL and Rolls Royce and Associates, other companies that were important manufacturers of equipment and services in the Trafalgar Class joined the Trafalgar Consortium and actively sought partners who might produce their equipment in Canada. Substantial progress was made and we were sure that in a reasonable time much would have been possible. Cynics will remark that it wouldn't have been so harmonious once orders were placed; that might well be but British industry did go into the thing telling Canadian industry what might be possible and not, like officialdom, how difficult and dour it all was. Frank Noah, helped by John Burgess, put the Consortium together and did much to foster this approach.

With the exception of Margaret Thatcher, Ministers of the Crown seemingly did more harm than good. I am forced to rely on Canadian ministerial aides for this information since no UK minister or minister's office ever bothered to tell me anything about the results of their visits. After all, why should they, I was now in industry and by definition, 'an outsider'. I suspected that ministers had been advised to 'steer clear of discussing the 1958 Agreement' which was perhaps the one thing the Canadians would expect a British Minister to discuss, so the silence must have been deafening. At best they were neutral: this even extended to ex-ministers as Frank Noah and I found when we had dinner with Jim Prior in Ottawa. They earned little respect.

And what of Canada? The time will surely come when this prosperous nation, so well endowed with natural resources will be better able to afford the trappings of advanced nation-hood than an overpopulated Britain in decline on the fringes of Europe. That's in the not too distant future. The extent to which the Minister's wish to acquire nuclear submarines exceeded Canada's ability to fund such an ambitious programme at the present stage in her development only became clear to the public at large in the months following the 1989 budget and are reported here in brief as seen by me.

The Nuclear submarine project having been cancelled it was announced that proposals would again be solicited for a new diesel-electric submarine for the Canadian

Navy. Our advisers suggested that we should take firm action with Mr Mulroney's office. They considered that he "owed Mrs Thatcher a favour" and that we should endeavour to capitalise on it. I doubted whether the Canadian PM felt that he owed favours to anyone but if the experts on the Canadian political scene whom we were paying for advice, so advised, who was I to ignore it. So we advanced our claim to supply Canada with a version of the Type 2400 and heard not one word in reply. Well not directly.

Chuck Thomas had told us on 23rd May 1989 that the navy had been given until 14th June and the army and the air force until 26th June to decide on their future material requirements as the result of the budget and that he knew what he wanted there and then. Meanwhile the Canadian navy was quietly asking the British and French navies what work they had done on low power nuclear reactors. The British made no reply and the French said come on in; hence, in due course, the Sillard-Healey letters. The Captain Submarine Requirements, Captain Sloane, volunteered that the inclusion of an under-ice capability in a new submarine requirement would be for political weight to justify the 1987 White Paper's emphasis on submarines, rather than for good operational reasons.

The end of July came with no reconciliation between the services needs. One problem was that the savings assumed in the budget from closing or reducing bases and other cuts proved difficult and, what is more, costly to achieve. Service chiefs found it difficult to meet day-to-day operational commitments within the financial limits that had been set.

General John de Chastelain became Chief of Defence Staff on 1st September 1989. He had practically a new team of senior officers within DND. His task was to present the changes in defence structure as logical developments of the 1987 paper, justified in some way by the reduction in international tension brought about as much by Mikhail Gorbachev's initiatives as by Michael Wilson's budget. They were caught between the obsolescence of equipment that would cost tens of billions of dollars to replace and the budgetary pressures to spend the money on social programmes.

The most intractable problem seemed to be the army. The 1987 proposal to withdraw from the commitment of troops to Northern Norway was to be softened by upgrading the Canadian brigade group in Europe to an armoured division with modern main battle tanks. The proposed acquisition of 250 main battle tanks had been swept away with the other Crown projects in the 1989 budget. Canadian ministers had a credibility problem with their NATO allies. As of the fall of 1989, the army demanded some definition of its role. There was no one better qualified than John de Chastelain to handle this difficult matter.

Ministers McNight and Mary Collins met with the DND chiefs at Meech Lake on 25th and 26th September 1989 to finalise and agree the DND operating priorities with proposals, reportedly in two parts, the capital projects that could be pursued within the budget and the "here's what we could do with just a little extra funding" list. The discussions reportedly failed to resolve the army's position.

The paradox was that in this uncertain situation there was now concern that the 2.5 billion dollars allocated for equipment in the 1989 budget would be substantially under spent; late in the year about 50% of the capital budget had been obligated mostly on programmes that were in train and had been approved before the budget cuts. Minister McNight was still expressing confidence that decisions would be made by the end of the year. It was now clear that the promised annual increase in defence expenditure of 2% above inflation until the year 2002 would go no-where near the true cost of equipping the Canadian forces to undertake the roles and missions envisaged in the 1987 White Paper. McNight insisted that this strategic basis still obtained while informing the DND chiefs that their equipment proposals were too costly ; the nuclear submarine had been cancelled because it would have absorbed too much of the available cash. It emerged that the cabinet Expenditure Review Committee had been told of this decision ten days before the April 1989 budget day. In the same interview he admitted that the series of base closures etc would fall short by some 500 million dollars of the planned cut of 2.74 billions planned over the following 5 years. The reason for the delay was the search for further economies. On October 6th it was confirmed that the DND recommendations had gone to the minister and he was considering these options before submitting his paper to the cabinet committees. Informed opinion was that he would be wise to first await the February 1990 budget.

Meanwhile, back in the UK we were asked by the MoD Director General Submarines to meet with his Director of Nuclear Propulsion to discuss a complaint that he had received from the American Authorities that VSEL had been discussing the design of a hybrid submarine in Canada using the AMPS low power reactor being developed by a small Canadian company. I was told that there was no possibility that VSEL would be permitted to manufacture components for such nuclear reactors in the UK. I said that our prime aim was to win orders and generate work for our countrymen and a small profit for our shareholders, but if the British government objected, there was no need for anything to be made in the UK, it would all be made in Canada and in the USA with whom arrangements were in hand to purchase the nuclear fuel from General Atomics Inc. I questioned whether the writ of the US Office of Naval Reactors under the 1958 Agreement would extend this far and repeated this in a letter to DGSM on 6th October.

I had assumed that the reason for this extreme sensitivity to US wishes was in the field of shared intelligence matters until it was revealed in a television programme that under the 1958 Agreement, President Eisenhower had authorised the supply of detailed design information on US nuclear weapons to the UK and that we had been copying them ever since. Even if there had once been pretence of having an independent design capability, the US information and then the test-ban treaty would have rendered the UK entirely dependent on the USA in this field.

In Canada, stories started to emerge again that the hostility of the US Navy to Canada getting Trafalgar Class SSN's was really on two counts, first they did not want a cheaper submarine to be built in North America and secondly they did not want the nitpicking, meticulous Canadian safety authorities probing the "Son of S5W" reactor.

An event that we observed with interest was the behaviour of the senior Canadian officers who visited the Royal Navy Equipment Exhibition at Portsmouth at the end of September 1989. The team consisting of Vice Admiral George, Rear Admiral Anderson, Commodore Broughton, and Captains Boyle and Slade, visited the VSEL stand but showed absolutely no interest in the submarine designs on offer. They showed great interest in the VSEL top-down approach to combat system design and asked that the presentation of this method earlier scheduled and cancelled when the nuclear submarine was cancelled, be reinstated. Suckers that we are, the VSEL weapons systems experts went to Canada and did their stuff and we heard not another word.

There was now little interest in defence topics in Ottawa beyond guessing where the cuts would fall. The Financial Post held its October 1989 Conference at which Associate Minister Mary Collins said that she "Hoped that the strategy for the armed forces would be defined by year end with the related procurement schedules to be worked out later" She added. "I don't think all the details will be available even by the end of this year". This made sombre hearing for the companies who hoped to manufacture equipment for the forces.

General de Chastelain and his senior service advisers appeared before the Parliamentary Defence Committee on 19th October. CDS explained that the Canadian forces had three roles, strategic, home defence and peacekeeping (for the United Nations). Although there had been no reduction in the size of the forces as yet, the provisions of the 1987 White Paper would not be realised. (He did not actually use those words but that's what he meant.). He then went on about unilaterally cancelling the commitment to northern Norway and so on through a whole litany of reductions.

That October there was a Commonwealth Prime Ministers Conference in Malaysia. The previous one had been held in Vancouver where Mulroney had led the chorus of demands for sanctions on South Africa. The dissenting voice had been Mrs Thatcher's and she had appeared on Canadian television and as good as said that her host, Mr Mulroney did not know what he was talking about. This had not exactly helped us in our quest to influence the Canadian government. An article published in The Sunday Times in July 1986, quoting 'palace sources' revealed that the Queen also disapproved of Mrs Thatcher's attitude.

Malaysia was a repeat performance. The Canadian TV, radio and press made much of the singular behaviour of Mrs Thatcher and the open rift that had developed between her and the Australian and Canadian Prime Ministers. Friends in the Canadian PM's office confirmed to me the profoundness of the personal dislike of Mrs Thatcher that had now developed and sympathy for the British officials whose discomfiture had been evident.

There are a number of occupations in which I am sure that I could have spent my time more usefully and pleasantly, but none more so than being a Senator in the Canadian parliament. This is the job to end all jobs, a good salary, an office and staff paid for by the state, liberal expense allowances and no upper retirement age. According to Sam Hughes they are not permitted to lobby on behalf of anything with which they have a pecuniary interest, no matter how remote. Imagine our surprise when Roger Harding of Defence Marketing invited Noel Davis and I to dine with a Canadian senator who was willing to advance our interests in Ottawa. He already represented a UK firm, which made tents or some such. We had no difficulty in saying "No thank you."

On 31st October an absolutely reliable source in Ottawa said that the papers setting out the DND recommendations from the navy had gone to the minister. They included six SSK's with a parallel study of air-independent propulsion systems. C$28 millions were allocated for the design phase including the AIP work and the Canadian Prime contractor who won the competition would select the submarine, plus a second choice. Throughout November speculation mounted that defence restructuring and capital programmes would likely post-date the 1990 budget. Mary Collins remarked at a private dinner party that "The disarray in the senior ranks of DND had to be experienced to be believed" and that "The forces had better accept that they would not get an additional nickel".

VSEL had long considered that St John Shipbuilders had the most mature management and technical capability of the Canadian yards to build submarines and had developed close links with the firm's management and a nodding acquaintance with the owners. Although the Quebec shipyard MIL's financial problems were becoming known, the true extent was startling, they were thought to be about C$ 150 millions in the red. They had been given a Department of Transport contract for a repeat Caribou ferry on which they had lost C$15 millions; they had not manned their Tribal Class frigate update and modernisation programme work (TRUMP) - for which they were being sued by the prime contractor Littons and they were much behind programme with the three Patrol frigates that the government had required St John to sub-contract to Quebec yards and for which they were being sued by St John Shipbuilders Limited. The SJSL writ was served on 6th July 1989 and claimed damages of C$1,759,593,000.00

I had much sympathy with the MIL President Robert Tessier who had inherited this can of worms. He claimed that the original contracts between companies had major hidden flaws and remarked to me that he had a personal commitment from Mulroney that MIL would continue to receive government work. Furthermore Mulroney was indebted to Bourassa and Bouchard. Tessier was not exactly helped by the speed with which all financial claims by MIL and its owners were passed on to the federal government by the provincial Industry Minister Gerald Trembly with the equivalent of 'Yours I think'. He it was who said, on 18th December that "The federal government grants 96% of the shipyard contracts in Quebec so if we don't have any more, how can we keep running the yards" and "The Quebec government is not there to subsidise the federal government as far as shipyards are concerned".

In January 1990 Mary Collins remarked in passing, in London, that she did not expect the capital equipment programme to be announced before the fall. Meanwhile the Canadian media speculated on whether defence funding would be required by the 1990 budget to absorb further cuts beyond the C$ 2.74 billions over 5 years imposed in the 1989 budget. With over 0.35 cents of every tax dollar going to service the massive national debt, government spending had to be curtailed. There was an air of relief when it was announced that the cut in defence funds would 'only" be C$ 210 millions in 1990/91 and C$270 millions in 1991/1992 to give defence budgets of C$ 11.87 and C$ 12.46 billions respectively. These savings would be made by further reducing personnel by 1,500 below the ceiling of 65,000 set in the 1989 budget and not yet achieved. The 1,500 reductions would be by voluntary retirement.

The most visible casualty of the budget was the proposed Polar 8 arctic icebreaker on which C$ 15 millions of government money and much more of industry's money had been spent on design studies. Thus in successive budgets all pretence of having a maritime capability in the arctic had been abandoned, first the nuclear submarine, then the patrol aircraft and now the icebreaker. What now of sovereignty, Mr Joe Clarke?

St John Shipbuilders were keen to present the government with an unsolicited proposal and it was agreed on 4th December 1989 that they would prepare this for a package of 4 or 6 SSK's to be built by SJSL to a VSEL design developed from the Royal Navy's Type 2400 Class. Following top-level negotiations preparation of the proposal was put in hand, with the intention that it would be submitted at the end of February 1990 when the government's defence update paper might be expected.

A significant problem that developed was St John's insistence that they had advice from the submariners in Halifax NS that what they wanted was the basic Type 2400 whereas we argued that the design offered must be the Type 2400 variant that we had prepared for the previous SSK competition, which met Canada's original 1986 staff requirements. We could not budge them on this; they believed that their contacts in Halifax knew best.

Relations with St John were not helped by changes introduced in the organisation in Barrow. Lord Chalfont had moved from being a non-executive chairman to an executive one.

Different VSEL directors appeared on the Canadian scene and thoroughly annoyed the St John management. Matters came to a head at the end of February 1990 following a visit by VSEL's Operations Director. SJSL's Chief Executive Arthur Nightingale met with Admiral Jock Allen and myself at the CIMA meetings in Montreal. He could scarcely contain his anger and indignation at the way he and his company were now being treated by VSEL Barrow. He could not wait until we got to our room but burst out in the corridor. He had persuaded the owner of St John Shipbuilders to agree this collaboration on the understanding that they would deal with Tony Peake and Jack Daniel who would accompany them to ministers. " Mr Irvine knew and trusted Jack Daniel. Now they were expected to deal with strangers who knew nothing about the Canadian scene and talked down to them on shipbuilding". To cap it all he had yesterday been accused of poaching VSEL's workpeople and warned to lay-off recruiting those who sought employment in Canada despite the fact that VSEL had just declared 500 people redundant at Birkenhead.

The proposed package was agreed at a meeting at St John on 20th March at which both Tony Peake and I were present at Arthur Nightingales insistence and was signed by the latter and Peake in New York on 6th April. It was handed to Minister McNight on 25th April. I learned soon after, that McNight had sent the proposal to a key official with a handwritten question "What do I do with this?"

Other nations made similar proposals. The German, Swedish, French, Netherlands and other ambassadors were in and out all the time in support of their companies whereas our High Commissioner seemed to have his hands tied by Whitehall. The UK alone seemed to treat its industry as people apart. There were also approaches by the Australian navy for Canada to adopt their new Swedish designed submarine.

St John issued a brief press release. There was no comment in the press except a short paragraph in 'The Wednesday Report' remarking on 'the curiously low key approach'. The fact was that Mr Irvine, the boss of St John Shipbuilders, was by now regretting the whole thing. The Canadian DND and DSS were pleased to have all the information on costs and construction but Vice Admiral Thomas told Jock Allen " He didn't think that it had done any good. On the other hand he didn't think that it had done any harm. But it's the wrong submarine, why didn't you offer a boat that met the requirements set out in the 1986 invitation to tender?". We had pleaded long and hard to do just that.

McNight finally replied to St John Shipbuilders an 26th June 1990, virtually rejecting the proposal and saying in effect, don't call us on submarines, we will call you. We knew that the old firm of Bowkett and Anderson had been drafting the letter in May and wondered why it took so long to emerge. Seasoned defence watchers were interested to note that it did not seem to bear the marks of the technocrats (strong on detail) or a minister (warm and insincere). It looked like a civil service Deputy Ministers hand, three pages of geo-politics straight from the Globe and Mail and a final paragraph "should our future …include submarines.. your proposal to participate in such a project will certainly be given careful consideration".

This effectively concluded the Canadian submarine exercise. Like the Australian submarine exercise it had cost VSEL and others a great deal of money and effort. Unlike the Australians whom we discovered had no intention of ever having a British design, the Canadians would have liked a British design but the US Navy could not be persuaded to agree. In the event they were right; the cost would have been too great for the Canadian budget to bear.

Some years later the Canadian Navy accepted the loan and eventual purchase of the RN's four Type 2,400 Class submarines.

Index